Grandmother's KITCHEN WISDOM®

TENTH ANNIVERSRY EDITION

by Dr. Myles H. Bader

Grandmother's Kitchen Wisdom®
Tenth Anniversary Edition

DR. MYLES H. BADER

© 2005 Bader Publishing, LLC

All Rights Reserved

Published by:
Creative Concepts Holdings, Inc.
307 East Church Rd., Suite 8
King of Prussia, PA 19406

Distributed by:
Creative Concepts Holdings, Inc.
307 East Church Rd, Suite 8
King of Prussia, PA 19406

Printed in the United States of America

First Printing February 2005

ISBN: 0-9767135-0-0

After ten wonderful years of presenting my books on QVC, I thought it was time to create a 10th Anniversary Edition that combines the very best of my five books including thousands of new facts not included in my previous books.

All five of my books were inspired by my mother and my grandmother and women like them whose recipes and home remedies relied on common items that were grown in their herb garden, kept in their cupboard, or bought at the general store. For more than twenty years I listened to my patients tell me their grandmother's household tips and solutions to health problems they encountered. I worried that this wisdom of the ages would be lost to future generations so I published my first Grandmother's Kitchen Wisdom for QVC ten years ago. Since then I have sold more than 10 million copies for which I am most gratified.

With this 10th Anniversary Edition, this treasured wisdom handed down from generation to generation, is passed on to you.

This book is organized into sections that will help you find exactly the cooking solution or home remedy you might need. In Section One: Grandmother's Kitchen Wisdom, you'll find new facts and solutions for household problems that range from how to get rid of pests and insects naturally to quick stain removal. Section Two: Grandmother's Penny Pincher, has countless penny saving tips and strategies to save money and prevent waste. Section Three: Grandmother's Cooking Secrets, is not intended as a cookbook but as Grandmother's guide to making recipes turn out just right. This section has tips on what to substitute if you are missing an ingredient, ways to keep food fresh longer and ways to repair burnt food. Section Four: Grandmother's Home Remedies, includes many of the secret remedies I learned from my grandmother and my mother who practiced as a nurse through her 92nd birthday. Our grandmothers didn't have a 24 pharmacy available so they improvised with ingredients found around the house and came up with home remedies that really work!

It is said that necessity is the mother of invention and the wisdom I have garnered from my patients, mothers, and grandmothers so often proves the point. They may not have had all our modern conveniences- no internet, no chemicals, no drug store shelves stocked full- but they had something that money can't buy, common sense.

I've taken the very best of grandmother's wisdom on all these subjects and combined them in this book. It is my hope that this 10th Anniversary Edition will help you continue their legacy.

Sincerely,
Dr. Myles H. Bader

Table
OF CONTENTS

Section 3   GRANDMOTHER'S COOKING SECRETS

A WORD ABOUT THE AUTHOR

Dr. Myles H. Bader (known as the wizard of food) has been interviewed on over 5,000 radio and television shows in the United States and Canada and is internationally recognized as a leader in Preventive Care and Wellness fields. Recent appearances on television shows include The Oprah Winfrey Show, The Discovery Channel, Crook and Chase, America's Talking, Trinity Broadcasting, QVC, Smart Solutions, and Help at Home.

Dr. Bader received his Doctoral Degree from Loma Linda University and is board certified in Preventive Care. He has practiced weight control, exercise physiology, stress management, counseled in all areas of nutrition and has lectured extensively on anti-aging for 25 years. He has established prevention and executive health programs for numerous safety departments, city governments, and Fortune 500 companies.

Current books Dr. Bader has authored include; Club the Bugs & Scare the Critters, Cookbook's Companion, 1,001 Secret Money Saving Formulas, 10,001 Food Facts, Chef's Secrets & Household Hints, 5,001 Mysteries of Liquids & Cooking Secrets, 250 Future Food Facts & Predictions for the Millennium, To Supplement or Not to Supplement, and The Wellness Desk Reference. Dr. Bader's books have been sold through Reader's Digest, Doubleday, Book of the Month Club and Barnes & Noble.

To My Readers

I want to thank you for the interest and loyalty you´ve shown me for so many years. Your support and valuable suggestions have been my inspiration. this 10th Anniversary Edition is my gift to you.

Sincerely,
Dr. Myles H. Bader

Section 1

Grandmother's
KITCHEN WISDOM

Vegetable
SECRETS

The Healthiest and most Nutritious Greens

Dandelion- Young leaves are the best.
Arugula- Has a slight mustard green flavor.
Kale- Young leaves are the best.
Romaine- One of the best lettuces.
Spinach- High in nutrients, but contains oxalates. Use in moderation.
Beet- Small young leaves are best.
Endive- Contains oxalates, use in moderation.
Iceberg- Most popular green and the least nutritious due to water content.

Snap, Crackle and Crunch
If cut-up greens need to be crisped, dry them and place them in the freezer in a metal bowl for 5-10 minutes.

Hail Caesar! He Invented the Salad

It wasn't invented in France by a renowned chef, nor did the "real" Caesar have anything to do with it. Caesar Salad was actually named after a restaurateur who lived in Tijuana, Mexico named Caesar Cardini. One day Caesar ran out of food, took a large bowl and placed everything he had leftover in the restaurant in the bowl, then served it as "Caesar Salad." Egg substitutes may be used to replace raw eggs in a Caesar salad. This will eliminate the risk of salmonella poisoning.

Pea Yew

Unless you really like the smell, try placing a few unshelled pecans in your saucepan when cooking kale, cabbage or collard greens to reduce the odor. When cooking onions or cabbage, boil a small amount of vinegar in a pan to remove the odor.

Vegetable Tenderizer

Next time you cook a fibrous vegetable, such as cabbage, celery or beets, try adding 2 tsp. of white vinegar to the cooking water. Vinegar is a mild acid and is able to breakdown the cellulose, which makes the vegetables stringy and somewhat tough.

Cancer-Fighting Vegetables

A number of fruits and vegetables contain compounds called "phyto-chemicals." These phytochemicals or "phytonutrients," as they are also called, are able to neutralize an abnormal substance that roams our body, causing havoc called a "free radical." Plants produce certain compounds to protect them from insects and other harmful microorganisms. Certain vegetables are presently being genetically altered to such a degree that they will contain a high enough level of phytonutrients to actually kill a cancer cell. The two vegetables at the forefront of this research are Brussels sprouts and broccoli. Both of these vegetables are capable of changing their phyto-nutrient, "siniqun" into the cancer cell killer, "isothiocyanate."

Snowdrops to the Rescue

A common flower called the "snowdrop" is being used to save a number of vegetable crops from aphids and other insects that can damage the crop. Snowdrops are able to produce the compound "lectin," which can kill insects that threaten the flower. Scientists in the near future will be transferring the gene that is instrumental in producing "lectin" to certain vegetables, such as cauliflower, to assist them in fighting off the aphids.

A Prescription for a Vegetable Instead of a Shot

Forget about the needle when you need a vaccine in the next millennium. Research is making progress in developing unique fruits and vegetables that when consumed will include compounds that will force the body to produce protein antibodies that are capable of fighting diseases. These specialized proteins will actually force the body to develop immunities to diseases.

The following vegetables have been chosen to be field-tested:
Corn will be grown to contain a rabies vaccine. Potatoes are also being modified to produce blood proteins that can fight viral diseases. Special bananas may contain a diarrhea cure and will be pureed and sold in small jars similar to baby food. Pharmacists may soon dispense genetically modified (GM) vegetables.

The End to World Starvation

A new product that should be inexpensive and plentiful should be available soon to feed all the starving people in the world. The new food will be prepared from corn and soybeans and will be a precooked powdered food that will not need any cooking and be fortified with vitamins and minerals. The powder can be made into a drink or porridge by adding water and will contain high enough levels of nutrition that it can be a person's complete source of nutrition for a minimal period of time. This will be especially helpful when crops fail or when people are forced into refugee camps.

Getting the Little Critters Out

When washing vegetables, place a small amount of salt in a sink full of cold water to draw out any sand and insects.

Bagged Salads to be Zapped

By the year 2005 all bagged salad products will be irradiated to reduce the possibility of harmful pathogens residing with the greens. The bagged vegetables are normally washed in a chlorine solution but it appears that all microorganisms are not killed.

Farming to Become more Biodiverse

Because of the new age of biotechnology in the food industry, farmers will be able to grow bigger yields per acre and produce a wider variety of foods on the same acreage they had used for only one crop. Modern agriculture will have fewer farms producing much higher yields by 2005.

Sweetens them up, too

Caramelizing vegetables will make the flavors and colors more intense. If you toss them in extra virgin olive oil, then roast them in a 500°F. oven for about 30-40 minutes, they should turn a nice golden brown. However, there will be a big loss of nutrients.

How about a Flower Petal or Two

Studies are being conducted to identify nutritious flowers and provide the public with guidelines on how to plant and care for the flowers. Some flowers contain excellent levels of nutrients, however, if they are not grown within special guidelines they may not be edible and may even be unhealthy. If you do eat flowers, never eat their pistils, stigmas or stamens. Some supermarkets may already be selling flowers for salads.

Popular Salad Flower

All parts of the nasturtium flower are edible, which include the flowers, leaves and even the seedpods. The flowers have a somewhat tangy, mustard-like taste and add a pleasant aroma to your salad. The flower should be used just as they open, but need to be swished in clean water before using in case a bug or two is hiding in them. Small whole leaves and the petals can be chopped up and added to cream cheese or salad oils for an excellent flavor. The seeds can be pickled and used on pizza.

Petroleum May be on its Way Out

Genes have been identified in plants that, if altered, will change the plant into a mini-factory to produce chemicals needed in a number of industries. The chemicals are the same ones that we are presently acquiring from oil. These chemicals can be used to produce plastics, lubricants, nylon, glue and detergents. By 2025, we may not need fossil fuels and will be using plants to produce the raw materials for a variety of energy uses.

Just a Wee Bit

Adding a small amount of sugar to vegetables when they are cooking will bring out the flavor. This is especially true with corn.

Need a Vegetable Prop? Grow One!

A genetic engineer at Stanford University has modified a mustard plant to create a substance called PHB, which is a close relative of polypropylene. By the year 2004, science may be able to genetically modify a vegetable to produce a plastic vegetable, instead of one high in starch.

Genetically Modified Plants - Timeline

1983 - The first genetically modified (GM) plant was created.
1990 - The first GM plants were grown for commercial use under
USDA supervision.
1996 - Almost 6 million acres of GM plants were grown in the United States.
1997 - Almost 25 million acres of GM plants were grown.
1998 - Over 58 million acres of GM plants were grown.
2002 - Over 100 million acres were grown.
2015 - Approximately 75% of all crops worldwide will be GM.

The Terminator Seed

A number of seed companies may be genetically modifying their seeds to become sterile after they have produced one crop. This will force farmers to purchase new GM seeds every year, instead of saving viable seeds from one year to the next.

Stop Boiling Over

Next time you are cooking greens, either stir constantly or rub a small film of butter or vegetable oil on the sides of the pan to prevent boiling over. The butter tends to stop the buildup of air bubbles.

Everything to Get Foamed

The foam on coffee has been so popular that companies will be foaming almost every food imaginable, as well as topping a variety of beverages with the foam. Vegetables will even be turned into foamy vegetable toppings.

It's Getting Tougher to be a Vegetarian

Trying to be a vegetarian has surprised more and more people, especially when they actually investigate the ingredients in a variety of products. Beef products are used in a number of biscuit and bread products, some Nestle desserts, potato chips and other snack foods, Max Factor lipstick and gelatin-based nutritional products.

Marine Algae to Stop Bleeding

A compound found in marine algae will soon be available and will be placed on dressings to control and stop bleeding from wounds. It will be produced in paper-thin sheets and derived from a sterile culture of marine algae. The compound is known as "poly-n-acetyl glucosamine" and does not contain any of the normal clot-forming ingredients or proteins associated with clot formation. Since it is not derived from any animal product, it has a low risk of disease transmission.

Meatless Corn Dogs Are Coming Soon

Worthington Foods will be marketing a new corn dog to compete with the hot dog/sausage dog rolled in pancake batter. The new dog will be 100% vegetarian.

Bagged Greens More Popular Than Ever

By 2005, bagged greens will account for almost 46% of all greens sold for salads. The nutritional content has been retained to an excellent degree. Some studies have even shown that "salad-in-a-bag" has a higher nutritional content than some of the fresh greens that sit out for days under the lights and are frequently washed. Media reports that these products are not safe due to higher bacterial contamination were found to be untrue, and no evidence to support these statements was ever presented.

Brain Food?

New research may be unveiled soon that will link certain fruits and vegetables with slowing down the loss of brain function due to aging. The new research is called "nutritional intervention" and testing is being done on laboratory animals, feeding them strawberries and spinach or a vitamin E supplement. Strawberries and spinach are very high in antioxidants and reduce free radical damage to the brain cells. Additional testing will be done with blueberries. The testing is being done by the Society for Neuroscience.

Color Set

Try adding a small amount of milk or vinegar to your cooking water. It will help retain the color of vegetables.

Attenshun

If your celery, carrots or potatoes get soft and limp, try placing them into a bowl of water with ice cubes in the refrigerator for 45 minutes. Sometimes adding a small amount of lemon juice may help.

A Small Amount of White Vinegar Wouldn't Hurt

It is always a good idea to line your refrigerator-produce drawers with a piece of paper towel to absorb excess moisture. Mold spores love moisture.

Shape Up!

Use a well-greased muffin tin to bake tomatoes, apples or bell peppers. This will keep them in shape.

Let's Have a Coming Out Party

In 2003, a new plastic wrap was released for sale that was developed by the USDA to extend the life of wrapped vegetables.

The Top 10 Fruits And Vegetables

Broccoli   Papaya
Cantaloupe   Pumpkin
Carrots   Red Bell Pepper
Kale   Spinach
Mango   Sweet Potato

ARTICHOKES TO WATER CHESTNUTS

Artichokes

Originated in Italy and was brought to the United States by the Europeans in the 1800s. Marilyn Monroe was the first artichoke queen in 1949, crowned in Castroville, California. Almost all artichokes sold in the United States are grown in California. The artichoke is an unopened flower bud from a thistle-like plant. The most tender and edible part is the "heart" or center of the plant. They tend to vary in size and produce a sweet aftertaste caused by the chemical, "cynarin." When artichokes are sliced and mixed with other vegetables, the cynarin will impart the sweet flavor to the other vegetables.

There are 50 varieties and it is best to purchase them March through May.

- Choose from compact, tightly closed heads with green, clean-looking leaves. Their size is not related to quality. Avoid ones that have brown leaves or show signs of mold.
- Leaves that are separated tell you that it is too old and will be tough and bitter.
- Best to wear rubber gloves when working with artichokes.
- Artichokes should never be cooked in aluminum pots, as they tend to turn the pots a gray color.
- They are easily burned and should be kept covered by water while they are cooking. However, they are also easy to overcook.
- Stainless steel knives should be used to cut artichokes. Carbon blades tend to react with the

chemicals and darken the flesh.

- A better flavor may be obtained when cooking artichokes if you add a small amount of sugar and salt to the water. They will have a sweeter taste and will retain their color better. If they are still too bland, try adding a small amount of fennel to the cooking water, about _ - $\frac{1}{4}$ tsp.

- Artichokes can be stored in an airtight plastic bag in the refrigerator, sprinkling them first with a small amount of water before placing them in the bag. However, after about 6 days, their flavor starts to deteriorate and they lose moisture fairly rapidly.

Be Gentle With the Babies

Baby artichokes can be purchased in most supermarkets, sold either loose or repackaged.

The sizes vary from walnut to large egg size; however, size is not related to the age of the artichoke. Make sure they are firm and heavy for their size or they will have lost too much moisture.

The Proper Way to Eat an Artichoke

This large globe-like vegetable tends to scare people away and many people never get to taste one. If you do eat an artichoke, remember that the best part to eat is at the base of the leaves, since the rest of the leaf is bitter and tough. Place the leaf into your mouth and draw the leaf through your teeth, removing the tender meat. After eating all the meat on the leaves, you will be left with the "choke" or the heart of the artichoke, which can be eaten with a fork and is the most succulent portion of the vegetable.

Artichokes, a Real Sweet Treat

Artichokes contain the chemical, "cyanarin." Any food that is consumed immediately after eating artichokes will taste sweet. Cyanarin stimulates the taste buds that are involved in the sweet taste and keeps them stimulated for 3-4 minutes. After eating artichokes, it's best to rinse your mouth with a glass of water.

The Color of Artichokes

When an artichoke is cooked, the chlorophyll in the green leaves reacts with the acids in the artichoke or cooking water and forms the compound, "pheophytin" which turns the leaves brown. This is why many cooked artichokes have a bronze tint. If the artichoke is cooked fairly rapidly, this reaction will not take place and it will remain green. Also, if you rub lemon on the leaves that have been cut, they will not discolor. Another method is to soak the artichoke for 20-30 minutes in a qt. of water with $1\frac{1}{2}$ tbsp. of white vinegar. The vinegar will stabilize the chemical that produces the color and the taste is also improved.

World's Greatest Artichokes

If you want the greatest tasting artichoke direct from the grower, just call Giant Artichoke in Castroville, California at (408) 633-2778.

ASPARAGUS

Asparagus can be traced back to ancient Greece and has been referred to as the "aristocrat of vegetables." It is a member of the lily family and related to onions and garlic. It is an excellent source of vitamins and minerals. There are two types of asparagus, white and green. Canned asparagus contains less vitamin C, due to losses by heat and water in the can. It is recommended to use the water in other dishes. White asparagus is the result of planting under a layer of soil, which does not allow the sun to reach the asparagus. Fresh asparagus stalks are more fibrous and need to be tenderized by removing a single layer with a potato peeler. Asparagus loses approximately 50% of its vitamin C content within 2 days after picking as well as some of its sugars. Fresh asparagus should be eaten within a day of purchase.

- When choosing asparagus, the stalks should be green with compact, closed tips and tender.
- Avoid flat stalks or stalks that contain white streaks.
- Never purchase them if they are being stored in water.
- The best time of year to purchase asparagus is March through June.
- Refrigeration will help to retain the nutrients providing you cut a small piece off the ends, wrap the ends in a moist paper towel and seal them in a plastic bag.
- Fresh asparagus loses sugar very rapidly and each day it is stored in a plastic bag in the refrigerator, it will lose about 10-15% of its natural sugar. As the natural sugars are lost, the asparagus will also become tougher.
- The tips should be kept as dry as possible or they will become mushy and fall apart when they are cooked.
- To tenderize the stalks, just use your potato peeler and remove the first layer of the stalk.
- To freeze asparagus, remove the last 2 in. of the stalk, then blanch in boiling water for 2-4 minutes depending on the thickness of the stalks. If you steam, blanch and then add 1 minute cooking time.
- If the asparagus is too thick, you can cut an "X" on the bottom of each one to speed-up the cooking time.

The Darker the Green, The Better

When choosing asparagus, always choose the asparagus that has the darkest stems, they will be the sweetest. The white-stemmed asparagus is usually bitter and somewhat tough. The greener ones also will have a higher content of vitamin A, C and potassium.

When It Comes to Asparagus, Males Are Best

Only male asparagus plants are sturdy enough for genetic engineering. The female plants do not respond well and are being weeded out. The female plants have been found to be tougher and not suitable for eating.

Asparagus to be Thicker and Healthier

The best asparagus are the thicker, heartier stalks. They contain more nutrients and are almost always more tender. The thin stalks will be phased out and new varieties that are at least $1/2$ in. in width will be available soon.

Asparagus, a Foul Odor; Beets are Colorful

Asparagus contains a sulfur compound that is converted during the digestive process into a foul-smelling sulfur compound. When some people urinate after eating asparagus, their urine may have a foul smell. Almost 40% of all people that eat asparagus have this problem caused by a specific gene that causes the harmless reaction. Beets contain a pigment called, "betacyanin," which will harmlessly turn the urine and feces red. Only 15% of the population has the problem of not being able to metabolize this substance.

Male and Female Asparagus Stalks

The male asparagus flower has a stamen that will produce a spore. The female asparagus flower has a pistil or ovary. The male asparagus stalks are thinner, while the female stalks are fatter. The darker the color of asparagus, the more tender, the greener or the whiter the better.

This will Straighten Them Out

Asparagus that has become limp can be revived by placing them in ice-cold water with ice cubes for 30-45 minutes. To improve the taste of asparagus, try adding a bouillon cube or a small amount of soy sauce to the cooking water.

Beans (Edible Pods)

This type of bean is picked before they are fully ripe and as the inner seed (bean) is just starting to form. These immature seeds contain a higher level of beta-carotene and vitamin C. The dried seeds are high in protein and carbohydrate. Beans may be green, purple or yellow and should have no scars or discoloration. When broken, they should have a crisp snap. They are available all year round, but are best May through August. Refrigerate whole and unprocessed beans to retain their nutrient content. Never leave beans soaking in water.

Legumes, a Pain in the Abdomen?

Almost all legumes, including beans, peas, and lentils (fresh or dried) contain a toxin called a "lectin," which is capable of causing abdominal pain, nausea, diarrhea, and severe indigestion. To destroy this toxin, legumes must be cooked at a rolling boil for 10 minutes before lowering the heat to a simmer. Peas and lentils only need to boil for 2-3 minutes to kill the toxin.

Lentils - Very Old Food

Lentils are one of the world's oldest cultivated foods going back 9,000 years. The Egyptians were lentil traders and mashed lentils were found on Egyptians tombs. Half of the world's supply of lentils are grown in India.

Plants Need Nitrogen, Legumes to the Rescue

A certain bacteria found in the roots of peas and beans are capable of absorbing nitrogen and converting it for plant use. These bacteria are being genetically modified and will be able to live and function in the roots of other plants, especially wheat and corn. This will reduce the amount of fertilizer needed since feeding will be natural and internal.

Chili-Making, it's Bean a Secret

The first aim is to soften the bean and turn it into mush, without it falling apart. The cell wall needs to be weakened and the starch granules need to be gelatinized. Initially, beans are soaked in water containing 1-2 tsp. fennel seed and $1/2$ tsp. of baking soda for 3-4 hours. This will soften the bean and allow the fennel seed to neutralize the complex sugars that causes flatulence. The beans are then cooked in boiling water with another $1/2$ tsp. baking soda added until they are tender but not overly mushy. The texture of the bean will remain more stable if the cooking is performed in a somewhat alkaline solution instead of an acidic one. This is why you add the baking soda to the cooking water. Chili sauce is too acidic a solution for the bean until it is fully cooked, since it will not soften any further in an acidic environment. Occasionally, cooks will try to save time by relying on the acid nature of chili sauce to complete the cooking of the bean and end up with hard beans.

Side Dishes will be Improved

Baked beans will no longer cause flatulence, since they will be treated with an enzyme called "b-oligo-saccharidase." This enzyme will neutralize the complex sugar in the beans. Potato salad and coleslaw will be high-pressure-treated with 80,000 psi for 2 minutes, which should inactivate any pathogens and bacteria and increase shelf life.

HIC, HIC

Instead of soaking beans in water overnight, try soaking them in cider, then use applesauce to thicken the syrup.

Roasted Beans

Only two legumes are commonly roasted, soybeans and peanuts. This is because of their high oil content, which compensates for their dryness. When roasted, both legumes tend to change flavor and texture. The low water content and the high temperature used for roasting are responsible for the browning of the outer coating. Unless you desire a very hard-bean after it is roasted, it is best to partially cook the bean first. This will partially gelatinize the starch, making it more crisp than hard as a rock. Beans are similar to nuts when it comes to roasting and they should be roasted slowly at 250°F. (121°C.) to avoid burning the surface before the insides are done.

Flatulence Levels of Common Beans

The following list provides information that was released by the USDA's Western Laboratory in Berkeley, California. The list of beans is in the order of those that produce the most gas, or are higher in the sugar that causes the problem, to the beans that are lower-rated on a scale of 1-10:

BEAN	GAS RATING
Soybeans	10 (gas mask, cork & muffler required)
Pea Beans	9
Black Beans	8.5
Pinto Beans	8.5 (will clear out the house)
California Small White Beans	8 (still dangerous)
Great Northern Beans	7 (a bit on the wild side)
Lima Beans	6.5
Garbanzos (chick-peas)	6
Black-Eyed Peas	5 (barely livable)

Goodbye to Flatulence

When it comes to eating beans, many of us have a problem with flatulence (gas). The gas is produced by the fermentation of the complex sugar, "oligosacchaide" found in beans and some other vegetables, such as cabbage and broccoli. The small intestine does not have the proper enzyme to break this sugar down and it passes into the large intestine where bacteria break it down and unfortunately ferment the sugar, producing hydrogen, methane, and carbon dioxide gases.

However, when you are in a Mexican restaurant eating refried or black beans, you don't stand a chance unless you consume an equal amount of rice. Rice has the ability to neutralize the gas in the beans. We found this out in Mexico when we asked a restaurant owner why no one ever seems to have a gas problem in Mexico, when they consume large quantities of beans daily. We were told about the rice and have tried it with perfect success every time.

The problem of flatulence was studied when it became a problem for pilots, since the gas expands at higher altitudes and can cause pain and discomfort. At 35,000 feet, the gas will expand to 5.4 times more than at sea level. Almost 50% of the gas is nitrogen with about 40% being carbon dioxide, produced by aerobic bacteria in the intestinal tract. The remains are a combination of methane, hydrogen sulfide, hydrogen, ammonia, and the really bad odor-makers, the "indoles" and "skatoles." In the late 1960s, astronauts had to be selected who would not produce large amounts of gas. The two beans that cause the most problems were found to be navy and lima beans with pinto beans coming in a close third.

The Vinegar Method
When cooking dried beans, try adding 2 tbsp. white vinegar to the pot.
This will tenderize the beans and will reduce the gas problem in susceptible individuals.

Bean Varieties

Chinese Long Beans- Mild-tasting, long thin-beans. These can be as long as 18 in. and have been called the "yard-long" bean. Best when young and tender.

Haricots Verts- A slender variety of a snap bean developed originally in France.

Italian Green Beans- Also known as Romano beans. Have a broad, flat, bright green pod and are popular frozen beans.

Purple Wax Bean- Has a dark purple pod that changes color to green when cooked. Looks similar to a small yellow wax bean.

Scarlet Runner Bean- Pods are broad and flat, the pod is green and the seeds are a reddish color. The blossom is also edible.

Snap Beans
Have tender, crisp pods that will easily snap in half. The ends are usually just "snapped off" instead of cutting them. These are the familiar green beans or yellow wax beans. Formerly known as "string beans." The string has been bred out from the inside and their name has been changed. Cooked beans have a refri-

gerator life of approximately 5 days. If you boil the beans whole without even removing the ends, you will retain 50% more of the nutrients. If you place a very small amount of sugar in the cooking water of beans, it will bring out the flavor. Baking soda should never be added to green beans while they are being cooked, as it will reduce the nutrient content of the beans. Acid foods, such as tomatoes will cause the color of green beans to be lightened.

The Early Bird Gets the Bean
If you want your snap beans to produce over a longer period of time, just pick them when the beans are about pencil-width. Make sure that the seeds are just visible. If you wait too long, the plant will make the seeds larger instead of the meat of the bean and use up all its energy.

Is it a Beanstalk or a Cornstalk?
If you plant pole beans next to corn stalks, the beans will use the corn stalk and wind its way up, making it easier to grow them without putting up poles for them.

Beans (Shell)
These are actually mature fresh seeds that are between the fresh seeds and dried seeds. Shell beans have a higher level of vitamins and dried beans are higher in protein, potassium and iron.

Bean Shell Varieties

Cranberry Bean- Identified by their red markings on the white pods as well as the actual bean.

Fava Bean- Fava beans are similar to Lima beans in taste and texture. Also called "broad bean" but the pods are longer than Lima beans. Popular favorite in salads.

Lima Bean- Lima beans are the most common shell bean in the United States. They originated in Peru and almost all the domestic crop goes for canning or freezing. They are very perishable and should be used as soon as purchased. If you add a small amount of sugar to the cooking water, it will help bring out the flavor.

Poisonous Lima Beans
Lima beans tend to produce an enzyme called, "cyanogens," which is a form of cyanide. Some countries have laws that restrict certain varieties of lima beans from being grown. European and American farmers have developed new breeds of lima beans that do not produce as much of the toxin and are safer to eat. These potentially harmful toxins may be removed by boiling the beans in a pot without a lid, allowing the hydrogen cyanide gas to escape with the steam. Neither raw lima beans nor their sprouts should be eaten raw.

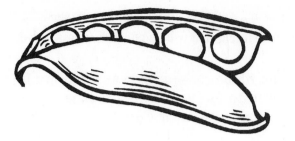

Soybeans

Usually sold as a dried bean, however, they are more popular in the Orient as a fresh bean. They have a high protein content and a mild flavor. Soybeans contain a complete protein, which makes it equivalent to animal products in relation to the quality of the protein.

Soybeans, Getting Popular

Soybeans are now the single largest cash crop in the U.S. producing more protein products and oil than any other source. The soybean originated in China and was popularized by the Buddhists who were vegetarians. They became popular in the U.S. after Commodore Matthew Perry's expeditions brought back two varieties in 1854 from the Far East. The bean has a high protein content of 40% and oil content of 20% and was originally used in paints, soaps, and varnishes. It was not used in foods due to an off-flavor until the process of hydrogenation was invented, which placed water into the soybean making it more acceptable as a food product. The first use in the food industry was in margarine to replace butter during World War II.

Super Bean to Fight Weeds

Soybeans will soon be able to control weeds. By the year 2004, the U.S. soybean harvest will have been genetically modified to produce a protein that will enable the bean to tolerate the herbicide, "glyphosphate." Farmers will then be able to use the herbicide without damaging the growing beans.

The Following are a Few of the More Common Soy Products:

How is Bean Curd, aka Tofu Made?

Tofu is prepared by boiling soybeans in water, then grinding the beans into a paste and adding calcium sulfate to coagulate the curd, making it a better source of calcium than raw soybeans. However, most Japanese and Chinese tofu is made without the addition of the calcium sulfate; instead they use an acid, such as lemon juice or vinegar. The protein in bean curd is 90% digestible, which is close to milk. The curds are compressed into blocks then stored in water under refrigeration or vacuum-packed. If you purchase tofu that is not in a package, be sure and change the water it is stored in daily.

Low-fat tofu is now being sold. If this is done, tofu will last for 3-5 days from the "sell date" and possibly 2 weeks, if it is very fresh when purchased. If you are going to freeze tofu, then it should be frozen as soon as it purchased in its original water and container. It can be frozen for about 2 months at 0^0F. After it is thawed it will, however, be a little bit more fragile and will disintegrate unless added to dishes just before serving.

Tempeh- Made from whole cooked soybeans that are infused with starter bacteria then allowed to ferment. This produces a product that is very dense and chewy with a nutty flavor. Can be fried, grilled or used for veggie burgers. Because of the fermentation process, it contains one of the only vegetable sources of vitamin B12.

Settan- Prepared from wheat gluten and may be called "wheat meat." Contains a very high level of protein and does not have to be cooked. It can be sliced and replace meat loaf in a sandwich.

Miso- This is a fermented soybean paste. It is high in protein, isoflavones, and antioxidants. Has high sodium content. Used more as a condiment and flavoring agent.

Soy Milk- Extracted from soybeans and consumed by people who have an allergy to cow's milk. Usually found supplemented with vitamin D and B12. Commonly found flavored with chocolate.

Textured Soy Protein (TSP)- Made from compressing soy flour. Excellent source of calcium and because of its consistency, it's used as a replacement for hamburger meat in many recipes. Try replacing 30-50% of your ground beef with TSP next time you make a meatloaf.

The Pot-Bellied Bean

Shell beans should have a bulge and a tightly closed pod. If the pods are sealed, they should last for 2-3 days. When they are cooked, add a small amount of baking soda to the cooking water to help stabilize their color.

What a Relief!

Gas-free lima beans are now being grown. They will contain less of the hard-to-digest complex sugar that causes the problem.

Beans (Pinto)

Pinto beans are a dried bean that is an excellent source of protein. They should have a bright uniform color. Fading is a sign of aging or long storage periods. When preparing pinto beans, try to purchase ones of uniform size; the smaller ones may become mushy before the larger ones are cooked. If you feel that this may be a problem, try adding a small amount of baking soda to the water while they are cooking.

Storing Dried Legumes

If legumes are kept in a dry, cool location below 70°F., they will last for up to 1 year and retain most of their nutrient content. They may be stored in their original bag or container or transferred to a sealed glass jar. Never mix old beans with new beans, as they will not cook evenly. It is not necessary to freeze dried beans, since it will not help to retain their nutrient content any longer. Beans in cooked dishes may be frozen; however, they may be somewhat mushy when thawed but can last for up to 6 months. Pinto beans contain about 22% protein while beef has only 18%, and eggs 13%.

Bean Overboard

When you are cooking dried beans, make sure you add 3 tsp. of a pure vegetable oil to the water. This will help prevent them from boiling over.

Cooking Tips

To tell whether a bean is fully cooked, squeeze the bean. You should never feel a hard core. If you are cooking the beans in an acid medium, such as with tomatoes, this will slow down the cooking time and testing the tenderness of the beans is a must. The taste of beans can be improved by adding a small amount of brown sugar or molasses.

Bean Cooking Time vs. Loss of Nutrients

Many people worry about the loss of nutrients due to the long cooking and soaking times for beans and other legumes. Studies performed by the USDA, however, have proved that legumes, even if they require 1-1$^{1}/_{2}$ hours of cooking time, will still retain from 70-90 percent of their vitamin content and almost 95 percent of their mineral content. The most affected were the B vitamins of which about 45-50 percent are lost.

BEETS

Beets, a relative of spinach, have the highest sugar content of any vegetable; however, they are low in calories and are an excellent source of vitamins and minerals. Both the roots and the leaves are edible. It is best to buy only small or medium-sized beets; the larger beets are not very tender and may have a stronger flavor. Never purchase beets if they look shriveled or flabby; they should be firm. Beet greens should be used as soon as purchased and the roots within 5-7 days. Beets should be cooked whole and not peeled to retain their nutrients. Beets contain the chemical pigment, "betacyanin," which gives them their red color. Some people cannot metabolize this pigment and it turns their feces and urine red for a few days; however, it is harmless. When preparing any dish that contains beets, be sure and add the beets last. Beets will lose some of their color and turn the other foods red.

Helping Beets to Stay Red

If you add a small amount of vinegar to the water you are cooking, it will stabilize the red color and it won't fade.

Better Beet Ware

Betacyanin or "beet red" is difficult to remove from your skin and disposable rubber gloves are recommended when working with beets.

Sweet Beet

Sugar beets are 20% sucrose by weight and have twice the sugar content of standard beets. It takes 100 lbs. of sugar beets to produce 5 lbs. of sugar.

Off With Their Tops

As with any vegetable with a leaf top, the top should be removed when they are purchased and stored. Otherwise, it will leach moisture from the root or bulb and shorten the shelf life.

If You Like Them Young and Tender

Try sowing the beets in a short row about every two weeks and begin four weeks before the last frost during spring.

How Sweet it is

Beets grown in the spring and fall are usually sweeter than beets grown in the summer. Cool temperatures tend to cause the beet to store more sugar. If you must grow beets in the summer and would like them sweet, then mulch them to keep the ground as cool as possible.

Boniato

The boniato is also known as the "tropical sweet potato." In the U.S., it is presently being grown primarily in the Southern Florida Area and is a popular vegetable.

It originated in Central America and has a pink-colored skin, which makes it easily distinguishable from its closest relative, the sweet potato, which has an orange-colored skin. The flesh is a whitish color and resembles a baked potato and it is not as sweet as the sweet potato. The nutritional content is lower than the sweet potato in most areas.

BROCCOLI

A member of the "cruciferous" family of vegetables, which includes cabbage and Brussels sprouts, it was first grown in United States in the 1920s and is one of the more nutritious vegetables. Presently, California grows 90% of the broccoli sold in the United States. Broccoli has a higher nutrient content if eaten fresh. Broccoli is available year round and is best from October through May. The stem should not be too thick and the leaves should not be wilted. If the buds are open or yellow, the broccoli is old and will have a significant loss of nutrients. The florets should be closed and should be a good solid green color.

The florets contain 8 times the beta-carotene as the stalks. One cup of broccoli contains 90% of the USRDA of vitamin A, 200% of vitamin C, 6% of niacin, 10% of calcium, 10% of thiamin, 10% of phosphorus, and 8% of iron. It also provides 25% of your daily fiber needs and even has 5 grams of protein. Broccoli should be washed in a good organic cleaner since the EPA has registered more than 50 pesticides that can be used on broccoli. Seventy percent of these pesticides cannot be detected by the FDA after harvesting. In a recent study, it was reported that 13% of broccoli still retained pesticide residues even after initial processing. Organic broccoli would be an excellent choice or else, consume in moderation.

Broccoli consumption has risen over 50% since 1983 to 25 servings per person in 2002. Cooked broccoli still contains 15% more vitamin C than an orange. Broccoli stems will cook in the same amount of time if you slice an "X" all the way down the stem before cooking. Broccoli should be cooked as quickly as possible to retain its green color. Broccoli's color is also very sensitive to acidic foods.

Breeding Broccoli to Fight Cancer

There are over 50 varieties of broccoli with only a few varieties containing enough cancer-fighting phytonutrients to be effective. Some varieties have as much as 30 times the phytonutrients than others. The University of Illinois is working on research that will produce a new breed of broccoli that will contain the most effective phytonutrients and the highest levels.

Storing Broccoli

Broccoli should be stored in a plastic bag in the refrigerator. It will keep for only 3-5 days before the florets start opening and a loss of nutrients occur. To freeze broccoli, the leaves need to be removed and the stalks peeled. The broccoli should be cut into small lengthwise strips and blanched for 5 minutes, chilled and drained well then placed in a sealed plastic bag. May be frozen for 10-12 months at 0°F. A recent study at the University of Kentucky compared the vitamin C content of whole broccoli and plastic wrapped broccoli. Broccoli that was left out in the air lost 30% of its vitamin C content in four days, while the broccoli that was wrapped in plastic only lost 17% and retained its color better. The respiration rate of the broccoli was slowed down, conserving the nutrients.

Broccoli May Stop Breast Cancer

Studies conducted at the University of California at Berkeley are showing promise that consuming broccoli and other vegetables in the same family may slow down the reproductive cycle of cancer cells in breast cancer. Studies are still ongoing and soon we may find out that eating broccoli may reduce the incidence of the disease significantly. Broccoli is also being genetically engineered so that you will never see yellow florets anymore.

Keeping Broccoli Green

Broccoli should only be boiled for 30 seconds, if you wish to retain its green color at the highest intensity. This short duration cooking causes the gases that are trapped in the spaces between the cells to expand and escape and the color can be seen more vividly. However, when broccoli is cooked for more than 30 seconds in boiling water the chlorophyll reacts with acids in the broccoli and the color is lost. The color may now appear to be more olive green, which is caused by a brown substance called, "pheophytin." Remember: always add vegetables to the boiling water. Never start them in cold water or you will lose nutrients and color. Baking soda may be added to the cooking water to turn broccoli green, but this only works for a short period of time, then the broccoli turns mushy. Baking soda will also destroy some of the nutrients.

Why is it the Longer I Cook Broccoli, the Worse it Smells?

Broccoli as well as Brussels sprouts contains the natural chemical called mustard oil or "isocyanates." This chemical, when heated, breaks down into a foul-smelling sulfur compound called hydrogen sulfide, and ammonia. In fact, you should never cook these vegetables in an aluminum pot or the reaction will cause an even more intense smell. The longer you cook the vegetables, the more chemicals are released and the smellier the kitchen. Cook them for as short a time as possible. If you keep a lid on the pot and place a piece of fresh bread on the top of the broccoli or Brussels sprouts while they are cooking, the bread will absorb some of the odor. Discard the bread afterwards.

Broccoflower

Broccoflower is a cross between broccoli and cauliflower and looks more like a cauliflower with a light green color. It has a milder flavor than either of its relatives. Make sure that the florets are tightly closed for maximum nutritional content.

BRUSSELS SPROUTS

This vegetable was named after the capital of Belgium, where it originated. A relative of the cabbage family, it even resembles small heads of cabbage. They were brought America in the 1800s from England and were first grown in Louisiana. They are an excellent source of protein, but not a complete protein unless you eat them with a grain.

They are easily overcooked and will become mushy. Best to store them in the refrigerator to keep the leaves a green color instead of yellow.

X Marks the Spot
If you cut an "X" on the stalk end of each Brussels sprout with a sharp knife before cooking, the sprout will retain its shape and not fall apart. The small opening will allow the steam to be released through the bottom instead of being forced through the leaves.

CABBAGE

It originated in the eastern Mediterranean region and was popular among the ancient Greeks. It's available year-round in three main varieties: red, green and savory, which has crinkly leaves.

*   Avoid cabbage with wormholes and be sure to smell the core for sweetness. Green and red cabbage should have firm tight leaves with good color.
*   Cabbage should be refrigerated in plastic bags and used within 7-14 days.
*   Cabbage, along with its other cruciferous family members, are being studied in cancer prevention, due to its "indole" content. Initial studies indicate that if you consume $\frac{1}{2}$ of a standard cabbage daily, you may prevent some cancers.

Leaf Removal a Breeze

An easy method of removing leaves to prepare stuffed cabbage is to cut around the core at the base, remove the core and remove the leaves from the base. Remove one leaf at a time very gently.

Freeze Me First

When you need cabbage leaves for stuffed cabbage, try freezing the whole cabbage first, then let it thaw and the leaves will come apart without tearing.

Bag Me

Cabbage will last longer if stored in the refrigerator sealed tightly in a plastic bag. It should stay for about 2 weeks. Cabbage is 91% water.

Cole Slaws, no Problem

To make sure that your coleslaw is crispy, just shred the cabbage and soak it in a bowl of salted ice-cold water for about 15 minutes.

No Gas Problem

Flatulence problems from cabbage can be eliminated by boiling the cabbage for about 5-6 minutes, then draining the water and continuing to boil it in fresh water. The chemical that causes the problem is released during the first few minutes of cooking.

If you serve pineapple with cabbage or beans, it will prevent bloating and gas.

Staying in Shape

If you are preparing a recipe that calls for cabbage wedges, try steaming them instead of boiling them and they will retain their shape better.

Sauerkraut to the Rescue

Sauerkraut was popularized by Genghis Khan when his marauding hordes brought the recipe back from China. The recipe found its way throughout Europe and to Germany, where the cabbage was fermented with salt instead of wine and given the name of "sauerkraut." However, sauerkraut became a real hero in 1772, when Captain James Cook who had heard of the possible health properties of sauerkraut decided to bring 25,000 pounds of it on his second journey to explore the Pacific Ocean. Since sauerkraut has vitamin C, he only lost one sailor to scurvy in over 1,000 days at sea. The sauerkraut supply lasted one year without going bad.

Making Sauerkraut

Sauerkraut is usually produced by placing salt between layers of shredded cabbage and then subjecting the cabbage to pressure, which will bruise the cabbage and squeeze out the juices, allowing it to ferment.

Removing Tartness From Sauerkraut

Rinsing sauerkraut that is in a jar or plastic bag will reduce the tartness. A more severe method is to pour boiling water over the sauerkraut and allow it to stand for 4-5 minutes.

Cabbage Varieties

Bok Choy- Looks like a cross between celery and Swiss chard. When cooked, bok choy will have a slightly sharp flavor, but the stalks are rarely bitter. They contain an excellent amount of calcium and vitamin A.

Green- Has smooth dark-to-pale outer leaves, while the inner leaves are pale green or white.

Napa- Has a more delicate flavor than most cabbages. Is high in vitamins and minerals.

Red- Has a solid red to purple outer leaf, usually with white veins or streaks on the inside leaves.

Savoy- Has a crinkled, ruffled yellow-green leaf and is less compact than most cabbage.

CARROTS

Carrots are the best source of beta-carotene of any vegetable. Studies show that carrots may lower blood cholesterol levels, however, and drinking an excessive amount may turn your skin orange, due to high levels of carotenoid pigment. Reducing the intake will alleviate this color problem. They are available year round and should have smooth skin, solid orange color and be well formed. Should be stored in the refrigerator and never placed in water for any period of time, especially if peeled.

If carrots are to be used in a stir-fry, try boiling them first, then place them in cold water until needed. It takes longer to cook the carrots, since they are so solid. To slip the skin off carrots, drop them in boiling water, let stand for 5 minutes, then place them into cold water for a few seconds.

Carrot Curling - a New Olympic Sport?
To curl carrots, peel slices with a potato peeler and drop them into a bowl of ice water. When grating carrots, leave a portion of the green top to use as a handle. This will keep your fingers from becoming shorter.

Drying Carrots
Best to wash and scrape the carrots and slice them into 1/8th inch slices. Boil water in a large pot and place the carrots in for 5 minutes, remove, dry and place in food dehydrator for 2-4 hours.

Why Soak Celery and Carrots?
A number of vegetables tend to lose their moisture before you are able to use them up and become limp. There is no need to discard them when all you have to do is immerse them in a bowl of ice cubes and water for 1 hour in the refrigerator. The cells will absorb the water and return to their normal size, thus making the vegetable hard and crisp again. Soaking fresh vegetables for long periods of time, however, may have the opposite effect because of excess water buildup in the spaces between the cells.

Why is the Beta-Carotene Increasing in Carrots?

According to the USDA, scientists have been improving carrots to such a degree that they presently have twice the beta-carotene level as they did in 1950. By the year 2004 the beta-carotene level is expected to double again, thanks to genetic research.

How Crisp I am

A new breed of carrots and celery will start appearing in the produce section of your supermarket by 2004. These new vegetables will retain their crispness for long periods of time, even if they are sliced.

Off with Their Tops

Carrots and beets need to have their tops removed before they are stored. The tops will draw moisture from the vegetable, leach nutrients from the carrot and cause them to become bitter, as well as reducing their storage life. However, leave about two inches of the root if it is still there to keep the bottom sealed. Carrots and beets need to be stored in a plastic bag with holes in the refrigerator. Both are very susceptible to a number of microbes that will cause them to decay. Carrots will freeze well with only minimal blanching. Beets should be boiled until they are fork-tender before freezing.

Why Carrots may Become Bitter

When carrots are stored in a sealed plastic bag, a chemical is released called, "terpenoid," that will reduce the sweetness and make the carrot somewhat bitter. Also, if carrots are stored with apples, melons, avocados, peaches, pears or green tomatoes, they will develop terpenoids faster. Those fruits and vegetables tend to give off more ethylene gas as they ripen.

Purple Carrots?

Originally, carrots were purple until the early 17th century when the orange color variety was developed in England. The beta-carotene levels were not always as high as they are today. Carrots were originally grown to have a higher level of beta-carotene to help the World War II British aviators acquire better night vision. The iron supply in carrots is also absorbed more efficiently than most other vegetable sources.

Carrots, Easier to Digest When Cooked

Carrots are not affected to any great degree by heat and cooking, therefore there is almost no loss of the vitamin A content. Carrots will retain their color, which is the result of the chemical, carotene. When carrots are cooked, a percentage of the hemicellulose (fiber) will become softer, making the carrot more easily digestible and allowing the digestive juices to reach inside the cells and release the nutrients for easier utilization by the body. Carrots should be washed well, then cooked in a small amount of salted water. To tell when the carrots are done, pierce them gently with a fork and place them into a bowl of ice-cold water for a few seconds to loosen and easily remove the skin.

Going for a Physical? Don't Eat Carrots

Your physician needs to be advised if you consume a large amount of carrots since your skin may have a somewhat yellow tinge due to the excess amount of the carotenoids you are consuming. (The physician may think you have jaundice.) Another problem which may cause concern you, is if you are asked to take a guiac test for occult blood in your feces. The active ingredient in the guiac slide is alphaguaiaconic acid, which turns blue in the presence of blood. Carrots contain the enzyme peroxidase, which causes a chemical reaction to take place reacting with the alphaguaiaconic acid, turning it blue and giving you a false-positive test showing that you have blood in your feces.

Fresh Young Ones are Best

A good rule to remember when purchasing vegetables for freezing is to purchase "young ones." The nutrient content will be higher and they will contain less starch. Freeze as soon as purchased. Remember, fresh produce has stronger cell walls and will handle freezing better.

Very Nutritious

Carrot greens are high in vitamin K and E, which are lacking in the carrot.

Cooking Slightly Helps Even More

The USDA has completed studies showing that 7 oz. of carrots consumed every day for 3 weeks lowered cholesterol levels by 11%. This was probably due to calcium pectate, a type of fiber found in carrots and usually lost during the juicing process.

Are You Suffering from Crusty Soil?

Crust tends to form on the ground and causes patchy carrot growth. The seedlings are not strong enough to break through in some areas. Never cover carrot seeds with soil, instead use peat, compost or vermiculite.

CAULIFLOWER

Another member of the cruciferous family, it has a very compact head and grows on a single stalk. It is surrounded by green leaves, which protect it from the sun and cause the cauliflower to remain white instead of producing chlorophyll. Cauliflower is best purchased September through January, but is available year round. Do not purchase if the clusters are open or if there is a speckled surface; this is a sign of insect injury, mold, or rot. Should be stored in the refrigerator, unwrapped. Cauliflower can be kept white during cooking by just adding a small amount of lemon or lemon peel to the water. Overcooking tends to darken cauliflower and make it tough. To reduce the odor when cooking cauliflower, replace the water after it has cooked for 5-7 minutes. Due to certain minerals that are found in cauliflower, it is best not to cook it in an aluminum or iron pot. Contact with these metals will turn cauliflower yellow, brown or blue-green.

Storing Cauliflower

One of the most important things to remember is never bump or injure the florets. This will cause the head to loosen and spread too fast, causing discoloration. Store the head in a plastic bag that is not wrapped too tight around the head and put it in the vegetable crisper. Don't wash cauliflower before it is stored and it should keep for 4-6 days. Before eating, wash the head thoroughly since a number of chemicals are often used to preserve their freshness. To freeze, just cut the cauliflower into small pieces, wash in lightly cold salted water; then blanch in salt water for 5 minutes. Drain and chill before placing in a plastic bag.

New Bland High Fiber Source

Since fiber is always low in most processed foods, there has been research conducted to try and find a bland source of fiber that was relatively inexpensive. Cauliflower will soon be the vegetable of choice to replace fiber in a number of products. It will be used in sauces and a number of deli foods to start with. Dehydrated cauliflower may replace certain food gums and even fats.

Stop Odors with Bread

If you break up a few pieces of fresh white bread and add them to the pot when you are cooking cauliflower, it will reduce the smell. Placing a piece of fresh white bread on top of the cooking cauliflower will also work.

Brown Out

It is a common practice to tie the leaves up around a cauliflower plant as it grows to bleach the heads. Instead of the old method, try gathering up the leaves and then place a brown bag over the head. The air will still be able to circulate and will prevent rotting that is common when the leaves are tied.

CELERY

Arriving in the U. S. from Europe in the 1800s, celery has a very high water content and is low in calories. It is available year round. Stalks should be solid, with no hint of softness along any of the stalks, which will denote pithiness. If even one stalk is wilted, do not purchase.

•   Celery will only store in the refrigerator for 7-10 days and should not be placed in water.

- Don't discard the celery leaves. Dry them, then rub the leaves through a sieve turning them into a powder that can be used to flavor soups, stews, and salad dressings. This can also be made into celery salt.
- Celery, carrots and lettuce will crisp up quickly, if placed into a pan of cold water with a few slices of raw potato.
- To prevent celery from turning brown, soak in lemon juice and cold water before refrigerating for only a few minutes.

The Greener, the Better

When you purchase celery, purchase the greenest you can find. It will be the healthiest and have the most flavor.

Celery Strings

Celery is easy to cook. The pectin in the cells will easily break down in water. However, the "strings" which are made of cellulose and lignin are virtually indestructible and will not break down under normal cooking conditions. The body even has a difficult time breaking them down and many people cannot digest them at all. Best to use a potato peeler and remove the strings before using the celery. When preparing stuffed celery stalks for a party, always be sure and remove the strings.

Medical Concerns with Celery

Celery contains the chemical, "limonene," which is an essential oil and known to cause contact dermatitis in susceptible individuals. This chemical is also found in other foods, such as dill, caraway seeds and the peelings of lemons and limes. Photosensitivity has also been a problem with workers who handle celery on a daily basis unless they wear gloves. The chemical that is responsible for this problem is "furocoumarin psoralens" and increased contact may make your skin sensitive to light.

How Did Celery Turn into a Swizzle Stick?

Placing a stalk of celery into a Bloody Mary and using it as a swizzle stick came about in the 1960s. A celebrity (who wishes to remain anonymous) needed something to stir his drink with and grabbed a stalk of celery from a nearby relish tray in a restaurant at the Ambassador East Hotel in Chicago. Celery was first grown in the U.S. in Kalamazoo, Michigan in 1874 and to popularize celery, it was given to train passengers free. Presently, 2 billion lbs. are grown annually.

Storing Celery in Aluminum Foil

One of the best methods of storing celery for a prolonged period of time (2-3 weeks) is to wrap the celery tightly in aluminum foil.

Celeriac

Celeriac is an edible root vegetable that resembles a turnip and may be prepared like any other root vegetable. It has an ivory interior and has a strong celery taste with a dash of parsley. Celeriac should be firm and have a minimum of rootlets and knobs. Excellent in salads and can be shredded like carrots.

Celtuce

A hybrid of celery and lettuce, it does not have a high nutritional content and is prepared similar to cabbage.

CORN

Corn was first grown in Mexico or Central America and was an early staple of the American Indian. Corn is a good source of protein and can be part of a complete protein by serving it with rice. When ground for tortillas, an excellent amount of niacin is released. Corn contains 5-6% sugar, making it a taste favorite. Americans consume about 25 lbs. of corn per person annually. It is available May through September and the kernels should be a good yellow color. Do not purchase if the husks are a straw color, they should be green. The straw color indicates decay or worm infestation. Yellow corn usually has a more appealing flavor than white and is higher in vitamin A content.

The easiest method of removing kernels from an ear of corn is to slide a shoehorn or spoon down the ear. The best tasting corn is grown in Florida and is known as "Florida Sweet."

New Corn Fiber Oil to Fight Cholesterol

New corn fiber oil has been extracted from the corn kernel hulls that may have the ability to lower serum cholesterol levels. ARS and the University of Massachusetts have applied for patents.

Why Does Corn Occasionally Turn Rubbery?

When corn is cooked, the protein goes through a chemical change called "denaturization," which simply means that the chains of amino acids (proteins) are broken apart and reformed into a network of protein molecules that squeeze the moisture out of the kernel, turning the corn rubbery. The heat also causes the starch granules to absorb water and swell up and rupture the kernel, thereby releasing the nutrients. Corn should be cooked just long enough to cause the kernels to barely rupture, which allows the protein to remain tender and not tough. When corn is boiled in water, 50% of the vitamin C is destroyed. However, if you cook it in a microwave without water, almost all of the vitamin C is retained. Worldwide there are 200 varieties of corn. However, corn ranks as a vegetable low on the overall nutritional scale.

Don't Store Corn

Corn is one vegetable that is always better if eaten when it is fresh, preferably the same day you purchase it. As soon as corn is picked, it immediately starts to convert the sugars to starch. The milky liquid in the kernel that makes corn sweet will turn pulpy and bland in only 2-3 days. Corn loses 25% or more of its sweetness in less than 25 hours after harvesting.

This is the reason that many people add sugar to the water when cooking corn. This guarantees the taste, which was probably lost after a few days in storage. Leftover fresh corn should be cooked for a few minutes just to inactivate the enzymes, then store the ears in a sealed plastic bag for 1-2 days before using. If you plan on freezing corn, it needs to be cleaned and blanched for 4 minutes in boiling water. First, allow the water to drain, Tray-freeze, keeping room between the ears so that the kernels will retain their shape and not be crushed when sealed in plastic bags. Frozen corn will freeze for 1 year.

Back to the Drawing Board

In an effort to protect corn from pesky insects that damage the ears, science has developed a genetically engineered ear of corn that has the ability to produce a bacterial toxin to kill the pests. A side effect, however, is that the toxin also kills monarch butterflies. The pollen from the corn enters the caterpillar larvae and kills it.

Corn Smarts

If you plan on storing corn, always keep it in a cool, dry location and, to avoid mold, try not to place the ears touching each other. Remember, as corn warms up, the sugar tends to convert into starch very quickly. In fact, when corn is piled high in bins in the market and is allowed to stand for days, the bottom ones will be less sweet due to the heat generated by the weight of the ones on top.

Making Polenta Without Lumps

Polenta is easy to make without lumps, if you just use cold water instead of warm or hot water, which is what most recipes call for. Cold, lightly salted water will not cause the starch to lump together. Then, as the cooking heats the water, the starch in the corn will remain in a state of semi-separation and tends to stay that way throughout the cooking process.

Cooking Corn?

Steaming corn for 6-10 minutes is one of the preferred cooking methods. To store corn longer, cut a small piece off the stalk end, leave the leaves on, then store the ears in a pot with about an inch of water, stems down.

Almost no Nutritional Value

The color of a corn or potato chip will not affect the calories or fat content. However, if the label reads baked, it will probably be a lower fat product.

Corn Fact

Cornmeal may be purchased in two varieties: steel-ground, which has the husk and germ almost all removed, and stone or water-ground, which retains a portion of the hull and germ and is usually only available in health food stores.

Cornstarch, the Ideal Thickener

Cornstarch is thick, powdery flour that is made from the corn's endosperm. It is an excellent thickener for sauces, but tends to form lumps easily unless it is mixed slowly into a cold liquid and then added to a hot liquid. Stir the cornstarch until it mixes thoroughly, then boil it for a few minutes to thicken the sauce or stew. When you are thickening a stew or soup, be sure to remove as much fat as possible before adding the cornstarch.

Kernel Corn

Choosing fresh corn can be a difficult task unless you have some "corn knowledge." If the corn still has its husk, it will be necessary to peel back a small area and examine the kernels. The kernels should be packed tightly together with no gaps between the rows. Gaps between rows mean that the ear is overmature. If the tip has no kernels, the corn was picked too soon and not allowed to mature. The kernels should always be plump and juicy and should spurt a milky, starchy liquid. If the center of the kernel is sinking inward, it is drying out and will not be as sweet. Always purchase corn with the smaller kernels at the tip of the ear, since larger kernels are a sign of over-maturity.

Don't Hurt Those Little Suckers

Corn suckers are the small shoots that grow out from the stalk at ground level. Many people remove them, but the latest research shows that they will not reduce yield and if there is a drought they will send nutrients to the main stalk. If you do remove them and don't remove them properly, you may cause diseases to enter the stalk.

POPCORN FACTS

What Makes Popcorn Pop?

When the popcorn kernel is heated, the moisture inside turns to steam and as the pressure builds, it has to vent and bursts the kernel. The explosion forms a fluffy white starch. Normal corn will not explode because it does not have as high moisture content as special popcorn. As soon as the popcorn is popped,

it is best to open the bag or remove the lid as soon as possible to avoid the popcorn absorbing the steam and becoming soggy. Popcorn should always be stored in a well-sealed container so that it will retain as much of its moisture as possible.

Calling Roto-Rooter, Help!

Popcorn is composed of a complex carbohydrate (starch), and includes insoluble fiber (cellulose), which may help prevent constipation. It is always best, however, to drink plenty of fluids when consuming any large amount of insoluble fiber. Insoluble fiber tends to absorb water from the intestinal tract and will add bulk. The only risk that might exist would be if you ate a large tub of popcorn without drinking any liquids, then you may have a major traffic jam.

Size Does Make a Difference

Raw corn for popping is sold in many different grades. Most of the corn products sold in the supermarkets to produce popcorn have an expansion ration of only 28:1, while those sold to movie theatres have an expansion ratio of 42:1. The oil to corn ratio of quality popcorn should be about 3 parts of corn to 1 part of oil.

Wising Up

The 2002 annual popcorn consumption in the U.S. was about 61 qt. of popcorn per person. In 1994 this figure dropped to about 40 qt. it was found that high-saturated-fat coconut oil was being used to pop the corn. Movies switched to canola oil and by 1995 popcorn consumption was back to its original level. Using canola oil did not change the fat content, just gave us healthier oil. New oils are presently being used to pop corn that reduce the amount of oil to be absorbed. One qt. of popcorn (a small bag) equals the calories in just 7 large potato chips.

Probably Needed Salt and Butter

The first recorded popcorn event in history was by the Aztecs. However, they used it for decoration instead of eating it.

Tough Popocorn?

Salt should never be included in packaged popcorn or placed in a popcorn popper. Salt should only be added after the popcorn has fully popped to keep the popcorn tender. Salt will cause the popcorn to become tough.

Pass the Popcorn Tenderizer

It may be healthier to air-pop your popcorn; however, all this does is make larger blossoms that are tougher and not as crispy.

Saving an old Maid

Old maids are kernels of corn that are too pooped to pop. The kernels usually have lost sufficient moisture and can be revived by placing a handful of them into a sealed container with 1-2 tbsp. of water, shake for at least 3-4 minutes. The container should then be placed in a cool (not cold) location for about 3 days. This should revive them, and you should have no problem popping them.

Too bad, Yuppies

Nutritionally, regular popcorn and gourmet popcorn is equal. The only difference is that gourmet popcorn pops into larger blossoms.

Air-Popped Popcorn may be a Good Snack

It would be wise to read the label on air-popped popcorn packages before you buy the product, if you're trying to cut down on fats. Some products are now sprayed with oil.

Popcorn with Ghee

If you want to give popcorn a new taste treat, just use ghee instead of the oil you are presently using. There will be no heavy oil taste and the popcorn will have a new light buttery flavor.

CUCUMBERS

Originated in Asia, cucumbers were brought to the Americas by Columbus. They are grown in all sizes from the smallest 1" gherkins to as large as 20" long. They have a very high water content and are an excellent source of fiber. The Greenhouse or English cucumber is becoming more and more popular. However, the price of this thin-skinned skinny "cuke" is considerably higher than the standard market cucumber. Cucumbers should be firm and a good green color, either dark or light, but not yellow. Purchase only firm cucumbers and refrigerate. Large thick ones tend to be pithy and will give when squeezed. Cucumbers only have 13 calories per $3^1/_2$ oz. serving due to their high water content.

Cucumber, Bitterness Remover

This fact really surprised me, and I thought it was just another old wives tale again, one that had been passed down through the years and really didn't work. To my surprise, it actually worked. Next time you purchase a standard cucumber, not the long skinny English variety, cut about one inch off the end and then rub the two exposed areas together in a circular motion while occasionally pulling them apart. This will cause enough suction to release a substance that causes some cucumbers to have a bitter taste. Then discard the small end you used to release the bitterness.

Why are Cucumbers Waxed?

Cucumbers tend to shrink during shipping and storage. The wax coating is to prevent the shrinkage and is edible. The skin should never be removed until you are ready to eat the cucumber or it will lose most of its vitamin C content. The cucumber is capable of holding 30 times its weight in water and is a member of the "gourd family." If you can remember back to the 1930s, "cucumber" was a slang word for a $1 bill.

Waxed Cucumbers and Pickling

Never use a cucumber that has been waxed when preparing pickles. The wax coating will not allow the liquids to be absorbed.

Do Cucumbers Sweeten After They are Picked?

Cucumbers do not contain any starch, therefore they are unable to produce sugar to sweeten them. They will, however, get softer as they age and absorb more moisture into the pectin. If the cucumber gets too soft, just soak the slices in lightly salted cold water to crisp them up. The reaction that occurs removes the unsalted, lower-density water from the cells and replaces it with the higher-density salted water.

How Does a Pickle get Pickled?

It all starts with a fresh cucumber arriving at the pickle factory. There are three processes to control their fermentation. The first is a type of processing that begins with the "curing" stage, where the cucumbers are stored for up to 3 years in large tanks filled with a salt-brine mixture. Next, they are washed and placed in a vat of fresh water, then heated to remove any excess salt residues. After being cleaned and heated, they are packed in a final "liquor" solution, which turns them into the dark green color we are used to purchasing. The second type of processing is for "fresh pack" pickles, which eliminates the holding tanks and speeds the cucumber into a flavored "brine" or "syrup." then immediately into pasteurization. The pickles emerge less salty than the cured pickles and are a lighter green in color. The third method of processing is done totally under refrigeration. These special pickles are known as "deli dills."

They are then cleaned and graded and proceed right to the flavored brine without any further stages. They are never cooked or pasteurized and remain very cucumber-like in flavor and texture. These pickles are always found in the refrigerated section of the market and must be stored under refrigeration. Sour pickles are completed in a solution of vinegar and special spices. Sweet pickles are just sour pickles that have been drained of all traces of brine and bathed in a mixture of vinegar, sugar and spices. The most popular are the small gherkins.

Pickled Calorie Fact
Pickled dill cucumbers have 3 calories per oz. compared to sweet pickles at 30 calories per oz.

Never Pickle with Table Salt
Table salt should never be used when pickling. Use only kosher salt, pickling salt or any other salt that is not iodized. Never use salt that is used on highways.

Storing Cucumbers Before Pickling
When cucumbers are stored below 50°F., they tend to deteriorate and cannot be used for pickling.

Don't Pickle Burpless
Burpless cucumbers do not remain crisp during pickling. They are best used for bread and butter pickles or relishes.

Getting Pickled
When making pickles, remove $\frac{1}{4}$ in. from each end. The ends contain an enzyme that may cause the pickles to soften prematurely.

When Pickling, Use the Right Pot
A number of metals will react with the acid in the vinegar when pickling. Never use brass, copper, iron or even any galvanized utensils. Glass or ceramic pots and plastic or wooden spoons are best.

Grandmother's Trick
If you add a small piece of horseradish to the pickle jar, it will keep the vinegar active while keeping the pickles from becoming soft.

Pickle them Fast
For the best flavor in pickles, make sure you pickle them within 24 hours of harvest. If this is not possible, ask your produce manager to notify you when a fresh shipment arrives. Farmer's markets are best for fresh cucumbers.

De-Blossom the Cucumber
Before using a cucumber for pickling, make sure you remove a small piece of the blossom end. The blossom end contains an enzyme that can make the pickle become soft and mushy.

Where, oh Where Did my Acid Go?
The longer you boil vinegar, the more acid will be released, weakening the vinegar. Boiling vinegar for long periods will result in a poor quality pickle and the preservation qualities will be lost.

Are your Cucumbers Gasping for Air?
Cucumbers should be stored unwashed in a plastic bag with holes to allow air to circulate around the cucumber or should be placed in the vegetable drawer if your refrigerator has one. Cucumbers will only keep for 3-5 days and do best in the warmest part of the refrigerator around 40°F. Cucumbers do not freeze well because of their high water content; too many cells tend to burst, making the cucumber mushy. Pickle juice should be saved and used for making coleslaw, potato salad, etc.

EGGPLANT

Eggplant is a member of the "nightshade" family of vegetables, which includes potatoes, tomatoes and peppers. It is not very high on the nutrient scale and varieties include Chinese purple eggplant, globular eggplant, Japanese eggplant and Italian eggplant. Eggplant contains the chemical, "solanine," which is destroyed when it is cooked. Best never to eat raw eggplant.

Males are Sweeter than Females, at Least in Eggplants!
Male eggplants contain fewer seeds than female eggplants. The seeds make eggplant bitter, but are difficult to remove effectively. To determine which gender the eggplant is, just look at the bottom where the flower is attached. The male eggplant will have a well-rounded bottom and the stem area will be smooth. The female will have a smaller, narrow bottom and an indented stem area.

Eggplant Bitter? Salt it
Since eggplants will only last a few days even under refrigeration, it is best to use them the same day or no later than the next day after they are purchased. Eggplants tend to be a bit bitter and the easiest method of eliminating this problem is to slice the eggplant in $1/2$ in. slices, then lightly salt the slices and

allow them to drain on a wire rack for 30 minutes. This will also reduce the amount of oil that is absorbed when frying. Eggplant is available year round but is best during August and September. Their outer purple-black skin should be smooth and glossy, free of scars and they should be firm. Soft eggplants are usually bitter. Keep them cool after purchase and use in 2-3 days.

Eggplant, the Fat Sponge
The cells in a fresh eggplant have a very high air content that will escape when the eggplant is heated. When you cook an eggplant in oil, the air escapes and the cells absorb a large quantity of oil. As the cells fill up with oil and as the eggplant is moved about, they eventually collapse and release the oil. Eggplants in a recent study absorbed more fat when fried than any other vegetable, 83 grams in 70 seconds, four times more than an equal portion of French fries, thus adding 700 calories to the low-calorie eggplant. Eggplant parmigiana is always served in a pool of olive oil for this reason. Eggplant should never be cooked in an aluminum pot; this will cause the eggplant to become discolored.

New Jersey Should be Called the Eggplant State
Almost 70% of all the eggplants in the world are grown in New Jersey.

Fennel
Fennel is a member of the parsley family and looks like a very plump bunch of celery. Fennel tastes like "anise" and has a sweet flavor. It is very low in calories, can easily be substituted for celery, and is high in vitamin A, calcium and potassium. The bulbs should be firm and clean with fresh-looking leaves. If any brown spots are seen, avoid the fennel. It tends to dry out quickly and should be wrapped and used within 3-4 days.

Horseradish
Horseradish is usually available year round and stores very well. Make sure that you purchase only firm roots with no signs of soft spots or withering. If tightly wrapped in a plastic bag, it should last up to 3 weeks in the refrigerator. If not used in 3-4 weeks, it may turn bitter and lose its hot bite. Try mixing a small amount of horseradish with applesauce as a unique condiment when serving pork. One tbsp. of horseradish has 6 calories and is recommended by the National Heart, Lung and Blood Institute.

Every year about 24 million lbs. of horseradish root are processed in the U. S., producing 6 million gal. of prepared horseradish, enough to season sandwiches that could reach 12 times around the world. A horseradish root was tossed over 80 ft. by Al Weider, which ended up in the Guinness Book of Records.

This Will Clear your Sinuses
The "hotness" from horseradish comes from the chemical, "isothiocyanate," which was given to people to clear their sinuses.

Horseradish to Help Anti-Cancer Drug
Scientists have discovered an enzyme in horseradish that can be utilized to make it easier to manufacture anti-cancer drugs. The enzyme, "horseradish peroxidase," combined with a derivative of chlorophyll has the ability to assist in the production of chlorins by eliminating the multi-stage process into just one step. Peroxidase will also clear certain pollutants from waste water.

Dagwood's Favorite
In the comic strips, Dagwood consumed horseradish regularly, much to the dismay of Blondie.

JERUSALEM ARTICHOKES

These are members of the sunflower family, also known as the "sunchoke." Do not buy them if they are tinged with green or have any soft spots.

- They should be firm and look fresh.
- They will stay fresh under refrigeration for about a week and are easily peeled with a vegetable peeler; however, they do contain a fair amount of nutrition in the skin.
- It has a somewhat nutty, sweet flavor and should be crunchy. It can be boiled, sautéed or even breaded and fried.
- Sunchokes contain no fat or sodium and is a good source of trace minerals.

JICAMA

Originated in Mexico and is becoming very popular in the U.S. It is a root vegetable that can weigh up to 5 lbs. or more. The skin is brown and the flesh is white. It can be used in salads, either diced or in small sticks. Choose only unblemished jicama with no soft spots. Jicama is excellent for stir-fries and an excellent source of vitamin C. It has a slightly sweet flavor and can be substituted for potatoes. One lb. equals about 3 cups. The texture is similar to a water chestnut.

LEEKS

Leeks are a close relative of the onion family, but are milder and sweeter. They are more nutritious, having a wide variety of vitamins and minerals. They are best purchased between September and November. The tops should be green with white necks 2-3 inches from the roots. Do not purchase if tops are wilted or there appears to be signs of aging. Refrigerate and use within 5-7 days after purchase.

LETTUCE

Lettuce can be traced back to Roman days and was originally named for the Romans (Romaine). Lettuce is second only to potatoes in popularity in the U.S. It is mainly used in salads and as garnish. It is available year round and should be heavy and solid, depending on the variety. The greener the leaves, the higher the nutrient content. Never add salt to lettuce prior to serving as this may cause the lettuce to wilt.

The Good and the Bad

Americans consume approximately 11 lbs. of lettuce per person, per year. Romaine lettuce has 6 times as much vitamin C and 8 times as much vitamin A as iceberg lettuce.

Lettuce Scrub

Over 60 chemical agents can be applied to lettuce. Most can be removed by washing with a good organic cleaner or by placing the head stem side up in a sink with 6-8 in. of cold, lightly salted water for a minute while shaking and swirling it around.

Ouch, Ouch

Before you store your lettuce, you should remove the core by hitting the core once against a hard surface, then twist the core out.

Salad Dressing Soaks into Lettuce, Why Won't Water?

Lettuce leaves as well as many plants have a waxy cuticle, which is a water-repelling mixture of various chemicals that are all related to repelling water and assisting the leaves from becoming waterlogged. This cuticle also protects the leaves from losing too much of their internal moisture. The oils in salad dressing are related to the chemicals that keep the water out and to at least allow the oils to stick to the surface. Water molecules also tend to bead up and fall off the leaf, while the oil spreads out and coats the surface. Always place the oil on the salad first, then vinegar, and the vinegar will remain on the lettuce. If you place the vinegar on first, the oil will slip off.

To Tear it or to Cut it

Recently, I watched two different cooking shows on television and watched one chef tear the lettuce and the other cut the lettuce with a knife. The chef who tore the lettuce mentioned that tearing it would extend the life of the lettuce before it would turn brown. After trying this, I found out that it makes no difference at all whether you tear or cut lettuce. It will brown and oxidize in the same amount of time.

Storing Lettuce

All types of lettuce love the cold and the closer the temperature gets to 32°F. without going below that, the longer it will last and the crispier the lettuce will be. Most refrigerators range between 35°-40°F., which is good but not the ideal temperature for lettuce. The lettuce should be stored without washing in a sealed plastic bag with a small hole or two for ventilation. Lettuce will turn brown easily if allowed to remain near most other fruits or vegetables, due to the level of ethylene gas given off by most fruits and vegetables.

Iceberg lettuce will remain fresher than any other type of lettuce due to its higher water content and will store for 7-14 days, romaine lasts for 6-10 days, and butterhead only 3-4 days. If you need to crisp lettuce leaves, place them in the freezer for no more than 2-3 minutes, any more and you may have to discard them.

Lettuce Varieties

Butterhead- Has a soft "buttery" texture and is a "loose" head lettuce. Also known as Boston or bibb lettuce. The leaves are a dark to a grass-colored green.

Iceberg- This is the most popular and extensively sold in the U.S. It is the least nutritious lettuce of all the green vegetables except Belgium endive, which has an even higher high water content. Best to choose any other lettuce.

Looseleaf- The leaves are loosely packed and joined at the stem. The leaves are usually green with a tinge of red near the edges. It is a crisp lettuce with a mild and delicate flavor.

Romaine- Has long green leaves and is usually very crisp. It is mainly used in Caesar salads. Romaine lettuce has 6 times as much vitamin C and 8 times as much vitamin A as iceberg lettuce.

Stem- Has a thick edible stem, approximately 6-8 in. long. Widely grown in China. The U. S. grown variety has been called Celtuce. It has a mild flavor.

Arugula- Solid green lettuce with a high beta-carotene and vitamin C content. Has small flat leaves on long stems and resembles dandelion greens with a somewhat peppery flavor. A cruciferous vegetable, it may be studied regarding cancer prevention.

Belgium Endive- Related to chicory and escarole. Has a bullet-like head with tightly closed creamy white or somewhat yellow leaves and is low in vitamins and minerals. It is even lower than iceberg lettuce.

Chicory- Has loosely bunched, ragged leaves on a long stem. The outer leaves are dark green and it has a somewhat bitter taste. The center leaves, however, are yellow and have a mild taste.

Escarole- Has broad, wavy leaves with smooth edges and a bitter flavor.

Mache- Has a delicate green-colored leaf, is very perishable, and more expensive than most lettuce. The leaves have a fingerlike shape with a mild taste and are only sold in small bunches.

Radicchio- A chicory-family member that looks like a small head of red cabbage with leaves in a variety of colors.

Watercress- Another member of the cruciferous family with dark green leaves and a mustard- like flavor. More popular as a garnish than for use in salads.

Throw the Lettuce in the Washing Machine

Greens need to be thoroughly washed before using them in a salad and they are not always as dry as they should be, if you are in a hurry to prepare the salad. When this happens, just put the greens in a clean pillowcase and place them in the washing machine on the fast spin cycle for no more than 2 minutes.

MUSHROOMS

Mushrooms can be traced back to the Egyptian pharaohs. They are an excellent source of nutrients and are a fungus without any roots or leaves.

- There are approximately 38,000 varieties of mushrooms, many toxic, and a few varieties that are edible. It is best never to pick and eat a wild mushroom.
- Mushrooms contain the chemical substance, "hydrazine," which is found mainly in the stems. Cooking tends to neutralize this chemical, therefore mushrooms should be cooked. However, most of the "hydrazine" is found in the stems.
- Studies from the University of Nebraska showed that mice developed malignant tumors from ingesting large quantities of mushrooms.
- Never eat the stems of raw mushrooms.
- They are available year round but are best November through March.
- Be sure that the caps are closed around the stem and refrigerate soon after purchasing.
- Mushrooms can be kept white and firm when sautéing, if you just add a teaspoon of lemon juice to each quarter pound of butter or olive oil.

Mushrooms Need Room to Breathe

Fresh mushrooms have a very short shelf life of only 2-3 days and need to be stored in an open container in the refrigerator. Plastic containers should never be used since they tend to retain moisture. Best to use the original container or a paper product to store them in. Never clean them before storing them; they will retain moisture and become soggy. If you need to keep them stored for a few days, place a piece of single-layer cheesecloth on top of the container. If they do become shriveled, they can be sliced and used in dishes. When freezing mushrooms, just wipe them off with a piece of damp paper towel, slice them, sauté them in a small amount of butter until they are almost done, allow them to cool, then place them in an airtight plastic bag and freeze. They should keep for 1 year.

Super Mushrooms

The common white button mushroom is not a very hearty mushroom and does not have a very long shelf life, which is one of the reasons it is so costly. Supermarket sales of the button mushroom is about $7 billion annually. However, strains are being genetically modified that will strengthen the mushroom's DNA to produce a stronger, more disease- resistant mushroom.

The Flavor of Mushrooms and MSG

The unique flavor of fresh mushrooms is caused by glutamic acid, the natural version of the same flavor enhancer used in the flavor enhancer, Monosodium Glutamate (MSG). Mushrooms, however, do not have any sodium.

Mushroom Varieties

Button- The standard mushroom that is widely cultivated throughout the world. A large majority of the production goes into jars and is canned and dried. They are a short, stubby mushroom with a round cap and gills on the underneath side. Sizes can vary from 1-10 in.

Cepe- Has a stout stem, a spongy surface instead of gills on the underneath, and a solid brown cap. It is also known as the Bolete, Cep and Porcino mushroom. They range in size from 1-10 in. and are one of the best-tasting mushrooms.

Chanterelle- These are shaped like trumpets. They are large with frilly caps and range in color from gold to yellow-orange.

Enoki- These are sprout-like and have very small caps on a long thin stem. Their color is a creamy white and they have a mild flavor. Best served raw in salads or soups. They're occasionally called "enokitake" mushrooms.

Italian Brown- These are less expensive mushrooms and are similar in appearance to the standard button mushroom. They have a good flavor and are not as tender as button mushrooms.

Kombucha- Also know as Japanese tea fungus. Claims have been made recently that it is a cure-all for numerous diseases and recommended for the prevention of hair loss, arthritis, psoriasis and cancer. According to recent information from the FDA, scientific evidence is lacking. Cornell University is studying the mushroom and has found it to have properties that may have an anti-tumor effect.

• A West African study showed that the tea fungus caused organ damage in rats. A report from the Iowa Department of Public Health stated that two women who drank the tea for several weeks suffered from acidosis.

Morel- These are one of the more high-priced mushrooms. Morels are a dark brown mushroom with conical-shaped spongy caps and have a honey-combed surface.

Oyster- A wild variety, ranging in color from off-white to a gray-brown, they grow in clusters and have a very dense, chewy texture. More flavorful when fully cooked!

Portobello- Also known as Roma mushrooms, they have a hearty flavor, circular caps and long, thick stems. Cut off the woody part. Never wash or soak a Portobello since their caps are like a sponge and will become water-logged. Clean them with a damp cloth or soft vegetable brush. If they are real dirty, just give them a quick rinse.

Shiitake- At one time these were only grown in Japan, but are now grown and are available in the U.S. They are grown on artificial logs and are umbrella-shaped and brown-black in color. They have a rich flavor and are excellent in salads. They may also be called golden oak, forest, oriental black or Chinese black mushrooms. Remove stems.

Wood Ear- May have anti-coagulant properties and health claims are presently showing up in the literature. There are no conclusive studies at present in relation to the avoidance of heart attacks. They are mostly sold dried and have flattened caps that tend to vary in size with a crunchy texture. They have also been known as tree ear, and black tree fungus.

Truffles- These are fungi that grow underground, and are only found by pigs and trained truffle-seeking dogs. They have an excellent flavor, and are a very expensive delicacy. There are two types, the black truffles from France and Italy and the white truffles from Northern Italy.

OKRA

Originated in Ethiopia or North Africa and brought to the U. S. in the 1700s. Okra has been a Southern favorite and is used in many Creole dishes. The taste is a cross between eggplant and asparagus and, because of its sticky juice, has been mainly used in soups and stews. It is a good source of vitamins and minerals. Okra pods should always be green and tender and should not be purchased if the pods look dry or shriveled, since they will lack flavor and be tough. Okra tends to spoil rapidly and should be refrigerated soon after purchasing. It is usually best between May and October. Never wash okra until you are ready to use it or the protective coating will be removed that keeps the pods from becoming slimy. Try grilling okra with a small amount of olive oil brushed on.

Okra is an Excellent Thickener

Okra is actually a vegetable that consists of numerous unripe seed capsules. It is a very high carbohydrate food that is high in fiber and starch and contains a good amount of pectin and gums. The combination of these food elements provide an excellent thickener for soups and stews. As okra is heated, the starch granules absorb water and increase in size. The starch granules soon rupture and release "amylose" and "amylopectin" molecules, as well as some of its gums and pectin. These then attract additional water molecules and increase the volume, thus thickening the food.

Rope me an Okra

Okra has the tendency to become stringy and tough, which is called "roping." To avoid the problem (roping), just add 1 tsp. of white vinegar to the cooking water.

Get out the Hammer and Chisel

Okra seeds have a very hard outer coat, which can hamper germination, resulting in an uneven patchy garden. There are a number of ways to avoid the potential problem:

- Barely nick the seed coating with a sharp knife.
- Place seeds on a piece of fine sandpaper and rub them with another sheet.
- The seeds can be soaked in tepid water at room temperature for 24 hours.
- The seeds can be placed in the freezer for about 12 hours, and then soaked in hot tap water for 30 minutes just before planting.

ONIONS

Probably originated in prehistoric times and was a popular favorite in ancient Egypt and Rome. Onions are a member of a family with over 500 varieties. They are low in calories and some are an excellent source of vitamin A.

Solid as an Onion

Onions should only be purchased hard and dry. Avoid onions with wet necks; this indicates decay. Also, avoid onions that have sprouted. They can easily be stored at room temperature or refrigerated.

Top of the Onion to you

If you are only going to need half an onion, use the top half, since the root half will store longer in the refrigerator.

How to Retain the Sweetness in Raw White and Red Onions

Place the raw chopped onions in a medium strainer, then dip the strainer into a bowl of cold water that contains a small amount of white vinegar (about $1/2$ tsp. to 1 qt. of water). The slight acidity from the vinegar is just enough to stop the onions from turning bitter.

Storing Onions

Onions should be stored ideally in hanging bags, which will allow the air to circulate around them. Never purchase an onion if it has the slightest hint of decay, since it will spread rapidly to healthy onions. The location should be cool and dry. If the weather is hot and humid, it will cut the storage time in half. Otherwise, they should last about 2-3 weeks.

- If you refrigerate onions, they will last for about 2 months but may pass their aroma on to other foods in the refrigerator, even eggs.
- Sprouted onions are still good to use, as well as the sprouts. To freeze onions, just slice (do not blanch them) and place them into a sealed plastic bag.
- They will freeze well for about 1 year.
- The smell of onions can be removed with a strong solution of salt water or a small amount of white vinegar.
- Chives need to be refrigerated and used within 3-4 days after purchase for the best flavor. If frozen, they can be added to any dish while still frozen. Chives can be stored in the refrigerator wrapped in paper towels in a plastic bag. They should last for about 1 week.

How Sweet it is

Vidalia onions are a variety of sweet onion, grown in Georgia and one of the best tasting onions. Sweet onions brown better in the microwave and most are over 12% sugar. Place 1 cup of sliced onions in an uncovered dish with 2 tbsp. of butter for approximately 15 minutes on high. No need to cover as there should be no splattering and they will not brown if covered.

Ring my Onion

When preparing onion rings, make sure you place the onions in the dish as evenly as you can to assure even cooking.

Pithy to Throw it Out

An onion that has become pithy and has started to sprout can be placed in a pot on a windowsill. As it continues to sprout, snip off the sprouts for salad seasoning.

Cooking Onions and Garlic Together

When sautéing onions and garlic together, be sure and sauté the onions first for at least $\frac{1}{2}$ their cooking time. If the garlic is placed in at the same time, it will overcook and possibly burn and release a chemical that will make the dish bitter.

Odor Remover

After cutting up garlic or onions, try rubbing a small slice of fresh lemon on the knife blade and cutting board to remove the odor.

Pop Goes the Onion, Insides Only

Have you ever cooked a whole onion only to have the insides pop out and ruin the appearance of the dish you are preparing? This is a very common occurrence and happens almost every time unless you pierce the onion with a thin skewer once or twice, allowing the steam to escape. Another method, similar to one that is done to chestnuts so they won't explode, is to cut an "X" on the root end, which will allow the steam to be released without damaging the onion.

Shedding a Tear for Onions

When you slice into an onion, a gas is released that affects the lachrymal glands in the eyes and causes a defensive reaction by the body against the chemical, "propanethiol S-oxide," which reacts with the fluid in your eyes, forming sulfuric acid. The body protects itself from the acid by tearing action, which washes out the eyes, ridding itself of the irritant. One of the best methods to avoid tearing is to wear solid plastic goggles.

Other methods, if you prefer not to shed tears, is to cut the root off last, freeze the onion for 10 minutes, or refrigerate for 1 hour before slicing. Other tricks that have worked are to ball up a piece of white bread and place it on the tip of the knife to absorb the fumes. Chewing gum may also help. Another method that works well is to light a candle to absorb the fumes.

Cooking an Onion

Cooking an onion will actually turn the sulfurs in the onion into sugars, which is why onions tend to have a sweeter flavor after cooking. As onions are browned, the sugars and protein change and become a deep brown color and caramelize, which also intensifies the flavor. The reaction is called the "Maillard Reaction." Onions will also change color when cooked and turn a creamy white color from the chemical, "anthocyanin." This chemical should not come into contact with metal ions from aluminum or iron pots or it will turn brown. When onions are sliced with a carbon-steel knife, the same reaction takes place and may change the color of the onion.

Onion Varieties

Bermuda- These are the most common large white onions. The flavor is somewhat mild and they are commonly used in salads.

Purple (red) Onion- These are usually one of the sweetest and have the strongest flavor. They are commonly found on hamburgers and in salads.

Spanish- These are light brown in color, are larger than most onions and the standard onion for cooking. When cooked, it caramelizes easily and is very sweet.

White- Smaller than most onions, they are usually used in soups, stews or dished that are creamed. These are normally used in Mexican cuisine. They will turn golden brown and have a sweet flavor when sautéed.

Yellow- These are full-flavored onions that can be cooked with any food. They will turn a rich brown color when cooked and are commonly used for French onion soup.

A Warm Chive is a Healthy Chive
If you start seeds in the late summer and keep them inside where they can get adequate sun, you will have a nice supply of chives during the winter months.

PARSNIPS

Looks like a top, heavy ivory-colored carrot. It has a celery-like, nutty flavor. Waterhemlock is occasionally confused with parsnips but is a poisonous root. Parsnips are more easily digested when cooked, since they are very fibrous and have strong cell walls.

PEAS

Peas are actually legumes, plants that are pod-bearing with inner seeds. Green peas are one of the best vegetable sources of protein and have been used as a food source since ancient times. Only 5% of all green peas arrive at the market fresh, almost all are frozen or canned. Always select pods that are well filled without bulging. Never purchase flabby, spotted or yellow pods and refrigerate and use within 1 week. When cooking fresh peas, always add a few washed pods to the water. This will improve the flavor and give the peas a richer green color. If peas are cooked in their pods, the pods will open, allowing the peas to rise to the surface. Either method is acceptable. When dried peas are placed in water, the good ones will sink to the bottom and the bad ones will float to the top for removal. Snow peas, however, can be served fresh in salads or cooked without removing the pea.

Peas Are Best When Used in Soups or Stews
The difference between fresh green peas and dried split peas is that the dried peas are actually mature seeds and usually have twice as much starch as the fresh peas. Dried peas contain an excellent source of protein. It is best not to soak split peas before using since the water you will discard will contain a good percentage of the B vitamins. When you use the split peas for soups or stews, you will normally consume the liquid, which will have some of the B vitamins still available.

What's a Wasabi Pea?
This is the Japanese version of horseradish. It is the hot green mound on a plate of sushi. It is usually called a condiment and has been sold to prevent tooth decay since it will kill bacteria in the mouth. A spoonful of "wasabi" will keep the dentist away and probably most of your friends.

PEPPERS

When purchasing peppers, be sure the sides of the pepper are firm. Do not purchase if the colors are dull. Refrigerate and use within 3 days. They are a good source of vitamin A and C; in fact, studies have shown that eating hot peppers does not cause stomach ulcers and may even speed the healing process by increasing circulation. Sweet red peppers contain more vitamin C than an orange. When making stuffed bell peppers, coat the outside of the pepper with vegetable oil and it will retain its color.

Why Won't the Color in Yellow or Red Peppers Fade?

Green peppers contain chlorophyll as the coloring agent, which is sensitive to the acids in the pepper and when the pepper is cooked, are released and cause discoloration. Red and yellow peppers rely on carotenoid pigments for their color. These pigments are not affected by the acids or the heat from cooking.

Red Peppers vs Green Peppers

Nutritionally speaking, sweet red peppers are superior by quite a bit. They are 11 times higher in beta-carotene and have 1-and-a-half times more vitamin C than a sweet green pepper. Hot red peppers contain about 14 times more beta-carotene than a hot green pepper. However, the vitamin C content is the same.

Pepper Protection

Some of the hotter peppers will cause eye irritation and it is recommended that you wear rubber gloves so that your hands will not touch the pepper and accidentally touch your eyes. Once you get hot pepper juice in your eyes, you will remember the experience for some time to come. If you do not have any rubber gloves and must work with the peppers, just coat your hands with vegetable oil. The vegetable oil will protect your skin from being burned. Recent studies have shown that New Mexico has one of the lowest incidences of cardiovascular disease. The study stated that chemicals in hot chili peppers may actually lower cholesterol levels and increase blood coagulation time. In New Mexico, over 55,000 tons are eaten annually. Chilies are probably the oldest known spice, having been found in archaeological digs in Mexico that have been dated to 7,000 B.C.

A Mole that Tastes Good

A "mole" is actually a Mexican sauce made from chili peppers and tomatoes. The combination of ingredients, especially the variety of chili pepper, will determine whether the mole is spicy or mild. The most popular mole is "mole poblano," which is a spicy red sauce that even includes unsweetened chocolate and is served over turkey. Green mole is made from green chilies and cilantro.

Like Hot Peppers? Start Counting the Days

Research into just how hot peppers can become and how long it takes them to develop their "hot bite" is making excellent progress. In the near future agricultural science will be able to advise pepper farmers as to the number of days a pepper needs to grow before it reaches an exact hot stage. Piquin peppers need to grow for 40 days to reach their "hotness" maturity, while Habanero peppers need 50 days to mature. If the peppers are harvested before those days, the peppers will be more acceptable to western tastes.

Indian Tear Gas

The American Indians burned chili peppers when they were fighting off the invading English. The fumes were so potent the English stayed away.

The Color and Hotness of Chili Peppers

The color of chilies is only an indication of the level of ripeness of the vegetable. If the chili is picked before full maturity, it will be green and contain more chlorophyll than a red chili that has matured and lost its chlorophyll. The highest concentration of capsaicin (hot stuff) is located in the white ribs that the seeds are attached to. If you remove the ribs and seeds and wash the insides a few times in cold water, you will eliminate 70-80% of the hotness. When the chili is then fried or boiled, it will lose even more. People that consume chilies frequently are less susceptible to the hot effects and tend to become immune to the bite. Remember, there are two liquids that will neutralize the hot bite: they are whole milk (most dairy products will work) and beer.

The Hottest of the Hot

The hotness of chili peppers is attributed to the chemical, "capsaicinoid" which acts directly on the pain receptors in the mucosal lining of the mouth and the throat. A single drop of this pure chemical diluted in 100,000 drops of water will still cause a blister to form on a person's tongue. This chemical is measured in parts per million, which are converted into heat units called Scoville units. This is how the degree of hotness of a chili pepper is measured. One part per million of capsaicinoid is equal to 15 Scoville units.

Black Olives Absorb Hotness

If you add sliced black olives to a dish that has been over-spiced toward the end of the cooking cycle, they will absorb a large percentage of the hot spice. Best to discard the peppers by straining them out before serving, unless you want to light up your guests. Thanks to Pastor Koch for this tip.

How Hot is Hot?

The following peppers have been graded as to their level of hotness. A grade of 10 will knock your socks off and curl your toes, 6-9 will only knock your socks off, and below 6 will still give you a pretty good kick but is palatable for most people. If your mouth is on fire, try to drink a small amount of milk or beer, since both will neutralize the hot bite. Most dairy products will work well.

PEPPER	SCOVILLE RATING
Habanero	10+ (200,000-300,000)
Thai Piquin	10 (100,000)
Jalapeno	9 (85,000)
Cayenne	8+ (50,000)
Tecpin Cayenne	8+ (50,000)
De Arbol	8 (25,000)
Hungarian Wax	(20,000)
Serrano	6+ (12,000)
Cherry	6 (7,500)
Cascabel	5 (5,000)
Ancho	3+ (1,500)
Anaheim	(1,000)
Pimiento	2 (500)
Peperoncini	(100)

Crisp Peppers

If you would like to keep peppers crisp when canning, just add a grape leaf or two to the jar.

Sweet peppers contain more vitamin C than an orange.

Sweet Pepper Varieties

Bell- Sweet bell peppers are available in four colors: green, red, orange or yellow. They are all relatively sweet but each has its own distinctive flavor difference. When the four are mixed in a salad, it is a real taste treat. Bell peppers contain a recessive gene, which neutralizes capsaicin, which is why they are not spicy. Bell peppers should be stored in the refrigerator in a plastic bag; they will stay fresh about a week. They can be frozen for 6 months and retain a good amount of their nutrients. To seed a bell pepper, hold on to it tight and hit the stem end on the counter hard. This will loosen the seed core and it should pull out easily.

Bell Peppers All Start Out Green- Every sweet pepper starts out as a green pepper and as it ripens, changes to the final color of that variety, which may be yellow, red, green, purple, brown, white or orange. The purple peppers will turn back to green when they are heated.

Hungarian Sweet Peppers Now In Markets- These peppers are long, skinny peppers that range in color from red to orange and even yellow. They are smaller than the American bell pepper and can replace bell peppers in any dish.

The King Kong Of Peppers- One of the largest peppers grown is the Italian Bull Horn Pepper. These peppers can grow to one ft. in length and can be purchased in red or yellow when fully ripe. It is an excellent pepper for sautéing and is very mild.

Well, Excuse Me- If you find that you "burp" too much after eating bell peppers, try peeling the skin off before you use them.

Banana- Mild yellow peppers resembling bananas are available fresh or pickled.

Cherry Peppers- These can be found in both hot and sweet varieties. They look like a small cherry tomato with a long stem.

Cubanelle- Long tapered pepper about 4 in. long. Sold in either green or yellow.

Pimento- Heart-shaped peppers, generally sold in jars and usually found in gourmet markets.

Hot Pepper Varieties

Anaheim- One of the most common chili with mild to moderately hot bite. Consumed in either the green or red stages of growth. Often found in long string of red peppers. Used for chili rellanos.

Ancho- Dried peppers that are flat, wrinkled and usually heart-shaped. Mild to moderately hot and usually ground, then used in sauces and salsa.

Cascabel- Moderately hot red chili with seeds that tend to rattle. When dried, their skin turns a brownish-red.

Cayenne- These are one of the hottest chilies. They are long with sharply pointed, curled tips and usually dried and made into a spice for chili and salsa.

Habanero- Lantern shaped peppers, which grow to about 2-3 inches. Their color is yellow-orange and are the hottest pepper grown. They are known for extending their bite for some time. Best to have milk handy for this one.

Hungarian Wax- Moderately hot yellow-orange pepper. May be purchased fresh or pickled.

Jalapeno- One of the most common peppers, they are usually moderately hot to very hot and are sold at their green stage. The red stage, which is the full maturity stage, is super hot. Canned jalapenos are usually milder because the seeds are removed and they are packed in liquid.

Serrano- Popular chili in Mexico! They look like a small torpedo and are very hot.

Give Them Something to Read

Next time you plant peppers, try wrapping each plant stem in 6x6-in. square of newspaper. Dip the newspaper in cool tap water before wrapping each pepper plant. When the roots are kept moist, it keeps away the cutworms.

RADISHES

Originated in China thousands of years ago. They are a cruciferous vegetable and contain phytochemicals that are under investigation relating to cancer prevention. Their green tops are edible and tend to have a peppery flavor. Radishes are a good source of vitamin C. They are available year round. Larger radishes tend to be somewhat pithy while smaller ones are usually more solid. Squeeze to be sure they are not mushy and don't buy if the tops are yellow or if there is any sign of decay. A number of varieties are sold: these include California Mammoth Whites, Daikons, Red Globe and White Icicles.

Daikon Radish Facts

Originated in the Mediterranean area and brought to China in 500 B.C. The roots can be 2-4 in. in diameter and from 6-20 in. long. The largest grown are between 40-50 lbs. More are produced in Japan than any other vegetable. In the U.S. they are mainly grown in the Houston, Texas area. To keep daikons white, cook the radish in water that has been used to wash rice or add some rice bran to the cooking water.

Radishes to the Rescue

Radishes have stronger sprouts and can break through the soil easier than carrot sprouts. If you plant radishes with the carrots, they will break through the soil crust and allow the carrots to sprout more easily.

Friends Forever

Radish seeds develop strong sprouts that are capable of breaking through the ground. Parsnips do not have very strong sprouts and need the radish sprouts to open up the soil for them.

RHUBARB

Popular vegetable for making pies! Its origins can be traced back to Southern Siberia. The plant has edible stalks with heart-shaped large leaves, which are poisonous. Rhubarb is occasionally referred to as a fruit since it is a common pie ingredient, but it is a true vegetable. Two varieties can be purchased, the hothouse and the outdoor types. Rhubarb does contain oxalic acid which may reduce the absorption of calcium and is not recommended in large quantities, especially for women who are close to or going through menopause.

Salsify

This odd-shaped plant has also been called the "oyster plant" since their appearance is similar to an oyster. The plants' blossoms always close at high noon and it is also known as the "Johnny go to bed at noon" plant.

SPINACH

Was first grown in the U.S. in the 1700s. It is high in vitamins and minerals, as well as being one of the best vegetable sources of protein. Spinach, however, does contain the chemical "oxalate" which tends to bind with certain minerals, such as calcium and limits their usefulness by the body.

The Eye in Popeye

Spinach contains two special antioxidants that belong to the carotenoid family: lutein and zeaxanthin. These antioxidants in recent studies have proven to be important in an age-related disease of the eye known as "macular degeneration." This form of blindness is prevalent in people over 65 and is the leading cause of blindness. Experts believe that overexposure to sunlight, pollution and smog over a period of years may contribute to this problem. Consuming foods that are high in these carotenoids, such as kale, collard greens, spinach, sweet red peppers, mustard greens, and hot chili peppers may significantly lower the risk by as much as 75%.

Color me Green

A trick to keeping the nice green color in spinach used by chefs is to cook spinach with the pot uncovered. The buildup of too much steam will cause the chemicals that create the color to lose their ability to maintain the dark green.

Should Spinach be Eaten Raw?

While most vegetables should be eaten raw, especially to retain their enzymes, spinach has a tough cellular wall that will only release the maximum amount of nutrients if it is cooked. Carrots are actually better cooked for the same reason. Our digestive system cannot break these two vegetables down sufficiently to gain the most from them. Cook in as little water as possible and for the shortest period of time. In fact, boiling in 1cup of water, instead of 2 cups will help the spinach retain twice as much of its nutrients.

Storing Popeye's Favorite

Spinach will only store for 2-3 days, providing it is stored in a sealed plastic bag. Do not wash it or cut it before you are ready to serve it. When purchasing spinach that has been prepackaged, be sure and open the bag and remove any brown or darkened leaves since they may cause the balance of the leaves to deteriorate at a faster rate. When freezing spinach, do not freeze the stems, only the whole leaves. This will allow the leaf to retain more of its moisture. To store spinach for a longer period, it should be washed in cold water, dried carefully and thoroughly with paper towel and stored in the freezer in an airtight bag. It should keep for 10-12 months, if the freezer is kept at 0°F.

RUTABAGA

To prepare rutabaga, just slice off the top end, cut into pieces, peel off the skin and the wax covering. To microwave, you will need to make small punctures in several places and wrap it in paper towel. It will take about 15 minutes on high before it is fork tender.

SPROUTS

When seeds are moistened, they change into edible sprouts or shoots. When this occurs, the seed utilizes its carbohydrates and fat and leaves a good percentage of its vitamins intact, making sprouts a healthy food. Their nutrient content, while preserved, is not appreciably high compared to most mature vegetables. They are healthy and a pleasant departure from the standard vegetables.

Little Sprouts

When purchasing fresh sprouts, remember that they can only be stored in the refrigerator for 7-10 days providing they are left in their original container, refrigerated, and placed in a plastic bag. They should be lightly moistened before putting them into the bag and sealed. Too much water in the bag will cause decay. Remember, the shorter the tendril, the more tender and younger the sprout. Sprouts cannot be frozen successfully: they become mushy and bland. Refrigerate for 1-2 days at 36°- 40°F. (20° - 40°C.).

Common Sprout Varieties

Adzuki Bean- Very sweet, small bean-shaped with grass-like sprouts. Has a nutty taste.

Alfalfa- Threadlike white sprouts that have small green tops and a mild nutty flavor.

Clover- Looks similar to the alfalfa sprout with tiny seeds that look like poppy seeds.

Daikon Radish- Have a silky stem and leafy top. The taste is somewhat peppery and spicy hot.

Mung Bean- Larger than alfalfa sprouts and has a blander taste. A thick white sprout used in many oriental dishes. Be sure these sprouts are crisp when you purchase them.

Soybean- Sprouts have a somewhat strong flavor but a good source of protein. They contain a small amount of a toxin and large amounts should be avoided. Cooking for at least 5 minutes tends to neutralize the toxin.

Sunflower
Crunchier than alfalfa and has a milder flavor.

SQUASH

Squash is a fleshy vegetable with a solid protective rind. It has been a staple vegetable for thousands of years. They are a low-calorie food and contain an excellent level of vitamins and minerals, which vary depending on the variety.

- It is available year round. The soft-skinned types should be smooth and glossy. The hard-shelled type should have a firm rind.
- Refrigerate all soft-skinned varieties and use within a few days. Summer squash varieties include chayote, patty pan, yellow crookneck, yellow straightneck and zucchini.
- Winter squash varieties include acorn, banana, buttercup, butternut, calabaza, delicata, golden nugget, hubbard, spaghetti, sweet dumpling, turan and pumpkin.
- The winter squash varieties tend to develop a higher beta-carotene (precursor for vitamin A) content after being stored than it has immediately after being picked. Also, the smaller the squash, the more flavor it tends to develop.
- Squash blossoms are edible and have an excellent flavor. They make a great garnish for many dishes and can even be battered and fried. Try stuffing them with cream cheese for a real treat.
- When pureeing squash, the strings should be easy to remove when you are using the blender. The strings will entwine around the blades and can easily be removed.

What is the New Freedom II Squash?

The Asgrow Company of Michigan has developed a new strain of squash called the "Freedom II" squash that is resistant to viruses transmitted by aphids. This is expected to make squash more available and lower the prices, due to less pesticide use. The company is also developing virus-resistant cantaloupe, watermelon and cucumbers.

"A" Winner

One of the best sources of vitamin A and beta-carotene is the pumpkin. An 8- oz., 40-calorie serving contains about 27,000 IU.

Jack-O-Lantern Miracle

One of the biggest problems every Halloween is that the pumpkin will get soft and mushy a few hours after it has been carved. The problem is the result of the air coming in contact with inside flesh, thus allowing bacteria to grow at a rapid pace. Spraying the inside of the pumpkin with an antiseptic spray will retard the bacterial growth and reduce the time of deterioration. Make sure you do not eat the pumpkin or the seeds, after it has been sprayed.

Pumpkin Pie? Or Squash Pie?

Manufacturers may be placing smaller amounts of "real" pumpkin into the cans that say "pumpkin pie filling." The reason for this is that they are finding out that "real" pumpkin does not retain its flavor well, so they are adding a large percentage of banana squash to the cans.

Board Up Your Pumpkins

When your pumpkins or squash start to mature, try placing a small board under each fruit. This will protect the fruit from soil-borne bacteria and fungus.

Taro

An underground tuber, similar to a potato. It is primarily used and grown in Hawaii and used to make a local dish called "poi." There are two varieties of taro: the wetland taro and the dry-land taro. Taro is high in carbohydrates and potassium and low in sodium. The dry-land taro is presently also being made into "taro chips."

Here Comes Hawaiian Spinach

A new snack food is now being produced called, "Hawaiian Spinach." The taro root is baked or roasted and turned into taro chips, which are low in calories and sodium and high in carbohydrates and potassium.

Tomatillos (Tomate Verde)

These look like small green tomatoes but with a thin parchment-like skin. They are also called Mexican green tomatoes and they have a somewhat lemon-apple flavor. They are popular in salads and salsas, and are usually available year round. Purchase only firm tomatillos. The smaller they are, the sweeter they will be. Make sure that the husk is light brown and fresh- looking, and remove the husks before cooking.

TOMATOES

The question of whether the tomato is a fruit or a vegetable was settled by the Supreme Court in 1893, when it was officially declared a vegetable. Botanically, it is still a fruit, actually a berry. It is a member of the nightshade family, making it a relative of potatoes, bell peppers and eggplant.

- It is available year round and should be well formed and free of blemishes.
- Green tomatoes will eventually turn red, but will not have a good flavor. Green tomatoes will ripen faster if you store them with apples.
- A vine-ripened tomato is best. Refrigerate, but do not allow it to freeze.
- To peel tomatoes easily, place them in boiling water and remove from heat. Allow them to stand for 1 minute before plunging them into cold water.
- Tomatoes will store longer if you store them stem down.
- Never allow tomatoes to ripen in direct sunlight. They will lose most of their vitamin C.
- Americans consume approximately 25 lbs. of tomatoes per person, per year. If you are expecting a frost and have tomatoes on the vine, pull them up by the roots and hang them upside down in a cool basement until the fruit ripens.

How Do You Reduce Acidity in Tomato Products?
Some people are unable to eat spaghetti sauces and other tomato-based foods due to their higher acidic content. When chopped, carrots added to any of these dishes will reduce the acidity without affecting the taste. The high fiber content of the carrot seems to do the job.

A New Tomato Paste

A new genetically modified (GM) tomato paste will soon be available in the U. S. The paste will have a richer natural flavor than present products in markets. The GM tomato paste is produced from tomatoes that are able to remain on the vine longer to ripen, instead of being picked green and forced to ripen after picking, which causes a loss of flavor.

Tomato Aroma Only Lasts for Three Minutes?

If you like the aroma of fresh tomatoes in your salad, don't refrigerate them. Tomatoes should be left at room temperature, if they are going to be used within 2-3 days after purchase. They should never be sliced or peeled until just before you are going to serve them. The aroma is produced by the chemical z-3-hexenal, which is released when the tomato is sliced open. The aroma chemical only lasts at the "maximum aroma" level for three minutes before it starts to lose its scent. If you do refrigerate a tomato, the chemical becomes dormant, but if you allow it to return to room temperature before you slice it, the aroma will still be active. If the storage temperature is below 50°F., it will interfere with the ripening process and stop it cold. Even if the tomato does turn from green to red, it will still not be ripe.

Dr. Miles Patent Medicines

One of the patent medicines of the early 1800s was "Dr. Miles Compound Extract of Tomato." Basically, they were selling ketchup as a medicinal product to treat any number of diseases.

Tomatoes, a Real Survivor

Studies in Russia have shown that tomatoes are able to survive 60,000 times the radiation damage as humans and still be able to reproduce.

The Best Dried Fruit and Tomatoes, Anywhere

The finest, all natural fruits and tomatoes can be found at Timber Crest Farms in Healdsburg, California. All products are unsulfured and packaged without any preservatives or additives. The farm is owned by Ron and Ruthie Waltenspiel, who have been producing the finest quality products for 32 years. Almost all the products come from their ranch with most grown under strict organic regulations of the California Health and Safety Code. This is one of the cleanest operations of its kind I have ever had the privilege of visiting. To order or receive a catalog call (707) 433-8251 or write to Timber Crest Farms, 4791 Dry Creek Road, Healdsburg, California 95448.

Skinning a Tomato

The easiest method of removing skin from a tomato is to first remove the core; cut an "X" on the bottom and place the tomato in a pot of boiling water for 10-12 seconds. Quickly remove and place into a bowl of ice-cold water (with ice cubes). Remove the tomato in 25-30 seconds and the skin will peel right off.

What is a Designer Label Tomato?

A new tomato is making an appearance in supermarkets everywhere called the "FlavrSavr™." This is a genetically engineered tomato that can be shipped vine-ripened without rotting and is the first whole food to be born of biotechnology. Most tomatoes are shipped green and gassed with ethylene gas to turn them red before they get to the market. The only downside is that the new tomato will cost about $2.00 per lb.

To Flower or not to Flower

If you would like early tomatoes, purchase plants with flowers. Don't be upset if the flowers fall off while you are planting them. They are in their reproductive stage and more flowers will appear shortly. If the plants are young and without flowers, they will bear fruit later but will give a better harvest.

Speedy Planting

The easiest method of planting tomatoes plants is to use a bulb planter. It will result in a deep hole and will not take a lot of work.

MOOOOOOO

Dry cow manure is the best fertilizer for tomato plants. It will give you a higher yield. Use about 100 lbs. per sq. ft. in plants that are spaced about 3 ft. apart.

Puree Concentrate

One oz. of tomato puree has twice the vitamin C and 20% more beta-carotene than one oz. of fresh tomato.

Whoa Catsup

Heinz catsup leaves the bottle at a speed of 25 MPH. Once you finally get it started!

Ka Boom, Ka Boom

Never place a whole tomato in the microwave: it will explode.

Reported Health Benefits:

- An antioxidant that is concentrated in tomatoes called "lycopene" is being studied and is showing promise in reducing the risk of heart disease, prostate cancer and even slowing mental decline with old age.
- Adding a small amount of olive oil also improves the absorption of lycopene. Processed tomato products contain more lycopene than fresh tomatoes.
- The lycopene level in tomato paste is 16 mg. per oz., tomato sauce has 5mg. per oz. and fresh tomato has only 1mg. per oz.
- One of the more popular foods consumed in the U. S., pizza is one of the popular sources for lycopene.
- Cooking tends to release more usable lycopene than eating a raw tomato.
- Tomato sauce is now at the forefront of a number of studies relating to protecting a person from heart attacks.
- The extraction of lycopene may show up in health food stores in shakers similar to salt and pepper shakers.

TURNIPS

Related to cabbage, turnips grow easily even in poor soil conditions and are a good source of complex carbohydrates. It is a cruciferous vegetable and can weigh up to 50 lbs. Turnips are a better source of fiber than an apple (but I'd rather eat an apple).

WATER CHESTNUTS

Chestnuts are actually grown underground and are the tip of a tuber. They are the carbohydrate storage-depot for plant growth. They must be kept cool or they will sprout and are an excellent source of trace minerals, especially potassium. Also, they contain vitamin C.

X Marks the Spot
Always remember to cut an "X" before you place chestnuts in the oven for roasting. If you don't, you may hear a small explosion. This also makes them easier to peel.

WATERCRESS

Watercress is a member of the mustard family and its natural location is Europe. It has a peppery flavor and contains oil of mustard. Watercress can easily be grown by just removing one or two from the bunch and placing them into a shallow tray of water. It will sprout in about 10 days and can then be transplanted to a pot. The water should be changed everyday for the best results.

FRUITS AND VEGETABLES

Carbohydrate Content Analysis

VERY LOW	LOW	MEDIUM	HIGH	VERY HIGH
Asparagus	Beets	Artichokes	Corn	Rice
Bean Sprouts	Brussels Sprouts	Kidney Beans	Dried Beans	Potato (sweet)
Beet Greens	Carrots	Parsnips	Lima Beans	Yams
Broccoli	Chives	Peas	Pickles (sweet)	
Cabbage	Collards	Apples	Avocado	
Cauliflower	Dandelion	Cherries	Bananas	
Celery	Eggplant	Grapes	Figs	
Chard, Swiss	Kale	Olives	Prunes	
Chicory	Kohlrabi	Pears	Raisins	
Cucumber	Leeks	Pineapple		
Endive	Okra	Mango		
Escarole	Onions	Blueberries		
Lettuce	Parsley			
Mushroom	Peppers			
Mustard Greens	Pumpkin			
Radishes	String Beans			

Complimenting Combinations

Certain vegetables go better with each other and will compliment the taste of the others when mixed together. Some of the tasty combinations are Brussels sprouts + peas + onions, green beans + carrots + mini-onions, peas + corn + zucchini, parsnips + peas + corn, celery + corn + peas.

The Best in Organics

One of the best quality organic farms in the U. S. is the Diamond Organics in Freedom, CA. Most of the fruits and vegetables are picked when ordered and shipped immediately.

Getting Low on Water?

When cooking vegetables in a pot of hot water, always add the hottest water you can if the water level gets too low. Adding cold water may affect the cell wall and cause the vegetable to become tough.

Fruit and Veggie Juices

The information contained herein, which suggests health improvement and uses of juices for other than general health purposes, is meant to be taken in a historical perspective and is not meant to be used to treat or imply that the juice will help any medical condition. Your family physician is still your first line of medical care and treatment.

FRUIT AND BERRY JUICES (APPLE TO PINEAPPLE)

Apple Juice

Almost 50% of all apples grown in the United States are processed into apple products or juice. The average American consumes about 30 lbs. of apples annually in the form of juice, applesauce and pie filling.

Juicing up your Baby

Most pediatricians tend to recommend apple juice as baby's first juice. Apple juice is a mild laxative and has a very acceptable sweet taste. It is also commonly fortified with vitamin C, which will allow the baby to absorb more iron, which is very important for growth.

Numero Uno Apple Juice Product

If you enjoy apples, then Martinelli's products are worth trying. They have produced quality products since 1868. Their sparkling cider can't be beat. All products are 100% pure juice and have no flavorings, concentrates or preservatives and are only lightly carbonated. They started out producing cider and carbonated soft drinks in California's first commercial orchard.

The Sauce from Apples

Whether your applesauce is smooth or chunky usually depends on when you add the sugar to the recipe. If you would prefer chunky applesauce, you should add the sugar before cooking the apples. If you prefer a smooth applesauce, then add the sugar after the apples have been cooked and mashed. Commercially prepared sweetened applesauce can contain as much as 77% more calories than unsweetened varieties.

Butter Me an Apple, Please

Apple butter, when prepared properly, does not contain any fat. It should be prepared with mashed apples, cinnamon and all-spice.

Apple Juice to the Rescue

When apples lose their moisture, just slice then up, pour apple juice over them and refrigerate for about 30 minutes.

Apricot Juice

Apricot juice is very high in vitamin A and contains a good amount of sulfur. The juice has been used to reduce the effects of aging, such as premature wrinkling of the skin. The combination of vitamins, minerals, oils, amino acids and enzymes may even be related to slowing the aging process. The juice is also being studied in relation to slowing the growth of cancerous tumors.

The Apricot Astronaut

The apricot was one of the favorite fruits taken on the Apollo moon mission. One oz. of the juice can contain 20% of your daily vitamin A requirement in the form of beta-carotene. They also contain a high level of iron.

Banana Juice

Banana juice has been known to ease the suffering of people who have colitis and heartburn. It is an excellent source of potassium, vitamin A and a number of other beneficial elements.

Berry, Berry Interesting, but not Funny

Bananas contain less water content than most other fruits. They are actually a "berry" from a plant classified as an herb tree, which is capable of reaching heights of 30 ft. The banana tree is also the largest plant in the world with a woody stem.

Berry Juices

In cultures that have to survive by adding a significant amount of berries and nuts to their diet, there is little if any incidence of cancer. Most berries and a number of nuts contain ellagic acid, which researchers are investigating to find out if the acid has an effect on cancer cells. In tests on mice, the mice that were fed ellagic acid had 45% fewer tumors. Berry juice is also an important source of iron.

Berry Baking: The Sinking Solution
When you make a dish with berries, be sure the batter is thick enough so that the berries can easily be held in suspension. If the batter is too thin, they will just sink to the bottom.

Berry Stain Removal
Berry juice stains can easily be removed from your hands by using a small amount of lemon juice.

Citrus Juice
The first citrus juice dates back to 500 B.C. and was prepared from the "citron," which resembles a knobby lemon and is somewhat tart. All citrus fruit must ripen on the tree, since they will not continue to ripen once picked. Before the fruit is picked, representative samples are taken and evaluated as to their sugar (brix) and acid content. As soon as the percentages are correct, the fruit will be harvested. Almost 98% of all citrus fruit is still harvested by hand using wooden ladders and sacks.

The Case of the Green Orange
It is not uncommon to see oranges with either a hint of green or quite a bit of green. The green color is caused by temperature changes. For an orange to be a nice orange color, it needs warm days and cool nights. If the nights remain too warm, the orange cannot turn as orange as we are used to. The fruit will continue to ripen normally; however, the green coloration remains. The fruit will be just as good even if it has the green tint. Another factor may be that the tree had an extra shot of chlorophyll in the spring, but here again it doesn't affect the quality or the sweetness of the fruit. When making juice, it doesn't matter whether the oranges are orange or somewhat greenish.

Storing Juice Oranges
Never store oranges in sealed plastic bags. If they are stored in too airtight a container, small drops of moisture will form and cause mold to grow. The best temperature to store any citrus is around 45°F. (7.2° C.). Refrigerators are the recommended location.

The Juiciest of the Juicy

The best oranges for juicing are the Hamlin and Valencia. Both will be found to have thin skins and either no seeds or very few seeds and will produce the most juice.

The Tropicana Story

Tropicana purchases almost 25% of Florida's oranges directly from the growers, which amount to over 500 truckloads per day that must be processed. The plant is capable of processing over 50 million oranges per day. The juice extractors are capable of extracting juice from 700 oranges per minute producing 1 million gal. of juice per day.

Lemon and Lime Juice Facts

Lemon juice is an excellent flavoring for many dishes and can replace salt in most of them. The high acid content tends to mask the need for the salty taste. Both lemon and lime have the ability to blend well with a number of foods, such as potatoes, rice, all types of salads and most cooked vegetables. When the juice is processed, it does tend to lose a good percentage of its flavor, so try and use the juice from fresh-squeezed for the best results and taste. A real treat is to use "key lime" juice, which may only be found in a health food store. They also are great in salads to replace vinegar.

Got a Throbbing Headache? Use a Lime

An old wives' tale that tends to work almost every time is to rub $\frac{1}{2}$ of a lime across your forehead a few times. There is a chemical in lime that tends to relax the muscles in the head.

Cooking Fish with Lime Juice and no Heat

Acids have a tenderizing effect on the meat of fish and when placed in lime or lemon juice for about 10 hours, the meat will turn white instead of translucent. There is no heat generated. However, the meat will look as if it were cooked. Two foods that utilize acidic cooking are pickled herring and seviche.

Natural Tenderizer

Both lemon and lime juice are natural tenderizers for any type of fowl dish.

Grapefruit Juice at its Best

The best grapefruit for juicing is the White Seedless. It has a thin yellow peel with almost white flesh and is almost seedless. Another good one is the Flame Grapefruit, which contains more soluble fiber in 1 grapefruit than 2 cups of popcorn.

The Best of the Best

If you are going to make orange juice in a blender, always use the white membrane just under the skin.

The membrane is called the "albedo" and contains a higher percentage of vitamin C than the pulp or juice. Albedo is also being studied for its cholesterol lowering qualities.

Don't You Dare Pucker up

Markets are starting to sell a sweet lemon grown in California called the "millsweet." They resemble a cross between a lemon and a lime. Now you will be able to make lemonade without adding sugar.

Cranberry Juice

Cranberries are just too tart to be used for juice without the addition of a sweetener. That is why it is rarely sold as pure 100% cranberry juice and usually mixed with other juices.

Bladder Be Healthy

There have been numerous studies regarding cranberry juice and its relationship to bladder infections. Studies have shown that cranberry juice does not abnormally raise the acid levels in the bladder, which was originally thought to lower the incidence of bladder infections. However, the latest studies now show that there exists an antioxidant compound that protects the walls of the bladder from bacteria adhering to it. Studies are still being conducted regarding both cranberries and wild blueberries in relation to bladder health.

Fig Juice

Fig juice is normally not a drink, but is used as a meat tenderizer. Fresh figs contain the chemical "ficin," a proteolytic enzyme that is capable of breaking down proteins with a similar action as that of "papain" from papaya or "bromelain" from pineapples. Ficin is effective in the heat ranges of 140°-160°F. (60°-71.1° C.), which is the most common temperature range when simmering stews. If you add a few fresh figs to the stew, it will tenderize the meat and impart an excellent flavor. If the temperature rises above 160°F. (71.1°C.), "ficin" will become inactive.

Grape Juice

Grape juice has more calories than any other fruit juice, due to its high sugar content. It contains no vitamin C once processed. Make sure the label reads "pure grape juice" or 100%, since grape juice is frequently blended with other juices that do not contain a high level of sugar. If you do purchase pure 100% grape juice, it can be diluted with water or seltzer for a great drink.

The Secret is out

Researchers are isolating the biologically active flavonoids (anthocyanins) that may lower the risk of heart disease and strokes. It was thought that drinking red wine was the reason the French had a lower incidence of heart disease, but it is actually the flavonoids in the red grape. The active flavonoids can be found in the skin, seeds and even the stem of the red grape plant. Drinking 8-10 ounces of red grape juice daily may reduce your risk without drinking the wine or taking aspirin. The American Heart Association does not recommend drinking red grape juice for any health benefit; however, the University of Wisconsin found that 10 oz. per day reduced the stickiness (clotting) of blood platelets better than red wine and aspirin together. In fact, there are more ongoing studies by the University of Illinois that are relating the phytochemical compound, "reservertrol," found in red grape skin (ends up in the juice) as a potent cancer fighter. Purple grape juice is also being investigated in relation to Lou Gehrig's Disease by the University of Wisconsin.

Grapefruit Juice

The heavier the grapefruit, the more juice it will hold. However, grapefruits grown in the western United States has a thicker skin and will have lower juice content.

Medical Alert

A researcher at the University of Western Ontario found that grapefruit juice caused a three-fold increase in absorption rate for a blood pressure medication. Some of the drugs that can be affected are calcium-channel blockers, such as Procardia, Cylosporine, Seldane and the estrogen, Estinyl. Researchers are trying to isolate the guilty ingredient causing the reaction.

Papaya Juice

The most effective papaya juice is derived from the "green papaya." This is the stage before it ripens to an orange-yellow color and turns sweet. At the green stage, the papaya contains a higher level of the chemical, "papain" and "fibrin." Green papaya juice has been used to heal ulcers and has been found to speed up the healing process. In the South Pacific, papaya leaves have been used to speed the healing of serious lacerations with phenomenal success.

Pineapple Juice

A nutritious drink that contains a number of minerals, including potassium, iron, phosphorus, and calcium. It also contains good levels of vitamins A and C. Pineapples also contain the enzyme "bromelain," which has been effective in treating an intestinal blockage condition called a phytobezoar and as an anti-inflammatory. Bromelain is used as an effective meat tenderizer in marinades.

Kona, Hawaii Island Juice

Yes, it's spelled right! This is a 100% juice product using a pineapple base in all its products. The drinks are non-pasteurized and contain real 100% juice with nothing added. This is one of the finest and most flavorful juice beverages on the market.

STORAGE OF JUICES

Frozen juices once thawed and reconstituted should be stored in well-sealed containers. The vitamin C content will only last for a few days at a decent concentration. Fresh squeezed orange juice will only keep for 24 hours before it loses a percentage of vitamin C. All juices should also be kept cold to reduce their nutrient losses. Juice purchased in paper cartons, glass or plastic containers from the supermarket should retain 90% of their vitamin C content for at least one week and up to 70% after two weeks. Opening and closing the container too often, however, will change these percentages significantly.

Additives/Preservatives

When purchasing any type of juice, it is always wise to check the label and read the list of ingredients. Many products, including lemon juice, add a number of preservatives to their products. While most of the preservatives and coloring and flavoring agents are harmless, it would be best to limit the use of products that contain these added chemicals. If possible, it is always best to use the raw, natural food. Even if the label reads 100% pure juice, it may still contain an additive. Even 100% pure pineapple juice still has an anti-foaming agent included or it would foam up so much, it would be difficult to pour.

NUTRITIONAL INFORMATION

The Musical Juice Drink

We are all too familiar with the fact that beans cause intestinal gas to form, but there are a number of fruit juices that will precipitate a real good attack of gas. This occurs when the natural sugar in the fruit called, "fructose," combines with the chemical, "sorbitol." If you want to avoid gas from fruit juices, you will need to stay away from apple, pear, cherry, plum, prune and peach juices. These are the juices that contain both fructose and sorbitol. Since these are healthy juices, my recommendation is to reduce the serving size, which may eliminate the problem. Also, sorbitol is a very common sweetener used in diabetic products, and if your consume one of those products and drink almost any fruit juice, you are combining fructose and sorbitol.

E. Coli is at it Again

When you purchase apple juice, it is pasteurized and not just "raw." The E.coli bacteria really gets around and anywhere a cow goes, the bacteria may follow. If the cow walks through an apple orchard and leaves manure, it may get on the apples that fall off the trees, which are the ones more likely to be used in apple juice and cider, since they don't look good enough for the market. If the product is not produced under strict, sanitary conditions, the E. coli found in the manure will contaminate the batch. Also, it is never wise to eat any fruit off the ground without really washing it good with an organic cleaner.

One of the Healthiest Juices

Eight oz. of orange juice contains at least 60 mg. of vitamin C, 20% of the recommended USRDA of folic acid, 15% of your fiber, and 12% of the recommended potassium. The National Institute of Health, however, recommends 200 mg. of vitamin C, which would be a little more realistic with our stressed-out lifestyles.

Putting a Label on it

The only three beverages that contain the required amount of nutrients and vitamins to be called a "healthy" drink are orange juice, grapefruit juice and skim milk, according to the FDA. For a food to be considered "healthy," it must be low-fat, contain no more than 60 mg. of cholesterol, have less than 480 mg. of sodium and contain at least 10% of the RDA of either vitamin A, vitamin C, protein or fiber.

A Safe Squeeze

Before oranges are squeezed, they are inspected for damage and contamination. The oranges are then kept chilled to help retain the vitamin C content. All fruit is then washed with a neutral detergent, sanitized and rinsed with pure water. The orange is then squeezed from the outside, which eliminates the bitter taste from the peel. As soon as it is squeezed, it is cold- chilled to below zero temperatures and placed in cold storage.

Don't Give your Bones a Break

Orange juice is an excellent source of calcium. One 8-oz. glass of Tropicana Pure Premium Calcium Juice contains 350 mg. of calcium. The calcium is of a type that is easily absorbed and useable. Orange juice is also an excellent source of folate, which is a B vitamin that studies show is very effective in reducing the risk of heart disease and certain birth defects.

Another Lime Disease?

If your child likes limes and gets the oil found in the skin on his skin, it may cause a rash that looks like a bad burn. In fact, the oil, "bergamot," if allowed to remain on the skin and then exposed to sunlight will actually cause the skin to burn. There are a number of other foods that contain the oil and will cause this phototoxic reaction that you should be aware of, such as carrots, celery, figs, parsley, parsnips, coriander, caraway seeds, fennel and anise.

An Apple a Day

A new study conducted at the National Public Health Institute in Helsinki, Finland found that an anti-oxidant, flavonoid compound in apples called, "quercetin," reduced the risk of lung cancer by 46%. Fruit juices are one of the best sources of flavonoids.

The Bad Side of a Good Food

Grapefruit and grapefruit juice should not be taken with certain medications and it would be wise to check with your physician, if you are on medication and consume grapefruit. The types of medications that may interact and increase absorption are channel blockers, antihistamines, sedatives, antiviral agents, hormones and immuno-suppressants.

Where's my Vitamin C?

Apples are not a good source of vitamin C and when they are processed into apple juice or cider, virtually all the vitamin C is lost. Many apple products fortify their products with vitamin C.

Nectar

Apricot Nectar- Apricot nectar is high in beta-carotene, which is instrumental in producing vitamin A in the body. Calories in apricot nectar are only slightly higher than orange juice and it is also a good source of potassium.

Peach Nectar- Most cans contain 100% of the RDA for vitamin C and some minerals. It is high in carbohydrates and sugar. Most products contain 35-40% juice with a lot of sugar added.

Papaya Nectar- Most contain only 25-30% juice. The vitamin C content is 100% of the RDA and the majority of the drink is sugar and water.

Strawberry Nectar- Most contain only 20-25% juice. The vitamin C content is 100% of the RDA and the rest of the drink is sugar and water.

Mango Nectar- Contains 25-30% juice and is higher in vitamin A and C content than most nectar, with the balance of the drink high in sugar and water.

JUICY FACTS

Christopher Columbus, the Orange King
Orange trees were brought to the Americas by Christopher Columbus in 1493, but were not introduced to Florida until about 1540 by Ponce de Leon. Grapefruit didn't arrive until the French brought a tree to Florida in 1806. The Chinese were actually the first to grow a citrus tree in 2200 B.C.

Florida, Only Number Two
The largest producer of oranges in the world is Brazil. Between the U.S. and Brazil, they produce 42% of the world's crop. Florida produced a record of 273 million boxes in the 2001-2002 season and will produce 1.9 billion gal. of orange juice and 158 million gal. of grapefruit juice. Nine out of every 10 Florida oranges are used for juice.

Best to be Thin-Skinned
At least when it refers to an orange! Florida oranges are thin-skinned which means that they will have more juice than all other oranges grown outside of Florida. The climatic changes in other growing states cause the oranges to develop a thicker, more protective skin and less juice.

This Will Take Care of a Really Big Cold
The Florida Department of Citrus unveiled the largest glass of orange juice in the world, holding 730 gal. of juice and standing 8 ft. tall and containing over 700,000 mg. of vitamin C.

How Dry I am
For citrus fruit to be "seriously" damaged by freezing, the dryness caused by the freezing temperatures must cause the fruit to appear dry more than $1/2$ in. from the stem. If the dryness extends only $1/4$ inch, then the fruit is considered only "damaged."

Sunny the "Delight" Only Lasts for 10 Days
Tangy citrus beverage that contains orange and tangerine juice! It has a pleasant taste and is enriched with vitamins A, C and B1. Additional flavors are also sold that combine a number of fruit flavors. Refrigeration is recommended by the manufacturer after purchase in order to retain the taste and preserve the drink. Sunny Delight's flavor will only last for about 10 days without refrigeration.

New York, New York
New York City is the biggest consumer of orange juice with the record of 64 million gal. per year. New York may want to consider changing its nickname to "The Big Orange" instead of "The Big Apple."

Clear the Aisles, Get out of my Way

Prune juice is an excellent source of vitamins and minerals, especially iron and potassium. Prunes also contain the chemical, "diphenylisatin," which is a relative of "biscodyl," one of the active ingredients in laxatives. Prunes should have the same laxative effect in most individuals.

Buyer Beware

As of 1993, labels on juice drinks must contain the percentage of actual "real" juice that the product contains. It is wise to read the label and look for the actual percentage of juice in that beverage, if you are interested in purchasing a drink with a high nutrient content. 100% means that the drink contains 100% of that particular juice. If the label reads 10%, the product only contains 10% of that juice and is not a particularly high nutrient product unless it has been fortified.

Up in the sky, Look! It's Super Nectar!

Super Nectars are now being sold in health food stores. These drinks provide a 100% fruit blend drink with different herbs and may contain up to 100% of the RDA of at least 8 different vitamins. These juices may contain Chi'I Green Tea, high levels of vitamin C, Red Guarana, Ginko Biloba or high protein levels. All are healthy drinks and make a good drink in place of soda pop.

Grain and Veggie Juices

Alfalfa Juice- Very rich in chlorophyll and traditionally used to increase resistance to infections! The juice is very strong and is best when mixed with a compatible juice, such as carrot juice and/or celery juice. In fact, the combination of all three have been used to strengthen the roots of your hair. Alfalfa juice also contains "saponins," a compound found in a number of herbs and grasses that may have a cleansing ability on the plaque deposits on the walls of the arteries.

Asparagus Juice- This juice contains an alkaloid known as Asparagine without which a plant cannot grow or even remain alive. Cooking or canning asparagus kills the alkaloid. However, when juiced, the alkaloid remains active and asparagus juice has been used historically as a diuretic. Asparagus juice is usually recommended combined with other juices, since it is a fairly harsh juice on the system. It is milder and a more potent diuretic, if combined with carrot juice.

Avocado Juice- The juice was used by the Mayans to keep their joints moving freely and to eliminate the diseases related to the joints such as rheumatism and arthritis. These diseases were unheard of in their culture as long as they consumed avocados. The juice may also lower total cholesterol while raising the good cholesterol (HDL). Hardening of the arteries was also not a problem for the Mayans and many South Americans who are lucky enough to have avocado trees on their property.

Beet Juice- In small quantities, this juice was used traditionally as a blood cleanser. Both the roots and tops may be used. However, a first-time user should mix the juice with carrot juice and use more carrot juice than beet juice. The combination of the beet juice with carrot juice and coconut juice will provide a drink that has been used as a kidney and gall bladder cleanser. Cucumber juice may also be substituted for the coconut juice.

Barley Grass/Wheat Grass Juices- Wheat grass is only used when it is in a young growth stage, while barley grass should mature to a point when it develops stems. It is at this point that the grasses have their highest level of available nutrients and are high in calcium, phosphorus, potassium and magnesium salts. The juice from these grains have been used to treat a number of illness, including liver disorders, cleansing of organs of drugs, increasing energy levels, fighting infection and improving the efficiency of the immune system.

Brussel Sprouts Juice- Historically, Brussels sprouts juice was consumed to help the pancreas regenerate cells that produce insulin. Before insulin, this juice was one of the only treatments available. When combined with carrot, string bean and lettuce juice, it tends to be more effective.

Cabbage Juice- Cabbage juice has been implicated in intestinal gas production and many people shy away from drinking it. However, the gas formation may be due to excess putrefied matter on the walls of the intestines that became loosened by the juice. Cabbage juice has high sulfur and chlorine content, plus a good level of iodine, all of which can provide a cleansing effect on the stomach walls and may possibly be effective in duodenal ulcers according to literature. Sauerkraut juice, because of its high lactic acid content, has a soothing effect on the intestinal tract.

Carrot Juice- Just 6 oz. of carrot juice contains over 400% of the RDA for vitamin A and is a good source of vitamin B6. Carrot juice would make an excellent alcohol chaser since vitamin B6 is destroyed by the alcohol. Carrot juice has been used for a body tonic for many years and was especially used by nursing mothers to improve the quality of their milk. It has even been used to reduce the incidence of cancer. The carotene, which gives the carrot juice its orange color, is one of the leading antioxidants in today's studies regarding cancer. Through the use of the latest electron microscopes, it has become evident that there is a relationship in the human blood molecule and the carrot molecule, which may account for its beneficial effects on a number of human ailments.

Celery Juice- Celery juice contains a high percentage of organic sodium (the good salt) that is needed to assist calcium to stay in solution for more efficient utilization. It may even have a protective effect from a number of other chemicals, such as oxalic acid, that tend to cause calcium to be excreted prematurely. Table salt is composed of inorganic, insoluble elements, which are not beneficial to the body. Celery juice has been used as a nerve tonic and may have a beneficial effect on the nervous system. Celery juice has also been suggested to relieve attention deficit disorder (ADD) in children.

Cucumber Juice- This juice is one of the best, known diuretics in the vegetable family. It was used long before diuretics to promote natural urine flow. It's high silicon and sulfur content has been related to hair growth, which is enhanced by adding carrot juice to the cucumber juice. Cucumber juice has also been used effectively on poison ivy and poison oak rashes to alleviate the symptoms. Sunburns can also be relieved to a degree with an application of cucumber juice.

Dandelion Juice- This juice is high in magnesium and iron and was used to prevent a number of bone disorders, especially osteoporosis. The juice has also been known to improve lung function.

Endive Juice- Endive is a relative of lettuce and dandelion and may be called chicory or escarole. The juice is normally used as an additive to other juices, such as carrot or celery, and used to improve the function of the muscular and nervous systems. It also may have a significant beneficial effect on the health of the eye and optic nerve in particular.

Fennel Juice- The only variety of fennel that is suitable to be juiced is the Florence fennel or Finocchio fennel. The sweet garden-variety fennel is not suited for juicing. The Florence fennel is a member of the celery family and has been used as a blood builder, especially during menstrual periods.

Garlic Juice- Garlic juice is high in mustard oils and has been used as a blood cleanser for hundreds of years. It has also been used effectively to rid the body of parasites. Garlic juice should not be made in a juicer since it will take days to get rid of the aroma.

Lettuce Juice- Iceberg lettuce can be used for juicing; even though it has a high water content, it still contains a number of minerals. Iceberg lettuce has a good iron and magnesium content. The juice assures the liver and spleen of an ample supple to produce new red blood cells. In World War II, an extract from lettuce, lactucarium was used to relieve pain and also as a cough suppressant.

Parsley Juice- Parsley is considered an herb, but will still be discussed under vegetables. The juice is one of the most potent juices and should always be mixed with other juices for the most beneficial results. Carrot, celery or lettuce juices are the most common mixers that work well with parsley juice. The juice is related to thyroid and adrenal function and to keep the arteries healthy. Drinking too much pure juice may adversely affect the nervous system.

Pea Juice- This juice when prepared is similar to soup and has been known to relieve the painful symptoms of irritable bowel syndrome. The common garden peas need to be juiced and warmed with a pinch of powdered cardamom and ginger root for added flavor.

Potato Juice- The juice of raw potatoes has been used to clear up a number of skin disorders and blemishes. Never use a potato that has a green tint since it may have high solanine content, which is a chemical that we should never consume. In fact, even consuming a greenish potato may affect the nerves controlling the sexual organs. A sweet potato has more beneficial qualities than the standard Idaho or Irish potato.

Spinach Juice- An excellent cleansing juice for the intestinal tract! Has the ability to relieve constipation almost as well as prune juice. Has a positive effect on the teeth and gums.

Spinach is best raw and, if at all possible, should not be consumed cooked. Cooked spinach releases a level of oxalic acid crystals that may not be beneficial to the body and can affect proper utilization of calcium. The oxalic acid crystals become inorganic when heated and may form the crystals in the kidneys.

Tomato Juice- A 6-oz. glass will provide you with a good supply of vitamins C, A and folate. Best to purchase the low-sodium variety. If you have an allergy to aspirin, you may have to avoid tomato juice, since it contains the same chemical, salicylate. It is an excellent tonic to keep your metabolism working at a healthy level. When tomatoes are cooked, a number of the beneficial elements change to the inorganic form and are not healthy. Kidney and bladder stones may be the result of consuming a diet high in cooked tomato products.

String Bean Juice- This juice may assist the pancreas in the production of insulin by keeping the cells healthy. This is an excellent vegetable to mix with other juices to enhance the overall benefits.

Turnip Juice- The leaves, as well as the root, should be used, since turnips contain a high level of calcium. The potassium content of the leaves is also high and the juice has been used for growing children and people who may be at risk of osteoporosis. Turnip juice in combination with spinach, carrot and watercress juices has been reported to alleviate hemorrhoids.

Watercress Juice- This is a high sulfur drink, which also includes a number of minerals and salts that make the drink an effective intestinal cleanser. Because it is so powerful, it should never be consumed without the addition of other juices, such as carrot, spinach and lettuce.

Watermelon Juice- Historically, watermelon juice was used to cure a number of ailments. The juice was squeezed out and made into a syrup and was given for arthritis, gout, colic in babies, fevers, and the Indians used it to soothe their stomachs. Skin problems, especially those related to over-acidic conditions, were treated with watermelon juice, which reduced the acidic condition.

HEALTH INFORMATION

The Minimum is a Lot

If you consume just 16-oz. of FRESH (not canned) vegetable juice each day, it will equal the same level of vitamins, minerals and enzymes found in two very large vegetable salads. The enzymes in the vegetable juices will assist the body in metabolizing and absorbing the nutrients in almost all foods consumed.

Juicing

This is one of the most efficient methods of adding vitamins and mineral to your diet, since it is only possible to eat a limited quantity of fruits and vegetables without overfilling yourself. The juice, which will contain a large percentage of the nutrients, is more easily consumed and allows the nutrients to be more easily absorbed. By assisting your body in breaking down the cell walls in fruits and vegetables, you allow more of the nutrients to be utilized. Fruits and vegetables are now being studied more than ever before to unlock the secrets of the phytochemicals they contain. There are over 100,000 of these phyto-chemicals, also called phytonutrients that may be instrumental in reducing the risk of many diseases, including cancer. Juicing provides you with more of these special nutrients than any other source.

Help, I'm Losing My Fiber

We all worry about not getting the fiber from the fruits and vegetables when we juice. However, the juice will still contain a good percentage of fiber and you will still need to eat foods rich in fiber, even though you are drinking healthy juices. Juices are one of the best sources of fresh, natural nutrients and in a quantity that most people never get.

How Much is Enough?

Most nutritionists recommend drinking 2-3 glasses of a combination natural juice drink every day to maximize your nutrient intake. Vegetable juice will contain less sugar and it is recommended that the majority of the juice come from vegetables.

Juicing Tips for the Beginner

- If possible, use organically grown produce. There is always the possibility of fertilizer or pesticide contamination.
- Wash all produce, even organically grown produce, with a good organic cleaner and remove any damaged areas.
- Many fruits and vegetable skins and greens are not good candidates for juicing. Best to learn the healthy way to go.
- Remove all pits and seeds.
- Some stems and leaves are acceptable, especially those from red grapes.
- Cut all produce into workable pieces to make it easier on your juicer.
- Mix produce with a smaller liquid content with produce with a better liquid content for a more drinkable juice cocktail.

Know Your Fruits and Vegetables

Some people think that you can just throw any fruit or vegetable into the juicer and come out with a healthy drink. Not true! If you are going to juice, I suggest you buy a book that tells you how to juice before starting. It is not healthy to eat too much of the skins of oranges and grapefruits. Apple and apricot seeds contain a small amount of cyanide. Rhubarb and carrot greens may also be toxic. Celery leaves are just too bitter. I think you get the idea.

Glossary of Juicy Terms

100% Pure or 100% Juice- If the label has either one of these percentage terms, the product must contain 100% of that juice. There can be no sweeteners or water added, just the juice from the fruit.

Acerola- Red berry found in the West Indies and known to be one of the richest sources of vitamin C.

Enzymes- Complex substances found in fresh fruits and vegetables that assist the body in breaking down and utilizing nutrients.

FDA- Food and Drug Administration.

Fresh Squeezed Juice- Fresh product that has not been pasteurized and is kept cold until purchased.

Canned Juice- The most common juices are orange and grapefruit juices, which are pasteurized and sealed in cans. This gives the product a shelf life of at least a year. Once opened, these juices should be refrigerated and only have a life of about one week.

Super
SPUDS

Potatoes (Sweet)

They are usually only available around Thanksgiving. However, yams are available year round. Sweet potato skins are normally a light copper color while yams are more reddish. They should not be purchased if they have any soft spots, visible mold, or white areas. Sweet potatoes and yams tend to decay faster than white potatoes due to their high sugar content. Yams originated in Asia and are a close relative to the sweet potato but are less sweet and contain 10-20% less nutrients. Sweet potatoes have 10 calories per ounce less than yams.

The Sweet Nature of Sweet Potatoes

Sweet potatoes cook somewhat different than regular white potatoes in that they tend to become sweeter, the more you cook them. A percentage of the starch in sweet potato converts to sugar when the potato is heated. The cells in a sweet potato are not as strong as those in a white potato and when it is boiled, it will easily absorb water and swell up.

Yam-a-Daba-Do

The best way to tell the difference between sweet potatoes and yams is to look at the flesh, which should be orange in a sweet potato and reddish in a yam. Supermarkets commonly label yams as sweet potatoes. Sweet potatoes contain the same number of calories as white potatoes; however, they contain more vitamin C and 3 times the beta-carotene. The best sweet potato is called a "boniato" or "Cuban" sweet potato and has a very light yellow flesh.

Crop Destroyer not a Problem Anymore

The Colorado potato beetle, which is capable of destroying 85% of a potato crop, will not be a problem anymore. A company called, "NatureMark" has developed a potato seed that carries with it the ability to resist the beetle as well as viruses. The potato is called the "NewLeaf™" potato.

African Farmers to Harvest more Sweet Potatoes

The sweet potato crop in Africa is one of the more important crops, but is damaged almost every season by the feathery mottle virus. The African sweet potato crop is now protected by biotechnology and is able to fight off the virus without the heavy use of chemicals.

The Bitter-Sweet Potato

A chemical in sweet potatoes is activated by temperatures below 40°F. and tends to make a sweet potato taste bitter. Best not to refrigerate that poor sweet potato.

Drop Them Skins

To peel a sweet potato easily, take them from the boiling water and immediately immerse them in a bowl of ice cold water for about 20-30 seconds. The skins should almost fall off by themselves.

A New Potato Soup Makes Its Debut Soon

New aseptic technology will soon be in place to produce extended shelf-life potato soup that will be low acid as well.

Space Spuds

Five tuber sprouts were sent into space on the Space Shuttle Columbia to see if they would grow in zero gravity and what, if any, the genetic changes might be. Four out of the five tubers were able to sprout and were determined to be a safe source of food.

Spud Storage

Sweet potatoes, yams and white potatoes are actually an enlarged stem called a "tuber" that extends from the plant underground and is the storage depot for the plant's excess carbohydrates. The potato plant bears a vegetable similar to a small mini-tomato and is not that good to eat. If potatoes are stored below 40°F., they tend to release more sugar and turn sweet. Potatoes will last longer and remain solid longer, if they are stored in a cool, dry location, preferably at 45°-50°F. Air must be allowed to circulate around potatoes since moisture will cause them to decay. Potatoes do not freeze well, since a large majority of the cells tend to burst, causing the potato to become mushy and watery when thawed. Commercially processed potatoes will freeze.

Genetically Modified Potatoes

Genes that control the amount of starch in potatoes will soon be under human control. The present level of starch allows too much oil to be absorbed when frying a potato. By genetic manipulation, a potato can be grown with a "higher starch" content that would be capable of reducing the amount of oil that the potato will absorb. This same potato will also be used to produce an all-natural, low-fat potato chip. Sweet potatoes will contain more protein and be even healthier than ever before.

How Sweet it is

Sweet potatoes, unlike white potatoes, will freeze without becoming mushy if fully cooked, either boiled or baked. They need to be placed in a well-sealed plastic container, with as much air as possible bled out. The container then needs to be placed into a large sealed plastic bag. They will keep for 10-12 months.

Potatoes (Red)

Red potatoes have smooth, thin skins with white insides and are very firm. It is the potato of choice for casseroles, salads, soups, boiling, steaming and roasting. They are easier to peel than the standard white potato and are more attractive. They are best when cooked using moist heat.

Potatoes (White)

White potatoes originated in South America and were introduced to Europe in the 16th century. They are one of the most nutritious vegetables and a member of the "nightshade" family. Americans consume approximately 125 lbs. of potatoes per person annually with the U. S. producing 35 billion lbs. per year. In the last 30 years, Americans have reduced their consumption of fresh potatoes by 40%.

Baked Potato May not be a Good Choice

Carl's Jr. has outdone itself by serving the worst baked potato in the U.S. Carl's Jr. Bacon and Cheese baked potato has 730 calories and 43 grams of fat, 15 of which is saturated. A Burger King Whopper would be better with 630 calories and 39 grams of fat, 11 of which is saturated. Not that either is a very healthy meal. If you want a good baked potato, have a Rax Cheese-Broccoli at only 280 calories and almost zero fat.

Jack Frost may be Guilty

If your red potatoes are too sweet, it may be due to a frost. When the potatoes freeze or even get close to freezing, a percentage of the carbohydrate turns to sugar.

Spud Facts

There are over 5,000 varieties of potatoes worldwide and only 4 varieties are sold and used in U.S. markets. The potato is the number one vegetable in the world, with potato chips ranking number 1 snack food.

Who Invented Potato Chips?

In the summer of 1853, a Native American by the name of George Crum, was the chief chef at the Moon Lake Lodge in Saratoga Springs, New York. A guest who had ordered French fries complained that they were too thick. Chef Crum sliced up another batch of potatoes, somewhat thinner and served them, only to have them rejected again. The chef was very upset and decided to slice the potatoes paper-thin to get even. The guest was delighted with the thin potatoes and they became a hit, and the trademark of the restaurant. They were called "Saratoga Chips." In 1997, the Frito-Lay Company used 7 million lbs. of potatoes a day in 35 plants to keep us supplied with potato chips.

Scrub-a-Dub Potato

Food stains will vanish if you rub a piece of raw potato over them, then wash with soap and water.

Sprouts are Poisonous

Never buy potatoes if they have a green tint and never eat potato sprouts, since they may be toxic and make you very ill.

Low-Fat French Fries

The J.R. Simplot Company of Boise has invented a method of producing a low-fat French fry. The potatoes are dipped into a solution of pectin, which is derived from fruit and is 100% natural, then allowed to dry before the French fries are fried in oil. The average small order of fries contains 220 calories and about 12 grams of fat. The new Simplot French fries have only 130 calories and 3 grams of fat. The fries are going to be sold as the "MicroMagic" fries.

Who Invented the Potato Chip Bag?

Before 1926, potato chips were sold from big barrels of chips, weighed and placed in bags. The first potato chip bag was invented by Laura Scudder in 1926 in Montgomery Park, California. She had her employees iron sheets of waxed paper and make them into bags, then filled the bags by hand and sealed them with a flat iron. In 1933 the Dixie Waxpaper Company of Dallas invented the "glassine" bag that then allowed the chips to remain fresher and have a better shelf life.

Save Those Stale Potato Chips

When the potato chip bag is left open and they become stale and lose their crispiness, just place the bag in the microwave for 45 seconds on high and then allow to stand for 2 minutes.

Hot Potato, Baked Potato

When baking a potato, many people tend to wrap the potato in aluminum foil, thinking that it will speed up the cooking time. After trying to bake potatoes a number of different ways to see which method was the fastest, I was surprised to find that by oiling the skin with vegetable oil, the skin reached a higher temperature faster and baked the potato in a shorter period of time than when it was wrapped in aluminum foil.

- One method that will speed up the cooking time is to insert an aluminum nail into the center of the potato, thereby transferring heat inside.
- You can place the potato in the microwave for 7-8 minutes before placing it into the oven, but be sure and make a few short cuts in the potato first.
- Another method is to allow the potato to stand in boiling water for 15 minutes before placing the potato in the oven.

Leftovers

Baked potatoes that are leftover can be re-baked if you dip them in water and bake them in a 350°F. oven for 15-20 minutes.

I Know Where the Yellow Went. . . .

If you would like your potato salad to have a richer color, try adding a small amount of yellow food coloring when you are mixing it. Mustard will also work.

Hide and Seek

Potatoes should be stored at room temperature in a dark area and not refrigerated. Refrigeration tends to turn potato starch to sugar. However, if the potato is removed from the refrigerator and left at room temperature, the sugar will convert back to starch.

Staying Fresh Longer

It is best to purchase potatoes in bulk bins and not in bags. It is too difficult to determine which ones are bruised. If ginger root is stored with potatoes, it will help them stay fresh longer. If half an apple is stored with potatoes, it will stop the sprouting by absorbing any moisture before the potato does.

POTATO FACTS

To boil potatoes in less time, remove a small strip of skin from one side. After they are cooked, the balance of the skin will be more easily removed. To keep peeled potatoes white, place them in a bowl of cold water, add a few drops of white vinegar, then refrigerate. White potatoes should have a small amount of sugar added to the cooking water, which will revive a percentage of the lost flavor. Potatoes prefer to be stored in pantyhose. Just cut a leg off and drop the potatoes in, then hang it up in a cool, dry location.

Refrigerated Potato

The only potato that can be stored in the refrigerator is the new potato. They will retain a good quality for 7-10 days.

Old Potato, New Potato, Best Potato?

A new potato will have more moisture than an old potato; however, both can be used for different dishes. A new potato should be used for dishes, such as potato salad, since it will absorb less water when boiled and less mayonnaise when prepared, thus adding less fat to the dish. It's stronger and won't break as easily when the salad is stirred. Idaho and other varieties of older potatoes are best for baking and French fries. They are drier, meatier and have more starch. Because of this, they will bake fluffier and have a lighter texture. When French fries are made with an older potato, the frying fat will splatter less because of the potato's lower water content. When baking a potato, make sure you pierce the potato to allow steam to escape otherwise it may become soggy.

Are Green Potatoes Safe to Eat?

When you see a potato with green spots or with a greenish tint, it would be best not to purchase it. Overexposure to light causes a chemical reaction that increases chlorophyll buildup and the production of the chemical, "solanine." Solanine will impart a bitter taste to the potato and high levels can actually cause serious medical problems, such as interfering with nerve impulse transmission, abdominal discomfort, nausea and diarrhea. When potatoes are stored, it is best to store them in a dark location to avoid solanine buildup. This may also be a risk factor for people with arthritis.

How a Commercial Potato Becomes a French Fry

The following is the step-by-step commercial production of French fries:

- **Peeling the potato** - Large, hot pressurized tanks are used that increase the pressure to such a point that when the pressure is released, the skins actually fly off. They are then sprayed with high-power jets of water to clean any skin residues off.

- **The assembly line** - The potato is then run by inspectors who remove the bad ones and any small bad spots and send the potato on to the next station.

- **The slicing station** - The potato flies through a centrifugal pump and is shot into the cutting blades at 50 m.p.h. to be cut into "strips." The strips are inspected again and rejects sent to the hash brown, dehydrated potatoes, or tater tot department for further processing.

- **Blanching is coming up next** - The real processing is now beginning with the blanching process. A conveyer belt carries the potato through a vat filled with very hot water, which removes excess sugars and cooks them just enough so that they are all a uniform color. Occasionally, sugar is added in this stage so that the potato will brown more uniformly as well.

- **Drying out the strips** - The strips are placed on a belt and go through a machine, which sends out blasts of hot air, partially drying the strip. The amount of drying depends on the water content of the potato strip and they need to be left a little damp and not completely dry. The water content must be regulated at about 73%, if the potato strip is to be fried; oven French fries must be 68% and microwave fries need to be only 57%.

- **Now the fries are par-fried** - Process which partially fries the French fry for about $1\frac{1}{2}$-minutes. This will add some fat to the fry but will make them faster to fry when they are fried just before being served. The final fry at the restaurant site basically finishes cooking the already cooked fry, then browns and crisps it.

- **The chilling ending** - The fries now go through a process called blast freezing, where the fries travel down a conveyer belt on which the air is cooled to -40°F. and only very small ice crystals form, which will not allow the fries to stick together. This method protects the flavor. French fries prepared in this manner must be served within 10 minutes of leaving the frying vat or they will become soggy and limp.

Don't Fry Your French Fry

When frying French fries, never allow the oil to go above 380°F. or the fry will burn on the outside before cooking the insides.

French Fries Were Actually Invented in France

The French fry was brought to the U.S. by Thomas Jefferson around 1788 after he returned from a trip to France.

French Fries Are Popular Worldwide

If you are a world traveler and want an order of French fries, the following information will help you to order them:

COUNTRY	COMMON NAME	CONDIMENT SERVED WITH
Albania	Patai	Solidified grease & salt
Australia	Chips	Ketchup, brown gravy, vinegar, salt
Austria	Pommes	Ketchup
Belgium (Flemish)	Fritten	Mayonnaise
Bulgaria	Parzheni Kartofi	Feta cheese
Canada	French fries	Malt vinegar, ketchup
China	Suu Teaw	Ketchup
France	Pommes Frites	Salt, ketchup, mayonnaise
Germany	Pommes Frites	Ketchup, mayonnaise
Ireland	Chips	Ketchup, curry sauce, garlic sauce
Israel	Chips	Ketchup
Japan	Foo-rai-doh pohtay-toh	Ketchup, salt
Mexico	Papas Fritas	Ketchup, lemon, hot sauce
Netherlands	Friet	Peanut sauce, ketchup, curry sauce
U. K.	Chips	Malt vinegar, brown sauce, gravy
U. S.	Fries	Ketchup, mayonnaise, gravy

Sprinkle them with Flour

For the crispiest French fries, sprinkle them with all-purpose flour before frying.

Going for Surgery? Don't Eat Potatoes

Researchers at the University of Chicago have found that when some patients eat potatoes, tomatoes or eggplant before receiving anesthesia, the anesthesia may not be as effective. There are chemicals in these vegetables that may interfere with the chemicals in some types of anesthesia.

That's a lot of Potatoes

The U. S. grows 2.6 million tons of potatoes annually, with 51% being used for French fries. The most common potato is the russet.

The Anti-Sprouting Apple

If you place an apple in a bag of potatoes, they will not sprout.

How Firm I am......

If you want to keep potatoes firm while you are boiling them, just cook them in 2 parts of water to 1 part of white vinegar and a small amount of kosher salt. Leave the skins on and peel after they are finished cooking to retain the nutrients.

Removing Indigestion from Potato Pancakes

For some reason, a number of people have a problem tolerating fried potato pancakes and always get indigestion. This problem is easily solved by just adding 1 tsp. baking soda to the potato pancake batter. If you don't get indigestion, don't add it.

World's Greatest Potato Pancakes (Latkas)

Potato latkas should be crispy and not overly greasy from frying, and flavored just right. The following is my grandmother's recipe. The ingredients needed are:

5 large fresh potatoes
2 large eggs (well beaten)
1/2 cup of all-purpose flour
1/4 tsp. freshly grated black pepper (powdered) (optional)

1 large onion (grated)
1/4 tsp. baking powder (fresh)
1/2 tsp. table salt

Peel and grate potatoes in a large bowl, cover with cold water and refrigerate. This needs to be done 2-3 hours before you plan on using the potatoes to allow the water to soak some of the starch out of the potatoes. The water should be changed every hour. When you are ready to prepare the latkas, drain the potatoes and squeeze out as much water as possible. Peel and grate the onion and add it to the potatoes, then stir in the eggs, flour, salt, pepper (optional) and baking powder. Heat enough vegetable oil in a heavy pan to cover the bottom (about 1/4 in. deep). Drop the potato mixture into the hot oil by the tbsp. and form 3-in. patties. Fry over moderate heat, turning to brown each side.

Why Soak Fries in Water?

The surface of a cut potato deteriorates very quickly when exposed to air. When this occurs, a layer of sticky starch is formed as soon as the potatoes are placed into the frying vat. The potatoes may stick to each other as well as the pan and it will be almost impossible to serve them. If you soak the potatoes in ice water for 5-7 minutes before frying them, it will wash off a large percentage of the surface starch and the problem will not occur. They should be drained on a paper towel and be good and dry when you fry them, otherwise you will have hot oil splatter.

Skinny French Fries: Is There a Reason?

A number of the fast food chains like McDonald's serve their French fried potatoes thinner than most other restaurants. When raw potatoes are thin pre-cut exposing the surface, a percentage of the complex carbohydrates have time to convert to sugar. The extra sugar causes the French fries to brown faster and the thinner fry will cook faster. If they tried to serve normal size fries, they would be too brown or undercooked.

What is a Newleaf Potato?

The Monsanto Company has genetically engineered a potato that provides the potato with natural resistance to the Colorado potato beetle, which will reduce the need for additional pesticides. They are also working on a new potato that will absorb less fat when they are made into French fries.

Can a Potato Explode in the Oven?

It is not unusual for a white potato to explode in the oven if the skin is not pierced. It doesn't really explode; however, it may crack open and make a mess since potatoes are very high in water content and will build up a good head of steam as they bake. It is best to pierce the skin with a fork before baking.

Potatoes and Onions: Not Good Friends

Onions should never be stored with potatoes in the same bag. Onions tends to release gases that will alter the flavor of a potato. Cooking the two together is not a problem unless you overdo the quantity of onions and it takes over the flavor and aroma of the potato.

Why do Cooked Potatoes Have more Nutrients Available?

Nutrients from raw potatoes are more difficult for the body to utilize. The potato cells tend to hold the nutrients until the potato is softened and cooked and our digestive systems are unable to break the cell walls down adequately to release the nutrients. Potatoes should never be cooked in aluminum or iron pots or they will turn yellowish, nor can they be sliced with a carbon-steel knife. Best to cook potatoes in a glass or enamel pot, if you wish them to be a nice pale color.

What are Duchess Potatoes?

It is a light, fluffy combination of mashed potatoes, egg yolk, sweet cream butter and seasonings to taste. The mixture is then placed into a pastry tube and piped around meats, poultry, casseroles or fish dishes as a decorative touch.

Chips Made from Dough

Pringles Potato Chips are produced from dough of dried potato flakes. The product may contain sugar, corn, wheat, colorings and preservatives. The cost is more than most other brands of potato chips.

That's all, Folks

If you store a boiled or baked potato in the refrigerator for 3-4 days, it will lose approximately 90% of its nutrient value. Potatoes should only be stored for 1-2 days. When boiling potatoes, place them into a mesh, frying basket to make them easier to remove and drain since they may get somewhat mushy.

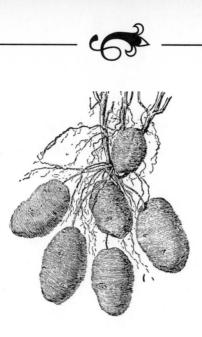

Getting Hard

To re-harden potatoes, try placing soft raw potatoes in ice water for $1/2$ hour or until they become hard. Brown areas on potatoes are the result of oxidation and vitamin C losses.

Long Digestive Time

The digestive time for a medium potato is approximately 2 hours. Cooking a potato with its skin will result in the retention of most of its nutrients. Recommendation is not to eat potato skins. They are one of the only vegetable skins that tend to hold pesticide and fertilizer residues even after washing and cooking. The EPA has registered 90 different pesticides for use on potatoes. The FDA laboratories can only detect 55% of these. Some of the problem pesticides are Chlordane, Aldicarb, and Dieldrin.

A French Fry Fit for a King

For the greatest gourmet French fries, try allowing crinkle-cut potatoes to stand in ice-cold water and refrigerate for 1 hour before frying. This will harden the potato, remove some of the starch and they will not absorb as much fat. Dry them thoroughly before frying, then fry them twice. The first time for only a few minutes, dry them well, sprinkle a small amount of flour on them and fry them until they are a golden brown.

Taking a Big Loss

Mashed potatoes that sit out on a buffet will lose up to 100% of all their nutrients after 1 hour. The loss is due to the constant heat, lights, mashing, exposing more of the surface to oxidation, and cooking in boiling water.

What Potato is Best for What?

The most popular potato is the Idaho or russet. They are starchy and mealy and best for baking, mashed potatoes and French fries. The "new potatoes" are thin-skinned potatoes that are somewhat waxy and young and are called red or white potatoes. These are best for boiling and make great potato salad, for use in stews and soups, and to prepare scalloped potatoes since they hold their shape better than russets.

Two Good Tips

If you have problems peeling the potato, drop it into a bowl of ice water for a few seconds to loosen the skin. To keep peeled potatoes white during cooking, add a small amount of white vinegar to the water.

Hot Potato, Cold Potato

Cold potato soup is called Vichyssoise and was invented when King Louis XV of France was worried about being poisoned. He insisted that his servants taste all his food before he ate it. When the hot soup was passed around, however, it got cold by the time it reached him. He enjoyed the cold soup and from that day on had it served that way.

Is it True or False?

With two people in the family working, potato products have been processed to make them easier to use. These products, which include flaked, frozen, and powdered potatoes, have risen in sales by over 500% in the last 30 years. Remember, the more you process a potato, the more nutrients are lost.

The Real Thing

To make a quality potato chip, cut potatoes in half crosswise, exposing two flat surfaces. A potato peeler is then used to cut paper-thin slices, which are sprayed with vegetable oil and placed on a cookie sheet. Brush the tops of the potatoes with a very small amount of fresh pure vegetable oil, preferably corn or safflower oil, then bake at 450°F. for about 10-12 minutes or until they are a light golden brown. Finally, place the chips in a brown paper bag with a small amount of sea salt ($^1/_4$ tsp. per whole potato) and shake. This will allow them to become somewhat salty and remove some of the fat.

3

Keeping Food
FRESH

Should I Freeze it?

There is always an uncertainty in the public's mind, regarding whether or not to freeze or refreeze a food and if it is frozen, how long it will retain its nutrient value, as well as its flavor and consistency. Many foods do not do well when frozen. Some get tough, some develop ice crystals shortly after being place in the freezer, while others get mushy when defrosted.

Freezing Alcohol

If you are going to try and freeze any dish that has alcohol in it, remember alcohol will not freeze like water and may need to be frozen at a lower temperature.

Save Those Nutrients

The longer a food is frozen, the higher the nutrient loss. Seal all freezer-stored foods, as well as possible to retain the nutrient level and avoid freezer burn, as well as the formation of ice crystals. While ice crystals are not a serious problem, they can affect the quality of the food as it is being thawed and make the food mushy.

Outsmarting a Power Failure

A good trick when you go away on vacation is to place a baggie with a few ice cubes in the freezer. If a power failure occurs while you are gone and the food thaws and re-freezes, it can affect the quality of the food as well as increase the bacterial growth. You need to be aware of this fact and discard the food.

Cold Damage

There are a number of foods that should never be refrigerated, since the cold causes either loss of flavor, sprouting, or the starch turning to sugar. These include garlic, onions, shallots, potatoes and tomatoes.

Freezing Sandwiches

Frozen sandwiches will thaw by lunchtime. If the bread is buttered prior to freezing, the bread will not become soggy and absorb any filling.

Freezer Temperatures and Foods

FREEZER TEMPERATURE	QUALITY CHANGES AFTER
30ºF.	5 Days
25ºF.	10 Days
20ºF.	3 Weeks
15ºF.	6 Weeks
10ºF.	4 Months
5ºF.	6 Months
0ºF.	1 Year

Food Preservation

The preservation of food is possible only if some method is used to destroy or control the growth of microorganisms that cause spoilage. There are a number of methods, which include drying, dehydrating, salting, smoking, radiation, heating, freezing and the use of chemical agents (preservatives, etc.). The microorganisms that cause food spoilage can be found everywhere. They are in the water, air, counter surfaces, brought home on foods, and even in the product itself. In many cases, the food is contaminated as a natural occurrence, such as salmonella being present in the chicken ovaries. Microorganisms can exist in two forms, either visible to the naked eye, such as in colonies or in small spores, which are for the most part invisible to the naked eye and carried by the air. There are three divisions of microorganisms: molds, yeast and bacteria.

Molds, Yeast and Bacteria

Molds are usually airborne "spores" or "seeds" that may light on a food product and start to multiply. They may also send out "feelers" or "filaments" and grow in colonies, which may be seen in many colors, depending on their food source. Mold spores will move from one food to another, especially fruits, so it would be wise to check your foods when you bring them home to be sure that none has any mold on them. Foods with a high acid content, such as tomatoes, pickles and fruits are especially susceptible to the growth of mold. Yeast is a small, one-celled fungus that produces enzymes, which convert sugars to alcohol and carbon dioxide in a process called "fermentation." It is also an excellent dietary source of folic acid. Yeast and molds can be destroyed by processing the foods at boiling temperature. Bacteria need only a small amount of organic material and some moisture to grow and multiply. They grow by splitting their cells and may develop either acid or alkaline properties. Bacteria grow rapidly between 40° and 140°F. The longer the food is kept in this zone, the more the bacteria will multiply. High temperature cooking will destroy most bacteria. When there is no moisture or the available moisture is used up, growth in all of these microorganisms cease, dry up and become dormant until moisture is again introduced.

Cooking to Kill Bacteria

FOOD	TEMPERATURE & DURATION
Egg in the shell	145°F. for 15 seconds
Fish & Beef	145°F. for 15 seconds
Pork	155°F. for 15 seconds
Poultry & Ground Beef	165°F. for 15 seconds

Was Napoleon Responsible for Food Preservation?

Napoleon's army was becoming sick and many of his men were dying from scurvy and other diseases related to lack of essential nutrients. Because of their long marches far from food sources, all they could bring with them was salted meats. Napoleon talked the rulers at the time to offer a reward equal to $250,000 in today's money, if anyone could develop a method of preserving foods. Nicholas Appert, a Paris confectioner, after 14 years of trial and error finally invented a method of preservation. His method was to place food in a glass jar, allowing for expansion, and place a hand-hewn cork in the jar attached firmly with a piece of wire. Each jar was then wrapped in a burlap sack and lowered into a pot of boiling water. The length of time the jar was left in seemed to vary with the type of food. He was successful in preserving eggs, milk products, fruits, vegetables and meats. He was awarded the prize money in 1810 by Napoleon and was labeled as "the man who discovered the art of making the seasons stand still."

Who Made the First Tin Can?

Canning was invented in 1810 by Peter Durand an Englishman, who called it a "tin canister." This would be an improvement over the glass jar, especially for transportation to outlying areas without breakage.

The first "tin cans" had to be made by hand with workers cutting the can from sheets of tin-plate, then soldering them together, leaving a small hole in the top to place the food in. The hole was then covered with a small tin disc and soldered closed. A tin worker was able to produce about 60 cans a day. The U. S. started a canning operation in the 1820s and within 20 years the canning of foods was being done all over the country. In 1860, Isaac Solomon in Baltimore found that if he added calcium chloride to the water when it was boiling, he could raise the temperature from 212°F. to 240°F. and thus reduce the processing time from about 6 hours to 45 minutes. A processing plant could now produce 20,000 cans a day, instead of 2,500. The longest food to date that has been eaten safely was canned meat that was 114 years old.

Freezing Baked Goods

Certain foods need care when freezing and also special preparation techniques after they have been removed from the freezer. The following foods are some of the more popular that most people freeze:

Biscuits Prepare as per instructions, then freeze in a well-sealed bag. Should be heated unthawed at 350°F. for about 20 minutes.

Coffee Cake Bake until the cake is a light brown only, then cool as quickly as possible and freeze. Thaw at room temperature in freezer wrapping. If the cake has been frozen in aluminum foil, heat at 400°F.

Muffins Prepare as per package directions, then freeze. Thaw at room temperature, then heat at 300°F. for about 15-20 minutes.

Doughnuts Prepare as usual and freeze. Remember that raised doughnuts will freeze better than the cake type. Glazed doughnuts do not freeze well. Thaw at room temperature for about 10 minutes before placing in a 400°F. oven to heat.

Bread (homemade) Prepare as usual and allow the bread to cool before placing in freezer. Thaw at room temperature and if wrapped in aluminum foil, bake at 300°F. for about 10 minutes.

Sandwiches (closed) If you are going to freeze sandwiches, use day-old bread and spread butter, margarine or salad dressing to the edge of the bread before adding any filling. Do not use crisp vegetables, cooked egg white, preserves, mayonnaise or tomatoes. Package in aluminum foil and freeze. Thaw at room temperature in original wrapping for about 3-4 hours or in a lunch pail.

Who Came up with the Name, "Birdseye?"

The Birdseye Food Company was founded by Clarence Birdseye, an American businessman who invented the process of freezing food in small packages. He discovered the process by accident while hunting in Labrador in 1915. Some portions of caribou and fish were frozen by the dry Arctic air and when thawed were tender and still tasty. He developed a process that duplicated the Arctic conditions and started a company. Birdseye Seafood was founded in 1923 and by 1929 had expanded its product line to other foods. In 1929, Birdseye sold the company to General Foods.

Negative Effects of Freezing Foods

When food is frozen, a percentage of the cells tend to burst releasing their liquids. This will occur in all foods, regardless of the method of freezing or the type of wrap. Ice crystals are formed from the lost liquid and the food never has the same texture or exactly the same flavor as it originally had when it was freshly prepared. Biologically, the process that occurs is referred to as "osmosis." Osmosis is the process by which a liquid passes through a semi-permeable membrane (cell wall) in order to equalize the pressure. When the food is frozen, the solids inside of the cell cause the water to become more concentrated, allowing the liquid from outside the cell to enter, form crystals, and eventually cause a number of the cells to burst. Since some of the flavor of the food is contained in each cell, a percentage of the flavor is also lost. Meats, fruits, and most seafood are more negatively affected than vegetables.

SMART FREEZING TIPS

There are a number of important facts that should be adhered to if you wish to freeze foods successfully:

- When preparing any vegetable for freezing, be sure and undercook it. Re-heating will complete the cooking.
- Freezing tends to intensify the flavor in spices, such as garlic, pepper, oregano and cloves, so you should use less, then add more before serving. Additional onions can be used, since freezing tends to cause the flavor to be lost. Salt should be used in moderation or not at all. Salt tends to slow down the freezing process.
- Never use quick-cooking rice in a dish that will be frozen, as it tends to become mushy. Use regular or converted rice.
- Artificial flavorings and sweeteners do not do well when frozen.
- Toppings should always be added before serving. Cheeses and bread crumbs on foods do not do well.
- Freezing causes old potatoes to fall apart. Always use new potatoes in dishes that are to be frozen.
- Gravies and sauces need to be made somewhat thicker than normal, since they will usually separate.
- Cool foods first in the refrigerator before freezing.

Why is a Full Freezer More Energy Efficient?

A freezer that is full will use less energy than a half-full freezer because frozen foods retain cold air for a long period. The freezer will run fewer hours per day and save considerable money in electricity.

Freezer Burn: Just the Facts

Freezer burn makes the surface of the food a lighter color than normal, dries out the food, makes it tough and takes away its flavor. Freezer burn may be caused by a damaged package, food that has been packaged in a product that is not moisturized or vapor-resistant or too much air was allowed into the package. Before sealing up foods to be frozen, be sure and remove all the air you possibly can.

Blanching Before Freezing: A Must

When vegetables are frozen, enzymes may still remain active and cause changes in the color, texture and taste in the vegetable even if they have been previously stored under refrigeration. Freezing will slow the changes down; however, it will not totally inactivate the enzymes. If vegetables are blanched by either boiling them in water that has boiled for 2 minutes first (to release oxygen) or steaming them for 3-4 minutes, it will not cook them but will inactivate the enzymes and the vegetables will retain their color, texture and taste. Of course, the enzymes are important to good nutrition and it would be more desirable to only purchase enough for a few days at a time.

Chest Freezer vs. Upright Freezers

This debate has been around for a long time; however, the answer has always been a fairly simple one. The chest freezer, even though the door may be larger, will retain its cold setting longer when the door is opened, since cold air is heavier than hot air and tends to stay put. The upright freezer tends to release most of its cold air the minute the door is opened. Chest freezers will maintain and hold the preferred 0°F. freezer level to maximize food storage times before spoilage.

Why is There a Gummy Liquid in my Frozen Fruit?

There are a number of reasons why this may occur. The fruit may have been frozen too slowly; the freezer temperature was not maintained at 0°F. or the temperature fluctuated too much by having the door opened too often, while the fruit was freezing.

Smoke-Curing Foods

Use of smoke to cure foods is one of the oldest methods of food preservation which, however, provides a number of risks to the body from the toxins that may be placed into the food from the smoke. Smoke may contain as many as 200 different chemical components, which include alcohol, acids, phenolic compounds, pyrobenzine and other carcinogenic chemicals. Many of these toxic substances do, however, retard microbial growth. Salt-curing methods and smoking are frequently combined to minimize the oxidation of the fats that cause rancidity.

New Storage Bags: A Must for every Kitchen

A new plastic storage bag for fruits and vegetables is now on the market. The bag contains hundreds of microscopic holes that allow air to circulate around the produce. The bag is also impregnated with "oya" which is a natural substance that will absorb ethylene gas, which is released by the produce as it ripens and helps the produce to ripen. Unfortunately, the more ethylene gas the produce expels and remains around the food, the faster the food ripens and spoils. The bags are tinted green to lessen the effects of light, reducing the potency of the vitamins. The bag is marketed under the name "Evert-Fresh™." Produce stored in these bags will last 10 times longer than standard plastic storage bags and in tests over a 12-day period 50% more of the vitamin C was retained.

Storing Margarine

Margarine will absorb odors from foods that are stored nearby very readily. It should be sealed as tightly as possible and should store for 4-6 months in the refrigerator. Margarine freezes well and will keep for 1 year if the temperature is kept at 0°F.

FREEZER STORAGE TIMES

Storage Times at 0°F.

FOOD	MONTHS	FOOD	MONTHS
Meats		**Dairy Products**	
Beef, Lamb	6-12	Milk	2 weeks
Chops, Cutlets, Beef Hamburger	3-5	Ice Cream	4 weeks
Ground Pork	1-3	Cream (40%)	3-4
Sausage	1-2	Eggs (not in shell)	7-10
Bacon (unsliced)	3-5	Margarine	2-4
Bacon (sliced)	1	Butter	2-4
Fish	3-6	Cheddar Cheese	5-6
Ham	3-4		
Liver	3-4	**Fruits**	
Poultry	4-6	Apples (sliced)	10-12
Giblets	3	Apricots	10-12
Duck, Goose	5-6	Berries	11-12
Rabbit	9-12	Cherries (sour)	12
Shrimp or Shellfish (cooked)	2-3		
Turkey	6-8		
Hot Dogs	2-3		
Luncheon Meats (ready-to-eat)	0		

Storage Times for Refrigerated Dairy Products at 0°F.

PRODUCT	DAYS	MONTHS
Butter	45-90	7-8
Butter, Clarified	60-90	7-8
Buttermilk	7-14	3
Cream	3-5	3
Cream, Whipped		
Commercial	30	Do Not Freeze
Homemade	1	2
Eggs (in shell)	20	Do Not Freeze
Eggs (hard boiled)	7	Do Not Freeze
Eggs (yolks)	2-4	12
Eggnog	3-5	6
Half and Half	3-4	4
Ice Cream, Commercial	2-3	
Frozen Desserts	1-2	
Mayonnaise	60	Do Not Freeze
Margarine		
Regular & Soft	120	12

Diet	90	
Milk	3-7	3
Non-Dairy Creamer	21	12
Non-Dairy Toppings		
Container	7	12
Aerosol can	90	Do Not Freeze
Sour Cream	14	
Yogurt	14	12

Storage Times for Baking Staples

PRODUCT	SHELF LIFE
Arrowroot	1 Year
Baking Powder	3-6 Months
Baking Soda	18 Months
Cornstarch	1 Year
Cream of Tartar	1 Year
Extracts	1 Year
Gelatin, Boxed	1 Year
Salt	Forever if Kept Dry
Tapioca	1 Year
Vinegar	1 Year
Yeast	Date on Package

Problems with Aluminum Foil

Foods wrapped in aluminum foil may be subjected to two problems. First, since aluminum foil is such a great insulator, it tends to slow down the heat transfer and food will not freeze as fast as you may want it to. Bacteria may grow and not be killed when the food is re-heated. Secondly, when you crinkle the aluminum foil to place it around the food, micro-cracks develop which may allow air and moisture to penetrate the food. If you plan on storing food for more than 2-3 days in the refrigerator in aluminum foil, you should probably wrap the food in plastic wrap first. Aluminum foil will also react with foods that are acidic or salty and may impart a strange taste to the food.

Which is Better, A Thermal Bottle or a Vacuum Bottle?

When a hot beverage is placed in a container for storage, the heat is lost to the colder air through conduction, and a cold beverage will lose the cold and gain heat from its surroundings. A thermal or vacuum bottle will slow the transfer of heat and cold between the beverage and its surroundings by placing a barrier between the food or beverage and the environment. A vacuum bottle places the food in a space within a vacuum surrounding the food. The unit is hermetically sealed between the bottle's inner and outer glass lining. In the thermal bottle, the exterior is solid and a poor conductor of heat, but not as poor as a vacuum bottle. Thermal bottles will not break as easily since they do not have the glass interior.

The Dangers in Raw Foods

The bacteria salmonella comes from the intestines of humans and animals and is often found in raw meats and eggs. Salmonella can be present after foods are dried, processed or frozen for long periods. The bacteria can also be transferred to food by insects or human hands, especially infants and people with poor cleanliness habits. Salmonella is easily killed with high heat, which is why raw meats need to be cooked thoroughly. Food preparation surfaces that are not cleaned adequately after preparing raw meats and egg dishes are usually the cause of most cases of salmonella- related illnesses.

Cold Facts

If ice cream thaws, it should not be re-frozen. Jelly, salad dressing and mayonnaise do not freeze well on bread products. The freezer in your refrigerator is not the same as a supermarket food freezer. It is best used for storing foods for short periods only. Foods should be frozen as quickly as possible and temperatures should be 0°F. or below. Potatoes become mushy when frozen in stews or casseroles. Their cells have high water content and break easily when frozen. However, mashed potatoes freeze well. Any bakery item with a cream filling should not be frozen. They will become soggy. Custard and meringue pies do not freeze well. The custard tends to separate and the meringue becomes tough. Waffles and pancakes may be frozen, thawed and placed in the toaster.

KEEPING FROZEN FOODS EATABLE

Meats and Fish

Rancidity is always a factor in meats and fish even though you freeze them. Meats with a higher level of saturated fat will freeze better than those with a higher level of unsaturated fat. Hamburger will have the shortest fresh-life of any meat due to the grinding and exposure of more muscle surface and fat to the air.

Vegetables

Since raw vegetables have enzymes, it is necessary to blanch the vegetables to kill the enzymes before freezing or they will turn the vegetables into mush.

Freezing Salsa

Uncooked salsa can be frozen without any problem if you drain as much water from the salsa as possible. If the salsa is not drained well, it will end up with a layer of ice on top.

Fruit

The cell wall of fruit contains pectin, which hold the fruits together. When you freeze fruit, the pectin tends to dissolve and the fruit loses its shape. To avoid this problem, just add some sugar or calcium to the fruit and it will retain its shape.

Eggs

You can freeze raw egg whites, but not the yolk. The yolk will turn into gelatin. However, cooked yolks will freeze well. Egg whites that have been cooked tend to get rubbery when frozen.

Dairy Products

Milk products that have less than 40% butterfat cannot be easily frozen. Heavy whipping cream can easily be frozen because of its high butterfat content. Cakes with icings that contain egg should not be frozen.

Emulsified Sauces

Products that have been emulsified do not freeze well. The water in the products tend to produce ice crystals and also to separate. Mayonnaise and salad dressings are good examples of products that should not be frozen.

Starchy Sauces

Any sauce or custard that has been thickened with flour or cornstarch should not be frozen. If the product has been thickened with arrowroot or tapioca, you can freeze it without a problem.

Starchy Foods

High starch foods, such as potatoes, pasta, rice and most grains after they have been cooked, should not be frozen. Most will turn mushy and not be very palatable.

Baked Goods

Baked goods that are low in moisture will freeze well with little or no change in texture. Pies that have not been baked also do very well.

Soups and Casseroles

Because of their high water content, both of these foods do well when frozen. The texture does not change enough to matter when thawing. Do not freeze these products, however, if they contain any dairy products.

COLD AND FREEZING FACTS

There are Icicles in my Ice Cream

Icicles or ice crystals in ice cream are usually formed from opening the door to the freezer too often. It doesn't take very much of a temperature drop to force the water molecules out of some of the ice cream cells and form the ice crystals. If the ice cream is stored for a prolonged period of time at 0^0F. $(-17.8^0$C.), the crystals will change their form again. Just scrape the crystals away since they are harmless.

Why Ice Must Float

When water freezes, the hydrogen molecules and oxygen combine in a loose fashion creating air pockets, which causes the frozen water to rise. When water remains in its liquid form, the air pockets do not exist, making water denser than ice.

Scrub Those Ice Cubes

When ice cubes remain in the freezer tray or the icemaker for more than a few days, they may pick up refrigerator odors or contaminants from the air when the door is opened. It would be best to wash the ice cubes before using them for the best results.

Masher to the Rescue

If you need to use frozen juice concentrate, just use a potato masher to soften it.

A Cold Solution

When you place a bowl of ice cubes out for a party and don't want them to melt too fast, try placing a larger bowl with dry ice under the cubes. The ice cubes will last through the entire party.

How Clear I am

To make clear ice cubes, boil the water first before placing the water in the ice cube trays. This will eliminate the impurities that make the ice cubes cloudy. Never use cloudy ice cubes in a gin and tonic. This is probably against the law somewhere.

Boy, am I Shapely

If you would like to make different shaped ice cubes, just freeze water in a small cookie cutter, then place the frozen shapes into a pan of very hot water for a few seconds to loosen them up.

Speedy Ice Cubes

Believe it or not, if you use boiling water to make ice cubes, they will freeze faster. Even though cold water is closer to the freezing point, the hot water evaporates faster, leaving less water to freeze. The evaporation also creates an air current over the ice cube tray, which tends to actually blow on the water, similar to the cooling effect when you blow on a hot spoonful of hot soup before tasting it.

You're Freezing my Enzymes

When foods are frozen, the enzymes go into hibernation. However, they are not destroyed. If enzymes were not inactivated by freezing, they would cause flavor and color changes in the foods. When blanching, the enzymes are destroyed. Blanching must be done if you want to produce top quality frozen vegetables. Enzymes in fruits are the cause of browning and can be neutralized with the use of ascorbic acid.

Rancidity Control When Freezing

Products that are frozen with higher fat content can become rancid to a certain degree and ruin the flavor of the food. Air is the guilty party, which means that the food must be wrapped properly to avoid air coming into contact with the food. If you use a freezer bag, try and squeeze as much of the air out of the bag as possible.

Help! My Texture is Changing

When you freeze foods, you are actually freezing the water that is in the food cells. As the water freezes, it expands and a number of the cell walls rupture releasing their liquid, which then freezes into ice crystals, thus resulting in the food becoming softer. These changes in texture are more noticeable in fruits and vegetables, since they have higher water content than most other foods. Certain vegetables, such as tomatoes, lettuce and celery are so high in water content they literally turn into mush when frozen. When cooked products are frozen, their cell walls are already softened, therefore they do not burst as easily. This is especially true when high starch vegetables, such as corn, lima beans and peas are included in dishes.

Quick, Freeze me Faster

The damage to foods when freezing them can be controlled to some degree by freezing them as fast as possible. When foods are frozen more rapidly, the ice crystals that are formed are smaller and cause less cell wall rupture. If you know you will be freezing a number of items or a food that you really want to keep in good shape, try setting the freezer at the coldest setting a few hours before you place the food in. Some freezer manuals also will advise you which shelves are in the coldest area.

It Feels like a Roller Coaster in Here

The temperature of your freezer should never fluctuate more than a few degrees to keep foods at their best. The temperature should be kept at least 0⁰F. below for the best results. Thawing and re-freezing is the worst thing you can do to foods. Every time the temperature drops in the freezer, some of those small ice crystals will convert to larger ice crystals and little by little, the dish will be ruined.

Microbe Alert, Microbe Alert

Most microorganisms are not destroyed by freezing and may even be present on fruits and vegetables. Blanching does help lower the microorganism count significantly but enough of them do survive and are ready and waiting to destroy the food as soon as it thaws. Inspect all frozen foods, which may have accidentally thawed by leaving the freezer door open or from an electrical failure. The botulism microorganism does not reproduce at 0⁰F.

Quick, Get the ALOE, I've Got Freezer Burn

Poorly wrapped food or slow freezing allows moisture to evaporate and cause freezer burn. This produces a grainy, brown spot on the food and that area becomes dry and very tough. The area will lose its flavor; however, the food is still safe to eat (if you really want to).

You Won't Like me if you Freeze me

There are number of foods that have a high liquid content. When these foods are frozen, they are not very palatable.

FOOD	PROBLEMS WITH FREEZING
Apple	Becomes soft and mushy and may turn dark
Celery	Becomes soft and only good for cooking
Cooked egg whites	Turns rubbery
Cooked macaroni and rice	Mushy, loss of taste
Cheese in blocks	Tends, to crumble too easily
Cheese, crumbled	Soggy
Cucumbers	Limp, water-logged, poor flavor
Custards	Get watery
Cream cheese	Becomes grainy and crumbly
Cream pies	Get watery
Custard fillings	Easily separates, watery
Egg whites (cooked)	Soft, tough, rubbery
Fried foods	Loss of crispness, soggy
Gelatin	Weeps
Grapes	Becomes soft and mushy
Gravy	Need to be re-heated if fat separates
Icings made with egg whites	Weepy
Jelly on bread	Tends, to soak into the bread
Lettuce	Loses shape and very limp
Mayonnaise	Separates
Meringue	Toughens
Milk sauces	Tends to curdle or separate
Onions, raw	Becomes watery and very limp, but OK for cooking
Potatoes, Irish	Soggy when frozen in soups or stews
Potatoes, raw	Texture is lost and they may darken
Radishes	Texture is poor and they become pithy
Salad greens	Lose crispness
Sauces with milk or cream	May separate
Sour Cream	Separates, watery
Tomatoes, raw	Watery and tend to lose their shape
Whole milk	Separates
Yogurt	Separates

THAWING 101

- Thawing is best done in the refrigerator at about 41°F. (50°C.). This will not expose foods to the temperature danger zone.

- Many foods can be thawed under warm water at about 70°F. (21.1°C.) providing it takes less than 2 hours. This method is reserved for poultry.

- If you thaw in the microwave, the food should be cooked immediately to be on the safe side.

- Room temperature thawing should never be done since it allows the food to reach a temperature that may cause bacterial growth.

Food Protect me, I'm Valuable

It is necessary to use the proper packaging materials, if you want to keep your food in good condition when you freeze them. Foods will lose color, flavor, nutrients and moisture unless you are careful. The wrapping material or container will vary depending on the type of food or dish you are freezing. Never freeze fruits or vegetables in containers over $1/2$ gal., since they tend to freeze too slowly and usually do very poorly. If you wish to have the best results, use packaging with the following characteristics:

- Should be resistant to oils, grease and water.
- Strong and leak-proof.
- Easy to seal up.
- Has a space to write date on.
- Needs to be moisture proof.
- Should not be too porous.
- Should not become brittle and crack at freezing temperatures.

Foiled Again

Aluminum foil should never be used next to a warm or hot meat product and frozen. It keeps the food warm for too long a period and bacteria may grow, and if the food is not re-cooked to a high enough temperature after it is thawed, the bacteria may be reactivated.

Also, aluminum foil develops micro cracks and is only good next to a cold food in the refrigerator for no more than 1-2 days. Moreover, never place aluminum foil on top of a meatloaf with tomato sauce. It will deteriorate from the acid in the tomato sauce. The acid in citrus fruits will also eat away aluminum foil.

We're Breaking Up, All Food Overboard

Standard glass jars are not recommended for the freezer and break very easily. If you do use glass jars, use only the ones made specially for freezing. Plastic containers are very good for freezing. When using a plastic container, remember to place a piece of plastic wrap next to the food after it has cooled or is newly frozen. This will slow any moisture loss and may prevent the formation of larger ice crystals. Also, use freezer tape whenever possible to seal around the lids of all containers.

I'm Expanding, I Hope I Don't Burst

Other than most vegetables that normally will pack loose, most foods should have a small air space to allow for expansion.

The Powers Gone, We're Lost

If you lose power, never open the freezer door unless you really have to. If the freezer is full, the foods will remain frozen for 2-4 days without thawing, depending on the size of the freezer. Half-filled freezers will only remain frozen for about 24 hours. Cover the freezer with a blanket and tape it around as best you can. Tape all around the door after placing aluminum foil in the door cracks. By placing a baggie with ice cubes in the freezer, you can see if it has thawed and re-frozen the food.

You Can Grow Old in Here

When foods are kept past the recommended freezer storage time, the food is still OK to eat; however, the taste, texture and nutritional quality will be reduced significantly. Rotating frozen foods are a must.

Well, Zip my Lock

Zip-type bags should not be used for freezer storage unless they specifically state that they are made for freezer use. Most are too porous and the seal is not airtight enough to really do the job.

I Want my Sweets

Fruits can be frozen without sugar. Sugar is used to maintain the sweet flavor and help to retain the texture and stabilize the color and is not needed as a preservative.

I'm not all Artificial

If you plan on using a sugar substitute with foods that are going to be frozen, it is not a problem. However, you should follow the directions for equivalents very closely. While the artificial sweeteners do provide sweetness, they do not provide the syrup and color stabilization that the real thing will.

Eliminating Brown Out #1

The best method of reducing or eliminating the browning of fruits can be achieved with the use of ascorbic acid or vitamin C. Pure ascorbic acid is available in most supermarkets or drug stores. While some people tend to use lemon juice, it is not as effective and may impart more of a lemon flavor, which may not be desirable for many foods.

Eliminating Brown Out #2

To stop potatoes, apples and pears from browning when they are cut and exposed to the air, just dip them into a bowl containing water and 2 tbsp. of white vinegar. This also works well with avocados.

Blanching in a Microwave

If you choose to blanch in a microwave, I suggest you read up on the procedure in your manual. It is not as efficient as boiling water blanching and cold spots are possible, which will not kill the enzymes that must be destroyed.

I Didn't Blanch at all

Vegetables that are frozen and not blanched are still good to eat; however, the quality, color, texture and flavor will be considerably lower than those that have been blanched before freezing.

Freezing Your Corn

Corn must be handled just right or it will not be very edible. Corn should be blanched according to directions and chilled immediately in a bowl of ice water until the cobs are completely cooled down. Before you cook the ears, allow them to partially thaw at room temperature and place a small amount of sugar in the water.

Cooking Frozen Veggies

Vegetables should be cooked right from the freezer for the best results. The only exception is corn-on-the-cob and leafy greens.

Cooking Meats that Have Been Frozen

Meat and fish may be cooked directly from the freezer.

Freeze that Commercial

Commercial fruit juice concentrates can be frozen at 0^0F. for 1 year and most vegetables for 8 months. Bread can be frozen for 3 months and ground beef for 4 months, roasts and steaks for 1 year. Whole chicken can be frozen for 1 year, while parts are only good for 6 months.

To Re-Freeze or not to Re-Freeze

Meat and poultry- May be re-frozen if freezer temperature was maintained at 40^0F. (4.4^0C.) or below and the meat has no odor and is not discolored.

Vegetables- May be re-frozen only if ice crystals are present or if the freezer temperature was 40^0F. (4.4^0C.) or below.

Fruits- May be re-frozen providing they do not show any signs of spoilage. If they have fully thawed, it would be best to use them in cooking or preserves.

Cooked foods- May be re-frozen only if ice crystals are present or the freezer was 40^0F. (4.4^0C.) or below. If questionable, the food should be discarded.

Ice cream- If even partially thawed, discard it. If temperature was above 40^0F. (4.4^0C.), the ice cream could be dangerous.

4

Condiments
& SAUCES

How Foods Become Emulsified

Emulsification is the process of combining two liquids that do not normally wish to come together. A good example of this is oil and water. Oil and vinegar is another example and if they are used to make salad dressing, you know that it takes a bit of shaking to bring them together before you can pour the dressing out of the bottle. When the oil and vinegar solution is shaken, the oil is broken into small droplets for a short period of time. There are a number of emulsifying agents that help keep the liquids in suspension. One of the best emulsifiers for oil and vinegar is lecithin. Lecithin, a natural fat emulsifier, can be obtained at any health food store in ampoules and only one or two of the ampoules emptied into the mixture will place the ingredients into suspension. Lecithin is found naturally in egg white, which is why egg whites are used in many sauces to keep the ingredients in suspension.

Gelatin, the Great Thickener

Gelatin can be acquired from a number of different sources; however, the most common sources are animal hoofs, muscle, bones and connective tissue. Other sources include seaweed from which agar-agar is produced and Irish moss from which carregeenan is made. Both of these are popular commercial thickeners. Carregeenan is especially useful for thickening ice cream products. Gelatin granules have the capability of trapping water molecules and then expanding to ten times their original size. The firmness of a product will depend on the gelatin/water ratio. If the product becomes too firm, a small amount of heat is all that is needed to change the firmness closer to a liquid. If you chill the product, it will become firm again. Since gelatin is high in protein, you can never use fresh figs, Kiwi, papaya or pineapple in the product, since these contain an enzyme that breaks down protein thus ruining the product. The enzyme in pineapple (bromelain) can be neutralized by simmering the pineapple for a few minutes. When using gelatin for a dish, be sure and moisten the gelatin first with a small amount of cold water, then use the hot water to completely dissolve the gelatin. When hot water is poured into the dry gelatin, a number of the granules will lump and some will not totally dissolve which may cause your dish to be somewhat grainy. The hot water should never be over 180°F. for the best results. If your recipe calls for an equal amount of sugar to gelatin, the cold water step is not required, since the sugar will stop the clumping. However, you still never pour the hot water into the gelatin. Place the gelatin in the water.

Who Really Invented Ketchup-or is it Catsup?
The original name for what we call "ketchup" was "ketsiap." The sauce was invented in China in the seventeenth century and mainly used on fish dishes. It was made from fish entrails, vinegar and hot spices. The Chinese imported the sauce to Malaya and it was renamed "kechap." The Malayans sold the kechap to the English sailors during the eighteenth century, and the sailors brought it back to England. Mushrooms were substituted for the fish entrails. In 1792, a cookbook by Richard Briggs, "The New Art Of Cookery" named the sauce "catsup" and included tomatoes as one of the main ingredients. Ketchup became popular in the U.S. in 1830 when Colonel Robert Gibbon Johnson ate a tomato on the courthouse steps in Salem, New Jersey and didn't die. Tomatoes at that time were thought to be poisonous. H.J. Heinz started producing ketchup in the early 1870s; the company today is a $6.6 billion company.

Handy Containers
Empty plastic ketchup and mustard containers are great for holding icings and oils. Allow a mixture of warm water and baking soda to sit overnight in the containers, then rinse thoroughly with hot water.

How Did Heinz Become the Number One Ketchup?
In the 1940s, Hunt's was the number one selling ketchup in the U.S., mainly because it poured more easily and this was viewed as a real asset, since you didn't have to fight with the bottle to get the ketchup out. Heinz was also selling ketchup, but sales were lagging far behind the Hunt's product. In an effort to change the public awareness that just because the Hunt's ketchup poured more easily that didn't necessarily mean that it is the best product. In the 1950s, Heinz placed simple TV ads stating that "Heinz, Slowest ketchup in the West....East....North....South." The public then started viewing the quality of ketchup as a measure of the

viscosity and Heinz with the thickest product took the market away from Hunt's. Hunt's has never regained it back even though all ketchup is now slow. Quality ketchup now flows at 4-6.5 centimeters in 30 seconds. Government standards (USDA) for ketchup flow is 3-7 centimeters in 30 seconds. Ketchup is a $600 million industry with sales of seven 14-oz. bottles sold per person in the U. S. annually.

The Jelly Thickener

Pectin, a carbohydrate, is the most common thickener for jellies. If your jelly doesn't set, it will probably be the result of too little pectin or the wrong proportions of other ingredients. For certain types of fruit jellies, only a small amount of pectin may be needed, since most fruits are relatively high in pectin. Some of the higher pectin fruits, include all citrus fruits, apples and cranberries. The ones with less pectin include peaches, cherries, raspberries, apricots and strawberries. To get the most out of the pectin that is found in the fruit, the fruit should be very fresh. The fresher the fruit, the more active pectin will be available for processing the jelly. Jelly requires a number of ingredients to set properly. Pectin is only one of the most important. The acid and sugar content will both affect the properties of the product in regard to setting up. Cooking the jelly at too high a temperature will destroy the pectin.

New Salt Substitute

A new salt substitute that actually tastes exactly like salt will soon be available to U. S. markets. The substitute was created at Michigan State University and will be called "HalsoSalt®." The new salt was a product of research into alternative uses for corn and produced lysine, which is a nutrient that has a salty flavor and is capable of masking the metallic flavor of potassium chloride.

Herbs to Battle Harmful Bacteria

New studies are showing that certain herbs can reduce the bacterial count in certain foods. Seasoning foods may reduce the risk even from E. coli in meats and other foods. Herbs, such as cloves, cinnamon, garlic, oregano and sage were all good active herbs. The most effective herb, however, in the study was garlic. The addition of 7.5% garlic and clove herbal mixture killed 99% of the pathogen that was added to the food. More studies are underway.

New Dressing to Contain Fish Flakes

A new dressing that will be used on vegetables will be produced from a soy sauce base and will contain fruit, mushrooms and dried cured Bonita fish flakes. The dressing is presently being sold in Japan and will soon be in U.S. markets. The recipe has hardly changed from its original 1835 one, using anchovies layered in brine, tamarinds in molasses, garlic in vinegar, chilies, cloves, shallots and as a sweetener, sugar. The mixture must still age for 2 years before being sold, with the solids filtered out, and preservatives and citric acid added.

HOT PEPPER SAUCES

One of the most common hot sauces is salsa. These sauces are very popular in Mexico and most of South America. They may be served either hot or cold.

Chef's Secrets

When handling hot peppers, always wear light rubber gloves and be careful not to touch your eyes. The chemical, capsaicin, in peppers can be very irritating to your skin and especially your eyes. The same chemical is used in police pepper sprays. One drop of pure capsaicin diluted in 100,000 drops of water is still strong enough to blister your tongue. To reduce the hotness, remove the seeds and the ribs, then wash the peppers in cold water.

Tabasco, the World's Favorite

Only three ingredients go into producing the most popular hot sauce in the world: they are fiery, hot Tabasco peppers, vinegar and salt. Sales total over 78 million bottles annually. The Tabasco pepper seeds were originally planted in the U.S. on Avery Island, Louisiana around 1865 and the product produced today is still using peppers planted from the first strain. The salt used in Tabasco Sauce is from the same island. The peppers need to be fermented for 3 years before they can be used in the sauce. Tabasco was first marketed in 1868.

This Dog Will Take a Bite out of you

If you really want fire-hot, try Mad Dog Liquid Fire Hot Sauce®. Just use it a drop at a time or it will take your toupee off and send it flying. The product contains jalapeno peppers and African Bird's Eye chili pepper. There are a few other secret ingredients and I think it's best we don't know what they are.

Hot Can Be Ice Cold

Salsa can be frozen, however, it must be uncooked and freshly prepared. Drain as much liquid off as you can from the tomatoes or a layer of ice will be formed on the top.

Vinegar

The earliest record of vinegar use dates back almost 7,000 years ago to ancient Babylonia when dates were made into wine and vinegar. Vinegar was used as a medicine, as well as a flavoring for a number of dishes. Other fruits became popular around the same period and these included grapes and figs. Laborers in ancient times were given small amounts of wine vinegar and water with a dash of salt to pep them up and work more hours. The Roman army was given vinegar rations to give them more stamina. In World War I vinegar was used to treat wounds. Vinegar does have certain antibacterial and antiseptic properties.

All About Vinegar

Vinegar is commonly produced from ethyl alcohol utilizing the bacteria, acetobacter, which feeds on the alcohol, converting it into acetic acid (vinegar). Vinegar, however, can be made from a number of other foods, which is the preferred variety to use, such as apples or grains. The distilled vinegars are best used for cleaning purposes and not as a food additive. Vinegar tends to stimulate the taste buds and make them more receptive to other flavors. The varieties of vinegar are endless, depending on the food that is used to produce it. It is a mild acid called "acetic acid."

The actual amount of acid in vinegar varies from 4-7% with the average being 5%. Common types include apple cider vinegar, plain white distilled, red and white wine, barley, malt, rice and balsamic. The acetic acid content of vinegar is referred to by "grains."

- Vinegar with a 5% acetic acid content is known as 50-grain vinegar. The 50-grain means that the product is 50% water and 50% vinegar.
- Vinegar with 6-7% vinegar will keep foods fresher longer because of the higher acid content.
- Vinegar has a shelf life and will retain its effectiveness for 18 months.
- Studies have found that excessive use of vinegar, which contains a mild acid, may cause digestive problems, liver disorders, ulcers and destroy red blood cells prematurely. In moderation, there should be no problem. However, if you can substitute apple cider vinegar in a recipe, it would be healthier. Apple cider vinegar contains malic acid, which is actually friendly to the human digestive process.
- One cup of vinegar is composed of 98.8% water, hardly any protein, no fat, 14.2 grams of carbohydrate, 14 mg. of calcium, 22 mg. of phosphorus, 1.4 mg. of iron, 2 mg. of sodium and 34 calories.

Kitchen Wisdom

Types of Commercial Vinegar

Apple Cider Vinegar- Produced from whole apples that have been ground into pulp, then cold-pressed and fermented in wooden barrels. It can be used in salad dressings, pickling and any dish that calls for white vinegar. Be sure and purchase a good brand since some apple cider vinegar is produced from apple cores and peelings and poorly processed. The best flavoring herb combination is dill, garlic and bay.

Balsamic Vinegar- Historically, balsamic vinegar can be traced back to 1046. A bottle of balsamic vinegar was given to Emperor Enrico III of Franconia. During the Middle Ages balsamic vinegar was used as a disinfectant. Most is produced in Italy and aged 3-12 years before being sold. The aging produces mellow, brown vinegar that is relatively sweet. Balsamic vinegar is produced from the unfermented juice of the Trebbiano grape. Some balsamic vinegar may be 50 to 100 years old and still be usable. It is one of the best cooking vinegars and is great for a salad dressing, bringing out the flavor of many vegetables.

Balsamic Grape Brew- There are two varieties of balsamic vinegar: artesian-made and commercial. True balsamic vinegar is more of a liqueur than vinegar and is almost like syrup. True balsamic vinegar can only be produced in the provinces of Modena and Reggio in northern Italy. Artisan-made balsamic vinegar can be traced back over 1,000 years.

It is made from boiled-down grape-must and legally cannot contain any wine vinegar.

The aging process is complex and the juice must be passed down through a series of progressively smaller wooden barrels for at least 6 years, which are kept in a cool, dry location. These special wooden barrels have small holes in their tops, which encourage evaporation, thus allowing the flavors to concentrate. This process also allows special enzymes to assist in the production of complex flavors. The vinegar must be aged between 12 and 20 years and the cost for a $\frac{1}{2}$ ounce bottle is between \$60.00 and \$250.00 for certain aged "aceto" balsamic vinegar. The best brands to purchase are Malpighi, Cavalli, Mamma Balducci and Giusti.

Commercial Balsamic Paint Remover- Commercial balsamic vinegar is not regulated and the amount of aging can vary. It may be a blend of artisan-made or even boiled grape-must combined with good quality wine vinegar. The real inexpensive commercial balsamic is produced from cheap wine vinegar, colored and flavored with caramel. The poor quality can be compared to a quality paint remover and might substitute for one.

Cane Vinegar- Produced from sugar cane extract and water that has been fermented. The acid level of cane vinegar is just barely within the legal limits of 4% acidity. Can only be purchased in some oriental groceries and is mainly used in the Philippines.

Champagne Vinegar- This is really not made from champagne, but from the grapes that are used to make champagne. These include Chardonnay and Pinot Noir. The methods used are the same methods that are used to produce wine vinegar. Acidity levels in champagne vinegar are relatively high and run around 6%. Most have excellent flavors and are usually used in delicate sauces. Flavoring herbs are lemon balm, lemongrass and lemon zest.

Coconut Vinegar- Tends to leave an aftertaste and has a very low acidity level of 4%. May only be found in Asian grocery stores. Frequently used in Thai cooking.

Distilled Vinegar- May be prepared from grain, wood pulp or oil by-products. Distilled vinegar has a somewhat harsh flavor and acidity level of 5%. Usually used in commercial processing of pickles and related foods. Best used for cleaning purposes around the house.

Fruit Vinegar- Prepared using good quality cider vinegar, which has fruits such as strawberries, peaches or oranges added.

Herb Flavored Wine Vinegar- Produced from white wine or a quality cider vinegar with the addition of any herb that is compatible. The most popular are basil, rosemary, dill, chive and oregano. Tarragon wine vinegar is commonly used by chefs for shellfish dishes and poultry. Rosemary wine vinegar is excellent with lamb dishes.

Malt Vinegar- Originally prepared using soured beer and was called "alegar" in Europe. Traditionally, it is used on fish and chips in England. Presently, it is produced from malted barley and grain, mash which is fermented and then combined with wood shavings, then placed into large vats with a vinegar bacteria. Acidity levels in malt vinegar are normally 5%. The best flavorings are a combination of tarragon, whole cloves and garlic.

Raspberry Vinegar- Produced by soaking raspberries in white wine, providing the vinegar with a pleasant fruity flavor. Commonly used with pork dishes, poultry, as a salad dressing, and on fruits. Vinegar can be produce from almost any fruit; however, the flavor of raspberry vinegar seems to be the most acceptable for a large majority of the public.

Rice Vinegar- The Chinese have produced rice vinegar for over 5,000 years. It has a mild, somewhat sweet taste and is produced from rice wine or sake. This is very robust vinegar that is somewhat bitter. The Japanese produce rice vinegar that is sweeter and much milder, using cooked rice. The Japanese rice vinegar is capable of neutralizing lactic acid in the body, which may relate to increasing endurance levels for athletes.

Sherry Vinegar- This is very mellow vinegar with a somewhat nutty flavor. More expensive vinegar, it is produced similar to the methods of producing balsamic vinegar. Acidity levels in sherry vinegar are 6-7% and blends especially well with olive oil in salad dressings. Chefs use the vinegar to de-glaze pans. The best flavoring combination is thyme, rosemary, oregano and basil.

Wine Vinegar- Wine vinegar is produced from white, red or rose wine and is common vinegar for salad dressings. White wine vinegar is milder than the red and goes well with fish and lighter dishes. The best flavoring combination for red wine vinegar is rosemary, savory sage, bay leaf, garlic and basil. The best for white wine is dill, tarragon, basil and lemon balm.

I'll Have a Shot of Vinegar with my Pearls

Cleopatra dissolved pearls in a glass of vinegar and drank it to win a wager that she could consume the most expensive meal ever.

I Was Pungent

Vinegar has the tendency to lose its pungency when heated. For this reason, when you add vinegar to a dish, it should only be added when you remove the dish from the heat. If the level of acidity in vinegar is not desired, just add the vinegar while the dish is cooking and the acidity will dissipate.

Mother can be a Producer

If you purchase better quality wine cider or malt vinegar, they may be used for a starter if the vinegar has not been filtered or pasteurized. Bacteria or "mother" may form on the surface, then sink to the bottom. If this occurs, the "mother" can be used to prepare another batch of vinegar similar to a sourdough starter.

Vinegar Tasting Party

One method of tasting vinegar is to place a square sugar cube into the vinegar for about 5 seconds, then suck out the vinegar. It is best not to try and taste more than 4-5 different varieties before drinking a small amount of pure mineral water to clear your taste buds.

Livening it up

If the dish you are preparing lacks the flavor you would like it to have, just add 1-2 tsp. balsamic vinegar to it.

I'm too Sweet for you

If you oversweeten a dish, try adding a small amount of vinegar until the flavor is more to your liking.

Vinegar Copter

If you want to eliminate cigarette smoke from a room, just very lightly dampen a dishtowel and swirl it around over your head, keeping your feet on the floor. This will clear the room of cigarette smoke as well as the smoker.

Phooey, I Forgot to Add Vinegar

When cooking cabbage, add a small amount of vinegar to the cooking water and it will eliminate about 70% of the cooking odor. If you get fish or onion smell on your hands, just rub a small amount of vinegar, toothpaste, salt or coffee grounds on them to remove the odor (lemon juice works too).

Old-Fashioned Revival

When vegetables become slightly wilted, revive them by placing them into a vinegar and water bath. Make sure the water is ice cold.

Fresher Water with Vinegar

Next time you go on a camping trip and want your water to remain fresher longer, just add a few drops of cider vinegar to the water to keep it fresher longer and it will also have a cleaner taste.

Household Cleaning Uses for Vinegar

Remove Water Rings- Mix vinegar and olive oil in a 1-to-1 ratio and apply with a soft cloth, using slight pressure in a circular motion.

Polish Leather Furniture- Boil 2 cups of linseed oil for 1 minute, then allow it to cool before stirring in 1 cup of white vinegar. Apply with a soft cloth, allow it to stand for 1-2 minutes, then rub off gently.

Remove Carpet Stains- Only works well if the stain is fresh. Combine 1 part of white vinegar to 3 parts of water and allow to remain on the stain for 3-4 minutes. Using a sponge, rub the area gently from the center out, then dry with a clean soft cloth. Try an area that is out of the way to be sure that the carpet is colorfast.

Chewing Gum Remover- White vinegar is capable of dissolving and softening chewing gum from a number of fabrics and carpeting.

Decal Remover- Apply warm vinegar on a sponge and allow it to stand for a few minutes, then wipe with a soft dry cloth.

Mildew Remover- For severe buildup of mildew, use white vinegar full strength. For all other mildew buildup, use a solution of vinegar and water.

Plastic Upholstery Cleaner- Combine vinegar and water 1-to-1 and wipe the furniture with a dampened soft cloth. Follow with a dry cloth to buff.

Metal Cleaner- Use a small amount of vinegar, baking soda or salt to prepare a paste and use the paste to clean bronze, copper or brass pots or utensils.

Clean Aluminum Pot Stains- Black stains on aluminum pots can be removed by boiling white vinegar in the pot up to the area of the stain. For large pots, boil the vinegar in a small pot and pour it on the stain.

Wash Windows- Mix 1 tbsp. of white vinegar to 1 qt. of water.

Grease Cutter- Place a capful of vinegar in the dishwasher to cut grease.

Crystal Clear Glassware- If you want your crystal to sparkle, just rinse them in a solution of: one part white vinegar to three parts warm water.

Remove Lime Residue- Coffee pots, teakettles and irons are notorious for hard water residue buildup. When they get really bad, fill them with white vinegar and run them through a cycle.

Drain Cleaner I- Boil 2 cups of vinegar and pour it down the drain a small amount at a time. Allow the vinegar to remain in the drain for about 5-10 minutes before pouring a pot of very hot water down the drain. The alternative is to use $\frac{1}{2}$ cup of baking soda poured into the drain followed by $\frac{1}{2}$ cup of warm vinegar, cover the drain and allow it to stand for 5-10 minutes before running cold water down the drain.

Drain Cleaner II- Drop 3-4 Alka-Seltzer® tablets down the drain, then pour a bottle of white vinegar down. After 3-5 minutes, run hot water down.

Clean Shower Head- Remove the head and place it in a container that will allow you to cover the head with vinegar. Let it soak overnight, rinse and replace.

Weed Killer- Pour white vinegar on weeds in sidewalk or driveway cracks and they will be killed.

Pet Flea Killer- Add 1 tsp. cider vinegar to every qt. of water. Fleas will not go near your pet.

Cement Remover- When you are working with concrete or cement, try cleaning your hands with vinegar. Works great.

Ant Remover- If you are having a problem with ants, just wipe your counters off with a solution prepared from equal parts of vinegar and water. Crawling insects hate vinegar.

Remove Scorch Marks- If you rub a scorched mark with a clean soft cloth that has been lightly dampened with vinegar. it may remove a scorch mark if it not too badly imbedded.

Brighten Clothes- If you add 1$\frac{1}{2}$ cups of white vinegar to your rinse water, it will brighten up the colors. If you are dying a fabric, add 1 cup vinegar to the final rinse to set the color.

Remove Crayon Stains- Moisten a toothbrush with white vinegar and rub the area lightly until the crayon is removed.

Eliminate Deodorant Stains- Perspiration stains can be removed by rubbing the area with vinegar before laundering.

Ink Stain Remover- Vinegar will remove most ink stains if they are fresh.

Rust Remover- To remove rust, just moisten the fabric with white vinegar, then rub the area lightly with salt. Place the garment in the sun to dry, then launder.

Medicinal Uses for Vinegar

Bunions- In a small bowl, soak 2 slices of white bread, 2 slices of red onion in 1 cup of vinegar for 24 hours. Place the bread on the corn (bunion) and place a slice of onion on top. Wrap with a bandage and allow it to remain overnight.

Dandruff- Massage white vinegar into the scalp 3-4 times per week, then shampoo.

Nail Polish Saver- To make nail polish last longer, just soak the fingernails in a solution of 2 tsp. white vinegar and $\frac{1}{2}$ cup of warm water for 1-2 minutes before applying the polish.

Sunburn Reliever- Place a piece of cloth that has been lightly dampened with apple cider vinegar on the burn. Replace every 20-30 minutes.

Athletes Foot- Rinse your feet 3-4 times per day in apple cider vinegar.

Morning Sickness- When morning sickness occurs, just combine 1 tsp. apple cider vinegar in a glass of water and drink it.

Indigestion- To relieve indigestion, just place 2 tsp. apple cider vinegar into a glass of water and drink during a meal.

Around the Kitchen with Vinegar

Storing Pimientos- If you want to store pimiento peppers after opening a can or jar, just place them into a very small bowl, cover with vinegar and refrigerate. They will last for 2-3 weeks.

Keeping Ginger Fresh- Prepare a clean jar filled with balsamic vinegar and add the grated ginger. Seal tight and refrigerate.

Flavor Enhancer- When preparing soup or tomato sauce, add one or two tbsp. vinegar to the soup or sauce during the last 5 minutes of cooking time. This will really enhance their flavor.

Over-Salted Foods- Add 1 tsp. vinegar and 1 tsp. sugar, then reheat the dish or sauce.

Mold Eliminator- Always remember to wipe down the outside of canning jars with vinegar to eliminate the possibility of mold growing.

Vegetable and Fruit Wash- Mix $2\frac{1}{2}$ tbsp. vinegar in 1 gal. of water and use the mixture to wash the outsides of fruits and vegetables before peeling or slicing into them.

Stops Food Discoloring- When boiling potatoes, if you add 1-2 tsp. vinegar to the water, they will keep fresh-looking (and not discolor) for a longer period.

Great Mashed Potato Trick- Once you have mashed the potatoes and added the hot milk, try adding 1 tsp. vinegar and beat a little bit more. It will fluff them up and they will hold their shape.

Firm Gelatin- In warmer weather, gelatin tends to lose its shape. Just add 1 tsp. vinegar to the gelatin to keep it firm.

Better Wear Dark Shades

If you would like the crust on your fresh baked bread to have a great sheen, just brush the top of the bread with vinegar about 5 minutes before the bread has finished baking. Remove the bread before brushing on the vinegar, as the oven can get very cramped.

All Cracked up over Eggs

To keep the whites where they belong when an egg cracks during boiling, just add some vinegar to the boiling water.

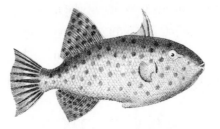

Fish Massage

Before you try and scale a fish, give the fish a vinegar massage and the scales will come off easier, as well as keeping your hands from smelling fishy.

Vinegar, Rising to the Occasion

Next time you steam vegetables, try adding 2 tsp. vinegar to the boiling water. It will prevent unwanted odors and stabilize the color of the vegetables.

Well, Pickle my Eggs

Pickled eggs are found in every English pub and will be sitting in a big jar of malt vinegar and spices.

STEAK SAUCE

A-1 Steak Sauce Rated One of the Best-Tasting
The ingredients are tomato puree, high fructose corn syrup, distilled vinegar, corn syrup, salt, raisins, spices, orange base (combination of orange, lemon and grapefruit juices), orange peel, dried onion and garlic, xanthan gum and caramel color.

New Kid on the Block
Grande Gusto™ is a new flavor enhancer that has been approved by the FDA and contains all-natural flavor and has no yeast or MSG.

WORCESTERSHIRE SAUCE

Who Invented the Sauce?
John Lea and William Perrins invented Worcestershire Sauce in England in 1835 by accident. They were managing a small drug store in Worcester, England when a customer, Lord Marcus Sandys asked them to reproduce his favorite Indian sauce he had liked in Bengal. They mixed up a batch of sauce prepared from vegetables and fish, but didn't like the aroma it gave off and placed the mixture in their cellar for storage. While cleaning the cellar two years later, they accidentally found the mixture and were surprised at the taste. Lea & Perrins Worcestershire Sauce is now one of the most popular steak sauces in the world. The recipe has barely changed from the original one using anchovies layered in brine, tamarinds in molasses, garlic in vinegar, chilies, cloves, shallots and sugar to sweeten it. The mixture must still age for two years before being sold. The solids are filtered out then, and preservatives and citric acid added.

SOY SAUCE

Soy sauce is one of the most popular condiments in the world. It is prepared from roasted soybeans and wheat (or barley), which have been fermented. The Chinese claim that ketchup was originally produced from a Chinese soy sauce recipe. There are four varieties of soy sauce:

- **Light soy sauce** that we normally see in the supermarkets.
- **Dark soy sauce**, which is not as salty but has a very strong flavor.
- **Chinese black soy sauce**, which is very thick and the color of blackstrap molasses.
- **Japanese tamari soy sauce**, which is very dark, thick and has a lower salt content than the Chinese variety.

The Soy Sauce Leader

Kikkoman International, Inc. is the largest producer of soy sauce in the world. Their latest product is a clear soy sauce that can be used in recipes without altering the color of the food. The company also produces soy sauce that is preservative-free and reduced-sodium, both available in powered or liquid forms.

MUSTARD

The mustard we know today can be traced back to 1726, and was produced by Adam Bernhard Bergrath in Dusseldorf. He combined strong brown mustard seeds with a milder yellow seed and added vinegar, water and salt. One of the finest quality mustards produced in the world is made by Appel & Frenzel under the name Lowensenf Mustard.

MARINADES

Marinades are usually prepared with one or more acidic foods, which are used to soften the food and allow the flavors to be more easily absorbed. They are usually thin liquids; however, most utilize oil as a carrier of the flavorings into the food. Marinades may be used for as little as 30 minutes and as much as 2-3 days, depending on the type of food and the recipe.

Love Meat Tender.........

Most marinades are used to both flavor the food, as well as tenderize it. The more common tenderizing acids are: papaya (papain), pineapple (bromelain), kiwi, lemon or limejuice, apple cider vinegar and wine.

A Tasty Morsel

The number of seasonings used in marinades is endless and really depends on a person's taste. The most common seasonings used are black or red pepper, garlic and onion.

Help! The Marinade is Drying out my Roast

Marinades will provide a small amount of moisture to a piece of meat. However, one of the major components of a marinade is acid. Acid will reduce the ability of the meat to retain its natural moisture when the meat is cooked. In some meat, the addition of the marinade will balance off this process and you will not notice any dryness. Always remember to allow your roast to rest for 10 minutes after you remove it from the oven so that the liquids that are left can return to the surface of the roast.

Chef's Secrets
Many chefs use a plastic bag to apply the marinade to meats and fish. Just pour the marinade into the bag, add the food and seal it up well with a rubber band, plastic strap or metal tie. The bag can easily be turned occasionally to be sure that all areas of the food are well marinated. Sometimes a chef will simmer the marinade after removing the food, thus reducing it and concentrating the flavors, and using the marinade as a sauce. One note of caution: if the marinade was used for raw meats of any kind or raw fish, it would be best not to use the marinade for a sauce unless it is boiled.

MAYONNAISE

Mayonnaise may be made using any type of vegetable oil. The preferred oil would be one that is low in saturated fat and ideally one that is high in mono-unsaturated fat, which would be olive or canola oil. If you wish to have a somewhat nutty flavor, you can use walnut or almond oil. Always use the highest quality of the oil you choose.

Who Invented Mayonnaise?
Mayonnaise was invented by a German immigrant, named Nina Hellman in New York City in 1910. Her husband, Richard Hellman operated a deli in the city where he sold sandwiches and salads. He soon realized that the secret to his success was based on Nina's recipe for the dressing she put on the sandwiches and salads. He started selling the spread he called "Blue Ribbon" for ten cents a dollop and did so well that he started a distribution business, purchased a fleet of trucks, and in 1912 built a manufacturing plant. The rest is mayonnaise history with Hellman's Mayonnaise becoming one of the best selling spreads in history. At present, we consume 3 lbs. of mayonnaise per person annually. To date, Hellman's has sold 3.5 billion lbs. of mayonnaise without changing the original recipe.

Step by Step, Drop by Drop, and Slowly I Stir
When preparing mayonnaise, always remember to add the oil drop by drop, which gives the emulsification enough time to fully form. As soon as the mixture begins to become more solid and looks somewhat white, you can then add the oil in a slow, thin, steady stream. Adding the oil too quickly will result in separation.

Curing a Separation
If the oil that is being added does cause a separation, the problem can be solved by either adding $\frac{1}{2}$ tsp. prepared mustard or 1 tsp. vinegar to the mixture. If this doesn't work, try using an egg yolk that has been beaten well. Whisk the egg yolk into the mixture a small amount at a time, just until the mixture is emulsified again. The balance of the oil then needs to be added in, a small amount at a time.

Tasty Sensations

Once all the oil has been added to the mayonnaise, flavorings can be added if desired. If you would like a more tart sauce, just add 1 tsp. lemon juice. Additional mustard may be added or any other condiment that appeals to your taste. Always serve mayonnaise at room temperature for the best flavor.

I Don't Like the Cold

Emulsions, such as mayonnaise, do not freeze well. The water in the products tends to freeze into ice crystals and separates from the oil. This causes the sauce to break up when thawed and cannot be put back into suspension easily.

Making Mayonnaise? Check the Weather Report First

When the temperature or humidity is high, it will cause the mayonnaise to come out heavier and greasier than normal.

Short Lifespan

Fresh mayonnaise will only remain fresh for about 3 days under refrigeration and should not be frozen. After 3-4 days, the mayonnaise will start to separate and there is no method to bring it back into a separation.

Please Don't Freeze Me

Mayonnaise will stay fresh in the refrigerator after it is opened for about 2 months, but does not freeze well.

Sauces

Sauces are only meant to complement the flavor or provide moisture for the dish. Sauces should never detract from the original flavor of the food. French cooking schools classify sauces in five categories: Espagnole, which is a brown, stock-based sauce; Velote, which is a light, stock-based sauce; Bechamel, which is a white sauce and usually milk-based; Hollandaise or mayonnaise is an emulsified sauce; and Vinaigrette is an oil-and-vinegar sauce. However, we place mayonnaise in the condiment class because it is usually always purchased as a commercial product and vinaigrette as a salad dressing.

THICKENING 101

To thicken any sauce, you will need to increase the solids and reduce the amount of liquid. This can be accomplished by boiling away some of the liquid. However, this will reduce the amount of useable sauce and may concentrate the flavors too much. If the sauce is high in water content, cooling it causes the water molecules to lose energy and they relax, thus thickening the sauce. There are, however, a number of good substances that will thicken sauces and depending on the type of sauce you are preparing one will surely be just right for the job. These include pureed vegetables, egg yolk, flours, gelatins, tapioca, pectin, okra, cornstarch, arrowroot, potato starch, kneaded butter, emulsified butter, cream, peanut butter, etc.

A Few of the Common Thickening Agents

Arrowroot- Purchased as a fine powder that is derived from the root stalks of a tropical tuber, it is prepared by dissolving a small amount in water. These stems are mainly composed of complex carbohydrates, which have the tendency to thicken at a lower cooking temperature than most other starches. The advantage of arrowroot is that there is less likely the chance of burning the thickener, due to its low protein content.

Tapioca- Extracted from the tropical cassava root and best used as a thickener if it is diluted with water before being added to a dish just before serving. The roots are finely grated, left to ferment, then pressed into cakes and baked. The baked cakes are then powdered into a pure starch. Tapioca is best when it is moistened, then heated and immediately used.

Vegetable puree- Vegetable puree is a healthier method of thickening gravies and sauces. Purees may be made with any assortment of vegetables that complement the dish it is to be used in. Vegetables need to be cooked first; some need to be sautéed fist, then pureed in a blender or food processor. Once the vegetables are pureed, they should be put through a sieve or fine mesh before using.

Cornstarch- Produced from the endosperm of a kernel of corn and should always be dissolved in cold water before using for the best results. May become cloudy when cooked and satiny when fully set. When used in place of flour, the sauce will be clearer.

All-Purpose Flour- Made from the endosperm of wheat and tends to turn opaque when cooked and somewhat pasty when set. Very effective in thickening gravies.

Rice Starch- This is sold in a fine white powder and is made from ground rice. It will turn white when cooked and creamy when it sets up. Usually found at Asian markets. Use only half as much as cornstarch for the same results.

Mung Bean Starch- Produced from dried ground mung beans. Becomes very clear when it is cooked and somewhat gelatinous when set. Commonly used throughout Asia to prepare jellied dishes.

Pectin

When using pectin in preserves, be sure and only use the pectin specified in the recipe. Different brands are prepared with different ingredients that will make a difference in the final product. Some pectin needs acid and sugar to set, while others need acid and only a small amount of sugar. Some pectin never needs either acid or sugar to set.

Real Easy and Thick, Too

A relatively new thickener, Thick & Easy® is now available. The thickener is made from modified food starch and maltodextrim with no additives or preservatives. The product can be used to thicken any type of cold or hot food, either solids or liquids. The product can be frozen and reheated by microwave oven. The thickening activity stops after one minute and retains its consistency. It is fully digestible, does not bind fluids, releasing 98% for consumption, while most competitive products only release 50%.

Commercial Thickeners

One of the better commercial thickeners is Textra™. Textra™ is a modified tapioca starch that has been designed to improve "mouthfeel" and texture of foods. It does not impart any taste to the product, while providing thickening for drinks, sauces and syrups. It is one of the more stable thickeners and will assist particles, such as fruit pulp to remain in suspension.

Instant Starch

There are two "jel" products that will do a great thickening job. These are ClearJel-310® and Rice Gel®. ClearJel-310® will thicken as soon as it is added to either water or milk and will provide a smooth, fully hydrated texture, as well as being heat-and-acid-resistant. Rice gel is produced from pre-cooked rice flour with no noticeable taste of its own. It has a high water capacity, blends well with dry foods and is non-allergenic.

Thickening a Sauce or Making Glue for the Kids

The easiest method to thicken a sauce is to prepare a small amount of "paste." The paste should be prepared separate from the sauce. Never try and add the paste ingredients to the sauce to hasten the procedure. The paste needs to be smooth and the consistency will vary, depending on the level of thickening needed. If the sauce is very thin, you will need a thick paste, etc. Add the paste gradually, allow the sauce to boil and stir until the desired texture is obtained. These pastes will work especially well with gravy and most other sauces.

Thin Paste	Use 1 tbsp. flour + 1 cup liquid
Medium Paste	Use 2 tbsp. flour + 1 cup liquid
Thick Paste	Use 3 tbsp. flour + 1 cup liquid

Use whatever liquid is compatible with the sauce you are preparing.

Hear Ye, Hear Ye, Hot Sauces Hate Egg Yolks

If your recipe calls for egg yolks, never add them to a sauce that is too hot. The instant change in temperature, resulting from placing the cool egg into the hot liquid, is just enough of a change to curdle the egg yolk and may ruin the sauce. To eliminate the possible problem, remove a small amount of the sauce and allow it to cool for a few minutes before mixing the egg yolk in. The cooled sauce can then be added to the hot mixture.

Whisk me a Ribbon

When sauce is finished cooking, it should fall from the whisk in a wide ribbon or sheet. This should take about 5 minutes of cooking.

Why Does Starch Thicken a Sauce?

Starch granules are a solid which, just by being there, will cause a certain degree of thickening. However, the small starch granules tend to trap water molecules, thus reducing the percentage of free-flowing water that is in the sauce or soup. When you heat the starch, it has the ability to expand and is capable of absorbing even more water.

Nervous Pudding

Kids call gelatin "nervous pudding" because it always shaking. Gelatin has been used as one of the primary thickeners for hundreds of years and is capable of increasing ten times its original size. Gelatin is the best water-trapping medium we have found. Care, however, must be taken when adding other ingredients to gelatin. Sugar reduces the absorption capacity of gelatin significantly and fruits, such as pineapple and papaya, which contain the enzymes bromelain and papain and will eliminate the gelatin's thickening ability.

Avoiding a Separation

If your egg-based sauce separates, remove the pan from the heat and beat in two tbsp. crushed ice to reduce the heat and place the eggs back into suspension, thus saving the emulsion. You can also change pans and add one tbsp. ice water to a small amount of the sauce while slowly whisking back the balance of the separated sauce. Additional ice water can be added slowly, but only as needed.

Two Times the Power of Flour

Cornstarch, arrowroot and potato starch should only be used just before you are finishing the sauce, since they have twice the thickening power of flour and can only be cooked for a few minutes before losing their thickening power.

Need Kneaded Butter?

This is an excellent thickener, especially at the last minute. If you wish to make a sauce from leftover liquids that have remained in the pan, just place an equal amount of butter (unsalted) and flour in another pan, then mix them together to make a thick paste. Use small amounts of the paste, adding it gradually to the leftover liquid.

The Fats in the Flour

Flour will not lump if you add the flour to any fat that is already hot. In fact, you can add flour to any hot liquid without the flour lumping.

Regular Flour vs Instant Flour

Regular flour tends to turn into a form of gelatin, when it comes into contact with hot water that tends to block the water from entering. Instant flour contains smaller, irregular-shaped granules that allow space for the water to enter.

How About a Quickie?

If you would like a hollandaise sauce that can be prepared in 10 minutes or less, try Knorr® Hollandaise Sauce Mix. The ingredients include modified food starch, wheat flour, non-fat dry milk, hydrolyzed vegetable protein, partially hydrogenated peanut oil, lactose, salt, fructose, onion and garlic powder, citric acid, vegetable gum, yeast extract, soup stock, spices and a natural flavor. It really is not too bad tasting, but nothing like the "made-from-scratch" original.

Don't Mock my Hollandaise

To prepare a "mock" hollandaise sauce, just use 1 cup of white sauce and add 2 slightly beaten egg yolks and cook until just 2 bubbles (not 3 or 4) appear on the surface. Remove the pot from the hot burner and beat in 2 tbsp. unsalted butter and 2 tbsp. pure lemon juice. Voila! Fake hollandaise sauce that will fool everyone but a chef.

Sauce Too Salty? Sugar Cubes to the Rescue

One easy method of reducing the salt level in sauces and soups is to dip a sugar cube into the dish and run it back and forth, covering the surface only once and before the cube melts. Salt is attracted to sugar and a percentage of the salt will adhere to the cube. Then discard the cube.

Hot is not Really Hot, It's Warm!

Sauces are never served hot, always warm. High heat will melt the butter too fast, ruin the emulsification and cause separation. You want the butter to turn into a foamy mixture, not a liquid. Start with cold butter, which will keep the mixture cool and reduces the risk of the butter melting, instead of foaming. Keep the pan moving on and off the heat if necessary, while beating the butter with a whisk. You can also use a double boiler, which is easier for the person who is not used to making a white sauce.

I'm Going Bad, my Starch is Freezing

Most sauces and custards that are thickened with flour or cornstarch do not freeze well. The starch, amylase, which is commonly found in grain starches, such as wheat flour and cornstarch, tend to freeze into a very firm, spongy-texture and allows the liquid to drain out. If the food is thickened with a root starch, such as arrowroot or tapioca, they can be frozen and thawed without any problem.

I'll Never Cook Again

If you accidentally burn your dessert sauce, don't fret. Just add a small amount of pure vanilla or almond extract in the sauce to cover up the burnt taste.

Chef's Secret to a Safe Hollandaise

Since eggs may be contaminated even if they are not cracked, it would be wise to microwave the eggs to be sure that there is no contamination before you make the sauce. The procedure will not harm the eggs and they will still be in good shape for the sauce. The procedure can only be done with 2 large yolks at a time and in a 600-watt microwave oven.

- The first step is to separate the egg yolks from the white and remove the cord. Then place the yolks in a small glass bowl and beat them until they are well mixed.
- Next, add 2 tsp. real lemon juice and mix thoroughly.
- The bowl should then be covered and placed into microwave on high and the surface observed.
- When the surface starts to move, allow the mixture to cook for no more than 10 seconds.
- Remove the bowl and whisk with a clean whisk.
- Return the bowl to the microwave and cook until the surface moves again and then another 10 seconds.
- Remove and whisk again with a clean whisk.
- Allow the bowl to sit for one minute before you use it for the sauce and it will be salm onella-free.

Are You Going to do it Again?

There are a number of rules to remember when re-heating soups, sauces and stews. Foods that contain fats tend to oxidize more readily and this may impart a less than desirable flavor. When re-heating, never place the food in an aluminum or iron pot and never add salt until the food is almost completely warmed. Soups and gravies should only be simmered for about 2 minutes. Creamed soups should only be re-heated at a slow simmer after it has reached a slow boil for about 2 minutes.

Am I Really that Bitter? I Try to be Sweet

Occasionally, sauces tend to taste a bit bitter and the reason escapes you. It may be from a tomato seed or two that ended up not being strained out. A crushed tomato seed will cause a sauce to become bitter.

Why is my Melted Cheese Solid?

When melting cheese, never cook it for too long a period or at too high a temperature. When this occurs, the protein separates from the fat and the cheese gets tough and rubbery. Once a cheese hardens, especially in a sauce, it would be wise to discard the sauce and start over. When you melt cheese, it would be wise to grate the cheese first. The cheese will then melt in a shorter period of cooking time.

Make Your Cheese Happy, Give it Some Wine

The reason cheese tends to form lumps or strings is that the calcium phosphate present in the cheese binds with the protein. This can be avoided if a small amount of wine, which contains tartaric acid, is added to the melting cheese. The tartaric acid prevents the calcium phosphate from linking the cheese proteins. If you prefer not to use wine, just use a small amount of lemon juice and the citric acid will accomplish the same thing.

White Sauce the Right Way

There are two types of white sauces: Béchamel, which is made from whole milk or cream and Veloute, which is made from chicken or fish stock to be sure it retains a white color. All white sauces are made with a roux - which is made by combining flour in clarified butter (or almost any fat) while cooking slowly until it combines. This is always done before adding any liquid; however, be sure the mixture doesn't brown and that it foams up slightly and remains a light color. As soon as this occurs, add the liquid at once and stir continually until it starts to boil, reduce the heat and allow the mixture to simmer for 5-8 minutes. The simmering is important since it will remove the taste of the flour. Cajun roux is cooked until the mixture of flour and fat turns black but does not burn. This is a very slow process.

Chef's Secrets to the Perfect White Sauce

- When you stir the liquid into the roux and lumps are formed, strain the mixture through a fine sieve before continuing.
- If the sauce is too thick, add a small amount of liquid while stirring slowly. If too thin, just simmer longer until it thickens.
- If you are preparing the white sauce and need to allow it to sit for a period of time, rub the top of the sauce lightly with the end of a stick of butter. This will result in a thin layer of melted butter on the top preventing a skin from forming.
- If a skin does form, skim it off carefully to remove it all.

Freezing White Sauce

If you do not use cream or eggs, the sauce will freeze well for 2 weeks but will only last for one day in the refrigerator. If you do freeze the sauce with egg, the yolk will separate from the sauce when thawed. Cream in the sauce may be too thin when thawed and will require 1-2 tsp. of arrowroot to be added.

Wine Sauce Tip

When wine is added to any sauce, be sure and heat the sauce long enough for the alcohol to evaporate, thus leaving the flavor only.

Giddyup Butter

Mounted butter sauces gain body from both the emulsification process and air that is beaten in.

Speedy, Almost Instant Sauces

Beef Sauce- Whisk 1 cup of heavy cream with 2 tbsp. a mild horseradish sauce, $1\frac{1}{2}$-tbsp. lemon juice and a small amount of salt and pepper as desired.

Chicken Sauce- In a small saucepan on low heat, whisk 8 ounces of sour cream with one can of cream of mushroom soup, then add one cup of de-fatted chicken broth.

Fish Sauce- Whisk together, one cup of mayonnaise with 2 tbsp. minced sweet pickles, 1 tbsp. minced onions and 1 tbsp. minced stuffed green olives.

Lamb Sauce- In a small saucepan over low heat, melt one cup of mint jelly with one cup of pure, pulp-free orange juice and one tbsp. mild prepared mustard. Heat and serve warm.

Low-fat Sauce- Combine one can of quality light evaporated milk with one package of onion soup mix and one tbsp. cornstarch in a small saucepan over low heat. Whisk in your favorite minced herbs or onion, remove from the heat and add one cup of non-fat sour cream.

Pork Sauce- In a small saucepan over low heat, melt one cup of current jelly with $\frac{1}{2}$ cup of ketchup and 1 tsp. pineapple juice. Serve warm.

Vegetable Sauces- Melt 6 or more oz. Velveeta® with just enough milk to make a smooth mixture, serve while it is warm. Slowly melt 6 or more oz. of regular or any flavored cream cheese with a small amount of milk on low heat in a small saucepan. Whisk one pt. heavy cream and one cup mayonnaise and blend well.

Lower-Fat Sauces

Barbecue Sauce- The American-style barbecue sauce is made with tomato sauce, mustard, onions, garlic, brown sugar or molasses and apple cider vinegar.

Bordelaise- Prepared with wine, brown stock, bone marrow, shallots and herbs.

Bourguignonne- French sauce prepared with red wine, onions, carrots, flour and bacon.

Coulis- Usually prepared as a vegetable puree.

Demi-Glace- Prepared as a reduced stock made with either sherry or Madeira wine.

Marinara- Prepared from tomato sauce, onion, garlic and oregano.

Sweet and Sour- Prepared with sugar, vinegar and seasonings.

Veloute- Stock-based white French sauce.

Higher-Fat Sauces

Alfredo- An Italian sauce prepared from cream, butter and Parmesan cheese.

Bechamel- White sauce prepared from butter, milk and flour.

Béarnaise- French white sauce prepared from white wine, tarragon, vinegar, shallots, butter and egg yolk.

Bolognese- Italian meat sauce prepared from meat, vegetables, wine, cream and herbs.

Hollandaise- Prepared with butter, egg yolk and lemon juice.

Mole- Mexican sauce prepared from onions, garlic, hot chilies and chocolate.

Pesto- Italian sauce prepared from fresh basil, pine nuts, garlic and Parmesan cheese.

Ragu- Prepared from tomato sauce, ground beef, onions, celery, white wine and herbs.

Vinaigrette- French oil sauce prepared from olive oil, vinegar and herbs.

Tomato Sauces

The French were the first to utilize tomato sauce in recipes after the tomato was discovered in Peru and brought to France by the Spanish Moors in the 1500s. If you are going to use fresh tomatoes in a recipe, be sure they are at room temperature for the best results. Tomatoes can be refrigerated for storage; however, they lose almost all of their aroma and flavor when cold. Allow the tomatoes to remain at room temperature for 30 minutes before using them. This will re-activate the aroma and flavor.

Chef's Secrets

Since most recipes call for removing the skin and seeds of tomatoes, there is an easy method of accomplishing this. Just place the tomatoes in a large pot of boiling water for 2-3 minutes. This will loosen the skin then remove them with a slotted spoon. To remove the seeds, cut the tomato in half and squeeze the halves into a fine strainer. This will catch the seeds and allow the juice to be saved. Homemade tomato sauce can be stored in the refrigerator for 2 days and will freeze for 3-4 months.

BARBECUE SAUCE

Barbecue sauces are prepared to provide a particular flavor to the food and is usually brushed on meat and chicken. They are not designed to tenderize the food and do not penetrate very deeply into the food. Almost all barbecue sauces contain oil, which keeps the surface of the food moist and helps avoid burning. The sauce is applied a number of times during the cooking process with a natural bristle brush or a special barbecue brush.

Grandma's Barbecue Sauce Recipe

2 cups ketchup or seasoned tomato sauce
3 tbsp. extra virgin olive oil (cold pressed)
1 tsp. canola oil
1/2 cup finely diced red onion
4 cloves of garlic, finely minced
1/2 cup unsulfured molasses
1/4 cup apple cider vinegar
1 tsp. powdered cayenne pepper
1 tbsp. lemon juice
1/4 cup quality mustard
1 tsp. soy sauce

Using a medium-sized pan, heat the olive oil with the small amount of canola oil (to raise the smoke point) over medium heat. Stir in the garlic and onion and sauté for 6-8 minutes before adding the rest of the ingredients. Mix the balance of the ingredients into the sauce, then allow it to simmer for about 15-20 minutes. The sauce may be applied either warm or cold.

Commercial Teriyaki Sauce

Commercial teriyaki sauce should contain the following ingredients if the quality is superior: soy sauce, dried garlic, concentrated pear or grape sweetener, dried onion, sesame seed, garlic powder, ginger powder, onion powder and natural vegetable gum. There should be no added salt.

Mole Sauce

This sauce is of Mexican origin and can probably be traced back to the Aztecs who used chocolate to sweeten dishes. However, originally a mole sauce was any sauce that contained hot chili peppers. The sauce is traditionally served with poultry dishes, but can be found on almost any dish in a Mexican restaurant.

SWEET SAUCES

Custard

One of the most popular sweet sauces is a custard sauce, which can be made in a number of great flavors, such as chocolate, vanilla, raspberry, mint, blueberry, apricot and lemon.

Chef's Secrets

When preparing custard, eggs are sometimes a problem if not handled properly. The eggs should be beaten first with sugar and set aside. The milk or cream must then be scalded until small bubbles form around the edges of the pot. Pour a small amount of the hot liquid into the eggs, mixing thoroughly, slightly cooking the eggs. Add the egg mixture into the hot milk and heat on low heat until it starts to thicken. The custard should then be strained into a bowl to remove any solidified egg or film that had formed. Custard must be stirred continually to prevent the bottom burning. Chefs always use a wooden spoon when stirring custard, since some of the eggs minerals may react with certain types of metal spoons. When stirring, always stir in a figure eight pattern to cover the complete bottom.

Chocolate Sauce/Syrup

When preparing chocolate sauces, there are a number of tips that you should be aware of. The following will help you obtain the perfect sauce:

Chef's Secrets

If a liquid is used in the recipe, always melt the chocolate in the liquid, not separate for the best results. Use low heat and stir continuously. The microwave is excellent for melting chocolate. Just place the chocolate in a large measuring glass and cook until melted while keeping an eye on it to be sure it doesn't cook too much. Most chefs melt chocolate in a double boiler over simmering (not boiling) water. Always use the type of chocolate called for in a particular recipe and always use the highest quality chocolate you can find.

Finger Lick'n Good

Ganache is one of the finest blends of chocolate sauce you will ever taste, when made properly. It consists of melted semi-sweet chocolate, heavy cream and unsalted butter. It is definitely not a healthy food, since it is high in fat, cholesterol and calories.

Ganache Recipe

In a small saucepan, heat 1 cup of heavy cream and 2 tbsp. butter to boiling. Place a 12-oz. bag of chocolate semi-sweet morsels into a medium-sized bowl and pour the hot butter cream mixture over the chocolate. Stir until smooth. When it is cool, it will remain somewhat soft and should not harden.

Grandma's Hot Fudge Heaven Sauce Recipe
4 oz. bittersweet chocolate (4 squares)
12 oz. can of quality evaporated milk
3 tbsp. salted butter
2 1/2 cups confectioner's sugar
2 tsp. pure vanilla extract

Combine the chocolate, sugar and evaporated milk on the top of a double boiler with simmering water in the bottom. Stir occasionally until the chocolate has melted completely. Remove from the heat and whisk in the pure vanilla and butter until the mixture is smooth. Enjoy!

Controlling Your Temper While Tempering

Tempering chocolate is the process of melting it, cooling it, then melting it again. This process produces a more lustrous, glossy and stable mixture and is called for in many chocolate recipes. This is an exact science to obtain the right consistency and takes some practice. However, there is a "quick-tempering" method that utilizes a small amount of oil that will speed the process up considerably. The end product will be a little thinner, but will not make a difference in most recipes and decorative uses.

We Love Chocolate

The U. S. is the largest purchaser of cocoa beans in the world. We average about 172,000 tons annually.

Finally! Low-Fat Chocolate Syrup

New low-fat chocolate syrup has hit the markets, which has all the flavor and taste of the real thing and 5 times less fat. The product is produced by New-Market Foods of Petaluma, California and consists of brown-rice syrup, honey, molasses and cocoa. The topping is syrupy and buttery and found in health food stores.

The Quick-Tempering Method

Use 1 tbsp. vegetable oil (preferable a neutral oil such as Canola or safflower) also clarified butter, is often used by some candy chefs, even a solid shortening. Stir 1 tbsp. oil into every 3 oz. of melted chocolate you use over low heat. Quick-tempered chocolate will only hold up for 2-3 days, but the candy is usually long gone before that.

COOKING EXTRACTS

Vanilla Extract

The FDA has established guidelines for vanilla extract and if you use vanilla extract in your cooking you should know the differences in the various ones that are sold. To be called a "pure vanilla extract," the list of ingredients must read "extractives of vanilla beans in water, alcohol (35%)." This will probably be the more expensive brand. Other labels may read "water, alcohol (35%), vanilla bean extractives and corn solids." The better brands may still use a small amount of corn solids; however, they will always have the vanilla bean as the first ingredient on the list of ingredients.

- To produce one gal. of pure vanilla extract it takes 13.6 oz. vanilla beans, 35% alcohol and water. The alcohol evaporates when you bake or cook with the vanilla extract.
- Sugar should never be listed on the label and may affect the product. Time (aging) will improve the flavor of pure vanilla extract.
- Vanilla extract sold in Mexico has been implicated in numerous studies, as containing contaminants from the harvesting of the bean and the processing procedures. Since there is no way of telling which are good and which are bad, it is recommended not to purchase any Mexican vanilla extract.
- The U.S. purchases more vanilla beans than any other country in the world, about 1,500 tons annually.

Well, Excuse my Infusion

Almost everyone is familiar with a simple "infusion" by just placing a tea bag in a cup of water and releasing the flavors and compounds. However, there are a number of other liquids that can be infused with essences, cinnamon sticks, vanilla beans, nuts, spices, dried fruits and even flower petals. Hot liquids tend to cause the herb or essence to release its flavors and occasionally their colors more readily than a cold liquid. The following is a simple method of infusion:

- Place the liquid you wish to infuse and the flavoring in a saucepan over moderate heat.
- The liquid may be milk, soup stock, sugar syrup, cream, etc.
- When the liquid is just about ready to boil, remove the saucepan from the heat, cover the pan and allow the mixture to steep until the flavor you desire is achieved.
- This process usually takes about 30-60 minutes.
- The mixture should then be strained and pressed hard through the strainer to extract all the liquid.
- The liquid is now ready to be used in your recipe.

5

All About
FATS & OILS

Fats (Lipids)

Fats are substances such as oils, waxes, lard, butter and other compounds that are insoluble (unable to mix with) in water. Some fats are readily visible, such as fat on meats, butter, cream cheese, bacon and salad dressing. Other fats are less visible, such as fat in egg yoke, nuts, avocado and milk. Fats are a combination of "fatty acids," which are their "building blocks" or basic "sub-units." The type of fat depends on the specific mixture of these fatty acids. The body uses fat as its energy storage reserves, padding to protect organs, as a constituent in hormones, an important building block of a healthy cell wall, and insulation.

Fats Fall into 3 Main Categories

1. Simple Fats: These are basic fats called a "triglyceride" and are composed of a glycerol base with three fatty acids.
2. Compound Fats: These are a combination of fats and other components. One of the more important is the lipoproteins, which are fats that combine with proteins. Lipoproteins are the main transport system for fats. They may

contain cholesterol, triglycerides, neutral fats, and fatty acids. Since fat is insoluble, it needs a vehicle to carry it around the body.

3. Derived Fats: Produced from fatty substances through digestive breakdown.

The Fats You Eat are Composed of 3 Chemical Elements:

Carbon	C
Hydrogen	H
Oxygen	O

The carbon atoms are like a skeleton and can be compared to the framework on a house. In a saturated fat, all the carbons are completely surrounded by hydrogen and oxygen atoms. Since the carbons are totally saturated, this type of fat is solid at room temperature.

In polyunsaturated fat, some of the carbons have a free space where an atom of hydrogen could be attached. It's because of these openings that polyunsaturated fat is liquid at room temperature. If all the carbons have hydrogen atoms attached, the fat is saturated and solid at room temperature. There is also a middle-of-the-road fat called a monounsaturated fat, which the body likes better than any other type of fat.

The 3 Major Types of Fats

Polyunsaturated Fats (PUFA) Good Fats- Always remains a liquid at room temperature. Examples are safflower, corn, and peanut. Studies have shown that some PUFA and MUFA fats may have a tendency to lower blood cholesterol levels.

Monounsaturated Fats (MUFA) Good Fats- These tend to thicken when refrigerated but are still liquid at room temperature. Examples are olive and canola oil. Recent studies show that MUFA oils may be more effective in lowering blood cholesterol levels than PUFA oils.

Saturated Fats (SFA) Bad Fats- Normally, these are either solid or semi-solid at room temperature. Examples are butter, lard, shortening and hard margarine. The exceptions to the rule are coconut oil and palm oil, which are liquid at room temperature and may be listed on the list of ingredients as "tropical oils." SFAs have the tendency to raise cholesterol levels, even though they may not actually contain cholesterol.

Medium Chain Triglycerides (MCT)

This oil is derived from vegetable oils and cannot easily be stored by the body. MCT oil does not raise cholesterol levels and contains 8 calories per gram instead of the normal 9 calories per gram in other fats.

The oil has shown to have anti-bacterial properties and can reduce the size of breast tumors in laboratory animals. The oil is extracted from coconuts, which contain about 15% MCT oil. MCTs, when ingested, tend to circulate until needed as a source of energy instead of being stored. The major supplier of the oil is Mead Johnson and sells for $40 per qt. Wholesale suppliers, however, such as Stephen and Huls America sell the oil for about $10 per qt. wholesale.

Studies are underway to relate the MCT oil to thermogenesis, which is the process by which the body creates heat by mobilizing fat stores. Presently, margarine is available in England that utilizes MCT oil as the main ingredient. Some ice cream manufactures may be substituting MCT oil for milk fat. MCT oil has too low a smoke point at 375°F. to be used for frying.

Good Fat?

Medium-chain triglycerides (MCT) are sold in health food stores for people who have trouble absorbing fats. They are for the most part produced from coconut oil, have a very low smoke point, and can be used for cooking without producing trans-fatty acids. Body builders tend to use this fat to increase caloric intake, but studies to date are not conclusive.

ESSENTIAL FATTY ACIDS (EFA)

The essential fatty acids are a part of the polyunsaturated fats and are considered a "good fat." They play a role in keeping the body tuned up and in good shape. If you are deficient in these good EFA fats, you may have symptoms that include loss of hair, elevated cholesterol and triglyceride levels, high blood pressure, nerve abnormalities and reduced immune system efficiency. Our bodies cannot produce these acids and they must arrive by way of the foods we eat. Some of the more important EFAs include Linoleic Acid, Linolenic Acid, vitamin F and the Omega group of fatty acids. Foods that are high in EFA's include seeds, grains, nuts and cold-water fish.

There are also a number of foods and disease processes that interfere with the breakdown and utilization of these fats, such as alcohol consumption, diabetes, a poor diet and aging. Supplements that are available include oil of evening primrose, flaxseed oil, black current oil and fish oils.

The more popular sources of Linoleic Acid (Omega-6) are soybeans, corn, sesame seeds, wheat germ and safflower. The best source of Linolenic Acid (Omega-3) is found in soybeans, walnuts, canola oil, pumpkin and flaxseed oil.

Hydrogenation

Many vegetable and baked good product labels state that they are hydrogenated. This simply means that the manufacturer has added hydrogen atoms from water to harden the fat in the product and make it more "saturated," thus adding a different texture to the food to make it more palatable and possibly last longer. A liquid fat can be turned into a solid in this manner. However, what you are doing is changing a good fat into a bad fat. The more hydrogenated a product, the higher the saturated fat level. Rearrangement can also be achieved during this process, combining two different oils to produce a product with different melting points.

The Bad Parts of a Good Fat

We have now covered a number of important points regarding fats and their relationship to the foods we eat. However, we now need to discuss the fact that those "good guys," the polyunsaturated fats and the monounsaturated fats, may have a bad side to them.

An example of this is eating at a fast food restaurant and ordering a potato patty for breakfast. Since it is early morning and the frying vat has just been filled with a good fresh vegetable oil (we hope), the majority of the fat will probably be a good polyunsaturated fat. However, when you go back to that same restaurant for lunch, they have now fried in that oil for 4 hours and the majority of the oil has converted to a bad oil called a trans-fatty acid. Studies have implicated this oil in the acceleration of the aging process, raising the bad cholesterol, and lowering the good cholesterol.

When you purchase oil from the supermarket, for the most part you're buying good oil or the "cis" form. The "trans" form should be avoided as much as possible.

Cis-Form Fatty Acids

A horseshoe-shaped molecule of polyunsaturated fat that occurs naturally in nature and is normally incorporated into a healthy cell wall. The health of the cell wall depends on a supply of cis-form fatty acids. When these acids are not available, the cell wall is constructed with abnormal openings (ports of entry) that may allow foreign substances to enter and cause a disease process to start.

Trans-Form Fatty Acid

Instead of the normal horseshoe form, trans-fatty acids are found in a straight-line shape. This form of the fat is difficult for the cell to utilize in the construction of a healthy wall. The blueprint calls for a horseshoe shape, not a straight line. Basically, trans-fatty acid is a product of processing foods that contain fat. When fat is heated, a percentage of fat converts to bad fat called a trans-fatty acid, which is really an artificial chemical. This fat is found in our food in such abundance to make it the number one artificial chemical in our food supply and a risk factor for heat disease. Margarine may contain up to 54% trans-fatty acids and shortenings as much as 58%. Heating and storage of these fats increases these percentages.

COMMON COOKING OILS

The following are some of the more common oils that are used for cooking and baking. Oils will vary as to the type of fats they are composed of, the color, aroma, nutrients, and smoke points. Oils may be categorized in many different ways, such as how refined the oil is, the plant or animal it was extracted from, the method of extraction (cold or hot), smoke point, consistency and color. All fat content figures are for one tbsp. fat or oil. Saturated fatty acids (SFA), polyunsaturated fatty acids (PUFA), monounsaturated, fatty acids (MUFA).

Almond Oil- Unrefined almond oil is commonly used in many dishes and is commonly substituted for butter. It adds an amber color to foods and has a mild sweet flavor. Refined almond oil is produced by crushing almonds and heating them until a thick, golden-colored paste is produced. The paste is then squeezed to produce the oil. This extensive processing makes almond oil one of the more expensive oils. Some people who are allergic to aspirin may be allergic to almonds and almond oil. The French almond oil is the highest quality.
SFA . . . . .3.2 g, PUFA . . . . . .3.3 g., MUFA . . . . . .5.7 g.

Avocado Oil- A light, nutty tasting fruit oil that is usually only used on salads. The oil does contain a small amount of saturated fat, but is mostly monounsaturated. The smoke point is too low to be considered for cooking and frying. Avocado is the highest fat fruit and should be used in moderation.
SFA . . . .1.6 g., PUFA . . . . . .1.9 g., MUFA . . . . . . .9 g.

Canola Oil- Produced from the rapeseed plant, which is a relative of the mustard family. It is normally found in the refined state, has a very high smoke point making it, one of the best all-around oils. This is the best oil for frying since it does not breakdown as easily as most other oils. The oil is high in monounsaturated fat and low in saturated fat. It is also one of the lowest priced oils. Canola oil is one of the few oils that contain omega-3 fatty acids. The name canola was derived from the word Canada and oil. The major source of canola oil, rapeseed, is Canada.
SFA . . . .1.0 g., PUFA . . . . . .4.1 g., MUFA . . . . . .8.3 g.

Shoot that Rapeseed Plant- Human genes are being shot into rapeseed plants to attempt to produce a plant (canola oil plant) that will be able to reduce the level of soil contamination. The plant is being forced into mating with the human genes.

Coconut Oil- This oil is very high in saturated fat and may be capable of raising cholesterol levels. Usually not sold for home cooking uses, it is present in numerous products, especially baked goods, candy and margarine. The oil has the ability to extend the shelf life of foods and it would be best to read labels to see if the product contains coconut oil or, as it is sometimes called, "tropical oil."
SFA . . . .11.8 g., PUFA . . . . . .0.2 g., MUFA . . . . . .0.8 g.

Corn Oil- One of the most common oils that is manufactured in large quantities and extracted from the corn germ, a by-product that is obtained from cereal and corn syrup producers. The oil is a light yellow color and has a mild flavor, which does not overpower recipes. This makes corn oil excellent for baking, pastries, and most recipes that call for vegetable oil. A darker corn oil is sold that is extracted from the whole corn kernel and has a stronger aroma, similar to that of popcorn. Other types of corn oil include unrefined, expeller-pressed oil that has a strong aroma and is not recommended for delicate dishes since it will overpower the flavors. This type of oil, however, is good for baking, as well as in sauces and dressings. It cannot be used for frying, however, since it tends to foam and boil over easily. Highly refined corn oil can be used for frying and has a relatively high smoke point. Corn oil is about 87% polyunsaturated fat and contains about 60% of the essential fatty acid, linoleic acid. Corn oil also contains more vitamin E than most other oils after processing, which normally reduces the vitamin E content significantly.
SFA . . . . . .7 g., PUFA . . . . . .7.9 g., MUFA . . . . . . .3 g.

Cottonseed Oil- This oil is normally not sold to the general public since it may be easily contaminated. The oil is heavily used in many products, such as shortening, baked goods, margarine and dressings. It was one of the most popular oils in the U.S. until the 1940s when more efficient processing methods were invented.
SFA . . . . .3.5 g., PUFA . . . . . .7.0 g., MUFA . . . . . .2.4 g.

Flaxseed Oil- One of the best sources of the essential fatty acids is omega-3. Has a strong golden color. And the flavor is not overpowering. The oil mixes well with most foods and imparts a pleasant flavor. Health food restaurants tend to use the oil in salad dressings, Cole slaw, dips, marinades and sauces for vegetarian dishes. Best not to cook the oil, as it tends to lose its flavor and aroma. The essential fatty acids are more active in this oil if it is not heated.

Grape-seed Oil- A light colored oil that is produced from grape seeds. The majority of the oil sold in the U.S. is imported from Europe; however, the U.S. is starting to produce larger amounts of the oil. Grape-seed oil has a very high smoke point and can be used for frying and in dishes that need to be cooked at high temperatures. Excellent for stir-fried foods.
SFA . . . . . .3 g., PUFA . . . . . .9.5 g., MUFA . . . . . .2.2 g.

Hazelnut or Filbert Oil- It is strong, full-flavored oil with a roasted nutty aroma. This oil has been used in France for hundreds of years and is one of the more popular oils. The unrefined hazelnut oil is difficult to refine, hard to find in the U.S. and very expensive. It is used by European chefs when preparing special hot sauces and for breading. Crushing the nuts, then heating them before squeezing out the oil, produces the refined oil.
SFA . . . . .1.0 g., PUFA . . . . . .1.4 g., MUFA . . . . . .10.6 g.

Hemp Oil- An excellent source of essential fatty acids, since it contains a balance of omega-3 and omega-6 fatty acids. The color of hemp oil tends to turn most people off since it is a green color, but it has a mild flavor and good texture. Like flaxseed oil, hemp oil is best when it is not heated and can be used in the same dishes and dressings as flaxseed oil.

Olive Oil- Olive oil is high in monounsaturated fat (77%) and is gluten-free. One tbsp. contains 8% of your daily requirement of vitamin E. Greece is one of the largest producers of olive oil with an annual output of 300,000 tons. The oil produced is of the highest quality, which is the low acid, extra virgin variety. Most of the Mediterranean countries produce olive oil of such poor quality that it must be refined to produce an acceptable flavored product. Look for oil from Greece or California that states "cold-pressed, extra virgin, pure organic."

Palm Oil- This is one of the highest saturated fat oils and may raise cholesterol levels. May also be listed on the list of ingredients as a "tropical oil" and is frequently found in baked goods with coconut oil. This oil is one of the most popular oils used for making soap. The oil is extracted from the pulp of the oil palm plant. Palm oil is normally a solid at room temperature, due to its high degree of saturated fat.
SFA. . . . . .6.7 g., PUFA. . . . . .1.3 g.., MUFA. . . . . . . .5.0 g.

Peanut Oil- Peanut oil is one of the more popular oils and one of the easiest to extract oil from since peanuts are about 50% fat. They tend to maintain their nutty flavor in recipes and especially stir-fried foods. Many chefs tend to mix the oil with unrefined sesame oil, which will complement each other's flavors and aromas. Peanut oil has a high smoke point and is a common oil for most cooking purposes, especially frying. However, 90% of peanut oil is saturated fat, which is higher than almost every other vegetable or nut oil. Also, peanut oil is low in vitamin E, trace minerals and essential fatty acids. Peanuts are actually from the legume or bean family and not from the nut family. Peanut oil is produced from pressed, steam-cooked peanuts and will not absorb or transfer flavors to other foods. Peanuts are also one of the ingredients in the manufacturing of dynamite.
SFA...........2.3 g., PUFA..........4.3 g., MUFA.........6.2 g.

Safflower Oil- Popular all-purpose oil that is relatively inexpensive and has a mild flavor. The thistle-like plant was used to produce a dye for garments in ancient times. Since the oil lacks flavor, it can be used in almost any dish that requires liquid oil without the risk of flavoring the dish. Unrefined safflower oil is best used cold in dressings, salads and sauces. The oil is high (80%) in essential fatty acids, especially linoleic acid. The oil is difficult to extract because of a very hard husk and hydraulic presses are required to extract the oil. The lower-priced safflower oil is usually extracted with the use of chemical solvents. However, the method of extraction is not required to be placed on the label, which means that you don't know whether you are purchasing a high quality product or not. Safflower oil is second only to canola in its vitamin E content. The refined oil has a high smoke point and is good for frying. Cold-pressed is the best oil to use in salads or dishes that are not heated.
SFA . . . . .1.2 g., PUFA . . . . . .10.1 g., MUFA . . . . . .1.7 g.

Sesame Oil- Sesame oil can be purchased in two distinct varieties: the type that is produced from roasting the bean, which is the dark oil, and the lighter oil that is recommended for use in salads and dishes that are not cooked. The more popular of the two is the dark variety, which is commonly used in many Chinese dishes and produces a nutty flavor. The lighter oil is produced from pressed, raw sesame seeds and is considerably milder and used when you desire just a hint of the sesame flavor. It only takes a few drops of sesame oil to add flavor to vegetables, soups, or salad dressings. One of the major advantages is that sesame oil is very stable and does not turn rancid easily, even in hot, humid climates. It is considered one of the more healthful oils and is high in polyunsaturated fats and especially essential fatty acids.
SFA . . . . .1.9 g., PUFA . . . . . .5.7 g., MUFA . . . .4 g.

Soybean Oil- Unrefined soy oil is one of the more difficult oils to extract, which makes the oil somewhat expensive. The oil is used in baking and

contains an excellent amount of lecithin, which is an emulsifier. The oil is also high in essential fatty acids and polyunsaturated fats. Unrefined soy oil tends to become rancid rather easily and should be used shortly after purchase, then stored in the refrigerator. The highly refined soy oil is lower in price and used extensively in the baking industry. Almost 80% of all oil that is used for baking is soy oil. If you see "vegetable oil" on the label, it is probably soy oil. Good source of omega-3 fatty acids.
SFA . . . . .2.0 g., PUFA . . . . . .7.9 g., MUFA . . . . . .3.2 g.

Sunflower Oil- Most sunflower oil is produced by a cold-pressed method, which only mulches the sunflower seeds, then presses the mulch to obtain the oil. Heat and chemicals are not used, thereby producing healthy, high nutrient oil. New Zealand is one of the major producers of sunflower oil. Russia produces as much as 80% of their usable oil from the sunflower. It has a low smoke point and is not recommended for high temperature cooking or frying.
SFA . . . . .1.4 g., PUFA . . . . . .8.9 g., MUFA . . . . . .2.7 g.

Walnut Oil- This is another expensive oil when purchased in the unrefined state. The finest grades of this oil are produced in the Perigord and Burgundy provinces of France. To produce unrefined walnut oil, the nuts are dried and cold-pressed. The oil is high in polyunsaturated fat and has a pleasant nutty flavor. Walnut oil tends to become somewhat bitter when heated and is best used cold in salads. Refined walnut oil is produced by crushing the nutmeats and heating them to produce a paste. The paste is then squeezed to extract the oil.
SFA . . . . .1.2 g., PUFA . . . . . .8.6 g., MUFA . . . . . .3.1 g.

Pure or Virgin, What's the Difference?- Law has set the standards for olive oil and the saturated fat levels it contains. Extra virgin olive oil must not contain more than 1% unsaturated fatty acid and virgin olive oil must not contain more than 3.3%. Pure olive oil is a combination of both oils.

Buyer Beware- The best quality oil is "cold-pressed" extra virgin olive oil. It is made from the plumpest, Grade A olives, has the best flavor, and is processed by pressing the oil from the olives with as little heat and friction as possible. The next best is virgin olive oil, then pure olive oil, which is a blend of both. Many companies are using "cold-processed" instead of "cold-pressed." Cold-processed may mean the olive oil is produced by using a chemical solvent to extract the oil. Chemical residues are not uncommon. Read the labels and watch for this intentional use of a similar phrase, which does not denote a quality processing.

Don't Let Olive Oil Have a Breakdown- Olive oil is one of the healthiest oils to use in salads or for low temperature cooking. It has a low smoke point, which means that it will break down easily and start smoking. You can extend the usable life of olive oil and slow its breakdown by adding a small amount of canola oil to the olive oil. Canola has a very high smoke point. This will also work well with butter, when you are sautéing.

Olive Oil vs. Cholesterol- Some nutritionists claim that olive oil has the ability to lower cholesterol levels; however, the only solid information reports that extra virgin olive oil tends to help the body preserve the good cholesterol, HDL and in some cases, may lower the bad cholesterol.

This, of course, is a good thing, but don't expect a cholesterol-lowering effect from any vegetable oil. Oat bran has been shown to lower the bad cholesterol by 26%.

Are my Taste Buds Working?- Peanut oil has very little flavor when used for cooking purposes. It has a relatively high smoke point, which makes it a good choice for frying. The mild nut flavor is popular with Asian cooks; however, it is not flavorful enough for most American dishes. The oil will remain fresh for about a year under refrigeration and if it becomes cloudy, will clear up in a short period of time, if allowed to remain at room temperature.

SMOKE, FLASH AND FIRE POINTS OF OILS

The smoke point of oil is the point at which the oil starts deteriorating. All oils have different smoke points: canola oil, having one of the highest, makes it the best oil for frying. Flavor would be another determining factor in using oil with a lower smoke point. The smoke point is the point at which the oil is starting to convert a percentage of the oil into Trans-fatty acids. The flash point is the point that the oil starts to show a small amount of flame emanating from the surface of the oil. This usually occurs at about 600°F. and should tell you that the oil has reached a dangerous level. The fire point is about 700°F., which is the point that you had better have a fire extinguisher ready and remember never to use water on a grease fire. The fire needs to be smothered to extinguish it.

Going up in Smoke - Quick Reference

OIL	TEMPERATURE
Canola Oil	525°F. (273.9°C.)
Safflower Oil	510°F. (265.6°C.)
Soybean Oil	495°F. (257.2°C.)
Corn Oil	475°F. (246.1°C.)
Peanut Oil	440°F. (226.7°C.)
Sesame Oil	420°F. (215.6°C.)
Olive Oil (blend)	375°F. (190.6°C.)
Vegetable Shortening	375°F. (190.6°C.)
Clarified Butter	350°F. (176.7°C.)
Butter	250°F. (121.1°C.)

Extraction Methods of Refined Oils

Extraction method will determine the color, level of nutrients remaining, the flavor and stability of the oil. Manufacturers do not have to state on their label which method is being used, leaving the consumer in the dark as to whether the oil is really of a higher quality or not. The higher quality oils do state the method, such as "cold-pressed" and charge a premium for their product. When oils are heat-extracted, all oils will lose a percentage of their nutrients. When processed at over 300°F., all proteins and vitamin E is destroyed. When processed at 120°F. to 160°F., almost all the protein and nutrients are retained in usable form. However, there is less usable oil produced, making these products more expensive. When vitamin E is retained in the oil, the oil will not become rancid as easily and will have a better shelf life. To overcome this problem, many companies add antioxidants to the oil.

Refined Oils

These are the best oils for frying and cooking dishes at higher temperatures, since they do not break down easily. Oils that are highly refined have very little flavor and usually have a light color. These oils are neutralized, bleached, deodorized and are low in nutrients.

• Neutralization process removes any "free fatty acids," which have separated from the triglyceride molecule. If the acids were allowed to remain in the oil, they would react with oxygen and produce rancidity. A washing and drying process to remove any moisture, which produces deterioration of the refined oil, further neutralizes the oil.

• Bleaching process involves removing impurities using an absorbent earth as a filter, leaving the oil clear. Another process called, "fractionation," can also be done to refined oils. This process can take liquid oil and cool it down under special controlled conditions, separating high melting point triglycerides from the low melting point triglycerides, providing solid, liquid fat at room temperature. The product can then be sold as margarine or liquid oil.

- Deodorization process involves removing any smell or taste that is not desired and is achieved by blowing steam through heated oil. A vacuum then removes the steam, which has trapped the smells and any off-taste.

Unrefined Oils

These oils are not heavily processed and cannot be used for high temperature cooking and frying. The only exception to this rule is safflower oil. Unrefined oils are by either cold-processed or expeller-pressed methods. Because of these methods of processing, the oils will retain their flavors and aromas. Many unrefined oils are used to flavor dishes that require the stronger oil flavors. Most of the unrefined oils retain a high level of essential fatty acids and nutrients.

Expeller-Pressed Extraction

The seeds or grains are squeezed under pressure of about 15 tons per square in., which generates considerable heat. Temperatures commonly exceed 300°F., which destroys all the protein and vitamins. Most of the oils sold in the U. S. are expeller-pressed extraction oils.

Cold-Pressed Extraction

This oil is still expeller-pressed; however, the process is not allowed to reach the high temperatures that are produced from the full extraction processing. Only three oils: olive oil, peanut oil and sesame oil can be processed by this method and obtain enough oil to sell commercially. The low-heat processing reduces the quantity of oil obtained significantly. Cold-pressed oils are the highest quality oils and contain the highest levels of nutrients.

Chemical Solvent Extraction

The less expensive brands of oils, especially the supermarket brands, may use solvent extraction methods. This is an inexpensive method of oil extraction, using the chemical "hexane" or another petroleum product to separate the oil from a food source. After the extraction takes place, the toxic solvent is boiled off. The oil is then refined, deodorized and bleached to an acceptable color at temperatures of over 400°F., leaving literally no nutrients in the oil. Preservatives and antioxidants must be added to give the oil a good shelf life and retard rancidity.

Packing Oils

If you would like to obtain the highest level of nutrition from oil, packaging is one of the most important factors to consider. Oils should be packaged in containers that do not allow any air or light to reach the oil.

Airtight Black Glass Containers

If you wish to obtain the highest level of essential fatty acids from the oil, then the oil must be packaged in a very dark or black container that is well-sealed. The oils should also be stored in the refrigerated section of the market. Quality oils processed at low temperatures will lose their nutrients very quickly.

Metal Cans

Metal containers have been used for many years to protect oils from the air and light. Most of these containers are of a very high quality and should not impart any metallic taste to the oil. Olive oil is the most common oil sold in metal containers. These containers are more common in Europe. Only metal container that the oil is sold in is safe for oils. These metal containers are specially lined with plastic polymers to prevent the oil reacting with the metal. Metal containers will cause rancidity very quickly if not coated.

Plastic Bottles

Almost all plastic bottles that are used to sell the lower quality oils are usually clear or translucent, allowing the light to penetrate the bottle. The oil will not retain its freshness for any length of time. Frying oil may be purchased in these bottles; however, these oils are rarely recommended for cold dishes or salads.

STORING OILS

Generally, all oils should be resealed as tightly as possible and stored in a cool, dry location. The best location, however, is the refrigerator. Cloudiness is common when oil is refrigerated and the oil will return to normal if allowed to remain at room temperature for about 15-20 minutes. If a container of oil is left out of the refrigerator for even a short period of time on a hot, humid day, the oil will start to become rancid very quickly. Oil that has been opened is only fresh for about 4 months and should be discarded after that. It would be wise to date the oil container when it is purchased. Rancidity will usually begin about 4 months after the oil is purchased, regardless of the method of storage. Exposure to light for long periods will cause almost any oil to turn brown.

Oil that is in a sealed, unopened bottle will stay fresh for 1 year. When oil is poured out of the bottle into any other container for any reason, it should never be returned to the original container and mixed with the clean oil. Contamination is possible and may ruin the balance of the oil left in the container. Unrefined oils high in essential fatty acids only have a high quality shelf life of 3-6 weeks and must be refrigerated. If you wish to freeze the quality oil, it will be good for about 12 months.

FLAVORED OILS

Flavored oils are sold in all food specialty stores and natural food markets; however, it is easy to prepare your own. The best base oils to use are olive, sesame or peanut oil. Any herb or combination of herbs can be added to the oil. All herbs should be thoroughly washed and dried before adding them to the oil, since cleanliness is an important factor to reduce the possibility of contaminating the oil. The most common herbs used in flavored oils are garlic, cayenne peppers, fennel, bay leaf, rosemary, oregano, cloves or citrus wedges. The herb needs to remain in the oil until the desired level of flavoring is reached.

When preparing flavored oils, it is necessary to be aware of the potential health problems that are associated with these oils.

The botulism bacteria is commonly found in the soil and brought into the home on vegetables and herbs. Certain precautions need to be taken when preparing flavored oils. Since the botulism bacteria thrives in a low acid, anaerobic atmosphere (low level of oxygen) environment, it is necessary to heat the oil with the herb to 240°F.(116°C.) to destroy any potential bacteria that may be present. If you are serious about making flavored oils, then you should purchase a book on the subject and adhere to the recipes and preparation and storage methods.

Digestion of Fats

The following is an example of how fats are digested:

Mouth- No digestion takes place here. Fats are just broken down into smaller particles by chewing action.

Stomach/Pancreas/Duodenum- Fat is separated from other foodstuffs by the action of hydrochloric acid, which makes it easier for it to be broken down by pancreatic lipase.

Small Intestines- The presence of fat in the duodenum (first section of the small intestines) stimulates the gall bladder to release bile salts. The fat globules are then further broken down by bile salts, which allows the enzymes to go to work and release diglycerides and monoglycerides and a few fatty acids. The bile salts then combine with pancreatic lipase, which helps to accomplish the breakdown process of the fats. Fats are then absorbed into the intestinal wall and are carried throughout the body by lipoproteins.

Liver- This is the main site of fat metabolism.

Essential Fatty Acids
Essential fatty acids (EFAs) are building blocks of all "good fats" and are necessary for optimum health. The body is unable to produce these "essential fats" and a quality source of the fat is required. The EFAs help the body to maintain a healthy cell wall around our cells and are critical to healthy functioning of the

central nervous system and our blood vessels. The majority of EFA oils are derived from fish oils and plant oils. While a low fat diet is recommended, we should not lose sight of the body's need for an adequate supply of EFAs. EFAs may also be sold and called vitamin F in some literature. Basically, the two most common EFA oils are linoleic and linolenic acids.

Omega-3 Fatty Acids

Essential fatty acids (EFA) are derived mainly from fish oils. Studies have shown that this type of oil has the ability to lessen the risk of a heart attack by reducing the possibility of a clot forming in an artery that has been damaged by plaque buildup. The omega-3 fatty acid also has the ability to reduce the level of bad cholesterol (LDL) circulating in the bloodstream. Some arthritis sufferers have found that increasing their intake of omega-3 fatty acids tends to have an anti-inflammatory effect and relieves some of the discomfort. However, people who are taking any anticoagulant medications need to consult their physicians before taking this supplement

Omega-6 Fatty Acids

This group of EFAs tends to compliment the omega-3 fatty acids and assist them in working more efficiently. These fats have been studied in relation to the same medical concerns with the addition of relieving pre-menstrual tensions and improving skin tone. The omega-6 group of oils is usually always derived from plant sources, the best of which are: black currents, evening primrose and starflower.

Flaxseed Oil

This plant has been around for over 5,000 years and the benefits are too numerous to mention in relationship to a healthy body. The oil is one of the best sources of EFAs and contains 60% omega-6 and 20% omega-3 oils. Studies have shown that the oil can reduce blood triglyceride (fat) levels.

Salad Dressing May be Good for your Heart

The latest information from a Harvard University study relates the use of salad oil to lowering the risk of heart disease by providing a good source of essential fatty acids. The salad dressing consisted of oil from a quality plant source and vinegar. Fat-free dressings on a consistent basis may not be in a person's best health interests. Alternating between a quality plant-oil-based dressing and a fat-free dressing may be the best way to go.

Processed Foods, a Major Problem

Burgers, fried chicken, French fries, baked goods, pastries, etc. may contain up to 25% of their fat in the form of trans-fatty acids. It doesn't matter whether the fat in the product is listed as polyunsaturated or saturated fat, it is possible that the 25% will include some of the good fats that have been converted.

Europeans May be Smarter than Americans

European countries and the World Health Organization, after investigating trans-fatty acids, have determined that they are a significant health problem and reducing them in our foods would substantially lower the incidence of heart and related diseases. The FDA and the U.S. food industry don't feel that the proof is sufficient and maintain that nothing need be done at this time.

Medical Test to be Used on Foods

Magnetic Resonance Scanning (MRI) equipment, using a lower level of magnetic resonance, will soon be used to investigate how water molecules react in foods. There are a number of foods that could be used to produce other products if we knew at what point water molecules change and affect the product's quality. This information could influence spoilage and change fat-containing foods significantly.

Hydrogenation to be a Process of the Past

New oil processing techniques are being studied that will change oil and create an oil that is a high-saturate oil. This will eliminate the need to hydrogenate oil and eliminate the trans-fatty acid. This new fat science will create fat that will have the same desired properties of the hydrogenated oil.

Stable Oil

Oil has the tendency to breakdown when used for prolonged periods or if heated to very high temperatures. This problem will be to a great degree solved with the increase of the oleic fatty acid content. The process of producing high-oleic oil has been too costly. However, scientists feel that the problem can be solved. This will provide oil for frying that will be a healthier oil and not breakdown to trans-fatty acids as easily.

Canola Oil to be Modified

The first oil to be genetically modified will be canola oil. The modified oil will have a higher level of "high-laureate" fat. This will increase the level of "good" usable polyunsaturated fat and reduce the level of saturated fat.

New Starch will be Replacing Fat

When food is processed, a product that is produced is "modified starch." This unusual starch can act as a food thickener and especially a fat substitute. The modified starch can provide the "mouth-feel" that people react favorably to when they eat a high-fat food. In the near future, however, chemically modified starch will not be needed. Plants are being developed that will make a new "modified starch," which will actually be harvested, then used as a natural fat-replacer.

Pricey Olive Oil

Because of a drought in olive-growing areas of the Mediterranean, olive oil prices have risen about 30-35%. The increasing demand for the high quality oil in North America is fueling the price hike.

Fat-Free Cooking to Be a Reality

You will not have to purchase expensive non-stick coated pots and pans ever again. A new product is now being sold that consists of a specially treated, anti-sticking sheet that is placed into the pan or baking tin or any other type of pot. You will be able to cook any dish or food on the sheet without the food sticking and it will allow uniform cooking. This will also eliminate the messy spray oils, which are being used to reduce fat intake. The sheet will not stick to the pan and can easily be cleaned and re-used over and over. The product is produced by Mapelli Srl and will be sold under the brand name, Maplon.

New Butter Will Spread like Margarine

Easy to spread butter may soon be available in the U.S. Studies in Australia are having excellent success with altering a cow's diet to include more polyunsaturated and mono-unsaturated fats. They have developed butter with almost the same consistency but easier to spread and lower in saturated fat. The butter still possesses the same "mouth feel" and flavor as the standard high saturated fat, hard-to-spread butter that has been produced for 7,000 years.

Frying Oil to Be Made into Diesel Fuel

Researchers at the U.S. Department of Energy in Idaho have discovered a method of re-cycling frying oil into a bio-diesel fuel. This environmentally friendly fuel can be produced through a less expensive process than is used to produce the standard diesel fuel and will be 100% biodegradable. The new diesel oil burns cleaner and will not pollute the air, and also have a nice aroma. In fact, the aroma is almost too pleasant, since it smells just like fried chicken. The new bio-diesel fuel is presently being tested by the National Park Service in some busses and seems to be working as well as the standard polluting diesel oil they had been using. Their only fear was that the park bears would chase the busses, since they smelled like fried chicken. Luckily, this did not happen.

Seaweed to Be more Popular

Monsanto is making progress in the development of new oil that will be used for baking. The "seaweed oil" will mainly be used in cakes and cookies, and the company is hoping that the new products will contain some of the healthy nutrients found in fish.

TRANS-FATTY ACIDS

Margarine and Trans-Fatty Acids

Margarine may contain the bad fat produced from the heat processing, trans-fatty acids, while butter has cholesterol. My preferred choice would be whipped, unsalted butter in moderation. The harder the margarine, the higher the percentage of saturated fat it contains. Even though margarine does not contain any cholesterol, saturated fats may assist in the production of cholesterol. The softer the margarine, the lower the level of trans-fatty acids, since air and water tend to replace a percentage of the fat.

Margarine Substitute in Supermarkets

A new product called "Benecol™" is now available to replace margarine and even lower cholesterol. The product is made from a plant, "stanol ester" and was invented in Finland. It has been sold in Finland since 1995 where studies have shown that the product actually blocks the absorption of the bad cholesterol, LDL. Johnson & Johnson's McNeil Healthcare has purchased the international rights to market the product. "Take Control™" is another new product that is also a margarine replacement that is already on the shelves.

Health Risk

Diets high in total fat and especially trans-fatty acids (from heated fats) have been related to cancer of the colon, the prostate and breast. Studies are also showing that the efficiency of the immune system may be depressed by high fat diets. Recommended dietary fat levels are 20-25% of your total daily calories; however, a person can actually survive on only 5% dietary fat if the fat is of the essential fatty acid type.

Who Invented Margarine?

Margarine was invented by a French chemist in 1870 upon the request of Napoleon III who wanted a low-cost fat. Originally, it was produced from animal fat, however, today it is made from vegetable oils (mainly soy), milk solids, salt, air and water. The name, "margarine," came from the original chemical used in the production of margarine, which was "margaric acid." Margarine was brought to the United States in 1873 and the production of "artificial butter" was started by the U.S. Dairy Company in New York City. By 1886, there were 30 manufacturers producing margarine. The U.S. government placed special taxes on margarine to protect the dairy industry, which almost eliminated the product.

How Much is too Much?

As a general rule, most products that state, "hydrogenated oil," on the list of ingredients have 30-40% of that oil as trans-fatty acid oil. The following is the approximate percentages of trans-fatty acids found in some of the more common foods:

FOOD	TRANS-FATTY ACID
French fries	40%
Cookies	35%
Crackers	39%
Doughnuts	38%
Hamburgers	45%
Potato Chips	38%

Good Fats in Jeopardy

Trans-fatty acids have been found to interfere with the conversion of some of the good essential fatty acids the body requires to remain in optimum health. The trans-fatty acids tend to block the conversion of omega-3 and omega-6 fatty acids into a form that is required by the body.

Avoiding Trans-Fatty Acids

The following are a few tips on how to avoid trans-fatty acids:

- Don't buy foods that contain "vegetable shortening" or "hydrogenated oils."
- Avoid fried foods as much as possible.
- Purchase low-fat or liquid margarine.
- Limit your intake of commercial cookies, pastries, cake and crackers.
- Purchase foods that are low in saturated fats or state "low or cholesterol-free."

A Few of the Harmful Effects

Trans-fatty acids have been implicated in the following:

- Lowers the blood levels of good cholesterol, HDL.
- Raises the blood level of the bad cholesterol, LDL.
- Raises the level of the type of fats that may increase risk of heart disease.
- Has the ability to raise cholesterol levels.
- Tends to lower the amount of available milk in lactating females.
- Tends to lower the quality of mother's milk.
- May affect the birth weight leading to a lower weight.
- Increase the risk of diabetes.

Trans-Fatty Acid-Free Margarine

A number of companies are now producing a margarine that does not contain any trans-fatty acids. Processing of the oil to protect it from high heat for a prolonged period makes this possible. The following are some of the more popular brands:

- Brummel and Brown Soft
- I Can't Believe It's Not Butter - Fat-Free
- Shed's Country Crock Light & Squeezable
- Spectrum Naturals with canola and olive oils
- Smart Balance (light and regular)
- Smart Beat Fat-Free
- Promise Fat-Free
- Fleischman's Fat-Free
- Parkay Squeeze

Choosing the Right Margarine

Lower fat margarine is produced, by adding additional water-thickening agents, such as gelatin, rice starch or guar gum to the mixture. Additional air may be pumped in to create addition volume. By changing the texture and consistency of margarine, it may not be suitable for all cooking needs. The following will provide a guideline to using margarine in a variety of cooking needs:

- **Baking and general cooking**

  Use the standard margarine, which is about 80% oil. The lower fat margarine has approximately 55% fat and does not work as well.

- **Spreading on bread**

  The light or low-fat margarine, which contain about 50% oil are fine.

- **Sautéing and frying**

  Never use fat-free margarine that has only $^1/_2$ gram of fat per tbsp. Stick margarine may work in some cases, but butter is preferred for sautéing. High smoke point oils, such as canola or peanut oil are best for frying.

Chef's Frying Secrets

Temperature Control

If frying temperatures are not controlled properly, the food will absorb more fat, the batches will not be consistent and the flavor will vary. The oil will also break down faster. The following are a few facts that should be followed when frying foods:

- A thermometer should be used to check the temperature of the oil and the oil should never exceed 380°F.
- If the time period is going to elapse between batches, it would be best to reduce the oil temperature to 250°F. to slow down the deterioration of the oil.
- When using shortening to fry with, always heat the shortening slowly. If you heat shortening too quickly, it will scorch. Always start shortening at 225°F. and keep it there until the shortening has completely melted, then turn the heat up.
- Too low a temperature will result in a poor coloring and usually a greasy product.
- When frying batches, remember to allow the temperature to go back up or return to the normal frying temperature before adding more food to be fried.

Why Frying Oil Darkens Prematurely

The following are the more common reasons for frying oil darkening:

- Your frying pan or fryer is not as clean as it should be.
- When you did clean it, you failed to rinse it well and there was some soap film left in the fryer.
- You are overcooking the food.
- The fat has been broken down and is mostly trans-fatty acids.
- The temperature has been consistently too high.

Why Fat Will Smoke

The following are the most common reasons:

- Foreign material has gotten into the fryer and burns while you are frying.
- Too much breading has fallen off and is building up.
- The fat has broken down and is no longer good.
- The temperature is too high.

The Case of the Foaming Fryer

There are a number of reasons why foam will form on the top of foods being fried. The following are a few of the more common ones:

- The fryer is not as clean as it should be and was not rinsed properly, leaving soap scum.
- Too much salt or food particles accumulating in the fryer.
- Using brass or copper utensils in the fryer, which react with the oil creating foam.
- Poor quality fat or old worn-out fat.

Less Greasy Foods

To make fried foods less greasy, just add 1 tbsp. of white vinegar to the pan or deep-fat fryer before adding the oil.

Reduced Fat vs. Standard Food

The reduced fat and fat-free craze is more advertising than a real nutritional benefit to most people. What you are basically doing is giving up fat and in most cases, replacing the fat with sugar. The calories almost end up the same and in some cases, the calories are even higher or the taste suffers to such a degree that the public refuses to buy the product.

REDUCED FAT FOOD	CAL.	REGULAR FOODS	CAL.
Non-fat frozen yogurt (1 cup)	380	Regular ice cream (1 cup)	360
Low-fat peanut butter (2 tbsp.)	190	Regular peanut butter (2 tbsp.)	190
Fat-free fig cookie (2 cookies)	140	Regular fig cookie (2 cookies)	200
Low-fat granola cereal (¹/₄ cup)	110	Regular granola cereal (¹/₄ cup)	130
Baked tortilla chips (2 oz.)	220	Regular tortilla chips (2 oz.)	260

Slows Down Aging

Cooking wine will stay fresher longer, if you add a tbsp. of very fresh vegetable oil to the bottle.

Grandmother's Frying Oil Trick, Not a Good One

When my grandmother fried foods, she always cleaned the oil out with a few slices of raw potato, then threw them away and stored the oil in the icebox to reuse it. When oil is reused, the level of trans-fatty acid rises until it is 100%, which doesn't take too long. Oil should never be reused.

Fat in the Fire

If the frying fat is not hot enough, food will absorb more fat. However, if you get it too hot, it will smoke, burn and produce trans-fatty acids. Use a thermometer; the temperature should be 360 to 375°F.

New Product Keeps Oil from Becoming Bad

In Europe, cooking oil breakdown has prompted laws regulating the amount of polar substances (dirty oil with trans-fatty acids), which are created by the breakdown of good oil. If the oil has more than 25% polar substances, the oil must be discarded. A new product, being used in Europe called Frypowder®, has recently been approved by the FDA as being safe in the U. S. and has the ability to reduce the breakdown elements, allowing the oil to have a longer, healthier lifetime usage.

Recipes Have Fat Points

Many recipes utilize fats for texture and to lend moisture. However, there are a number of foods that can replace fat without the food losing its flavor or taste sensations. If you experiment with other products to replace the fat, you may be surprised at the results. The "fat point" is a point at which fat is not needed and a replacement food can take its place for the balance of the suggested fat. Some of the best substitutes are fruit and vegetable purees. Yolks can easily be omitted in many recipes as well and only the whites used as a binder. When omitting a yolk, don't replace it with additional whites or the dish may turn out on the tough side.

Pig Abs
Lard is derived from the abdomen of pigs and is used in chewing gum bases, shaving creams, soaps and cosmetics. Future studies may implicate lard in shortened life span, as well as a factor in osteoporosis. Leaf lard is derived from the kidney area of the pig and is a higher quality than all other types of lard (best for piecrust).

Fatty Pate
Pates are bordered with pork fat from the flank of the pig.

Putting on the Ritz
Some of the highest fat content crackers are Ritz, Town House and Goldfish, which contain about 6 grams of fat per oz.

Lard Has Larger Fat Crystals
Lard can be stored at room temperature for 6-8 months. If you substitute lard for butter or shortening, reduce the amount you use by 25%.

Lard Oil Replaces Whale Oil
During the 1800s, California lighthouses used "sperm oil" from whales to light their lights. By the late 1860s, the oil became too expensive as the Sperm whale became an endangered species and the lighthouses switched to lard oil.

Crispy Critter
When you are greasing a pan, make sure you don't use too much grease or you may cause the food to overbrown.

Pigs in a Blanket
The age-old favorite of small pancakes wrapped around sausages was 60% fat and almost all saturated fat.

A Real Whopper
Every oz. of fat contains 250% more calories than an oz. of carbohydrate or protein.

Not the Bottom of the Churn
Buttermilk can be substituted for 2% or whole milk in most recipes. Buttermilk is less than 1% fat, almost equal to skim milk; however, it has a thicker consistency.

And Away it Goes

A high fat intake has been related to calcium losses through the urine.

Beat me, Beat me

Butter will go farther and have fewer calories per serving if you beat it well, increasing the volume with air.

Yolks away

When preparing any recipe or omelet, try replacing the egg yolks with an equal amount of egg substitute or just reduce the number of yolks.

Longevity

The most popular oil is olive oil with soy oil coming in second. Olive oil will stay fresh longer than most oils, while soy oil tends to lose its flavor the longer it is stored, due to the linolenic acid it contains.

Yummy, Yummy

Eight oz. of potato chips is the equivalent of eating 16-20 tsp. of fat.

Needs Shades

Only purchase oils in containers, if you cannot see the oil. Oil is very sensitive to light and will become rancid. All oils with the exception of cold-pressed olive oil start oxidizing as soon as it is heat-processed, then continues to breaks down until it becomes rancid.

Why Carob?

When carob is made into candy products, fat is usually added to improve the texture. This usually brings the fat content close to real chocolate. In fact, cocoa butter used in real chocolate is 60% saturated fat while the fat used in a carob candy is 85% saturated fat.

Margarine Fact

Most margarine contains over 90% fat. Diet margarine usually contains 80% fat, 16% water, 2% salt, and 2% non-fat milk solids. Margarine is naturally white, colorings and additives are added to all margarine. Liquid diet margarine, however, may contain only 40% fat.

A Fatty Separation

If you are going to make your own mayonnaise, be sure that the weather report is clear. If the temperature or humidity is too high, it will cause the mayonnaise to come out heavier and greasier than normal.

New Frying Shortening Lowers Cholesterol

This new fat is called "Appetize 2" and is a shortening that has had the animal fat removed and then re-formulated to actually lower cholesterol levels. In the very near future, expect to see fast food chains advertising that their fried foods have been fried in Appetize 2. This should also eliminate the trans-fatty acid problems.

The Debate

The margarine vs. butter controversy is still going on, with neither side really winning. Margarine has the bad fat, trans-fatty acids due the method of heat processing they must go through and butter contains cholesterol. My preferred choice would be whipped, unsalted butter in moderation.

Where, oh Where Have my Vitamins Gone?

Refined corn oil is a chemical extraction, a triglyceride, with no relationship to the nutrients in a "real" ear of corn. The vitamins that would normally assist with the digestion of corn oil are absent, even the vitamin E is lost.

Applesauce Replaces Fat

In most recipes, applesauce can be used to replace fat almost on a 1-to-1 substitution basis. If the recipe calls for 1 cup of oil, you can use 1 cup of applesauce, especially in baked goods.

Good Fat, Bad Fat?

Recent studies have shown that stearic acid, one of the saturated fats, has little effect on raising cholesterol levels. As our laboratory tests become more sophisticated, more information about which fats will actually raise your cholesterol will be forthcoming. Then we can avoid only those foods that may be harmful.

SALAD AND COOKING OIL USE	MARGARINE USE
1909 - 1.5 lbs. per person	1950 - 6 lbs. per person
1972 - 18 lbs. per person	1972 - 11 lbs. per person
1990 - 29 lbs. per person	1990 - 16 lbs. per person
1999 - 36 lbs. per person	1999 - 22 lbs. per person
2002 - 41 lbs. per person	2002 - 25 lbs. per person

Ask for Mocha Mix!

Most non-dairy creamers are made from coconut oil, which is high in saturated fat. Mocha Mix is your best bet.

Fats are More Satisfying

Studies now show that dieters miss fats more than sweets.

Education a Must

Americans consumed 53 lbs. of hard fats (meats, etc.), shortenings (baked goods, etc.) and cooking fats (oils, etc.) per person in 1972. In 2002, the consumption rose to 76 lbs., not a good direction. Poor nutrition education and the increased eating at fast food restaurants are to blame. There are 312 fats that are available for use in frying alone.

Top Frying Oil

Rapeseed (canola oil) for years has been grown as a forage crop for animals in the U.S. and Canada. Originally, it was banned in the U.S. when imports from Canada showed high levels of "erucic acid." However, new varieties have shown to contain lower levels of eruric acid and the oil is now being produced and sold in large quantities. It is high in monounsaturated fat and has a high smoke point, making it the preferred oil for frying.

The Color of Fat

Current studies show that if your body is higher in "brown fat" rather than "white fat," you have a higher percentage of the more active type, which may relate to why some people are able to control their weight easier than others.

Insomnia

Most fat should be consumed either at breakfast or lunch, and few, if any, for dinner. High fat meals late in the day may cause the digestive system to overwork while you are sleeping, causing restless sleep patterns.

Sugar in, Fat out, Calories the Same

The new reduced-fat peanut butter has the same number of calories per serving as the regular peanut butter, about 190 per serving. Sweeteners were added in place of the fat.

Work like a Pro

Purchase empty plastic ketchup bottles to use for your oils. The narrow spout makes it easy to pour oils when cooking. Label them with a permanent felt-tip marker.

Fat Science

When oils are refrigerated and become cloudy, it is due to the buildup of harmless crystals. Manufacturers will sometimes pre-chill the oils and remove the crystals in a process known as "winterization." These oils will remain clear when refrigerated. Lard has larger fat crystals than butter, which has a lot to do with the texture of these fats and is controlled during processing. The large fat crystals in lard will make it the choice for a number of baked goods where a flakier crust is preferred, especially pies. Moderation in eating these lard products, however, is the key word.

More Fat Science

Oxygen has been found to be 8 times more soluble in fat that in water, which is why fats tend to oxidize so easily and turn rancid. Every time you open a bottle of oil, more oil leaves and is replaced by oxygen.

Typical American Diet

The average American diet is about 44% fat. Dietary guidelines suggest no more than 30% of total calories. My recommendation is no more than 20% or less with the type of fats leaning toward the PUFA and MUFA types. The 30% figure is workable if the fat calories are all of the best type of fat, which may be difficult for most people.

Good Fat?

Medium-chain triglycerides (MCT) are sold in health food stores for people who have trouble absorbing fats. They are for the most part produced from coconut oil, have a very low smoke point, and can be used for cooking without producing trans-fatty acids. Body builders tend to use this fat to increase caloric intake, but studies to date are not conclusive.

Fat-Replacers

In 2000, the new "fat substitutes" started appearing in our foods. These synthetically produced products should be viewed with caution and used in MODERATION only. There are three categories of fat-replacers: protein-based, carbohydrate-based and fat-based.

Protein-Based Fat-Replacers

Simplesse®- This fat-replacer only contains 1-2 calories per gram and is made from whey protein or egg protein. The product is digested as a protein and is used in ice cream, salad dressings and many other dairy products. Dairy-Lo® is produced from a modified whey concentrate and used in dairy products, baked goods and salad dressings.

K-Blazer®, Lita®- Produced from milk and egg protein or corn protein and mainly used in frozen desserts and baked goods.

Carbohydrate-Based Fat-Replacers

Avicel®, Methocel™- Produced from a purified form of cellulose and has "mouth feel" and other properties similar to "real" fat. Used in dairy products, sauces and salad dressings.

Slendid™ (1991)- Produced from gums, such as guar gum, locust bean gum and carrageen an. Contains no calories and used in fat-free dressings, desserts and processed meat products.

Fruitafit®- Contains only 1 calorie per gram and used as a fat and sugar replacer. The main ingredient is inulin, which is extracted from chicory root and used in yogurt, cheese, baked goods, whipped cream and dairy products.

Oatrim, Beta-Trim™- This fat substitute is made from hydrolyzed oat flour and may even be good for you. It is oat flour that has been treated with water to break down the starches into individual sugars. This causes a change in the texture and provides the fat texture that people like in their foods. The flour is high in "beta-glucan" which may have a cholesterol-absorbing ability. The product was developed by the USDA and contains only 1 calorie per gram instead of the usual 9 calories per gram in fat. Studies have shown a definite cholesterol-lowering correlation in the 24 volunteers that took part in the study. Over 40 new products are being developed and it will be necessary to read the label to find it. It may also be called "hydrated oat flour" or by its brand name "Oatrim." It may soon be found in cookies, cheeses, low-fat hot dogs and low-fat lunch-meats. It is a safer alternative than the Olean products.

Z-trim™- Contains no calories and is produced from insoluble fiber extracted from soybeans, peas, oat or rice hulls. It is very heat-stabile and used in baked goods, hot dogs and dairy products.

Nu-Trim™- Produced from oats or barley and contains beta-glucans, a soluble fiber. Beta-glucans have been known to lower the bad cholesterol (LDL) and the total cholesterol. Meets all specifications of the FDA for a food product.

Fat-Based Replacers

Olestra (Olean®) (1996)- Olestra is a large, synthetic fat molecule, so large that it passes through the intestinal tract undigested. This increase of undigested material may cause diarrhea. Olestra, as it goes through the system, however, tends to attract the fat-soluble vitamins A, D, E and K and may bind with them. Proctor and Gamble, the inventor of the product, is familiar with the problem and may have to fortify the products with vitamins. However, this may not solve the problem. A more significant problem may be that the carotenoid family are also fat-soluble and the over-500 carotenoids may also be in trouble. A percentage of carotenoids may be washed out of the body. These include beta-carotene, alpha carotene, lutein, lycopene and the rest of the family. Since these are not considered to be essential nutrients, P & G does not feel that they have to include them through fortification. The carotenoids are a nutrient that is under investigation as a possible cancer preventive nutrient. The official name that will appear on products with olestra is "Olean." Olean has only been approved for snack foods. It is being added to snack-chips, crackers, tortilla chips, cheese puffs and potato chips initially.

The FDA is requiring a warning label be added which reads: "This product contains Olestra. Olestra may cause abdominal cramping and loose stools. Olestra inhibits the absorption of some vitamins and other nutrients. Vitamins A, D, E and K have been added." The "fake-fat chip" will have a caloric reduction of about 34%. The downside to this is that people may consume more junk foods and still end up with the same number of total calories. P & G presently is marketing the product under the brand name "WOW." A number of intestinal problems (diarrhea and abdominal cramping) related to products that contain Olestra are now being reported in medical journals and my recommendation is to consume the Olestra-containing products in moderation until further studies are concluded. Additional information has been released in 1999, stating that people who have bleeding disorders or persons taking blood-thinning medication should avoid products that contain Olestra since vitamin K may be adversely affected.

Salatrim, Benefat™- This new fat substitute will be marketed under the brand name "Benefat™." Salatraim is a complex mixture of specific triglycerides that only contain 5 calories per gram instead of the normal 9 calories per gram in fat. The product does not contain any trans-fatty acids and has excellent "mouth-feel." When used in baked goods, the new fat substitute can be used 1:1 in relation to normal fat. Rearranging the fat molecules reduced the calories and produces better fat.

Caprenin™ **(1992)-** Produced from canola, coconut oil and palm-kernel oil. Contains no long-chain fatty acids unless they are natural. Presently used in Milky Way II candy bars.

Fat by the Teaspoon

Sometimes it is hard to visualize the amount of fat we really consume. The following chart will actually provide the amount of fats in some common foods in teaspoons. The fat content of foods is much easier to comprehend in teaspoons rather than grams. If you wish to calculate the fat content in the foods you eat in teaspoons, the rule is that 5 grams of fat equals about 1 tsp. fat.

Food Serving Size Teaspoons

FOOD	TSP. FAT	FOOD	TSP. FAT
Bacon (1 strip/thin)	1.3	Hot Dog/All Beef (1 medium)	2.5
Big Mac (1)	7-9	Lean Beef (3 oz.)	2
Bologna (1 slice)	2	Medium-Fat Beef (3 oz.)	4.5
Canadian Bacon (1 strip)	1	Pork Chop (3½ oz.)	6.5
Chicken Breast/No Skin (4 oz.)	1	Sirloin TV Dinner (1 medium)	7
Chicken Breast/Skin (4 oz.9	2.5	Trout/Raw (3 ½ oz.)	3
Chicken TV Dinner (1 medium)	7	Turkey (3½ oz.)	2
Hamburger (¼ lb.)	3.5	Turkey Pot Pie (12 oz.)	6
Ham/Lean (2 slices/thin)	1.3		

Shortening vs. Oil

Shortening is just a solid form of fat and is always a solid at room temperature. It can be made from either an animal or vegetable source or a combination of the two. Shortenings that are made from vegetable sources are hydrogenated, which is the addition of water to a liquid fat until it becomes the consistency that is desired by the manufacturer. The term "pure shortening" means that the product can contain either vegetable or animal sources or a combination of both. If the product is labeled "pure vegetable shortening," it has to be made from only vegetable sources. If the product does not have the word "pure" on the label then a number of additives were added to increase the shelf life. However, when this is done, it lowers the smoke point and is not as good a product. One of the best shortenings is Crisco, which has a balanced saturated fat to unsaturated fat of 1-to-1.

The Longest Shelf Life of any Oil

The shelf life of Crisco is 2-3 years, longer than any other shortening. Cold pressed olive oil, however, if stored in a cool dark location and in a glass colored bottle, may last up to 10 years and still be useable.

Why Frying Oil Lands on the Inside of Lenses

If you wear eyeglasses and fry foods, you may have noticed that the oil droplets collect on the inner surface of the lens, rather than the outer surface. The reason for this is because when you are frying, the minute droplets become airborne and then fall back toward the floor. When you are bending over, working at your cooking task, the oil droplets fall on the inside of the lens.

Why Oil Can't Be Used for Baking

Because of its liquid nature, oils tend to collect instead of evenly distributing through the dough. This may cause the baked goods to become grainy. When solid fat is used, baked items tend to be more, fluffy and retain their moisture better. Especially bad are the "all-purpose" oils, which even though they say that they can be used for baking and frying, are not up to the standards that most cooks desire. To produce these oils, a number of additives are used which may affect the flavor and taste of the food.

Frying Temperatures are Critical

It is never wise to fry at too low a temperature, especially if the food is breaded. The oil will not be hot enough to seal the breading or outer surface of the food and too much of the oil is allowed to enter the f o o d before the sealing takes place. When the oil is too hot, then the food may end up being burned on the outside and not allow the insides to be cooked through. Most breaded foods that are fried are normally fried at 375° F. It is best to check the recipe for the particular food you are frying for the correct frying temperature. Chicken should be fried at 365°F. for 10- 20 minutes for the best results and meats at 360°F.

Who Invented Margarine?

Margarine was invented by the French chemist, Hippolyte Mege-Mouries in 1869, upon request by Napoleon III who wanted a low-cost fat. Originally, it was produced from animal fat; however, today it is made from vegetable oils (mainly soy), milk solids, salt, air and water.

The Difference Between Fats and Oils

The difference between fats and oils is basically that fat is usually solid at room temperature and oil is liquid. If the fat is from an animal source, it is usually solid and from a vegetable source, it is usually liquid. However, all fats are similar in their chemical structure and vary more due to their type of fat saturation. Shortening is solid fat at room temperature and can be either an animal or vegetable fat. The best shortenings will have the word "pure" on the label. If the word "pure" is not on the label, the product may contain a number of additives that are capable of lowering the smoke point.

Fats and oils should be as pure as possible to obtain the best results when baking or preparing any dish.

Vegetable Oils

The best vegetable oils to use for cooking are those that are lowest in saturated fat. However, some dishes require that certain oils or fats be used to produce the desired flavor of the dish. In those instances, the recommended oil should be used. In all other instances, olive oil is highly recommended since it is high in monounsaturated fat, which is fat the body prefers over other types of fats. Throughout the book, when recipes call for cooking with olive oil, you should note that a small amount of canola oil is usually recommended along with it. The canola oil raises the smoke point of olive oil just enough so that it slows down the breakdown of the olive oil.

Spray Oils - Money Savers

For many years, the only spray oil that was sold was Pam. The markets now are selling many different brands, as well as different oils available in spray containers. The latest to hit the shelves has been olive oil. If you find these products too pricey, all you have to do is stop by a kitchen supply store and purchase an oil spray bottle. These are small pump action spray bottles that you can easily fill. Use any oil and an equal amount of lecithin to keep the oil in suspension. Lecithin may be found in the vitamin section of your market or any health food store. Most of the market brands contain lecithin, which helps keep the propellant and the oil from separating. However, it is best to purchase the pump-type sprays to protect the ozone layer. Never spray the oils on too hot a surface or an open flame, since they are flammable. Also, be careful of inhaling the oil spray, as it is capable of coating the lungs and could be fatal.

Garlic/Olive Oil Alert

The government has issued an alert regarding placing raw garlic in olive oil for more than 24 hours. Garlic may harbor bacteria, and it tends to multiply in an atmosphere that lacks oxygen. Even though the risks are minimal, it would be wise not to store garlic in this manner. For additional information, regarding this problem, call (800) 232-6548.

NUTTY OILS

The Hawaiian Nut

Macadamia nut oil is now becoming more available. The oil is high in monounsaturated fat and is great in salad dressings and add a great flavor to dishes when you sauté. The smoke point is somewhat higher than olive oil so you may not have to add canola oil to it to raise the smoke point.

Gravy

Gravy is always best if you use the pan drippings, which contain the flavor of the meat or poultry. Many people avoid using the drippings because of the high fat content; however, the fat content can easily be reduced by separating the fat from the flavorful liquid; using a separating cup to pour off the fat. Other methods include placing ice cubes in a piece of cheesecloth and swirling it around to trap the fat. Or, if time allows, the drippings can be placed into the freezer for a few minutes until the fat rises and can easily be removed.

A Legal Separation

A common problem with gravy is that it almost always separates, especially as it cools down. To keep the gravy in suspension, all you have to do is add a pinch or two of baking soda to the gravy and stir.

Getting Rid of your Lumps

You will never have lumpy gravy, if you just add a pinch of salt to the flour and mix it in before adding any liquid.

Quick, Put me in a Suntan Booth

If your gravy is not brown enough and you need a quick fix, just add 1 tsp. hot instant coffee. There will not be any flavor of coffee in the gravy.

This Salt is Killing me!

To improve the taste of over-salted gravy, just add $1/4$ tsp. brown sugar to the gravy.

Repairing Burnt Gravy

If you accidentally burn the gravy, all you have to do is add a tsp. of peanut butter to the gravy. You won't notice the taste of the peanut butter at all.

Gravy Perker Upper

If you would like your gravy to have a rich, dark brown color, just spread the flour on a cookie sheet and cook over a low heat, stirring occasionally until the flour browns. Just before serving the gravy, add 1 tsp. coffee to the gravy to firm up the color permanently. Another method of browning the gravy is to add onion-skins to the gravy while it is cooking.

Grandmother's Gravy Recipe

The rule of thumb to remember is to use the same number of tbsp. of fat (need to use a little) drippings to flour.

- *The pan drippings should be taken from the pan before you remove the fat.*
- *The following recipe is for about 2 1/2 cups of gravy and should be adjusted depending on the number of people to be served. This amount usually serves 8 people comfortably.*
- *Unsalted butter may be used in place of the fat drippings and be sure to start with the butter at room temperature, do not microwave.*
- *In a medium-sized saucepan over low heat, place 4 tbsp. pan drippings and 4 tbsp. all-purpose flour.*
- *Cook the mixture until brown stirring occasionally. Add 2 cups de-fatted drippings and continue to cook over low heat until the desired thickness is achieved.*

FAT FACTS

Greece-ing up for Health
In Greece, people consume 40% of their calories as fat, however, their risk of heart disease is low. They consume most of their fat as olive oil.

How Much Fat Can Your Stomach Clear?
Approximately 10 grams of fat is cleared from the stomach per hour. Two scrambled eggs, bread and butter, coffee, and milk = 50 grams of fat. Assimilation time is 5-6 hours. An example of high fat foods; are bacon and cheddar cheese. The percent of fat to calories in each is 75% fat. Americans spend $3.2 billion per year on bacon.

The Quality of Butter
Butter is sold in three grades, depending on the flavor rating and milk-fat content. The best grade is U.S. Grade AA, next is U.S. Grade A, which has a lower flavor rating and U.S. Grade B, which is made from sour cream. The milk-fat rating of butter must be at least 80%.

Sqeeeezing The Last Drop from a Can
If you want to get the last drop of shortening from a can, just pour boiling water in the can and place it in the refrigerator for an hour or until the fat rises to the top. Then just skim off the fat.

Going up in Smoke

Oil will deteriorate very quickly, depending on the smoke point of that particular oil. When any oil deteriorates, it starts smoking and develops into bad fat called a trans-fatty acid. To test the oil while it is hot to check on the level of deterioration, just drop a piece of white bread in the oil. If the bread develops dark spots, the oil has gone bad.

Turn out the Lights

When purchasing liquid oil, only purchase oil that is packaged in opaque containers. Oil deteriorates very quickly and the light will hasten the process.

The Hotter the Oil, the Fewer the Calories

Tests have been conducted that prove that the hotter the oil, the less oil will be absorbed by the food. The frying time is also lessened, which also contributes to the fewer fat calories retained.

The Higher the Fryer, the Lower the Temperature

When you fry above sea level, it is necessary to lower the frying temperature 30°F. for every 1,000-ft. increase in elevation. If you live in Denver, Colorado, you will need to lower your frying temperature by 15 degrees.

Piecrust to Die for

Leaf lard has large fat crystals, which will produce a flakier piecrust. The lard is derived from the kidney area of pigs instead of the abdomen, which is where lard is usually derived from. When substituting lard for butter or shortening in a recipe, reduce the amount of lard used by 25%.

The Legal Fat Suet

Suet is fat that is derived from the kidneys of sheep and cattle. It may be substituted for lard in many recipes and has large fat crystals similar to lard, which is why suet is very popular in certain baked goods, such as piecrust.

Mashed Potatoes with Schmaltz and Gribenes (UFOs)

"Schmaltz" is a traditional Jewish food that is prepared from rendering down chicken fat and skin. The fat has an excellent flavor and after it has finished rendering, the small UFOs (unidentified fried objects) are called "gribenes." The gribenes are actually the remains of the skin that has been turned into small, crunchy fat balls. In moderation, these fats are very tasty when added into mashed potatoes. Don't knock it till you try it.

Brown-Out

When greasing a pan with oil or butter, try not to overdo the amount you are using. A common problem of over-browning baked goods and other foods is caused by placing too much of an oil in a pan.

How to Stop up your Drain

Fat should never be poured down the drain unless you pour at least one qt. of boiling water after the fat. Cold pipes will solidify animal fat very quickly.

Why Fat is Used in Baked Goods

Fat is used to produce tender baked good products by coating the gluten strands. The more the strands are coated, the more tender the product. Fat is also needed to add texture to baked goods and other products. Chilled solid fat is recommended when preparing flaky pasty dough, since it does not combine with the flour. This creates a flaky texture effect of alternating layers of fat and flour, which is why lard is the preferred fat for piecrusts.

Fried Food Protector

Fried foods will not pick up and retain as much fat, if you add a tbsp. vinegar to the fryer or skillet before adding the oil. Coat the pan as best you can and leave the balance of the vinegar on the pan.

Trapping Air

Room-temperature fat, when creamed with sugar, has the capability of trapping air in a cake batter, creating very light-textured cakes.

Frying Foods? Hide the Salt Shaker

Never salt a food before placing the food into a fryer. The salt tends to draw moisture out of the food and will cause splattering. The moisture will also cause the oil to decompose more readily.

Togetherness

When you shake oil and vinegar together, the oil breaks into smaller particles, which allows the two to mix together temporarily. As soon as you stop shaking, the fat droplets start to combine again and come out of suspension, rising back to the surface. However, if you use an emulsifying agent, it will hold the oil and vinegar in permanent suspension. The best substance to keep these two together is lecithin. Just break open two lecithin ampoules and mix the liquid into the oil and vinegar. The shaking will break down the fat globules again into very small particles and the lecithin will grab them, encircle them and keep them from combining again. Lecithin is the emulsifying agent in egg yolks, which keeps Hollandaise sauce in suspension.

Not Just Hot, Really Hot

Frying at too low a temperature will cause the breading to fall off many foods. Also, too much of the oil will enter the food since the hot frying oil is supposed to seal the food. If the oil is too hot, the food may burn or not be fully cooked. Breaded foods need to be fried at 375^0F. (190.6^0C.). Chicken needs to be fried at 365^0F. (185^0C.) for 10-20 minutes depending on the thickness of the piece. Meats should be fried at 360^0F. (182.2^0C.).

Good Snack Food

A great new snack food is now available on the market shelves. It is called "Seaweed Crunch." A serving has only 3 grams of fat and 130 calories. The texture and flavor is excellent. The snack food is being sold through health food stores and produced by Soken Natural Foods.

Snack Food History Timeline

1853- Chips invented by accident by George Crum in Saratoga Springs, NY

1861- Pretzels were brought to the U.S. from Germany where they were called "bretzels."

1885- A gasoline-powered popcorn popper was invented for commercial use, making popcorn a popular and accessible snack food.

1892- In Cleveland, potato chips were delivered house- to- house by horse-drawn wagons making them easily accessible.

1906- Planter's started selling Planter's Peanuts and invented the commercial process to produce them at a reasonable cost.

1926- The first potato chip bag was invented by Laura Scudder. The bags were filled with waxed paper, stuffed with chips, then ironed shut.

1950- Korn Kurls were invented by the Adams Corporation. Pork rinds also hit the snack scene.

1960- Frito-Lay started producing corn chips and Cheeto's cheese snacks. Lay's Potato Chip were sold in 1965.

1964- Doritos corn curls were introduced and were a big hit.

1983- The thicker, ridged chips made for dipping were produced by Frito-Lay.

1995- The low-fat snack foods appeared in all categories.

1998- Fat substitutes become popular and attract new snack converts only to find out that the artificial fats may be harmful.

Fat and Cholesterol in your Favorite Snacks

FOOD	TOTAL FAT(G)	CALORIES FROM FAT(%)	CHOLESTEROL(MG)
Apple Pie (2 crusts $\frac{1}{3}$)	13.8	42	0
Cheesecake ($\frac{1}{6}$)	18.0	63	44
Chocolate Bar (1oz.)	8.7	54	6
Chocolate Cake (frosted, $\frac{1}{3}$)	10.5	40	9
Chocolate Pudding ($\frac{1}{2}$ cup)	5.7	27	5
Fudge (1oz.)	2.4	20	10
Ice Cream (vanilla, $\frac{1}{2}$ cup)	7.3	50	29
Ice Milk ($\frac{1}{2}$ cup)	2.3	19	9
Lemon Meringue Pie ($\frac{1}{6}$)	9.8	9	51
Popcorn (with oil, 1oz.)	8.0	51	0
Potato Chips (1oz.)	9.8	58	0
Pumpkin Pie ($\frac{1}{6}$)	10.4	41	22
Orange Sherbet ($\frac{1}{2}$ cup)	1.9	13	5

Purees to the Rescue

One of the easiest methods of reducing fats in baked goods is to use fruit or vegetable purees to replace a percentage of the fat. The recipe will determine what type of puree you choose to use and it should relate to the other ingredients and complement them. For example, if you are making banana bread, you could use banana puree and only use about 2 tbsp. oil per loaf.

The Flip-n-Fry™ Does the Breading

If you bread your food, you may want to try a handy gadget for breading almost any kind of food. The plastic bowl has an inner core and a well-sealed lid that makes it easy to completely bread your food without a mess.

The Egg Binder

Many recipes call for eggs to be used as binders to hold everything together. However, egg yolks are high in fat. They can be eliminated in almost all recipes and it is not necessary to add additional whites to replace them. If additional whites are used, it will make many dishes dry and tough. If the egg yolks are needed for flavor, just eliminate some to reduce the fat.

New Microprocessor to Check for Bad Oil

Many people get ill after eating fried foods and feel that it is their system that does not handle these foods properly. However, new research has proven that in many cases it was the fault of the oil, not the person's digestive system. A newly invented microprocessor will soon be placed in all frying systems, even for home use that will alert the user when the oil is not fit for human consumption. As oil decomposes, free-fatty acids are released, some of which may be harmful when consumed in large quantities.

Whoooosh

A good test to tell whether hot oil is still usable and not high in trans-fatty acids is to drop a piece of white bread into the pan. If the bread develops dark specks, the oil has reached an unsafe level of deterioration. Never allow oil to heat to the smoke point, as it may ignite. It will also make the food taste bitter and may even irritate your eyes. The oils with the highest smoke points are canola, safflower and corn.

Slows Down Aging

Cooking wine will stay fresher longer if you add a tbsp. of very fresh vegetable oil to the bottle.

Sucking up to Fat

A few pieces of dried bread placed in the bottom of the broiler pan should absorb fat drippings. This will eliminate smoking fat and should reduce any fire hazard.

Buyer Beware

The best quality oil is "cold-pressed" extra virgin olive oil. It is made from the plumpest "Grade A" olives, has the best flavor, and is processed by pressing the oil from the olives with as little heat and friction as possible. The next best is virgin olive oil, then pure olive oil, which is a blend of both. Many companies are using "cold processed," instead of "cold-pressed." Cold processed may mean the olive oil is produced by using a chemical solvent to extract the oil. Chemical residues are not uncommon. Read the labels and watch for this intentional use of a similar phrase, which does not denote a quality processing.

Lighten-up

When you deep-fat fry, try adding $\frac{1}{2}$ tsp. baking powder per $\frac{1}{2}$ cup of flour in your batter to produce a lighter coating and fewer calories.

Mayonnaise or Salad Dressing

Mayonnaise must contain at least 65% oil by weight, any less and it must be called salad dressing. Most fat-free mayonnaise contains more sodium than "real" mayonnaise. A tbsp. of mayonnaise contains only 5-10 mg. of cholesterol since very little egg yolk is really used.

Increasing the Fat

Fast food restaurants may deep-fat or par-fry French fries before they arrive at the restaurant to save time. This may cause a higher level of trans-fatty acids in the fries. As much as 10 grams of fat may come from the par frying.

Good to the Last Drop

If you really want to get all the shortening out of a can, try pouring 2 cups of boiling water into the container and swish it around until all the fat melts. Place the container into the refrigerator until it sets up and the fat is on the top, then just skim off the fat.

Log Jam Ahead

Used oil should never be poured down the drain. It may solidify and clog the drain. Save the oil in a metal can and dispose of it in the garbage.

Keeping Butter, Better

If you would like to have your butter ready and easy to spread at all times, go to a kitchen store and purchase a "British" butter dish. It is a butter dish made from terra cotta, the top of which needs to be soaked in cold water every day.

Additive Helps

Cooking wine will stay fresher longer if you add a tbsp. of very fresh vegetable oil to the bottle.

Chef's Secret

If your recipe requires that you cream shortening with a sugary substance, try adding a few drops of water to the mixture. This will make it easier to stir. When creaming butter in the blender, cut the butter in small pieces.

Butter Fact

The highest quality butter is U.S. Grade AA, which is produced from fresh sweet cream. U.S. Grade A is almost as good but has a lower flavor rating. U.S. Grade B is usually produced from sour cream. The milk-fat content of butter must be at least 80%.

Forcing your Breading to Stay Put

Chefs never have a problem making breading stay on a food. There are a few secrets that will really make the difference:

- When using eggs, make sure they are at room temperature.
- Always place the breaded food in the refrigerator for 45 minutes. then allow it to return to room temperature before placing the food in the fryer.
- Never overbeat the eggs, the more air you put in, the lower the binding ability of the egg.

- Always use the smallest breadcrumbs you can purchase. Large breadcrumbs do not adhere well.
- Homemade breadcrumbs are coarser and always adhere better.

Fat from Down Under

Copha is a coconut shortening that is commonly found in Australia. If your recipe calls for copha, just use a solid shortening.

Stop Crowding me, Wait your Turn

One of the first rules a chef learns is not to place too much food in a deep-fat fryer. Smaller batches will not cause the frying temperature to drop too low. When you do fry, remember to always make sure the oil is about 150°F. (-9.4°C.) above the temperature that you want to fry in. Foods that are placed into the fryer at room temperature will cause a drop of about 150°F.(-9.4°C.). Never place food directly from the refrigerator into the fryer since this will cause splattering and may cause a 30°F.(-1.1°C) drop in temperature

Clarified Butter

Clarified butter is far superior to regular butter because you are able to fry it at higher temperatures and it will store longer, even at room temperature. One of the drawbacks, however, is that you do have to give up some of the butter flavor, which comes from the protein (casein) in the part of the butter that is lost during the clarification process. The smoke point of butter will be raised from 250° to 350°F. (121.1° to 176.7°C.) since it is the protein that tends to cause the butter to scorch and smoke. The protein also reduces the storage time of butter. When you clarify butter, you separate the fat from the non-fat ingredients. When butter is heated, it tends to breakdown into three different ingredients: a layer of foam, the thick middle layer of fat (the clarified butter) and a light-colored bottom layer of water, carbohydrates and protein (casein). The bottom layer contains no fat at all. The top layer contains similar ingredients to the bottom layer and trapped air keeps it from falling to the bottom.

How to Make Clarified Butter

- Cut up $\frac{1}{4}$ pound of unsalted butter into very small chunks.

- Place the butter into a clear ovenproof bowl.

- Cover the bowl and place it in the oven on the lowest temperature setting possible.

- After the butter has completely melted, place the bowl in the refrigerator for one hour and do not disturb.

- The middle fat layer (clarified fat) should be solidified.

- Remove the middle fat layer, remove the top foam and the bottom slimy layer, and then rinse the middle fat layer under cold water.

- Dry the fat layer gently with paper towel and store in the refrigerator for up to 3-4 weeks.

Ghee, it's Butter

Ghee is similar to clarified butter and is made using real butter. Ghee has a big advantage over butter in that you can cook and especially sauté with it without it breaking down and burning too easily. Therefore, you are able to treat ghee similar to oil. The smoke point of ghee is around 375^0F.(190.6^0C.), which is still lower than most oils but it is still much better than plain butter. Ghee tends to impart a great flavor to many sautéed foods, which is not possible with standard butter. To prepare ghee, just place some butter in a saucepan on high heat and heat until all the water evaporates. Butter is approximately 19% water. Continue cooking at the lowest heat point until the milk solids start to coagulate and caramelize (turn a light brown). The excellent flavor is released into the ghee when the milk solids turn brown. The milk solids are easily skimmed off and removed and you are left with the ghee. Strain the final mixture through a few pieces of cheesecloth to remove any remaining milk solids.

Drawn Butter, Picture Perfect

When you see drawn butter used on a menu, it means that it is clarified butter with the sediment drawn off. It is a very clear butter that has a refrigerator life of about 2 weeks.

Compound Butter

A compound butter is just a butter that has added ingredients and flavorings. It is usually prepared from unsalted butter. However, unless you prefer a sweet slightly sour taste, you might prefer using salted butter for most recipe variations. Basically, the butter is softened and beaten and beaten to add air and create a degree of fluffiness before adding any ingredients. When preparing a compound butter, it would be best to start with the highest quality butter available. Many pasta dishes are served using a flavored compound butter, instead of a sauce.

Brown Butter

Basically, this is an unsalted butter that has been heated until it is light brown and has a somewhat nutty aroma. It is prepared just before serving the dish and usually used on vegetables and fish dishes. The butter is easily burned and should not sit after it is prepared, since it may deteriorate very quickly.

Black Butter

Black butter is prepared the same as brown butter, except it is heated a little bit more and has a few drops of apple cider vinegar added and possibly a few capers. Care is necessary so that the vinegar will not cause splattering.

Chef's Secrets

When softening the butter, always allow the butter to soften at room temperature. The butter should be soft enough to be stirred with a wooden spoon. Never soften butter in a microwave or in a pan on top of the stove, since these methods will affect the flavor of the butter. When adding the other ingredients, never use a blender, mixer or food processor. This will affect the overall texture of the final product.

Would Someone Caul Fat?

A "caul fat" is a strip of fat that is used to wrap meats. It is sold in French, Asian or Italian markets. A good substitute would be bacon strips.

SAUTEING SECRETS

•   Chefs will never use salted butter when they are sautéing. The salt in butter may separate from the butter and impart a somewhat bitter taste to the food being sautéed. Always use unsalted butter.

- Always use a small amount of oil and heat the oil to a high temperature before adding the food. Try placing a small sample of the food (at room temperature) into the pan. If it sizzles, the fat is hot enough.
- If the food is cold, it will stick to the pan.
- Move the pan gently back and forth while sautéing.
- Parboil any dense foods, such as carrots or potatoes first. This will assure that all the food will be done at the same time
- Never salt food that is to be sautéed. That will retard the browning.
- Before sautéing meat, sprinkle a small amount of sugar on the meat. The sugar will help the browning and caramelize and will also improve the taste.
- Never overcrowd the pan.
- Remove any excess fat with a bulb baster.
- Never cover the pan or the food will become mushy.

One Pound of Fat

One pound of solid shortening is equal to 2 cups.

Soups,
STEWS AND GRAVY

The varieties of soup are endless; however, there are a few common types that most of us are familiar with:

Bisque- A relatively thick, creamy soup that is prepared from a variety of shellfish, fish, tomatoes and seasonings. Bisque can be served as a main meal dish.

Bouillon- This is clarified, concentrated soup stock that is made from any type of meat, meat bone or poultry meat.

Broth- This usually is a clear liquid that is made from simmering meats or vegetables in water.

Chowder- Relatively thick soup that is made with a fish or clam base with vegetables, especially potatoes. Cream is usually used in the base and all the contents are stewed.

Consomme- Very strong, clarified soup made from a heavy brown stock, which has been produced from meat or poultry.

Cream Type Soups- Usually made with the addition of milk, cream or butter. Sometimes all three are used. They can be thickened with tapioca or flour. Make sure you never boil cream soup or it will develop a film on the surface.

Pottage- These are broths that are laden with ingredients such as meat, pasta, vegetables, etc.

E.Coli Loves Swimming in Hot Gravy

New studies from the Agricultural Research Service reported that E.coli bacteria are getting tougher and some strains cannot be killed with low heat. Gravy with E.coli was heated to 115°F. for 15 to 30 minutes and E.coli was still swimming around and enjoying the hot bath. To kill the E. coli, it took a temperature of 140°F.

Go for Paul's

Spaghetti sauces are really best if they are homemade. Commercial sauces are for the most part higher in fat content and calories. Prego Extra Chunky with sausage and green peppers is 47% fat. Ragu Marinara is 40% fat. The only sauce I recommend is Newman's Own. The mushroom sauce is only 22% fat.

SOUPS

You Will Never Curdle Again

It is not uncommon for tomato soup to curdle, since all the ingredients-cream, salt, and tomatoes-are capable of changing the ratio of acid to cream as the soup is heated. To avoid the risk of curdling, just heat the liquefied tomatoes separate from the cream. The hot tomato mixture should then be added to the cream very slowly, mixing constantly just before you are finished cooking the soup. The salt should not be added until just before serving or this may also increase the risk of curdling.

When Should Soup Bones Be Added to Soup?

A frequent mistake made by people when they are preparing soup is to place the animal bone into the boiling water. In most instances, this tends to seal the bone to some degree and not allow all the flavor and nutrients to be released. The soup bone should be added to the pot when the pot is first placed on the range in cold water. This will allow the maximum release of the flavors, nutrients and especially the gelatinous thickening agents to be released. Store soup bones in the freezer.

Cool it! Quick

The best method of cooling soup or stock is to place the pot in an ice bath that reaches at least halfway up the pot. Stir the soup or stock continually, since it will cool faster by allowing all areas to come into contact with the sides of the pot. As soon as it is cool, the soup or stock should be refrigerated until you are ready to use it.

Something Different for a Change

The stock called for in pea or onion soup recipes can be replaced with the same amount of apple cider.

Freeze me, Freeze me

Soups and stews can be refrigerated for 3-4 days safely and can be frozen with little or no problem for 2-3 months. A texture change can easily be corrected. However, it is advised to whisk in any dairy product after thawing to avoid curdling. That goes for egg yolks as well.

Canning Soups

The best soups for canning are vegetable, dried bean, dried pea, meat-based and seafood-based. Meats should be cooked in a liquid until tender, then strained to remove all debris. Vegetables should be fully cooked to the consistency desired. Cover the meat and vegetables with water and boil for 5 minutes. Never thicken soups to be canned; however, you can add some salt to taste. Fill your jars halfway with the solid mixture, then add the remaining liquid, allowing 1-in. headroom for expansion.

Chef's Secrets

- When a chef needs to thicken soup, he/she will usually use flour, tapioca, tomato sauce or cream of wheat, depending on the type of soup needed to thicken.
- If you wish to blend the flavors in the soup, be sure and cook the soup with the cover on.
- Always use salt and pepper toward the end of the cooking time. Both of these seasonings will intensify the more they are heated. If too much salt is added, just place a piece of raw potato in and mix it around to absorb the salt, then discard it.
- Chefs usually prepare soups the day before they serve it to allow the flavors to blend.
- Always use a warmed bowl for hot soups
- If the soup becomes lumpy, just place it into the blender for a few seconds and then re-heat it.

Old Fashioned Beef and Barley Soup

3 tbsp. vegetable oil
2 cups red onions, minced
1 lb. of lean beef round,
cut into small pieces
5 cups of pure water
3 cloves chopped garlic
2 cups brown stock
1/2 cup barley
salt and ground black pepper to flavor

1 tsp. paprika
2 medium carrots, chopped
3 small stalks of celery, chopped
1/3 tsp. marjoram
3 medium potatoes, cut into small chunks
16 oz. can seasoned stewed tomatoes
3/4 cup mushrooms, sliced
1 small package of frozen peas

Combine the beef, garlic and onions in a medium-sized saucepan and sauté until just tender. Add the water, stock, paprika, barley and marjoram, then simmer with the pan covered until the meat has become tender. Add all the vegetables and continue to simmer until they are tender. Be careful not to overcook or the vegetables will become mushy.

The Original Chicken Noodle Soup Recipe

3-4 lb. chicken, cut into quarters and washed in cold, salted water
3 qt. pure cold water
1/2 cup red onions, sliced
2 large carrots, chopped
3 small celery stalks, chopped
1 tsp. salt
1 bay leaf
2 cloves garlic
3 stalks parsley, chopped
2 oz. thin noodles
Add pepper to taste, if desired

Place the chicken and salt in a large pot and bring to a boil slowly. Remove any foam or debris that rises to the surface. Simmer for about 1 hour uncovered and continue to add cold water as the water evaporates. Add the vegetables and seasonings, bring to a boil and simmer for another hour. Strain the soup and cut up 1 cup of the chicken into small pieces and add to the soup. Place the soup in the refrigerator until the fat rises and remove the fat. Cook the noodles in salted, boiling water. Don't overcook, then add to soup, heat and serve.

CHOWDERS

Basically, chowders are very thick, chunky and hearty soups. Many times they tend to resemble stews more than soups. The majority of chowders are prepared with shellfish, fish or vegetables or a combination of all three. Most chowder recipes call for the addition of potatoes and milk or cream. The vegetables most commonly used in chowders are corn, celery and onions.

Clam it up!

New England clam chowder was first prepared in the United States by early colonists who were watching wild pigs dig up clams for food. They realized that these were a good food source and started making soup from them. Different groups made the "chowder" with milk and some with tomatoes and neither agreed on which recipe was the best. The one thing that they agreed on was that the chowder had to have a very strong clam flavor with lots of clams and most was made with potatoes. Quahogs (named after the wild pigs) are hard-shelled clams and are preferred.

Old New England White Clam Chowder Recipe

4-5 dozen hard-shelled clams or 3 cups of shucked clams chopped into small bits
1 cup pure water
2 potatoes, medium size, diced
1 large red onion
1 oz. minced cooked bacon
2 cloves garlic
1/4 tsp. thyme
2 1/2 qt. whole milk
1 tsp. salt
1/4 tsp. fresh ground black pepper

Clean the clams thoroughly under running water with a brush. Using a large steamer or covered kettle, place the clams with 1 cup water and cook over medium heat until all the shells open. Stir occasionally then remove clams from heat and allow it to cool. Cook the remaining broth until it is reduced to 1-2 cups and place aside as a "reserve broth" or clam liquor. Using a medium-sized saucepan, place in the potatoes and cover with water and boil with a small amount of salt. Cook only until just tender not mushy. In another small, covered saucepan, place the onion, garlic and thyme in a small amount of butter and cook slowly until they are transparent. Remove the lid and allow it to brown slightly. Remove the clams from their shells and separate the harder meat from the soft center meat. Chop the harder meat only into very small pieces. Place the softer meat aside.

In a medium-sized pot, heat the milk until it is just scalded and a thin skin forms on the top. Remove the skin and add the chopped clams, potatoes and onions. Increase the heat to scald the milk again, then strain the "reserve broth" through a double thickness of cheese-cloth and add to the pot. Add the chopped up soft clam pieces, salt and pepper, simmer for 3 minutes and add any additional seasonings you desire.

If it's Cold, Go for it!

When preparing cold soups, you will need to add additional seasonings, since heat will increase the release of flavors in vegetables, seasonings and herbs.

To Prevent Scorching, Use Platform Cooking

To avoid scorching your soup when simmering for long periods, try placing two or three bricks under the pot. This slight elevation will prevent a boil-over from occurring.

Soup Floaters and Bobbers

The best floaters to use to top off soups are croutons, small pieces of bacon, broccoli, small celery chunks, mushrooms, crushed hard-boiled egg, parsley, parmesan cheese, miniature onions, a dollop of sour cream or yogurt or chives.

Rafting on the Consomme

Consommé should be crystal clear when served. To clarify the consommé, egg whites are added to the stock and the result is that the egg protein and the protein in the consommé stick together. When this occurs, they trap particles that cloud the soup and are just floating around. When you add the egg whites, whisk the mixture. When it comes to a boil, stop whisking and allow the solids to rise to the top and take the shape of a "raft." Allow the raft to continue acting as a filter and growing, as the soup simmers for about an hour. Ladle off the entire "raft" carefully so as not to unduly disturb the raft and release some of the unwanted materials.

Tail of the Soup

Oxtail soup is actually made from the tail of an ox, which is very flavorful. It is clear soup, which includes carrots, turnips, barley, carrots and celery. Occasionally, whole soft-cooked chicken or duck eggs may be found floating in the soup, especially in Europe.

Help! My Peas are Drowning

Next time you prepare pea soup, try placing a piece of white bread in the water while the peas are cooking. The bread will prevent the peas from falling to the bottom and sticking or burning.

BISQUES

Bisques are considered one of the more difficult soups to prepare and are more expensive when ordered in a restaurant. Lobster bisque prepared properly has no match when it is compared to any other soup. They are thick, creamy soups, usually prepared with shellfish. Shrimp and lobster are the shellfish of choice for most chefs when preparing bisque.

Stocks

Stocks are the basis of many soups and sauces. There are four basic stocks: brown, white, poultry and seafood. Stocks are prepared from a liquid that fish, meats or poultry are cooked in. The liquid is then seasoned and usually cooked for 8-10 hours to assure that the flavors are adequately incorporated into the stock. The liquid is then removed, leaving the flavored residue or stock. Stocks may be frozen and used as needed.

Brown Stock-Usually prepared with beef and veal bones. The bones are grilled, producing a rich brown color and should be included in the initial stages of preparation whenever possible.

Brown Stock Recipe

3 1/2 lbs. beef shank (butcher will easily supply)
3 tbsp. vegetable oil
3 red onions, sliced
4 fresh celery stalks, diced
3 medium carrots, sliced
4 sprigs parsley, whole

8 fresh peppercorns
4 qt. pure water
2 bay leaves
1 3/4 tsp. sea salt (iodized salt is OK)
1/2 tsp. ground black pepper
1/2 tsp. dried thyme

Step One:
Using a large pan with 1 1/2 to 2-in. sides, add the vegetable oil and the beef bones that have beef broken into chunks and bake in a 450° F. (232.2°C.) oven until they are brown, turning occasionally. This should take about 10 minutes. When the bones are brown, add the onions, carrots and celery to the mixture and bake until the vegetables start to brown. Remove from the oven.

Step Two:
Place the mixture into a large pot. Add 1 cup of boiling water to the baking pan and scrape all the residues into the water. Add this to the large pot, then add the thyme, bay leaves, peppercorns, parsley and 4 qt. of water. Bring the stock to a slow boil over medium heat, then reduce the heat and allow the stock to simmer for 5 hours. Remove any fat that rises to the top for the first hour using a piece of white bread as a sponge or a thin wooden spoon. Remove from the heat and strain the mixture.

Allow the stock to cool to room temperature. Stock will freeze for 6-8 months but will only last for a few days in the refrigerator. If any more fat rises to the top, allow it to remain until you are ready to use the stock, then remove it. The fat will protect the stock from outside contamination.

Chicken Stock- This is a clear liquid stock prepared from chicken or other poultry parts and usually simmered with vegetables, herbs and spices.

Fish Stock- Prepared from fish bones and poached fish or shellfish.

Vegetable Stock- Usually prepared from onions, carrots and celery and flavored with garlic and other herbs. The formula for making the stock is 60-20-20 with 60% onions and 20% celery and carrots. Strong-flavored vegetables, such as broccoli and cabbage should be avoided.

Poultry Stock
Prepared from any kind of poultry, but usually chicken. Vegetables are used and include onions, carrots and celery.

White or Veal Stock- Originally prepared with only veal bones, providing a clear stock that contains very little flavor of its own. The stock, however, is now made with veal, beef or poultry bones or a combination.

White Stock Recipe

4 lb. bones, broken into small chunks, meaty if possible	2 bay leaves
1 cup red onions, chopped	1/2 tsp. thyme
2 large carrots, chopped	3 cloves
5 celery stalks, chopped	1 tsp. black peppercorns
3 cloves fresh crushed garlic	Small bunch of parsley
	Add salt to taste

Place the bones in a large stockpot and cover the bones with water to about 4 in. above the top of the bones. Cover the pot and bring to a boil, then pour off the water with foam and residues. Cover with water again to the same level and simmer for 7 hours, adding cold water as the water evaporates. Continually skim the surface to remove the foam and debris. Only stir the pot 2-3 times to make sure that the bones do not stick to the bottom of the pot. Add the vegetables about 2 hours before the cooking time is completed, then add all the seasonings 30 minutes before the end. Cover a large bowl with three layers of cheesecloth and strain the stock. Discard all the bones and vegetables. Cool the stock as rapidly as possible. The stock will keep for about 2-3 days in the refrigerator and may be frozen for 4-6 months.

Chef's Secrets

- Never use salt, since salt will concentrate and ruin the stock as the liquid reduces. Salt may be added later, if desired.
- Always simmer with the pot uncovered. Condensation may affect the final result. Stock should never be boiled or it may become cloudy.
- Gelatin from the bones is important, since the stock should become completely gelled when cooled down. The stock can be spooned as needed.
- Stocks should be kept frozen until needed, especially if they contain an animal product. If refrigerated for storage, stock can be kept for about 6 days. For more than 6 days in the refrigerator, the stock should be boiled for 8-10 minutes before using.
- Brown stock can be reduced until it is syrupy or even very dark, if desired. Brown stock is usually very concentrated and very little is needed to flavor sauce. It is easy to overpower with a brown sauce and detract from the flavor of the dish. Any stock can be more concentrated, the more you boil it down.
- All fat should be trimmed off before placing the meat and bones into the stockpot. The stock should only be stirred 3 times during the first hour or the stock may become cloudy.
- When dissolving dry gelatin, never pour hot water directly on the gelatin. This causes clumping and reduces the ability of the gelatin to dissolve properly. Try using a small amount of cold water until they are dissolved, then add the additional hot water.
- For the best results, the hot water added to gelatin should never be over 180°F. (82.2°C.). If your recipe calls for an equal amount of sugar to gelatin, the cold water step is not required since the sugar will stop the clumping. However, you still never pour hot water into gelatin; place the gelatin into the water.

Pure Salt, a Must for a Quality Stock

Kosher salt is the preferred salt that most chefs use when preparing a stock. Kosher salt contains no additives, which may cause the stock to become cloudy. Also, salt should not be added at the start of the cooking, since it is impossible to estimate the amount needed. Salt is important to stock but should be added after it has cooked for 10 minutes. Salt will help draw the albumin (a protein) from the bones to keep the stock clear.

One of the Top 10 Tips

Next time you prepare soup or stock, try placing a pasta basket into the pot, or just use a large pasta pot. The basket can be removed and will contain many of the ingredients you may wish to dispose of or keep.

Well, Simmer my Bones

When you simmer bones to extract the flavor, it may create foam on the surface, which is composed of a protein (albumin) and a number of impurities (mineral residues) that are released from the bone. This foam is usually bitter and needs to be completely removed. Even leaving a hint of the foam may alter the desired taste.

Faster than a Speeding Chef

If you are really in a hurry and need a stock that can easily be prepared in about 30 minutes, the following should solve your problem:

Recipe for Speedy Stock

2 cans low-salt broth	1 large stalk celery, chopped
1 tsp. beef stock	1/2 large onion, sliced
1 1/2 cans pure water	1/3 tsp. thyme
1 medium carrot, chopped small	1/3 tsp. celery powder

Place all the ingredients in a large saucepan and bring to a slow boil, then reduce the heat and simmer uncovered for about 20-30 minutes. Strain the stock through a fine sieve.

Clarification Please!

All stocks need some degree of clarification. First, strain the stock through a piece of cheesecloth or very fine sieve, then for each qt. of stock, add 1 slightly beaten egg and a crumpled up eggshell. Stir the eggs and shell into the stock and bring to a slow simmer (do not stir). Foam will form on the surface as the heat rises. Allow the stock to simmer for 15 minutes, remove from the heat and allow the stock to rest for 30 minutes. Gently move the crusty foam aside and spoon the stock into a sieve lined with 3 layers of lightly moistened cheesecloth.

Old Cows Are in Demand

The bones and meat from older cows will have more flavor for stock and their bones will have 8 times more gelatin than their meat. The bones are more important to making stock than the meat.

Don't Strain too Much

When the stock is finished, you should strain it once only through a fine mesh strainer before refrigerating for 2-3 hours. Remove the stock and skim off the fat that has risen to the top, producing an almost fat-free broth with the flavor intact. Stock that will remain refrigerated for more than 3 days should be re-boiled or it will spoil.

Stock by any Other Name

If you prefer to purchase stock in the supermarket, it may be sold under a number of different names: these are bouillon, broth or consommés. There are two types of canned broth to choose from: ready-to-serve, which has liquid added and condensed, which requires that you add the liquid. Canned broth should be placed into the refrigerator overnight to allow the fat to rise. Remove the fat before using for a low-fat broth.

Save That Carcass

An excellent poultry stock can be made using the turkey carcass from Thanksgiving dinner. If you don't have the time right away, just freeze the carcass, well-wrapped in freezer paper. Try to use it within 2 months for the best results.

Aluminum Pots and Stock are Enemies

Preparing stocks in aluminum pots should be avoided. The aluminum tends to impart a bitter taste to stocks and will stain the pot if the stock is stored in it.

Bouncy, Bouncy

If your gelatin develops a thick rubbery skin, it is probably because it sat out in the air too long without being covered. The only other reason is that it has aged too long before being used.

Don't Use Hot Tap Water

Cold water is usually more pure than hot water. Hot water tends to leach more impurities from water pipes.

Veal Bones are Number One

Chefs always prefer veal bones when preparing stocks since they tend to provide a more delicate flavor than beef bones. Veal bones contain more collagen and therefore have a better thickening ability.

What Can You Do to Stop Curdling?

There is always the risk of curdling especially if you are preparing cream soups and sauces. To avoid the problem, you should always wait until you have thickened the mixture with flour or cornstarch before adding any ingredients that are acidic, such as wine, any type of citrus or tomatoes. Remember: heavy whipping cream won't curdle when you boil it.

A Chemical Buffet

When at all possible, make your own sauces and gravies. Packaged products are lower quality convenience items that contain numerous additives, preservatives and coloring agents.

Little Bone a Little ????????????

Spaghetti sauces that contain meat may not really have much of the actual muscle protein. By law, companies only need to include 6% actual meat. It would be best to add your own meat and you will know what you are eating.

The Secret to Saving a Curdled Hollandaise Sauce

The secret to saving the hollandaise sauce is to catch the problem and nip it in the bud. As soon as the sauce starts to curdle, add 1-2 tbsp. of hot water to about $^3/_4$ of a cup of the sauce and beat it vigorously until it is smooth. Repeat this for the balance of the sauce. If the sauce has already curdled, just beat a tbsp. of cold water into the sauce and it will bring back the smooth texture.

A Sauteing Secret

Never use salted butter for sautéing. Always use unsalted butter since the salt separates from the butter when heated and may impart a bitter taste to the dish.

In Olden Times

A method used in the 19th century was to add onion skins to the gravy, while it is cooking to give it a brown color. Just make sure you remove them after a few minutes and discard.

Shake It!

To help a semi-solid soup slide right out of the can, try shaking the can first then open it from the bottom.

Testing, Testing

High-fat gravy (which should only be eaten in moderation) will have a better consistency, if you add $^1/_4$ tsp. of baking soda to it. If it has a high starch content, don't add baking soda or it will turn it black. Try a small amount first before going the distance.

Amazing, But True

If your stew meat gets tough, it may be because when you add water to the cooking stew, you add boiling water. Always use cold water since boiling water may toughen the meat.

Easy Does it

For the best results and to keep the flavors intact, soups and stews should only be allowed to simmer, never boil.

Do-it-Yourself

Make your own TV dinner by just placing leftover stews into individual baking dishes or small casserole dishes, cover with pie crust or dumpling, then mix and bake.

Up, up, and away

Basil is a common spice for use in soups and stews; however, basil tends to lose much of its flavor after about 15 minutes of cooking. For the best results, add it about 10 minutes before the food is done.

Keep 'em Handy

To make dips and sauces, try using dry soup mixes, which are usually additive-free and only contain a few dried vegetables and seasonings. However, they are usually high in salt.

Removing Lumps

Wire whisks work better than any other kitchen tool for removing lumps in soups and sauces.

Stretching it out

To make soup go farther, just add pasta, rice or barley to it.

Stir Gently Till the Lumps are Gone

If you need to thicken a stew or sauce, try mixing 2 tbsp. cornstarch, potato flour, or arrowroot in 3 tbsp. water, then adding the mixture to the food. Do this for every cup of liquid in the product. If you just wish a medium amount of thickening, reduce it to 1 tbsp. cornstarch mixed with 2 tbsp. water for every cup.

Chihuahua Approved

To change your stew just a little, try taking a stack of tortillas and cut them into long thin pieces. Add them to the stew during the last 15 minutes of cooking. If you don't want the extra fat, use corn tortillas instead of flour.

Tea as a Tenderizer

The tannic acid in strong tea can tenderize meat and reduce your cooking time. Just add $1/2$ cup of strong tea to the stew.

Old Time Trick

Grandmother used to freeze leftover soup in ice cube trays, then use the cubes in soups and stews at another time.

Thick 'n Easy

An easy method of thickening stews is to add a small amount of quick-cooking oats, a grated potato, or some instant potatoes or onions.

Don't Drown Them

When preparing vegetable soup, only pour enough water into the pot to cover the vegetables by 2 in. Too much water makes the soup too watery.

Salt Reduction

If you have a problem with over-salting your soup or stew, just add a can of peeled tomatoes. Other methods include, adding a small amount of brown sugar or placing a slice or two of apple or raw potato in, mixing it up, then discarding them.

How Sweet it is!

Instead of sugar, to give your soup or stew a sweeter taste, try adding a small amount of pureed carrots.

Bad Bones

Dark-colored bones should never be used for cooking. They are probably too old and have deteriorated.

A Milk Curdling Experience

To avoid curdling when you are making tomato soup with milk, try adding the tomato base/soup to the milk instead of the milk to the tomato base. If you add a small amount of flour to the milk and beat it, it would also help.

A Real Winner

Next time you make soup or stew, try using a metal pasta cooker basket. Just place the basket into your pot and cook all your ingredients. When you remove the basket, it will contain all the veggies or bones you may not want.

The Parsley Magnet

When you overdo the garlic, just place a few parsley flakes in a tea ball to soak up the excess garlic. Garlic tends to be attracted to parsley.

On a Clear Soup, You Can See Forever

To make clear noodle soup, cook the noodles, then drain before adding them to the soup. When noodles are cooked in the soup, the excess starch will turn the soup cloudy.

Real Smooth

Next time you make cream soup, try adding a little flour to the milk. it will make it smoother and it will work even with 1% milk.

Soup Secrets

Always make soup at least a day ahead of time, so that the seasonings will have time to improve the flavor. Never use salt or pepper to season soups until you are almost finished with the cooking process. Both of these seasonings will intensify and may give the soup too strong a flavor. When cooking soup, always cook with the lid on to help the flavors become better absorbed. When you make cold soup, remember that cold soup needs more seasoning than hot soup. The heat tends to drive the flavors into the product more efficiently.

GLAZES

Glazes are actually just a stock that has been reduced to a point that it will coat the back of a spoon. They are used as flavorings in many sauces and used in moderation, since they are a concentrated source of flavoring. Glazes are the original bases and are still thought of as a base. Even though the glaze has been reduced from a stock, it will not taste like the stock. The types of glazes are basically the same as the stock they were prepared from such as, chicken, meat or fish.

Guidelines for Preparing a Glaze

- The stock should be reduced over medium heat.
- The surface should be skimmed frequently to remove any debris or skin.
- When reducing by at least $1/2$, a small saucepan should be used.
- Continue reducing over low heat until the glaze is syrupy and coats the back of the spoon.
- Glazes will store well in the refrigerator for at least 3-4 weeks if not contaminated and sealed well. Glazes may also be frozen for 2-3 months.

STEWS

Stews are basically prepared from almost any combination of meats, vegetables and seasonings you enjoy. Stew should always be relatively thick and not watery.

Tough Stew Meat? Should Have Used Cold Water

If you have a problem with tough stew meat, you may have added hot water, instead of cold water. Studies have shown that hot water added to boiling or simmering stew may cause the meat to become tough. Cold water does not have the same effect.

Timing is Everything

Basil is a common spice used in stews: however, it does not hold its flavor very long when subjected to heat for as little as 15 minutes. Basil should be added during the last 10 minutes of cooking.

Mulligan's Irish Stew Recipe

2 lb. potatoes, sliced to about 1/2 in. thick
3 lb. shoulder lamb, cut into 1-in. cubes
3 stalks celery, chopped
2 medium carrots, chopped
4 large red onions, sliced into small chunks
1/4 tsp. thyme
2 cloves garlic
1 tsp. freshly ground black pepper
2-3 tsp. salt
6 cups of pure cold water

Irish stew is normally prepared in layers. Using a large stew pot (or preferably a large, covered casserole that can be placed directly from the oven to the table), place a layer of potatoes on the bottom of the pot, then add a layer of onions and then the lamb (or other meat). Sprinkle on the seasonings and add the garlic cloves. Place any remaining onions on top of the lamb, then the rest of the potatoes on top of the onions. Add just enough cold water (about 4-5 cups) to cover the last layer of potatoes. Slowly bring the stew to a boil, cover the pot and reduce the heat to barely a simmer for 1-2 hours. Stop the cooking as soon as the meat and vegetables are tender and not overcooked and mushy. If the water is evaporating, add a small amount at a time as it is being lost. Preheat the oven to 350°F. (176.7°C.). Place the stew into the oven and check regularly to be sure that it is not boiling, only simmering.

Never Cook Stew at a Full Boil

Stew should be cooked at a medium heat and not allowed to boil. The turbulence causes all the ingredients to be blended with each other and flavors intermingle, instead of picking up the flavor of the base. Stew meat or chicken should not be too lean or the taste will suffer, since the taste for the most part comes from the fat. Fish stew is made with some olive oil and needs to be boiled somewhat vigorously to blend the oil in with the ingredients. Bouillabaisse is a good example.

7

Meat Facts
& TIPS

GENERAL INFORMATION

Americans have always been a society that consumed large amounts of meats and poultry, as far back as colonial days. The cattle industry during the 1800s thrived, and methods were improved as to transportation and preservation of meats so that the entire country could have their beef. Meat and poultry were the most important main dishes and this has stayed with us until recent years, when we discovered that excessive meat intake may increase the blood fat levels of fat and cholesterol to such a degree as to cause serious health problems. Recently, other factors have brought meat and poultry into the media in a negative light. The fact is that the inspection procedures may be lacking the tools and manpower to do an efficient job. Mad cow disease, E. coli contaminated meats, salmonella in chickens and eggs, and hormone residues in meats are just a few of the problems that may exist.

Education is the key factor if you are to continue to consume meat and poultry. The public must learn what types of meats are the healthiest and the safest, how to prepare the meats, what signs to be aware of, and even how to clean up after you work with meat and poultry. Americans consume 34% of all meat products in the world even though we are only 7% of the world population. We presently eat 184 lbs. of beef, pork and poultry per person, per year amounting to over 43.6 billion lbs. Red meat consumption, however, has declined since the 1970s and poultry has increased significantly to a 50/50 level. Numerous medical studies have surfaced in recent years that leave no doubt that a high red meat diet high in saturated fat is one of the key factors in causing colon cancer. Meat does provide a number of significant nutrients and in moderation should still be considered a healthy food. Meats should be treated more of a side dish and not the main course. Meat and poultry are composed mainly of muscle, which is approximately 73% water, 21% protein and 6% fat in beef, and 3% fat in poultry.

In the last few years, the bacteria E. coli has been associated with the risks of eating beef. However, more of an explanation is needed regarding the actual risk and how it can be eliminated, if it is present at all. The bacteria: E. coli is an intestinal bacteria that may not be washed off the beef after processing. It is capable of causing severe illness or even death. The bacteria, if present, would normally be found on the surface of the meat and searing or cooking a piece of meat on both sides would easily kill the bacteria. When you cook a steak or roast, all sides are normally cooked and the risk is eliminated. This means that if you wish to eat a medium or medium-rare steak, there is no risk, if the meat is properly cooked.

The problem is more significant in regard to hamburger or raw meat dishes, such as steak tartar. Since hamburgers are ground beef, if the bacteria is present on the surface, it will move to the inside during grinding. Then, if the hamburger is not cooked thoroughly, the bacteria may still be lurking inside. The following facts are meant to be usable in the choosing and preparation of meat and poultry, as well as providing some general information that might be of interest.

MEATY FACTS

USDA Meat Grading

Prime- Very tender, due to higher fat (well- marbled) content and comes from young cattle that are well fed. Prime is the most expensive cut of beef. Not widely available to the general public, since most prime is sold to better restaurants.
Calories from fat = 50%.

Choice- Relatively tender, still fairly expensive and becoming harder to find in supermarkets.
Calories from fat = 39%.

Good- Due to its present pricing, it has become the most common grade in supermarkets. Has less fat and may need some tenderizing. A common hamburger meat.
Calories from fat = 30%.

Commercial- Tougher beef from older animals, used mainly in TV dinners, hot dogs, cold cuts, sausage and canned meat products.

Utility, Cutter and Canner

These are usually leftover bits and pieces used in processed meat products. May be very tough. Includes neck bones and lower shanks.

Protein May Get a bit Buggy

The popularity of acquiring protein from bugs is gaining interest in the United States. Bugs have been a common, relatively good protein source in many countries for hundreds of years; however; you need to put up with the feelers, wings and hairy legs. A cricket-insect farmer in Louisiana is selling Cajon-spiced and chocolate-covered crickets.

Great Source of Protein

One of the best eating bugs is the locust, which contains 31% more protein per lb. than a porterhouse steak.

Salami Facts

Salami is really a dry sausage and can be prepared, using either beef or pork or both. It is seasoned with garlic, pepper, salt and some sugar. Depending on the origin of the salami, other seasonings are added. Cooked salamis are not dry sausage and must be refrigerated.

Genoa Salami
An Italian dry sausage made from mostly pork and may have a small amount of beef added. It is usually moistened with wine or grape juice and seasoned with garlic. It is always found with a cord tied around it.

Italian Salami
The varieties are endless and most take the name of the town or city where it is made. It is usually made from cured lean pork that is coarsely chopped and moistened with red wine or grape juice. It is highly seasoned with garlic and other spices and has a chewy texture.

Kosher Salami
This is always all beef salami that was processed under rabbinical supervision, making it high quality salami. It is usually seasoned with coriander, nutmeg and mustard, as well as either red wine or grape juice and garlic.

Mash that Meatloaf
To mix meatloaf easier, try using a potato masher.

What is in Red-Flannel Hash?
This is a favorite New England treat prepared from onions, potatoes, beef or lamb, all cubed and cooked together in a skillet with the addition of beets to make it red.

How About some Bubble and Squeak?
This is the name for a particular type of British hash made from mashed potatoes, cooked cabbage and beef.

Gator Burgers, not a Fast Food Item
Don't be surprised when you sit down at that upscale restaurant and see alligator steak on the menu. This is a tasty treat that has been served in the southern U.S. for many years. An Idaho catfish farmer is developing an excellent alligator ranch and will be supplying the West Coast upscale restaurants and specialty food stores with ample alligator meat. The choice tail meat will sell for about $10 per pound and the thigh meats for $5 per pound. To order your alligator for a unique barbecue, call (208) 543-6047 and ask for Gator.

Buyer Beware
Supermarkets are using their own wording on meat packages to make you think that you are buying a better grade than it really is. Most of the major chains are buying more "Good Grade" beef and may call it by a number of fancy names, such as "Top Premium Beef," "Prime Quality Cut," "Select Choice," "Markets Choice," or "Premium Cut." Since the public does not want to pay the higher price for USDA Choice, they have found a way to make the "Good Grade" sound better.

THE INSIDE STORY OF A COW

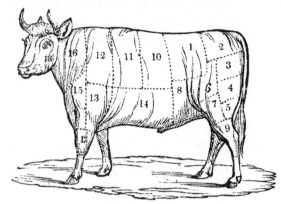

There are eight major cuts of beef butchered in the United States: they are called shank, flank, brisket, chuck, round, rib, plate and loin. The eight cuts are given a number of additional names, which will be more recognizable to the consumer. These include names, such as sirloin, porterhouse, top round, eye of the round, New York, T-bone, etc. These explain the way the eight major cuts are actually cut up. The tenderness of beef will depend on the location of the cut and the method of cutting. Some cuts are tougher than others. These include: pot roasts (chuck roasts), which are cut from the neck area of the cow and will be the least expensive.

Beef, Lamb, Venison and More

Chuck Cuts (Roasts)- These are the toughest cuts and should be cooked in a small amount of liquid and may need to be tenderized.

Rib Cuts (Ribs)- Markets may label these as baby back ribs, rib steaks, rib roasts, or just back ribs. For the best results, they should be prepared by grilling or placed in the oven and cooked slowly. The taste can be improved by adding a sauce or using a marinade.

Loin Cuts (Tenderloin)- Cut from behind the ribs they are the most tender. They include filet, Spencer, porterhouse and New York steaks. A New York steak is a sirloin steak that has been cut about 1" thick and was popularized in New York City.

Round Cuts (Roasts)- Most of these will be tender and can be cooked a number of different ways. They include: top round, eye of the round, and bottom round. They can be pot roasted or spit barbecued.

Flank and Plate Cuts- Most of the time, if USDA Good grade is purchased, it will need tenderizing. Prime and Choice are much better choices for these cuts are usually cut in strips and used for stir-frying. London broil is made from flank steak, best if marinated.

Brisket Cuts- The brisket is cut from behind a cow's front leg or may be cut from the leg itself. Normally, a tough cut of beef needs to be cooked in liquid for about 2-3 hours. If you wish to get the best results when preparing a brisket, rotate the roast ¼ turn every 25 minutes. The brisket is fully cooked when you see the fat just starting to roll off. However, if the fat can easily be removed with your fingers, the brisket is overdone.

Consume it or Freeze it

Small cuts of meat will spoil more rapidly and should not be kept in the refrigerator without freezing for more than 2-3 days. Liver, sweetbreads, cubed meats, and marinated meats should be used within 1 day or frozen.

The Case for Well-Done Beef

When meat is cooked, it becomes more easily digested and utilized by the body. Cooking meats to medium-well (170°F.) will increase the availability of vitamin B1 by 15% over well-done beef (185°F.). Amino acids, the building blocks of protein, will be absorbed more efficiently and more fully utilized when they come from beef. The absorption-rate of beef is about 90%; grains are 80% and legumes (beans) at 60-75%.

Pasteurized Beef

A Milwaukee slaughtering company (Emmpak Foods) is experimenting with a new steam pasteurization process to reduce the number of pathogens in beef. The company steams the beef trimmings before they are processed into hamburger and deli meats. The process employs hot water at 180°F. for 2-3 minutes. This process will probably be used on eggs and all seafood by 2005. More companies need to follow in their footsteps.

Tenderize Beef Stew with Wine Corks

If you add 3-5 wine corks to your beef stew it will tenderize the meat very quickly. The cork is a fiber material from a tree and contains enzymes that have the ability to tenderize meats. Best to remove the corks before serving the stew; they are not very appetizing.

There's Danger in Pigs' Ears

Cases of salmonella food poisoning have been traced to the handling of "pigs ears," a popular pet treat. Many of the pet toys and chews are made from beef and pork products and it would be best if you washed your hands after handling these items. People with chronic illnesses, babies and small children are especially susceptible.

Kosher Meat and Food Products Getting Popular

Kosher foods used to be found only in Jewish markets; however, the trend is to purchase more kosher foods and by 2005 will be moving ahead at high speed. The public is becoming more aware of the safety of kosher foods, due to special processing steps that the food must go through to be called kosher. There are now about 41,000 kosher-certified foods available.

Here Comes the Burger-Dog

It will be coming to your favorite movie theatre soon and will be called the "RollerBites," unless someone comes up with a better name. Basically, it is a tube of hamburger meat that may have a cheese filling and resembles a hot dog. It will be served on a regular hot dog bun. Supermarkets will be selling the "RollerBites" pre-packaged and pre-cooked in their own bun. Three varieties will appear at your favorite supermarket: Original Beef, Beef 'N Cheddar and Grilled Chicken.

Wet Your Hands

When you work with ground beef, try wetting your hands first and your hands won't stick to the meat.

Americans are Still Big Meat Eaters

In 2002, Americans consumed about 211 lbs. of meat annually per person, which included red meat, poultry and fish. Americans consumed 24 lbs less red meat in 2002, than they did in 1999.

Who Invented the Hamburger?

In 1885, Charles Nagreen, age 15, who lived in Seymour, Wisconsin was selling meatballs from an ox-drawn cart outside the Outagamie County Fair. Business was poor since people couldn't walk around carrying meatballs. He decided to flatten the meatballs and place them between two pieces of bread and called it a "hamburger." He sold the hamburgers at the fair until he died in 1951 and was known as "Hamburger Charlie."

Explosive Shock Waves to Tenderize Beef

A new method of tenderizing beef employs high-pressure underwater shock waves with pressures of 25,000 pounds per in. The method is known as "hydrodyne" and can tenderize meat that is of lower quality. This will eliminate the need to purchase beef that is high fat for tenderness. A tougher grade of beef can be tenderized to at least 50-70% improvement. Presently, the company can tenderize 600 lbs. of meat at once placing large cuts of beef in a pressure-resistant wrapping, lowering the beef into a tank of water then setting off an explosive charge about 2 ft. from the meat. Call (301) 504-8463 for more information.

Americans insist on tender cuts of meat, which is not always the case when a market sells beef that is not choice or prime. The most popular grade of meat sold in markets is the standard grade, which may be sold under a number of different names to make you think that it is choice. Two popular names are "market choice" or "select cut." However, since the complaints are mounting, the beef industry will soon be using a method of high voltage electrical stimulation to tenderize beef before it is sold.

Electronic Pasteurization of Beef

Another method of reducing and eliminating the incidence of contamination in beef is called "electronic pasteurization." The process is similar to the new method of pasteurizing dairy products and can be altered to sterilize meats, possibly in place of irradiation. The Titan Corporation is at the forefront of this new method.

Rub-a-Dub-Dub

A common method of seasoning the exterior of meats and poultry is called a "rub." This is simply a blend of various herbs and spices that do not penetrate the meat. It never blends with the flavor of the meat; however, it does provide a tasty coating which usually forms a brown crust of these concentrated flavors. Rub the seasoning on before you begin to cook and allow it time to take hold.

Now They're Fingerprinting Meats

In Canada, a new test for "adulterated" meats is being performed on random samplings. The new technique is called "protein fingerprinting" and was developed by A. Robin Robinson at the Nova Scotia Agricultural College. When samples were tested, it was found that 20% were adulterated. The test actually provides the exact level of contamination in the meat. The process is called "gel electrophoresis."

Freezer Burns on Meats

The white-patches on your meat or poultry indicates that the product was poorly packaged or been frozen for too long a period. The flavor will be gone from those areas but the product is still safe to eat.

Dunken Lamb?

Lamb stew will have a great flavor if you cook it in black coffee. The meat will come out dark and more flavorful.

Buying Meats? Location is Important

If the meat has been cut from near the head or the hoof, the meat will be tougher, than if it is cut from other locations. The most tender cut of beef is the "filet mignon," which means "dainty ribbon." The toughest cut is the "chuck."

Bison Burgers?

Beware of the wording on meat packages. If the steak packaging reads "lean," the steak cannot have more than 10% fat, "extra lean" cannot have more than 5% fat. The only time I have seen this low a fat content in a steak was a Buffalo steak. Ground beef when labeled "lean" is allowed to have as much as 22% fat.

Uniformity is Best

If you would like all your burgers to be the same size, just use an ice cream scoop to measure the meat out.

Grassfed Beef is Best

There is a healthy movement going on to educate the public in the benefits of grass-fed cattle, bison and chickens. This is definitely the healthier way to go, if there will be enough to go around and the products are easy to obtain. Animals that are grass-fed are higher in a number of antioxidant nutrients as well as omega-3 fatty acids. There are no hormone residues to be concerned about and no feed antibiotics to stimulate their growth. These animals live a normal life and provide us with the best quality meats.

My Roast has Darkened, is it Safe to Eat?

After a few days, the exterior of a roast will start to change color when refrigerated due to oxidation. The roast is still good, but try not to refrigerate meats for more than 2-3 days before cooking them.

Chasing a Cow Down the Football Field

It takes 3,000 cowhides to supply the National Football League with footballs for 1 year. The hides are made into special leather used for the footballs.

T-Bone Connected to the.........

The T-bone is on the top of the short loin cut of beef. The bone is shaped like a "T" is a flat bone. All flat bones are associated with the more tender cuts of beef. The round bones are associated with the tougher cuts of beef.

Cow Cartilage to Replace Sharks

In the next century, sharks will become an endangered species and cow cartilage will take over. Scientists are working to identify a factor in cow cartilage that may reduce the ability of cancer cells to develop blood supplies, as well as spread throughout the body. CSIRO Australia is doing this research.

How About a Wild Boar Burger?

Exotic meats will be even more popular than ever before. The public has been asking for some time for more variety and they are going to get it. Meat products that will be available will include: alligator legs, bear shoulders, antelope saddle, pheasant, deer steaks, wild boar burgers, buffalo tenderloins, duck breasts, lion chuck, ostrich prime, water buffalo steak, elk chuck, quail, rattlesnake meat, turtle loins, emu roasts and wild turkey.

Cooking Tips for Emu and Ostrich at $10.00 per Pound

Ostrich and Emu steaks are similar in taste to veal and never have the gamy flavor that accompanies many wild game meats. The steaks should be consumed medium rare for the best flavor and tenderness. If the meat is cooked above 160°F. internal temperature, it will become tough and somewhat dried out.

However, for safety's sake, be sure and reach the 160°F. level. A 4-oz. serving of either steak will contain 26.4 grams of protein, 120 calories, 66.1mg of cholesterol and only 1.9 grams of fat. The ostrich is the only animal with eyes that are larger than their brain.

Ostrich eggs weigh in at 3¹/₂ lbs. each and will make an omelet for 8-10 people.

What is Jerky?

The word "jerky" was derived from the Arawak Indian word, "charqui." It refers to meat that has been dried and cured. The best jerky is made with wood smoke and sunlight.

A Vegetarian Cow

Beef will be appearing in the supermarket with an "organic" sticker on the package. The cows will be fed pure vegetarian diets, which will be free of pesticides, fertilizer residues and antibiotics. They will be allowed to roam on the range and not be cooped up. The USDA has approved the new labeling "certified organic beef."

Buffalo Herds Increasing

After becoming almost extinct in 1900, there are presently over 200,000 head in the United States. By 2005, estimates are that there will be adequate buffalo meat to be sold in the supermarkets. Buffalo meat tastes better than beef and has about 80% less fat and half the cholesterol of beef. There are also no known human allergies that can be related to buffalo meat.

E. Coli Problem Solved with Hay

Researchers are finding that when cattle are fed grain diets, E. coli is stronger, more resistant and able to survive the acid medium in the human stomach better and may cause disease. If the diet of cattle is switched to hay, 5 days before slaughtering, the bacteria loses a high percentage of its ability to survive in the human stomach. The majority of E. coli bacteria are normally killed by stomach acid. Studies are presently ongoing at Cornell University.

Cherry Hamburgers Will Be Very Popular

Don't be surprised to find a cherry burger at all your favorite fast food restaurants. The latest studies prove that when you add cherries to hamburger meat, the burger will be healthier and will even taste better. When hamburger is cooked, a carcinogen may be formed in the meat called a heterocyclic aromatic amine (HAA). This is a risk factor you can do without. Cherries reduce the formation of this suspected cancer-forming compound and also reduce the fat content, make the burger juicier and even more tender. For additional information, contact American Chemical Society.

Fats may be used to Fight Diabetes

Within the near future, certain foods containing fat may be recommended to fight diabetes. Conjugated linoleic acid (CLA) found in red meat and cheese is being investigated and may have the ability to prevent certain forms of diabetes, especially adult-onset diabetes. Unfortunately, the foods containing the fat are also high-fat, high-cholesterol foods. When the fat is extracted and given to animals, beneficial results regarding; diabetes, weight control and even cancer can be obtained. The fatty acid is being used to regulate glucose metabolism. Studies are being conducted at Purdue University.

Honor Amongst Beefs?

In 2002, the USDA monitored only 1-2% of all beef carcasses for illegal drug residues, or in about 1.5 lbs. out of the 89 lbs. each person consumes each year. There are almost 2 million beef producers, which for the most part control themselves, regarding the use of hormones. If a problem with hormones is found, it is usually too late and the beef has been sold. The problem rarely surfaces, since it exists more in older cattle, which are processed for canned meat products, soups, beef stews, potpies and packaged frozen dinners.

Color Matters

All meat should be thawed as quickly as possible, preferably under refrigeration, then cook immediately. The color of fresh beef should be a bright red color, which is from the muscle pigment. The darker the red color, the older the cow. Beef fat, if fresh, is always white not yellow.

To Irradiate or not to Irradiate

There are only two ways to be sure that the meats you eat will be 100% safe: irradiation or complete cooking. Processing red meat without any contamination has been found to be almost impossible. Irradiating foods does not make the foods radioactive! Radiation is from cobalt 60 and cesium 137, neither of which can cause the foods to be radiation contaminated. Radiated foods will be labeled, using a "Radura" emblem. This will eliminate the E. coli problem completely. However, there may be a bad side to irradiated foods, since the radiation may cause a release of byproducts, such as benzene and even formaldehyde, both of which are capable of causing genetic abnormalities and even cancer in susceptible individuals. Most scientists conclude that more research is needed before irradiated foods reach the public.

Glandular Fat

If you have ever wondered what sweetbreads are, they are derived from the thymus gland of a calf. The gland assists the young animal in fighting disease. It then atrophies and disappears six months after they are born. They are a high fat food with only 3 oz. containing about 21 grams of fat or 189 fat calories.

Guinea Pigs May End up on the Barbee

The Peruvian favorite roasted guinea pig, usually served with boiled potatoes and corn, may soon be appearing at your favorite supermarket. The animal was brought to the New World by the Spanish and was one of their favorite food dishes. Presently, they are being farm-raised for food in almost every South and Central American country.

Roast Meat Tender . . . .

Sealing in the juices by lightly flouring the surface of meats works very well. When storing a roast, always place the roast back into its own juices whenever possible. When re-heating meats, try placing the slices in a casserole dish with lettuce leaves between the slices. This will provide just the right amount of moisture to keep the slices from drying out.

Tender Fact

Tomatoes or tomato sauce will act as a natural tenderizer for all types of beef. Meat should always be cut across the grain whenever possible, the meat will be more tender and have a better appearance.

Is it "Time for Dinner™" Yet?

New, fully cooked meat entrée meals are now appearing in supermarkets. They are being sold under the brand name "Time for Dinner™." These are meat main dishes, consisting of turkey breast, beef pot roast, barbecue beef, beef teriyaki, corned beef and pork loin roast. All dinners can be cooked in a microwave in 7 minutes.

The Beefing up of America

Restaurants and fast food outlets are doing a record business selling more hamburgers and cheeseburgers than ever before. New record sales of these high fat foods are reaching unbelievable sales figures with no end or slowdown in site. New medical research information was released in the year 2002 that should create a new awareness toward the health risks associated with these foods and force the restaurants to offer more veggie burgers and cherry burgers. Sales of hamburgers and cheeseburgers topped 6.8 billion sold in 2002.

Supermarket Sales of Meats 2002

MEAT	ESTIMATED PERCENT OF STORE SALES
Beef/Lamb	5.84%
Delicatessen	5.88%
Poultry	3.64%
Seafood	1.97%
Packaged Sliced Meats	1.98%
Pork/Bacon	1.01%

HOT DOG FACTS

Tennis and Baseball Fans Love Dogs and Burgers

Based on previous sales figures from the U.S. Open Tennis competition, estimates are that tennis fans will consume over 110,000 hamburgers (most with cheese) and over 160,000 hot dogs at the tennis event. Over 26 million hot dogs were consumed at major league ballparks in 2002. On the 4th of July, we eat 150 million hot dogs.

Best Hot Dog in America

The American Culinary Institute and the American Tasting Institute in San Francisco have judged hot dogs and found that the number 1 hot dog based on taste, freshness and appearance was produced by Best Kosher Foods and sold as Shofar Kosher Hot Dogs. Over 1 million Shofar hot dogs are produced every day.

Best Not to Eat Ready-to-eat Hot Dogs

The bacteria, Listeria monocytogenes may be lurking in a number of foods, such as hot dogs, sausage, raw milk, chicken, and deli-prepared salads and sandwiches. Listeria first became noticed when 48 people died from eating a Mexican-style cheese in 1985. The number 1 food-related risk in the U.S. is from bacterial food contamination, not pesticides or fertilizers. The Listeria organism can survive refrigeration or freezing and over 1,900 cases of food poisoning are reported annually. People with weak immune systems are more at risk. To avoid the problem, the following should be adhered to:

- Be sure to cook all ready-to-eat hot dogs, sausage, and leftovers until good and hot.
- Chicken and turkey dogs should be cooked.
- Hot dogs should always be kept hot (above 140°F.) until they are ready to eat.
- Be aware of "Sell by" and "Use by" dates on all processed food products.
- In 2002, Americans consumed about 68 hot dogs per person.

Moist Buns
When boiling hot dogs, try using the top of the double boiler. Keep your buns warm.

Big Doggie
The U. S. consumes more hot dogs than the rest of the world put together. This amounts to almost 2 billion hot dogs per year, almost enough to circle the globe.

Hot Doggie, We're Getting Fatter

1937 Frankfurter		2002 Frankfurter	
Fat	19%	Fat	26%
Protein	20%	Protein	11%

Most Are Poor Source of Protein
If hot dogs are labeled "All Meat" or "All Beef," they must contain at least 85% meat or beef. The "All Meat" variety can contain a blend of beef, pork, chicken or turkey meat. It can also contain bone, water, etc. Kosher hot dogs are only pure beef muscle meat and are the better source of protein. However, they all still contain nitrites.

Yum, Yum, Powdered Bone
One of the worst sources of protein is the hot dog. They have less protein in a $3^1/_2$oz serving than any other type of meat. Legally, they can contain up to 56% water, edible offal, and 3% powdered bone, which may even be listed on the list of ingredients. Sugar is a very popular ingredient in hot dogs and may show up on the label as corn syrup.

Coddled Cattle
In Japan, they can brag about having the most expensive per lb. priced cattle in the world. Their Kobe beef are fed a specially prepared diet of soybeans, rice, and beer and then given a massage daily. The meat has almost 3 times the fat content of USDA Prime Beef.

Premature Aging

Meats may turn a grayish color if they are cooked in a pot with insufficient room. Overcrowding tends to generate excess steam. Give them some room to breathe for better results.

Fat Rating of Non-Vegetable Proteins

1. Fish
2. Turkey
3. Chicken
4. Veal
5. Buffalo
6. Venison
7. Lamb
8. Pork
9. Goat
10. Beef

Meat Market Treasure Hunt

When purchasing a chuck roast, look for the white cartilage near the top of the roast. If you can spot a roast with this showing, you have found the first cut, which will be the most tender. When purchasing an eye of the round roast, look for one that is the same size on either end. This will be the tenderest one. However, with round steaks, purchase ones that have uneven cuts and you have found the one closest to the sirloin.

Celery to the Rescue

Roasts will never stick to the bottom of the pan again, if you just place a few stalks of fresh celery under the roast. This works great with other meats and meatloaf as well.

Just the Facts

17.2 billion lbs.of raw beef were sold in the U.S. in 2002 compared to 19 billion lbs. in 1976. During the same period, raw chicken sales increased from 43 lbs. per person to 81 lbs. per person.

Uncle Sam was a Meat Packer

His friends knew Samuel Wilson of Troy, New York as Uncle Sam. During the War of 1812, the government started stamping beef with "U.S." and the beef was referred to as Uncle Sam's beef or pork and the term was applied to any product that was related to the U.S. Government. In 1961, Congress made it official that Samuel Wilson was the original Uncle Sam.

Easy Math

When purchasing meats, you should figure the cost per lb. and realize that boneless cuts usually cost less per serving. The bone weight contributes considerable cost to the meat, making the cost per serving higher in most instances.

Sprucing it up

When preparing fatty-looking roasts, refrigerate the roast after it is partially cooked. The fat will then solidify and can easily be removed. Then return the roast to the oven and complete the cooking time.

GELATINS

Gelatins are sold in two forms: powdered gelatin, which is the most common, and leaf gelatin, which is only sold in bakery supply stores and is produced in brittle sheets. Leaf gelatin is rarely called for in most American recipes and is usually only required in European recipes. Leaf gelatin, however, does have a better flavor and produces a clearer gelatin. Both types are interchangeable in recipes. Gelatin dishes are only at their best for about 12 hours. They will keep for about 2-3 days when refrigerated, then allow them to stand at room temperature for 30 minutes to soften them up before serving. Never freeze a gelatin dish since they will crystallize and separate.

Softening Them up

When using either powdered or leaf gelatin, it must first be softened in a cold liquid. Water is usually the liquid of choice.

To soften powdered gelatin:

Place the gelatin in a dish and gently drop cold water on the gelatin. For every tbsp. of gelatin, use $^{1}/_{4}$ cup of cold water, then allow to stand for 5 minutes until rubbery.

To soften leaf gelatin:

Place the sheet in a bowl and cover with cold water. Allow the leaf to remain in the water for 5 minutes or until it is very soft. Remove the gelatin with your hand and squeeze out the excess water, then return it to a dry bowl. If the gelatin will be added to a hot liquid, it will not have to be further melted in a hot water bath.

Melting the Gelatin

To melt either type of gelatin, just place the dish with the gelatin into a pan of hot water and heat over a burner. You are allowed to shake the mixture gently, but never stir the gelatin or it will become stringy. To check the gelatin, just remove a small amount and there should be no visible crystals. Gelatin should never be dissolved over direct heat, since it will stick to the pan.

The 3 Stages of Gelatin

Partially Set - The gelatin appears syrupy and has the texture of beaten egg whites. Add additional ingredients, such as nuts, fruits, beaten eggs or vegetables.

Almost Firmed-Up - Almost set-up, but still able to flow when the pan is tipped. Able to add additional layers of gelatin if so desired.

Firm - Should remain fairly solid when the pan is tipped. Does not lose its shape when sliced. Ready to serve.

Stiffen up for Aspic

Gelatin needs to be really stiff for aspic. If you are curious as to whether the gelatin will be set up enough, just place a small amount in the freezer for 5 minutes. If it jells up in that period of time, it will make good aspic.

Loosening it up

To release the gelatin from a mold or pan, just place the bottom of the mold in very warm (not hot) water for a few seconds to loosen the sides.

Quick, Set me up

After completing the gelatin and placing it in the mold, try putting the mold in the freezer for 20-30 minutes before placing it into the refrigerator. Remember: gelatin will crystallize if frozen, so keep an eye on it occasionally.

Send in the Sub

Apple juice can be substituted for water in most Jell-O recipes.

Whoops, There Goes my Stage

If you accidentally set gelatin to a stage that is not desired, just place the mold in a pan of very hot water and stir the gelatin until it melts. Place the gelatin into the refrigerator and keep an eye on it until it jells to the stage you desire.

Staying Toooo Loose

Many fruits and vegetables will affect the setting up of gelatin. They all posses an enzyme that has the tendency to keep the protein in a liquid state and not allow it to become a semi-solid. These include: pineapple, papaya, kiwi, ginger root, figs and mangoes. If you would like to use any of these fruits, just cook them for about 5 minutes to destroy the enzyme. However, some of these fruits tend to lose their color and flavor when heated. If you use too much sugar, it will also stop the gelatin from setting up.

Throw me a Lifeline, I'm Sinking

If you are having a problem with your ingredients that have been added and are sinking to the bottom and not staying put, they were probably added at the wrong time. When this occurs, try melting the gelatin until just syrupy, then stir the mixture until the fruits, etc., are back where they belong.

Bouncy, Bouncy

If your gelatin set up too solid and rubbery, you probably used too much gelatin. When this occurs, the only way to fix it is to melt it and add more liquid.

Ouch!

If you need to cook hamburgers really fast, try puncturing the burgers with a fork a few times to allow the heat to enter more easily.

Secret to Thin Slices

If you would like to have thin meat slices for sandwiches, just place the roast in the freezer for 30 minutes before slicing.

L'il Doggie

The source of veal is from young milk-fed calves. Veal is very low fat, tender and more costly, but contains less hormones than most beef. It contains 1/10th the fat of lean beef and the cholesterol content is lower.

GAME MEATS

Venison Tip

Game meats dry out quickly and should not be overcooked. They usually have less fat content than pen-bred cattle. If you want to eliminate the gamy flavor, pour a small can of ginger ale in the pot. You can also soak the meat in canned evaporated milk for 30 minutes before cooking to tenderize tough cuts as well as removing the gaminess.

Another Gam-y Fact

The flavor of wild game can be improved by soaking the meat in a solution of $^1/_2$ water and $^1/_2$ white vinegar for 1 hour before cooking. This also tends to tenderize the meat somewhat, similar to marinade.

The Juciest Burger

To make your burger juicy, try adding $^1/_3$ cup of very cold water per lb. of meat before mixing and putting it on the grill. Do this in a colander so that the excess water runs out.

Keeps it Moist and Safe

When you are preparing meatloaf, try rubbing a small amount of water on top and on the sides instead of tomato sauce. This will stop the meatloaf from cracking as it cooks and dries out. The tomato sauce can be added 15 minutes before it is fully cooked. Make sure that you do not place aluminum foil on top of the tomato sauce or it will melt from the acid.

Shaping up

When you are going to make hamburger patties or meatballs, place the meat in the refrigerator for 30 minutes before forming the patties or meatballs and they will form better and stay in shape when cooking. If you place a small piece of ice inside your meatballs before browning, they will be more moist.

Ouch!

When you burn or scorch a roast, remove it from the pan and cover it with a hot, dampened towel for about 5 minutes to stop the cooking. Remove or scrape off any burnt areas with a sharp instrument and finish cooking.

Waste of Resources

Pigs require about 8 lbs. of grain to produce 1 lb. of meat. It requires 16 pounds of grain to produce 1 lb. of beef, while chickens only require 3 lbs. to bring them to market size. The latest statistics are that there are 1.6 billion cattle worldwide. These cattle consume 3rd of all the world's grain, which is not a very efficient use of a natural resource.

Must be Clean Living

The USDA has now published information stating that only 1 in 1,000 pigs are now found to contain the trichinosis parasite. My recommendation, however, is to still cook pork until the internal temperature is 160^0F. The trichinosis parasite is killed at 137^0F.

The Super "Trans-Genetic" Pig

One food science laboratory tried using a human growth hormone on a pig and ended up with a sickly pig with high blood pressure instead of a super pig. In this case fooling with Mother Nature did not pay off.

Basic Bacon Chemistry

Bacon is a meat that is highly nitrated. The higher nitrite content is found in the fat, which means you need to choose the leanest bacon you can find. Bacon can be prepared in the microwave on a piece of paper towel or under the broiler so that the fat drips down. When shopping for a bacon substitute, remember that almost all of these products still contain nitrites. Check the label and try to find a "nitrite-free" product.

Mineral Bath

Cured hams are immersed in a solution of brine salts, sugar and nitrites, which are injected into the ham. The ham will increase in weight due to these added solutions and if the total weight goes up by 8%, the label must read "ham, with natural juices." If the weight of the ham increases more than 8%, the label must now read "water added."

High Fat and Freezing Don't Mix Well

Most sausage products may contain up to 60% fat. If you purchase a pork ground product, they only have a freezer life of 1-2 months.

Damage Control

To stop sausages from splitting open when they are fried, try making a few small punctures in the skins while they are cooking. If you roll them in flour before cooking, it will also reduce shrinkage.

Yummy Sausages

If you would like extra-crispy sausages, just dip them in flour before frying.

Tender Liver

The acidic nature of tomato juice will tenderize liver. Just soak it for 1-2 hours in the refrigerator before cooking. Milk will also work on young calves liver.

Lamb Facts

If you're buying lamb, be sure it comes from New Zealand, since they do not allow the lamb to be injected with hormones. When buying leg of lamb, always buy a small one (two, if need be), since the larger legs are from older animals and have a stronger flavor.

Sitting Around

Stews are usually best if prepared the day before, allowing the flavors to be incorporated throughout the stew.

Dark Cutting Beef

Only 1-2% of all beef fall into this category. The fresh beef tends to turn a dark color very quickly making it unsuitable for sale at the supermarket, since we like to see our beef red instead of brown. It is caused by the cow being under too much stress before being slaughtered and drawing on glycogen stores to covert the glycogen to lactic acid. Normal lactic acid levels in beef will cause the meat to become red.

Stewing

Bones from poultry and beef should always be frozen and saved for soups and stews. Allow them to remain in the soup or stew from the start of the cooking to just before serving.

It's a Matter of Taste

Beef and veal kidneys have more than one lobe, while lamb and pigs have only one lobe. They should be firm, not mushy and should have a pale color. Before you cook them, be sure to remove the excess skin and fat.

How Brown I am

If you would like nice brown meat, be sure and blot any excess moisture from the surface of the meat before cooking it. A light dusting with flour also works well after blotting.

Naughty, Naughty

Meat products that are "ready-to-eat" usually contain more fat than fresh meat. When these products are manufactured, more of the meat by-products can be added which increases the fat content.

Where's the Beef Chop?

The beef chop is really a T-bone steak, which is much larger than a pork chop or a lamb chop.

Love me Tender.....

Some of the best tenderizers for meats have an alcohol base, such as beer and hard cider. The fermentation chemical process gives the products the tenderizing quality. Other meat tenderizers are made from papaya (papain), pineapple (bromelain) and Kiwi.

To Freeze or Not to Freeze

When any type of meat or lunchmeat that contains fat is re-frozen, the salt content may cause the fat to become rancid. This is one reason why meats should not be refrozen. However, leftover cooked meats can be kept refrigerated safely for 4-5 days.

Overexposure

Any meat that has been ground up has had a large percentage of its surface exposed to the air and light. Oxygen and light cause a breakdown in the meat and tend to change the color, as well as making the meat go bad in a very short period of time. Exposure to oxygen especially, leads to deterioration known as "self-oxidation." Grinding meats also speeds up the loss of vital nutrients.

Baa-Ware

When purchasing a lamb shank, be sure that it weighs at least 4 lbs. Any smaller and it will contain too high a percentage of bone and less meat.

Improving Your Recipe

When preparing hamburger or meatloaf, if you have purchased very low-fat meat, try mixing in one well-beaten egg white for every lb. of meat. Also, adding a package of instant onion soup mix will really make a difference. A small amount of small curd cottage cheese or instant potatoes placed in the center of a meatloaf makes for a different taste treat while keeping the meat moist.

High Fat Food

The most commonly purchased meat in the U.S. is hamburger. It also provides us with most of our meat fat intake and most of the fat is of the saturated type.

BUFFALO MEAT

Cooking up a Buffalo Roast

When cooking a beef roast, which has a high fat level, you would normally cook the roast at 325°F. However, due to the lower fat content of a buffalo roast, you only need to cook the roast at 275°F. for the same period of time. The roast will also be naturally more tender. In fact, once you taste a buffalo steak, you will never go back to beef steak.

Beeffalo is Great! Buffalo is even Better

Beefalo is a cross between a cow and a buffalo and is excellent meat; however, pure buffalo meat is even better. Game meats of all types are lower in fat than most of the beef we normally purchase. Many game meats also contain appreciable amounts of omega-3 fatty acid. However, game meats are more difficult to find in the stores.

A Low-Fat Meat Treat

Buffalo (bison) meat is gaining in popularity throughout the U. S. The meat is low in fat, cholesterol, and even calories compared to beef. Today's herds total about 190,000 head and are growing steadily. The National Bison Association has 2,300 members.

Nutrititional Facts About Buffalo

3 oz. Serving	Calories	Fat mg.	Cholesterol mg.
Buffalo (bison)	93	1.8	43
Turkey	125	3.0	59
Chicken	140	3.0	57
Beef	183	8.7	75

Scientific Fact

A study performed by Dr. Martin Marchello of North Dakota State University, Department of Animal and Range Sciences, found that in 26 species of domestic game meat, bison meat was lower in fat than beef, pork or lamb. A 3 oz. portion of bison contained only 93 calories, only 43 mg. of cholesterol, was low in sodium, and high in iron. Bison does not have the gamy flavor of many of the game meat animals.

Rabbit Facts

The American rabbit that is domesticated and sold in markets is mainly white meat. It does not get very much time to exercise. The European rabbit is more moist and tender since they do get their regular exercise period. Rabbits are smaller and better eating than their relative, the "Hare."

COOKING A SAFE BURGER

While undercooked burgers may pose a risk of E. coli, a well-done burger may pose a risk of a potentially harmful carcinogen called a "heterocyclic aromatic amine (HAA)". This compound is formed when meat is cooked to high temperatures.

- If you microwave the meat for a few minutes before cooking, this will make the meat safer and remove a large percentage of the HAAs.
- Choose a lean cut of beef. Have the butcher remove all the visible fat from around the edges and grind it through the meat grinder twice. That will break up the remaining fat.
- Place the hamburger in a microwave oven just before you are preparing to use it for 1-3 minutes on high power.
- Pour off the excess liquid, which will contain additional fat and the creatine and creatinine that form the HAA's.

- Reduce the meat content of the burgers by adding mashed black beans or cooked rice and you will have a safer, great-tasting medium-well burger.

Skeletal Problem Alert

Any type of beef consumed in large quantities may inhibit the absorption of the mineral manganese, as well as cause an increased loss of calcium in the urine.

Super Glued

If you're going to buy a canned ham, purchase the largest you can afford. Smaller canned hams are usually made from bits and pieces and glued together with gelatin.

Why Hamburger is Brown on the Inside

When hamburger meat is packaged, the exterior of the meat that is covered with plastic wrap still remains red since it is contact with a certain degree of oxygen. When no oxygen is present, the meat turns brown and is not able to retain its "bloom." Fresh hamburger meat will still be red on the inside since enough oxygen has been introduced during the grinding process.

Was Hamburger Named for a City in Germany?

The name hamburger originated in Hamburg, Germany in Medieval days, when the beef was ground up and consumed raw with a bit of seasoning. Originally, it was raw steak Tartar. It originated when the Baltic people started to grind up the steak Tartar into hamburger.

We're Losing our Forests for a Hamburger?

Presently, in the continental U.S., we are cutting down our forests at the rate of 12 acres every minute. The land is needed to produce feed for livestock, or for grazing. The deforestation is seriously reducing land that is the habitat for thousands of species of wildlife. Animals are actually being slaughtered during the reforestation process. The same problem, but on a much larger scale, is occurring in Central and South America to produce more feed and livestock.

Like a Juicy Steak, Don't Sear it

Searing a piece of steak does not help in any way to retain the juices (many chef's won't agree). In fact, the steak dried out faster because of the more rapid higher temperature cooking. The investigation found out that if the steak is cooked at a lower heat and more slowly, it would be more tender and retain more of its juices.

How is Veal Produced?

Veal is from a calf that has been fed a special diet from the day it completes its weaning to the time of slaughtering which is usually at about 3 months old. Its diet lacks iron, which normally turns meat red which is an undesirable color for veal. The animal is placed into a stall and not allowed to even lick a pail or anything else, which might contain the slightest amount of iron. It is not allowed to exercise and is fed a formula of either special milk (milk-fed veal) or a formula, consisting of water, milk solids, fats, and special nutrients for growth. When the calf is about 3-4 months old, the texture of the meat is perfect for tender veal. The most desirable is the milk-fed at 3 months old. However, the second formula is being used more, since the calf will be larger at 4 months resulting in more salable meat.

Old Fashioned Head Cheese

This is actually the head of a calf with the eyes, ears and brains removed. The head is boiled to obtain the meat and prepare a dish that is somewhat gelatinous.

Why is a Steak Called Chicken-Fried?

Not too many people can agree as to how this dish got its name. The closest we can come to an answer is that the dish came from the southern U. S., probably Mississippi, when someone breaded a small cube steak with a breading similar to fried chicken and fried the steak. The meat used was a tough cut of beef and required pounding into submission with a hammer.

Is There a Black Market in Drugs Sold to Livestock Producers?

The FDA cracked down again in 2001 to reduce illegal drug traffic to livestock producers; however, the problem may still exist. The FDA is still trying to control the problem with only minimal success. FDA testing of beef has shown that a number of drugs are still being used. One common unapproved drug is the antibiotic,"chloramphenicol," which. if it shows up in your beef in sufficient amounts can cause aplastic anemia and a number of nervous disorders. A number of other illegal livestock drugs that are still showing up. These include: Carbadox, Nitrofuazone, Dimetridazole and Ipronidazole, all known to be carcinogens.

What is Mixed Grill?

Basically, it is just a combination of different meats and a few kidneys and sweetbreads thrown in for extra flavor. The dish originated in England, but is also popular in South America.

Is a Rare Steak Really Bloody?

No! The blood in meats is drained at the slaughterhouses and hardly any ever remains in the meat. There is a pigment called myoglobin in all meat that contributes to the reddish color of the meat. Myoglobin is found in the muscles not the arteries. Blood obtains its color from hemoglobin. Those red juices are for the most part colored by myoglobin (and water), not hemoglobin. Beef will have a more reddish color than pork, since it contains more myoglobin in the meat.

Testing for Doneness

The experienced chef rarely uses a thermometer when cooking a steak. Meat has a certain resiliency that after testing thousands of steaks, the chef will just place his/her finger on the steak and by exerting a small amount of pressure, will know if the meat is rare, medium-rare, medium, medium-well, or well done. When meat cooks, it tends to lose water and loses some of the flabbiness. The more it cooks, the firmer it becomes.

Scrapple by any Other Name is Sausage

This is a type of sausage-like pork that is prepared from leftover parts of the animal that are difficult to sell any other way, except to grind it all up and make scrapple. The parts are boiled, ground up and fried in oil or butter.

Why is the "Fell" Left on Larger Cuts of Lamb?

The "fell" is a thin parchment-like membrane or thin piece of tissue that covers the fat on a lamb. It is usually removed from certain cuts, such as lamb chops before they are marketed. However, it is usually left on the larger cuts to help retain the shape of a roast and to retain the juices, producing a more moist roast.

Is a Fatty Marbled Steak the Best?

Those white streaks running through the meat is fat. It is a storage depot for energy and for the meat to be well-marbled, the animal must be fed a diet high in rich grains, such as corn, which is where the old saying that corn-fed beef was the best. The fat imparts a flavor to the meat and provides a level of moisture, which helps tenderize the meat. The presence of fat means that the animal did not exercise a lot and the meat will be more tender.

Best Way to Thaw Meat

When thawing meat, there are two considerations to be aware of: first, you want to reduce any damage from the freezing process and second, you need to be cautious of bacterial contamination. Rapid thawing may cause excessive juices to be lost, since some of the flavor is in the juices, which is now combined with water and ice crystals. To thaw the meat, avoid excessive loss of flavor and reduce the risk of bacterial contamination, it is best to thaw the meat in the refrigerator once it is removed from the freezer. This means that you will have to plan ahead. Placing the meat in the microwave to quick defrost will cause a loss of flavor and possibly a dried out piece of meat, after it is cooked.

What is a Coney Island Chicken?

In New York City, the Coney Island Chicken is actually the nickname for a "hot dog."

Which Came First? The Hot Dog or the Sausage

Actually, the sausage was first on the scene in 900 B.C. Hot dogs were first called a number of names, such as Frankfurters and Weiners in Germany and Austria and even "Dachshund Sausages" in the U.S. Hot dogs, as we know them, were first sold at Coney Island in Brooklyn, New York in 1880 by a German immigrant by the name of Charles Feltman who called them, "Frankfurters." The actual name "Hot Dog," was coined at a New York Giants baseball game in 1901 by concessionaire Harry Stevens. The weather was too cold to sell his normal ice cream treats, so he started selling "Dachshund Sausages" and instructed his sales team to yell out "Get 'em while they're hot!"

A newspaper cartoonist drew a cartoon showing the sales people selling the sausages, but since he didn't know how to spell "Dachshund" called the food a "Hot Dog." Hot dogs were sold at Coney Island from carts owned by Nathan Handwerker (Nathan's Hot Dogs). His employees sold the dogs dressed in white coats and wearing stethoscopes to denote cleanliness. In 1913, it was a dark year for hot dogs since they were banned at Coney Island when a rumor was started that they were made from ground dog meat. The rumor was cleared up and they were allowed to be sold again a few months later.

How Many Names are There for Sausage?
The following are a few of the names for sausage: Blood Sausage, Bologna, Bratwurst, Cervelat, Chorizo, Cotto Salami, Weiners, Genoa, Kielbasa, Knackwurst, Liver Sausage, Pepperoni, Bockwurst, Mettwurst, Braunschweiger, Kiszka, Liver Loaf, Yachtwurst, Mortadella, Krakow, Prasky, Smoked Thuringer, Teawurst, Vienna, Frizzes, Kosher Sausage, Lebanon Bologna, Lyons, Medwurst, Metz, Milano and Thuringer.

The Wahoo Wiener, One of the Last Handmade Hot Dogs
The finest, homemade hot dogs are made by the O.K. Market in Wahoo, Nebraska. The hot dogs have no preservatives or fillers and the ground hamburger and pork are placed in Australian sheep casings. The casings are expensive and imported, but make the finest hot dog with just the right texture and flexibility. The market has been in business since 1926, and if you want to taste a hot dog without nitrites, call Harold Horak at (402) 443-3015.

Spam, Hawaii's Favorite Canned Meat
In 1937, Spam, a spiced ham canned product was introduced by the Geo. A. Hormel & Company. Spam was extremely popular with the troops during World War II as a military ration. It is actually scraps of shredded pork, with added fat, salt, water, sugar and a dose of sodium nitrite as a preservative and bacterial retardant. The consumption of Spam in the U.S. is about 114 million cans annually. Hawaii outdoes itself with an annual consumption of 12 cans per person. Alaska comes in second with 6 cans per person with Texas, Alabama and Arkansas, all tying for third place with an average of 3 cans per person.

Buying the Best Hamburger Meat
Hamburger meat really depends on your taste. The news is full of information telling you to purchase only the

leanest hamburger meat you can find. Over the years I have been telling my patients the same thing. However, after reading of experiments that were conducted on hamburger meat relating to fat content and flavor, I have decided to change my mind and start purchasing the ground chuck, instead of ground round. For the most part, the extra fat content tends to be released from the meat during cooking, if the meat is cooked on a small platform or grate, allowing the fat to drip below the cooking surface. The flavor of the hamburger is far superior to the ground round, since the chuck cut is from an area of the animal that is more exercised. However, make sure that the ground meat is very fresh to avoid bacterial contamination.

How Many Hamburgers Do Americans Order in 1 Second?

In 2002, estimates are that 324 hamburgers are ordered every second, 24 hours a day in the U. S. at the over 152,345 fast-food outlets. About 48.1 million people order the hamburgers.

What is Wool-on-a-Stick?

If you are a Texan, you will know this phrase. It refers to lamb, and in Texas, that's a nasty word. However, there are 100,000 sheep farms in the U.S. producing 340 million pounds of lamb. New Zealand and Australia are always thought of as large exporters at about 40 million pounds per year. In Colorado, sheep ranchers are using llamas to protect the sheep, which are more effective than dogs.

Is Mutton the Same as Lamb?

Mutton is produced from a lamb that is only 3-12 months old, while lamb is produced from lambs that are at least 2 years old. Mutton also differs in that it is a deep-red color and well marbled. Cooking times for mutton should be increased about 8 minutes per lb.

Fried Rattlesnake

Rattlesnake is actually a good eating meat. To prepare it, just cut off the head and make sure you bury it in a hole at least 12-18 inches deep. Slit the skin near the head and peel it back an in. or so, then tie a cord around the peeled back area and hang the snake on a tree limb. This will allow you to have both hands free to peel the skin off using a sharp knife. Just loosen the skin from the flesh on the balance of the snake, then slit the belly open to remove the intestines. Rinse the snake in cold, salted water several times, then cut into bite-sized pieces, flour and fry as you would chicken or add to soups or stews.

The Room Temperature Roast

When a roast is brought to room temperature or at least near room temperature, it will cook more quickly than one that is placed into the oven directly from the refrigerator. Also, it will protect the roast from the exterior becoming overcooked and dried out before the inside is cooked. The only caution is that if the roast is very thick (over 6 in. in diameter), there may be a problem with bacterial contamination from spores in the air. Leaving a refrigerated roast out for about 1 hour should be sufficient to warm it without risking contamination. However, this should not be done in a warm, humid climate.

Cooking the Perfect Pot Roast

- Lightly coat the roast with seasoned flour
- Slowly brown the roast on all sides in a pan with a small amount of oil
- Add about 1-2 cups of broth to the pan, bring to a boil, then reduce heat.
- Cover the pan and simmer gently in a pre-heated 325°F. oven

Why is Liver Only Recommended Once a Week or Less?

The liver acts as a filtration plant for the body and may concentrate toxins in its cells. These may include pesticides and heavy metals, depending on what the animal's diet consists of. The liver is also extremely high in cholesterol, more than any beef product. A $3\frac{1}{2}$ oz. serving of beef liver contains 390 mg. of cholesterol compared to $3\frac{1}{2}$ oz. of grilled hamburger at 95 mg.

Resting Your Roast

A roast should never be carved until it has had a chance to rest and allow the juices to dissipate evenly throughout the roast. When you cook a roast, the juices tend to be forced to the center as the juices near the surface evaporate from the heat. A roast should be left to stand for about 15 minutes before carving. This will also allow the meat to firm up a bit, making it easier to carve thinner slices.

Should you Eat More Wild Game?

Restaurants, mail-order food catalogues and gourmet stores nationwide are now selling more wild game than ever before. The most popular are buffalo, venison, wild boar and pheasant. The majority of the wild game sold is farm-raised, not hunted, since the supply would be too limited. Venison hamburger is selling for $4.00 per lb. while a steak sells for $14.00 a lb. Most game has a high price tag; however, it seems to be selling and gaining in popularity. Most wild animals don't get fat, therefore their meat is lower in fat, calories and cholesterol than our conventional meat fare. The lower fat content of wild game may require marinating to produce the tenderness we are used to. To remove the "gamy flavor," just add some ginger ale to the marinade or soak the meat in the ginger ale for 1 hour before cooking. Beware of overcooking, because this will cause many of the cuts to become tougher.

The Scotch Love Haggis

Haggis is a full-bodied pudding prepared from a variety of innards (liver, lungs, heart, etc.) chopped up and mixed with oatmeal or bread and seasoned. The stuffing is then placed into the belly of a sheep or pig and boiled until a thick pudding is produced. Haggis tastes very similar to the traditional giblet dressing that is prepared for Thanksgiving.

Porkers Like to Play with Pigskins

In England, pigs are now given footballs to play with, which is keeping them from chewing on each other's ears and tails. Pigs do like being penned up and pester each other all day. The pigs are more content and are gaining weight at a faster rate.

The Colors of Fat

The color of fat that surrounds a steak can give you some insight as to what the cow ate and the quality of the beef. If the fat has a yellowish tint, it indicates that the cow was grass-fed, and if the fat is white, the cow was fed a corn and cereal grain diet. The meat with the white fat will be more tender and probably more expensive.

Re-Wrap me

Always remove meat from store packaging materials and re-wrap, using special freezer paper if you are planning to freeze the meat for more than 2 weeks. Chops, cutlets, and hamburger should be freezer-wrapped individually. This will assure maximum freshness and convenience.

Prehistoric Burgers?

Russians claimed to have recovered a Mammoth with its meat still edible in the ice of Siberia. The Mammoth is estimated to be 20,000 years old. If they decide to clone it, we may be eating Mammoth burgers. In the Yukon, frozen prehistoric horse bones, estimated to be 50,000 years old, were discovered in the ice. The marrow was determined to be safe to eat and was served at an exclusive New York dinner party.

Why is the Beef Industry Forced to Hormonize Cows?

If the beef industry did not use growth hormones, the price of beef would increase about 27 cents per lb. With the use of hormones, cows increase in size at a faster rate and have more body mass that is converted to usable meat. This will reduce the cost of raising cattle by about $70 per steer. Over 90% of all cattle raised for beef in the U.S. are given hormones. The hormone capsule is implanted in the skin on the back of the animal's ear.

Cooking vs. Meat Color

As we cook beef, we can see that the color of the meat changes, depending on how long we cook it. The red pigment of the myoglobin changes from a bright red in a rare steak to brown in a well-done one. The internal temperature in a rare steak is 135°F., medium-rare is 145°F., medium is 155°F., and well-done is 160°F.

Is the Surface of Meat Being Treated?

In many instances, when we purchase meats, the outside is a nice red color and the insides are darker almost with a brownish tint. Butchers have been accused of dying or spraying the meats; however, it is really not their fault. Actually, when the animal is slaughtered and the oxygen-rich blood is not pumped to the muscles, the myoglobin tends to lose some of its reddish color and may turn a brownish color. Then when the meat is further exposed to the air through the plastic wrap, oxidation tends to turn the myoglobin a red color. Butchers call this process the "bloom" of the meat. If you would like to see the insides a bright red color, just slice the insides open and leave the meat in the refrigerator for a short period of time. The air will turn the meat a reddish color. Remember, however, that if the meat is exposed for too long a period, the oxygen will eventually turn the meat brown.

The Splattering Bacon

If bacon was still produced the old fashioned way by curing it slowly and using a dry salt, it would not be splattering all over the place. Today's bacon is cured using brine, which speeds up the process. The brine tends to saturate the bacon more, causing the grease to be released and splatter more. To reduce splattering, use a lower heat setting. This will also reduce the number of nitrites you will convert into a carcinogen, since the higher heat tends to convert the nitrites faster. Another method that might work is to soak the bacon in ice cold water for 2-4 minutes, then dry the bacon well with paper towels before frying. Also, try sprinkling the bacon with a small amount of flour, if that doesn't work, as a last resort poke some holes in them with your golf shoes.

Pork Better Than Beef

The Chinese farmers knew that pork was one of the most efficient forms of livestock in providing meat over 2,000 years ago. Pigs are efficient at converting fodder into edible meat and far surpass the cow.

- For every 100 lbs. of food a pig consumes, they produce 20 lbs. of edible meat.
- For every 300 lbs. of food a cow consumes, they produce 20 lbs. of edible meat.
- More of the pig is also edible than any other animal.
- Fish farmers can produce a lb. of fish for every lb. of feed and chickens only need 2 lbs. of feed to produce a lb. of meat.

Beef Being Zapped to Tenderize it

A percentage of the beef in the supermarkets are being zapped to tenderize the beef with electrical charges of anywhere from 50-100 volts to 400-500 volts, depending on the meat's fat content.

How to Ruin Wild Game

How many times have you seen a deer strapped to a bumper of a car and being transported home with the proud hunter grinning all the way! Well, he may have enjoyed the macho feeling, but what he has done to the kill is to destroy it before he got it home. The heat from the car engine can increase the level of bacterial growth 10-fold and render the meat worthless by the time he gets it home. The animal should be bled in the field, cleanly gutted, cooled if possible, and placed on top of the car, covered on a rack.

Why Bad Meat Smells Bad

Bacteria, spores and mold may all be either airborne or already on the surface of the meat because of poor sanitary condition when the animal was slaughtered and processed. These contaminants break down the surface of the meat, liquefying the carbohydrates and proteins and producing a putrid film on the meat. This film produces carbon dioxide and ammonia gases, which result in a noxious offensive odor. The meat may also be discolored by this action on the "myoglobin" (red coloring pigment) in the meat, converting the myoglobin into yellow and green bile pigments. The more the reaction is allowed to take place, the farther the breakdown occurs and converts the protein into "mercaptans," a chemical that contains a substance related to "skunk spray," as well as hydrogen sulfide which has the "rotten egg" smell. Meats must be kept refrigerated and not allowed to remain at room temperature for more than a short period of time.

Marinade Facts

If you ever wondered why meats turn brown too quickly when they are cooked on a shish kebab or similar method of cooking, it's the marinade. Marinade has a high acid content that tends to react with the myoglobin (muscle pigment) and turns it brown very quickly.

The lower the temperatures, the slower the marinade will react, turn brown, and tenderize the meat. If you marinade at room temperature, it will take less time than if you do it in the refrigerator. However, it's safer under refrigeration. The acid in most marinades may reduce the moisture-retaining properties of the meat, and the meat may not be as moist as you would expect. This problem is usually countered by the fact that the meat will have a better flavor and may contain some of the marinade. Marinades may be a product that contains papain, bromelain, tomato juice, lemon or limejuice, white vinegar, etc.

Large pieces of meat should be placed into a large, tightly sealed plastic bag to conserve the amount of marinade needed. Smaller foods can be marinated in a glass container with excellent results. The acidic nature of the marinades may react with metals and give the food a poor flavor. Never baste the food with marinade that the food was in. Bacteria from the food may contaminate the cooking food and the food may not cook long enough to kill the new bacteria. Always cover the food that is marinating, and keep it refrigerated. Also, make sure the food that is in the marinade is fully covered with the marinade.

Marinade Times Under Refrigeration

Fish	20-40 minutes
Poultry	3-4 hours
Meat	1-2 days

If the pieces of meat are cut into small pieces, the marinade time should be shorter.

The Cooler the Meat, the Tougher

When meat cools on your plate, it will get tougher because the collagen, which has turned to a tender gelatin, thickens and becomes tougher. The best way to counter this problem is to be sure you are served steak on a warmed plate. After carving a roast, it would be best to keep it in a warmer or back in the oven with the door ajar.

Bacteria Risks: Ham Compared to Chicken

Recent studies have shown that a typical piece of pork found in a supermarket may only have a few hundred bacteria per square centimeter, compared to over 100,000 bacteria in the same area of a piece of chicken. This is one of the reasons it is so important to clean up well after handling poultry.

I Wonder Where the Flavor Went

When cooked beef is refrigerated, the flavor changes noticeably. After only a few hours, fat, which is the main source of the flavor, tends to produce an "off-flavor" within the meat. This "off-flavor" is caused by the heating process, which tends to release reactive substances from the muscle tissue and produces oxidation of the fats, especially the phospholipids and the polyunsaturated fats in the muscle itself. One of the reasons this occurs is that the iron in the muscles is broken down and released from the hemoglobin and myoglobin and encourages the oxidation reaction. To slow the process down and fight the "off-flavor" problem, try to avoid using iron or aluminum pots and pans, and try not to salt meats until you are ready to eat them. Pepper and onions, however, seem to slow the process down and even inhibit them.

Can a Cow Be Tenderized Before Slaughtering?

A number of slaughterhouses in the United States are injecting animals with a papain solution shortly before they are slaughtered. The solution is carried to the muscles via the bloodstream and then remains in the meat, since it does not have time to be broken down before the animal is killed. When the meat is cooked, the enzyme is activated at 150°F. This method does have drawbacks, however, since the flesh occasionally becomes mushy and lacks the firmness we are used to.

Never Salt or Pepper Before Cooking?

The rule is never to use a seasoning that contains salt or pepper before cooking. The salt tends to draw liquid from the meat, the liquid then boils in the pan and the surface of the meat may not have the desired texture or brown color you desire. The salt does not work its way into the meat to flavor it unless you puncture the meat, which is not recommended. If you wish the flavor of a seasoned salt, the best method is to season both sides of the meat just before serving. Ground pepper should never be placed on any meat that is cooked in a pan using dry heat. Pepper tends to become bitter when scorched.

The Difference in Freezer Life Between Chicken and Beef
Chicken has a shorter freezer life, due to its higher polyunsaturated fat to saturated fat content. Polyunsaturates are more prone to destruction by oxidation and subsequently rancidity. There are more hydrogen sites in polyunsaturated fat for oxygen to attach to. Beef is higher in saturated fat and has hardly any open sites.

Why Are Certain Cuts of Beef Tenderer?
There are a number of factors that relate to the tenderness of a piece of meat. They are: the actual location the meat is cut from, the activity level of the animal, and the age of the animal. The areas of the animal that are the least exercised are the areas that will be the most tender. However, even if a steak is labeled sirloin and expected to be tender, it will still depend on which end it is cut from. If it is cut from the short loin end, it will be more tender than if cut from the area near where the round steaks are cut. Activity levels in most beef is kept to a minimum so that they will develop only minimum levels of connective tissue. Kobe beef from Japan actually are massaged by "beef masseurs" to relax them since stress and tension may cause muscles to flex, thus resulting in exercise that would increase the level of connective tissue.

To Age or not to Age
Aging meat causes the enzymes in the meat to soften the connective tissue and the meat to become more tender. When aging beef, the temperature is very important, and must be kept between 340 and 380°F. The meat should not be frozen since the enzymes are inactivated. Also. too high a temperature will cause bacterial growth.

How Much Meat to Buy for Each Person?

TYPE OF BEEF PER SERVING	POUNDS PER PERSON
Chuck Roast/Rib Roast	$^1/_2$ lb.
Filet Mignon	5 oz.
Hamburger	$^1/_4$ lb.
Pot Roast with bone	$^1/_4$ lb.
Ribs	1 lb.
Round Beef Roast with bone	$^1/_4$ lb.
Round Steak	$^1/_2$ lb.
Sliced Lunch Meats	$^1/_4$ lb.
Steaks without bones	7 oz.
Steaks with bones	12 oz.
Stew Meat	$^1/_4$ lb.
Tenderloin of Beef	$^1/_2$ lb.

Relax the Animal Before Slaughtering

The mental state of the animal hours before they are slaughtered is important to the storage life of the meat. When you slaughter an animal that is stressed out, tense, or afraid, its body gears up for the flight or fight reflex and starts to convert glycogen (carbohydrate) into glucose for quick energy needs. This will provide the animal with greater strength, but when it is slaughtered the excess glucose shortens the storage life of the meat. The glycogen is needed to remain in the muscles to convert to lactic acid and help retard bacterial growth. When you are hunting, the meat will be better if the animal is killed instantly instead of wounding it and allowing it to live and convert the glycogen. Most slaughterhouses are aware of this problem and see to it that the animal is well relaxed, most of the time by playing soothing music, before they kill it.

Rigor Mortis and Tenderness

The process of rigor mortis occurs in all animals and is characterized by the stiffening of the meat and occurs a few hours after slaughtering. If meat is not consumed immediately after it is slaughtered, then you should wait at least 15-36 hours, which gives the enzymes a chance to soften the connective tissue.

Will Freezing Raw Meat Make it Safe to Eat Rare?

Unfortunately, freezing will not kill all the bacteria in meat or chicken and you will still have a risk, if the meat is consumed without fully cooking it. Some microbes will survive the freezing and will multiply very quickly as the meat is thawed. If you desire a rare hamburger, just purchase a steak, sear it well on both sides, grind it in your meat grinder and cook it immediately.

That's a Lot of Meat

In 2002, beef and poultry was a $107 billion industry. Beef and veal accounted for more than 12.2 million metric tons, more than any other country on earth. The U.S. exported about 2.4 billion lbs. of beef and veal, 3.2 billion lbs. of chicken, and 261 billion lbs. of turkey.

Why Should Meats Be Wrapped Tightly When Freezing?

When you freeze foods, evaporation continues and fluids are lost. The entire surface area of the meat needs to be protected from the loss of moisture with a moisture-resistant wrap. The best wrap for freezing meats is plastic wrap with a protective freezer paper over the wrap. This does not protect the meat 100% from a percentage of evaporation taking place in which water vapor causes freezer burn. A good tight wrap will reduce the risk of oxidation and rancidity.

Tenderizing Meats

Since the main problem with tough cuts of beef is the level of collagen (protein substance) in the connective tissue, it is necessary to use a moist heat to break down the collagen and soften the connective tissue. A slow moist heat will solve the problem; however, if you cook the meat too long, it will actually cause the meat to get tough again due to another constituent in the connective tissue called "elastin," which does not soften and become tender. The best method of slow cooking meat is to cook it at 180°F. for about 2-3 hours using a moist heat. Boiling is not effective, nor is slow cooking at 140°F. for an extended period. Baking soda is the easiest product to use when tenderizing beef, since all you have to do is rub it on the meat and allow it to stand for 3-5 hours before you rinse and cook it.

What is a Chitlin?

Chitlins, chitlings or chitterlings are all the same southern delicacy made from pigs' intestines. One 3-oz. serving of simmered chitlings contains 260 calories, 222 of which come from fat.

Should a Roast Be Cooked in a Covered Pan?

When cooking a roast, there are two methods that are normally used: either using dry heat (without liquid) or moist heat (with liquid). When the meat is covered, it is cooked with steam that is trapped in the pan. Many cooks use this method to prevent the roast from drying out. Dry heat with the lid off will keep the outside of the roast crisp, instead of mushy and if you wish, the roast can be basted every 15 minutes to provide the desired moisture. This is the preferred method by most chefs. However, if you do roast with a lid on and in liquid, you must lower the temperature by 250°F. Roasts should always be cooked on a rack or stalks of celery and never allowed to stand in the liquid on the bottom of the pan. This gives a mushy bottom to the roast.

How About a Squid Pizza?

Pepperoni is at the top of the list. Americans consume 300 million lbs. on pizza every year. If you placed all the pepperoni pizzas eaten in the U. S. next to each other, they would take up an area the size of 13,000 football fields. The favorite pizza topping in Japan is squid.

Ham it up

The Italian name for ham is "prosciutto." Prosciutto is never smoked and is prepared by a salt-curing process, seasoned and then air-dried. Prosciutto, means that the ham has been cooked and is common terminology in a deli.

Release me

The flavor of a fully cooked ham can be improved by cooking. Cooking releases the juices.

Hambrrrrrr

If you want thin ham slices, place the ham in the freezer for 20 minutes before you begin slicing.

Baste me, Baste me

When cooking a pork loin roast, place the fat side down for the first 20 minutes. This will cause the fat to release juices, then turn the roast over for the balance of the cooking time to allow the fat to baste the roast.

Cola Hits the Spot

If you want a moist ham, place the contents of a 12-oz. can of cola in your pan and wrap the ham in tin foil. About 30 minutes before the ham is done, remove the tin foil and allow the ham juices to mix with the cola.

Bacon Facts

Sliced bacon will only stay fresh for 1 week under refrigeration once the package is opened and the bacon is exposed to air. If you allow bacon to sit at room temperature for 20-30 minutes before cooking, it will separate more easily. Never buy bacon if it looks slimy; chances are that it's not fresh.

Baaaaaaaa

Lamb is graded Prime, Choice, Good, Utility or Cull. Prime is only sold to better restaurants. Most supermarket lamb is Good.

Meat and Poultry Hotline: (800) 535-4555

Fowl Facts
& TIPS

The first chicken was related to the Asian red jungle fowl and was domesticated about 2,000 B.C. However, the chickens raised in the U.S. are relatives of the British Cornish hen or White Rock hen originally bred in the New England States. In the year 2002, there will be more chickens in the world than people. Most chickens in the U.S. are processed in long metal vats with a controlled water temperature of 125°F. to 132°F. This is the temperature that bacterial growth is at a high level. Hot water also opens the pores in chickens and may allow the entry of undesirable matter that is floating in the hot bloody water of this communal bath. Commercial chickens must be cooked to an internal temperature of 185°F. to kill any bacteria that may be present. If the chicken is fully cooked and you see traces of pink near the bone, it is not a sign of undercooking. It is probably only the bone pigment that has leached out during the cooking process. This is more common in smaller birds or ones that have frozen and defrosted. The meat is perfectly safe to eat and can be avoided by purchasing older birds.

Any kitchen item, whether it is a washcloth, sponge or the counter must be thoroughly cleaned after working with chicken to eliminate the possibility of contamination of other foods and utensils, if any harmful bacteria is present. Recent television shows have uncovered the fact that there is a potential health risk with chicken, due to present processing techniques. Most of the pathogens related to poultry are rarely detected using the present poultry inspection procedures. Studies conducted by the National Academy of Science reported that 48% of food poisonings in the U.S. are caused by contaminated poultry. One person in every 50 who eats chicken is at risk of some form of food poisoning. In 1997, the USDA ordered food inspectors to increase inspections of all U.S. chicken-slaughtering plants. However, due to budget restraints the overall number of inspectors has decreased. As of 2002, things are finally getting a little better, but not much!

How Are Chickens Slaughtered and Inspected?

When the chicken is approximately six weeks old, they are ready for harvesting. The live chickens are packed into cases of 22 birds per case and sent to the slaughterhouse. The cages are dumped onto a conveyer belt, workers grab the bird and hang them upside down with their feet hooked into a type of locking device. Workers can grab a bird and lock it up in about one second. It is then dampened with a spray and sent past an electrically charged grid that it cannot avoid; the charge is only 18 volts, just enough to stun them so that they won't put up a fight. As the limp chicken moves on the conveyer, it passes a mechanical knife that slits its throat and allows it to bleed freely. After a minute, the blood has drained and the conveyer reaches a scalding water bath in which it is literally dragged through. The 135°F.- water temperature loosens their feathers.

Next they pass the de-feathering machine, which consists of six-in. spinning rubber projections, which literally flogs all the feathers off the bird. The bird now arrives at the point where a machine or a worker cuts off the chicken's head, cuts open the cavity and removes the entrails. The USDA inspector will inspect the bird at this point for diseases, tumors or infections. The inspector is given a whole 2 seconds to accomplish this task that should take at least 20 seconds or more. If the bird has one tumor, it is removed and the bird is passed. If it has two or more, it is rejected. Cleaning is then done with 5,000 chickens to a bath of chilled water. One billion lbs. of chicken are shipped in the U.S. every week.

The Processing of Kosher Poultry

Kosher poultry is de-feathered in cold water, not warm or hot water. It is then soaked, totally submerged for 30-40 minutes in ice-cold water, hand- salted inside and out to clean it out, then allowed it to hang for about 1 hour to remove any remaining blood residue. The birds are then salted and rinsed 3 more times to remove any remaining salt. Kosher chickens have a fresher, cleaner taste than the standard market chicken. Many Kosher-processed chickens never make it to the marketplace, even when passed by government inspectors. The quality control differs from most other processors and the standards are higher.

Food Fact

When purchasing chicken, be aware that a 3 lb. chicken will yield about $1\frac{1}{2}$ lbs. edible meat.

Making Great Fried Chicken!

Most chefs agree to the following method as being the best. Place the chicken pieces in buttermilk in the refrigerator for 45 minutes, drain and dry well before breading. Combine all-purpose flour, pepper, salt and any other seasoning you prefer in a brown paper bag and place the chicken pieces in the bag and shake. The bag will absorb any excess moisture and coat the chicken in the process. Frying oil should be exactly 375°F. Be sure not to crowd the chicken pieces.

Don't Be Too Speedy

When you make chicken or turkey salad, make sure that the meat has been cooked to 180°F., then allow the meat to cool in the refrigerator before adding the salad dressing or mayonnaise.

Chicken Tenders

Lemon is a natural tenderizer for chicken and gives it a unique flavor, also. You might try basting it with a small amount of Zinfandel. Remember: a low-to-moderate cooking temperature will produce a juicier chicken, since more fat and moisture are retained.

Time to Vaccinate the Chickens

A new vaccine should be available in the near future that will be used to control salmonella in poultry. The vaccine will be sprayed on chicks in the hatchery and will stimulate immunity in chickens, preventing an infection from salmonella. The vaccine is called "Megan™Vac 1" and was invented by Megan Health Inc. of St. Louis, in cooperation with Washington University. This will be the first food safety vaccine.

Fowl Cubes

Do-it-yourself bouillon cubes can be made by freezing leftover chicken broth in ice cube trays. They can be stored in Baggies and kept frozen until needed for a recipe or soup. They are easily thawed in the microwave.

Short Timers

Raw poultry and hamburger meat should not be kept in the refrigerator for more than 2 days without being frozen.

Clip, Clip

If you want to save money when buying chicken, buy whole chickens, then cut them with a poultry scissors and freeze the sections you want together. When you purchase whole birds, try not to buy the larger ones, they are older birds and not as tender. Young chickens and turkeys also have less fat.

Try it, You Will Notice the Difference

Chefs tenderize and improve the taste of chicken by submerging the chicken parts in buttermilk for 2-3 hours in the refrigerator before cooking.

Only Buy 4.0 Chickens

Chickens are Grade A, Grade B, or Grade C. Grades B and C are usually blemished and only used in canning, frozen foods, and TV dinners. Grade A chickens are sold in supermarket meat departments.

Call the Masseur

Poultry in foreign countries are never subjected to the conditions we allow in the U.S. You will also notice a difference in taste. If you do notice an odor from the market production chickens, try rubbing a small amount of lemon juice into the skin. The bird will enjoy this and it will totally remove the odor.

Ask the Butcher

When you see a chicken labeled fresh, you should ask the butcher whether it was previously frozen. If it has been frozen once, it would be best not to re-freeze it.

Mass Chicken Production

One chicken farm is capable of shipping 26 million chickens per week and over 43 million chickens are processed in the U.S. every day according to the National Broiler Council.

Not a Healthy Food

Chicken wings, alias "Buffalo wings" usually supply up to 25 grams of fat in a serving of 3 wings.

Staying Power

If you want to store chicken for 3-4 days in the refrigerator, change the wrapping to plastic wrap or waxed paper. The supermarket wrapping often contains blood residue.

Home, Home on the Range

A free-range chicken has an average of 14% fat, compared to a standard cooped-up production chicken at 18-20% fat.

Brown Parts

If you wish your chicken or its parts to be browned, try brushing them with a low-salt soy sauce.

Here a Duck, There a Duck

A farm-raised duck will have more meat than a wild duck. Ducks are not a good candidate for stuffing. Their fat content is so high that the fat is absorbed into the stuffing when you are cooking them.

Mini-Chick

Miniature chickens are called Cornish game hens. These are chickens that are only 4-6 weeks old and only weigh about 2 lbs. each.

Great Chicken Ranch

One of the finest chicken ranches in the U.S. is Shelton's in Pomona, California (909) 623-4361. They raise only free-range chickens, use no antibiotics and hand-process every chicken.

Your Turkey May Be Zapped

It is possible to see turkeys and chickens with the new radiation logo on the packaging. In 1992, the USDA approved irradiation for poultry. The word "Treated with Radiation" or "Treated by Radiation" will also be on the package.

Buyer Beware

It would be best to compare nutrition labels when purchasing ground turkey, chicken or pork. You may be surprised that in most instances, they will have as high a fat content as lean hamburger.

Scrub-a-Dub-Dub

The safest method of thawing poultry is to place it in a bowl of cold water. If you add salt to the water, it will improve the flavor of the poultry as well as providing additional cleaning.

Colonel's Prairie Chicken

The millennium may see a comeback of the old American stable "prairie chicken" which fed the settlers during the 1800s. They feasted on so many prairie chickens that they almost completely eliminated the species. The bird is making a comeback, after being totally extinct in Canada and had been reduced to only a few hundred birds in the Plains states.

Some Fowl Facts

Americans averaged 92 lbs. of chicken in 2002, about 27 birds per person. Approximately 38% of all meat sold in the U.S. is chicken, with 6.1 billion lbs. of the total 7.9 billion lbs. produced being sold by fast food restaurants. Chicken farming is a $16.8 billion industry.

Like Dark Meat? Eat Wild Fowl!

The dark meat on fowl is the result of using the breast muscles more, providing them with a greater blood supply. The breast muscles are rarely used in a production bird since they are cooped up all of their lives. The breast meat on wild fowl is always dark since these fowl must fly for long journeys and use the muscles extensively.

Fowl Antibiotics

Because of the way chickens are cooped up and the questionable sanitary condition they must endure, diseases are common occurrences. Almost all poultry, approximately 85% of all pigs, and 60% of all beef in the U.S. are fed either penicillin or tetracycline. Almost 50% of all antibiotics manufactured are used on animals. The fear is now that the animals will develop antibiotic-resistant bacteria. In Europe, many countries will not allow the indiscriminate use of antibiotics for this reason.

Bacteria Haven

Never stuff a turkey or other fowl and leave it overnight in the refrigerator thinking it´s safe. The inside of the bird acts like an incubator allowing rapid bacterial growth to occur. When the bird is cooked all the bacteria may not be killed. This results in hundreds of cases of food poisoning annually.

Is Ground Poultry Regulated?

At present, there is no set standard for fat content in poultry. However, the National Turkey Federation does have guidelines, especially where fat is concerned. Ground poultry must not have any added fat, other than the normal amount of fat found on the bird. No additional fat can be added. A turkey contains about 15% fat and a chicken has about 20% fat. This amounts to about 10-15% fat by weight of the product.

Chubby Chicken

According to the latest USDA reports, chickens are being marketed at higher weights than ever before. Using forced feeding and hormones may be the answer why they arrive at markets at top weight in only 7 weeks. Five years ago, it took 12-14 weeks. Turkeys reach maturity in 14-22 weeks and are usually more tender than chickens, as well as having less fat.

Fowl Plucking

If you need to pluck a duck, make sure the water that you dip the duck in is at least 155°F. It's easier to pluck out the feathers, if they are hot and wet. If you are plucking a goose, pheasant, or quail, the water should be at least 135°F.

Types of Chickens Sold

Organic chickens- May only be raised on land that has never had any chemical fertilizer or pesticide used on it for at least 3 years. They must also be fed chemical-free grains and are for the most part free-range chickens.

Mass-produced chickens- Commercially raised in crowded coops and never allowed to run free. They are marketed in exact sizes in the same number of months.

Kosher Chickens- Chickens that have been slaughtered and cleaned in compliance with Jewish dietary laws.

Broilers/Fryers- These are 7-week old birds that weigh from 3-4 lbs.

Roasting Chickens- These are usually hens that weigh in at 5-8 lbs. with more fat than broilers.

Stewing Hens- Usually weigh 4-8 lbs. and are 1-year-old. Basically, these are retired laying hens. They are tough old birds and need to be slow-cooked but are flavorful.

Capons- These are castrated roosters, which average 10 weeks old and weigh 8-10 lbs. They usually have large white meat breasts from making a lot of noise.

Poussins- These are baby chicks only 1month-old and weighing about 1 lb. They lack flavor and are only used for grilling.

Rock Cornish Game Hen- These are small broilers or fryers and weigh about 1-2 lbs. They are best grilled or roasted.

You're in a Muddle if There's a Puddle

When choosing meat or poultry in the supermarket, make sure that there is no liquid residue either wet or frozen on the bottom of the package. If there is, it means that the food has been frozen and the cells have released a percentage of their fluids. When cooked, the bones will be noticeably darker than a fresher product.

Which Came First, the Chicken or the Turkey?

According to the history books, the chicken was forced to come to the Western Hemisphere by Spanish explorers who weren't sure what kind of meat they would find when they arrived and wanted meat they were familiar with. The turkey, however, is a Native American and was introduced to Europe by the same explorers. The Europeans didn't know what to call the turkey and the Spanish were not sure where they landed. Thinking that it was India, they called the turkey "Bird of India" or "Calcutta Hen."

Which Came First, the Chicken or the Egg?

This is a relatively easy question to answer. The egg came first through a series of DNA changes in the relatives of the present-day chicken. Thousands of years ago, there were no chickens, just fowl that resembled the bird. As time passed and evolution took place, two non-chickens produced DNA that was different and when two non-chickens produced similar DNA and there evolved a male and female of the new species, they found each other and mated. They became the present-day chicken.

What is the Pink Liquid in a Chicken Package?

This is not chicken blood, but is mostly water that was absorbed by the chicken during the chilling process. All blood is drained from the chicken and if there were blood left, it would denote a poorly processed bird and the skin would also be a bright red.

Sticky Chicken Skin

When cooking chicken on a barbecue rack, always grease the rack well first. The collagen in the skin will turn into a sticky gelatin, which causes it to stick to the rack. To really solve the problem, try baking the chicken for 15-20 minutes in a preheated oven, breast side up, allowing the gelatin time to infuse into the fat and meat or to be released into the pan.

How Fast Do Bacteria on Chicken Multiply?

If a piece of chicken has 10,000 bacteria on a 1-square centimeter area when it is processed and reaches the supermarket, it will increase 10,000 times that figure, if left in the refrigerator at about 400°F. for 6 days. The Center for Disease Control in Atlanta estimates that 9,000 people die each year from food-borne illness with thousands of other becoming ill from bacterial, chemical, fertilizer, and pesticide residues left on foods and poultry. According to the USDA, 40% of all chickens are contaminated with salmonella and even if contaminated, they can still pass the USDA inspection. Almost 50% of all animal feed may contain salmonella.

Mini-Pigeon?

If you ever wondered what a squab is, it is just a "mini-pigeon" that is no more than 1-month-old. They are specially bred to be plump and raised to be marketed. They are usually sold frozen and will not weigh over 1 lb. Look for birds with pale skin and the plumper the better. Squab will store frozen for about 6 months at 0°F.

Best Method of Cleaning a Chicken

Chickens need to be cleaned thoroughly inside and out before cooking to remove any residues that are left from the slaughtering process. While it is impossible to completely clean the bird, you should at least do the best you can. The preferred method is to place 1 tbsp. baking soda in the water that you will use to clean the chicken and rinse the bird several times with the water, then clean water several times. The mild acidic action and abrasives of the baking soda will do the job.

How Much Chicken to Buy for each Person

TYPE OF CHICKEN	AMOUNT PER PERSON
Broiler/Fryer	$^1/_2$ lb.
Capon	$^3/_4$ lb.
Cornish Game Hen	1 bird
Whole Chicken with bones	1 lb.
Breast	$^1/_2$ breast
Drumstick	2 drumsticks
Thighs	2 thighs

5 lbs. of chicken will provide about 3 cups of meat.

Heavy Rooster

The heaviest rooster is the male White Sully, which can weigh in at a maximum weight of 22 lbs. Roosters are called a "cockerel" and are descendents of the Red Jungle Fowl of Southeast Asia. Their lineage can be traced back 8,000 years.

Can Chicken Be Re-Frozen After it is Defrosted?

Yes! Providing the chicken has been defrosted in the refrigerator and has not remained in the refrigerator for more than 2 days.

Begone Salmonella

A new device has been invented that will reduce the level of airborne salmonella by 95% in chicken coops to protect the hatchlings. The system employs a negative electrostatic charge to collect the dust particles and deposit them on plates that are cleaned regularly.

Skin Color vs. Quality

The public would prefer to see a nice, yellowish-colored chicken skin, instead of a bluish-white, sickly looking skin. Farmers are now placing marigold petals into the chicken feed to make their skin yellow. Production chickens are never allowed to run free and soak up the sunlight to make their skins yellow, thus their skins are actually a sickly bluish color. Since the marigold petals are "all-natural," they do not have to be listed anywhere on the packaging. Free-range chickens always have yellowish skins, as well as being more flavorful.

Get a Good Grip

The easiest way to skin a chicken is to slightly freeze it first, then grip the skin with a piece of paper towel. The skin will come right off with hardly any effort.

Quail: A Dangerous Bird

Over the years, a number of people have become ill with symptoms of nausea, vomiting, shivers and even a type of slow-spreading paralysis from eating quail. The problem may be the result of their diet in certain parts of the country. Occasionally, a quail may consume hemlock, which may be toxic to humans, as part of their feeding pattern. The green quail of Algeria has caused a number of illnesses. If you do experience illness after eating quail, it would be best to contact the local health authorities.

Cooking White Meat vs. Dark Meat

When you cook white and dark meat chicken parts together, remember that the white meat cooks faster than the dark, so start the dark meat a little sooner. The higher fat content in the dark meat is why this occurs. The white meat may be too dry, if you cook them together.

Giblet Cooking

When you cook giblets, make sure that you place the liver in during the last 20 minutes. The liver tends to flavor all the giblets when cooked with them from the beginning.

Meat and Poultry Hotline: 1-(800) 535-4555

9

Sounds
FISHY

The popularity of fish has risen since the 1980s and more varieties of fish have become available. Consumption of fish in 2002 averaged 24.1 lbs. per person. More fish than ever are now raised in aqua-culture fish farms. The fats in fish are high in polyunsaturates and contain the omega-3 fatty acids that may protect us from heart attacks by keeping the blood from coagulating too easily. Studies show that even canned or frozen fish retain most of their omega-3 fatty acids. However, many fish and shellfish may still harbor certain bacteria and parasites. Cooking is a must for fish and shellfish since they should never be eaten raw. Also, never consume the skin or visible fat on fish as most of the contaminants, if present, will be located there.

Choosing Fresh Fish in the Supermarket

Skin- The skin should always have a shiny look to it and when finger pressure is applied, it should easily spring back to its original shape. The meat should be firm to the touch with no visible blemishes. Never buy fish if the skin has any dark discoloration.

Eyes- When you look into the fish eyes, they should be bulging and not sunken into the head, which is a sign of a dried-out fish. The eyes should also be clear and not cloudy. If the fish winks at you, this is a very good sign.

Scales- The scales should not be falling off. If you notice loose scales, don't buy the fish. The scales should also have a healthy, bright and shiny appearance.

Gills- The gills must look clean with no sign of any slime. Their healthy color is a reddish- pink. Gray gills are a sign of an old fish that has seen better days.

Odor- A fresh fish never smells "fishy." If the fish does have a strong odor about it, it is probably from the flesh decomposing and releasing the chemical compound "trimethylamine." Seafood should be as fresh as possible, usually no more than 2-3 days out of the water.

Choosing Frozen Fish in the Supermarket

Odor- If frozen fish has an odor, it has probably thawed and been re-frozen. When it is thawed, it should have hardly any odor.

Skin- Be sure that the skin and flesh are frozen solid and that there are no discoloration or soft spots. The skin should be totally intact with no areas missing.

Wrappings- The wrapping should be intact with no tears or ice crystals, and be sure that the fish is frozen solid.

Common Forms of Supermarket Fish

Whole Fish- Complete with entrails, needs to be sold shortly after it is caught.

Drawn Fish- Whole fish with only the entrails removed.

Dressed Fish- Totally cleaned up with entrails removed and ready to party or cook.

Fish Fillets/Steaks- Large pieces of fish with the bones removed. When both sides are removed, they are sometimes called butterfly fillets.

Cured Fish- These are usually sold as smoked, pickled or salted fish. If the fish is sold as "cold smoked," it was only partially dried and will have a very short shelf life. If the label reads, "hot smoked," the fish was not fully cooked and should be kept frozen until used.

Dried Fish- Fish that has been processed using dry heat, then salted to preserve it.

Salted Fish- These fish are used mainly for pickling in a brine solution.

A Word to the Wise

If you see a seafood product with "USG INSPECTED" on the label, report it to authorities. This is not a legal designation. The label should read, "Packed Under Federal Inspection" or (PUFI). This means that it was packed in the presence of, or at least inspected by a Federal Inspector.

SHELLFISH

Pollution and Shellfish Still a Problem

Presently, about 34% of all shellfish beds in the U.S. have been officially closed because of pollution. All coastal waters worldwide are in jeopardy of also being closed to fishing. One of the world's better known seaports, Boston Harbor, is so polluted that fisherman are advised not to fish there anymore. Mutant fish are being caught in Boston Harbor with tumors and bacterial infections. The sewage problem is so bad in the Gulf States of Louisiana and Florida that 67% of the oyster beds have been closed to fishing. In Europe, about 90% of the sewage is still dumped into coastal waters.

Safe Shellfish a Must

Shellfish harvesters and aquafarms must now have a "harvest license" to sell shellfish. Make sure that your market purchases their shellfish from a dealer who has a license from the National Shellfish Sanitation Program.

Just a Sweetie

For the most part, shellfish are sweeter tasting than fish. The reason is that they have a higher percentage of glycogen, a carbohydrate which converts to glucose. The amino acid, glycine, is also capable of providing some degree of sweetness from its protein. Lobsters are the sweetest shellfish, while crab and shrimp come in second and third. However, if they are stored for more than 1-2 days, the sweetness will be reduced.

Abalone

Abalone is becoming one of the rare shellfish to find off the coast of California. The "foot" is the tough edible portion, which must be literally pounded into tenderness. The price is high and they must be cooked 12-24 hours after they are captured, otherwise they will become bitter.

Expensive Chewing Gum

The method of tenderizing abalone is to cut the abalone into the thinnest slices possible and then pound those slices even thinner, using a special meat-tenderizing hammer. If this is not done properly, the abalone will be tough.

Times up

When abalone is cooked, it should never be cooked for more than 30 seconds on each side. Overcooking makes it tough. Before cooking, place small slashes about an in. apart across the whole piece to avoid curling.

Southern Exposure

When purchasing abalone, make sure that the exposed foot muscle moves when you touch it. Never buy shellfish if it is dead.

CLAMS

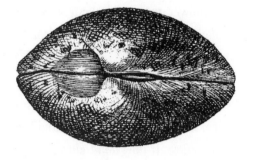

The most popular clam is the hard-shell clam. The geoduck clam, a soft-shell clam, is unable to close its shell because its neck sticks out too far and is too big. It can weigh up to 3 lbs. and is not as tasty as the hard-shell clams. Packaged soups and canned clam products are produced from large sea clams.

Know Where They Are Raised

All shellfish are called "filter feeders." They rely on food entering their systems in the water that goes by them, which may contain almost any type of toxic material and even sewage. Over time, any toxic material that is ingested may increase to a harmful level to humans, if adequate amounts of toxic shellfish are consumed.

- Diseases, such as hepatitis can be transmitted if the shellfish were feeding in areas that were contaminated with sewage.
- Shellfish are capable of filtering up to 20 gal. of water a day looking for food.
- Shellfish are rarely, if ever, inspected. Some of the contaminants are rendered harmless if the shellfish is cooked.
- Raw shellfish should only be eaten in moderation, unless they are aquacultured.

Open Wide, Say Ahhhh #1

To open shellfish, rinse them in cold tap water for 5 minutes, then place them into a baggie and place it into the freezer for about 30 minutes. They should be cooked in heavily salted water to draw out the sea salt. Remember, shellfish are naturally high in sodium and not recommended for a low-sodium diet.

Open Wide, Say Ahhhh #2

Another method of opening clams is to place the clams in a single layer on a cookie sheet and place them into the freezer for 15 minutes. The clams' muscles will relax, making them easier to open.

Fresh Waters, A Killer

Once saltwater clams are dug up, they must be cleansed of sand and debris or they will not be eatable. To accomplish this, the clams should be allowed to soak in clean seawater (never fresh water) for about 20 minutes. Change the water every 4-5 minutes to clear the debris from the water.

Dead or Alive

A healthy clam should have its shells closed when being cooked; however, it should relax and open after it's boiled. If you keep the clams on ice, they will probably relax and open their shells. To test their condition, just tap the shell and they should close. If they don't close, then they are sick or dying and should not be used. After they are cooked, if the shells do not open, they should be discarded and the shell never forced open.

Claw Renewal

Crabs and lobsters have the capability to regenerate a new claw when one is broken off. The crab industry in many areas now catch crabs and break off one of the claws, then release the crab to grow another one. The crab is able to protect itself and forage for food as long as it has one claw.

This Clam Will Really Fill You up

In 1956, the largest clam on record was caught off the coast of Manila and weighed in at 750 lbs. Clams are all males unless they decide to change to female later in life; luckily, many do.

The Chowder Trick

Chefs will always add the sliced clams during the last 15-20 minutes of cooking time. When clams are added early in the cooking of chowder, they tend to become tough or too soft.

CRAB

Different species of crabs are found in different oceans or seas. Crabs caught in the Gulf of Mexico or Atlantic Ocean are called Blue Crabs. Crabs caught in the Pacific Ocean are known as the Dungeness. The most prized crabs and the largest are the King Crabs; these are caught off the coast of Alaska and Northern Canada. The smaller Stone Crab is found in the waters off the coast of Florida. Crabs should only be purchased if they are active and heavy for their size. Refrigerate them as soon as possible and cover them with a damp towel. Live crabs should be cooked the day they are purchased.

The soft-shell crabs can be found in a variety of sizes. The smallest are called "spiders," which are almost too small to keep. They only measure about $3^1/_2$ in. across, which is the bare legal size. The "hotel prime" measure in at about $4^1/_2$ in. across and the "prime" at $5^1/_2$ inches. The largest are called "jumbo" and measure in at a whopping 6-7 in. across.

- If canned crabmeat has a metallic taste, soak it in ice water for 5-8 minutes, then drain and blot dry with paper towels.

Jimmy Marries Sally

Male crabs are known as a "jimmy" (T-shaped apron) and female crabs are known as a "sally" (V-shaped apron). The female crabs may also be called a "sook" and will always have their fingernails (or claw tips) painted a bright red. Males will never have red-tipped claws.

What is Imitation Crab?

Hundreds of years ago the Japanese invented a process to make imitation shellfish called "surimi." In recent years, it has become a booming industry in the U.S. Presently, we are producing imitation crab, meat, lobster, shrimp, and scallops. Most are made from a deep ocean whitefish, pollack. Surimi contains less cholesterol than the average shellfish and contains high quality proteins, and very little fat. Unfortunately, most surimi does contain high levels of salt (sometimes 10 times that of the real shellfish) and in some products, MSG is used to bring out the flavor. The processing also lowers the level of other nutrients that would ordinarily be found in the fresh pollack.

Cool it!

If crab shells are orange after they are cooked, the crabs were old and may not have the best flavor. Their shells should be a bright red after cooking, which means that the chemical in the shell was still very active.

CRAYFISH/CRAWFISH/CRAWDAD/MUDBUG

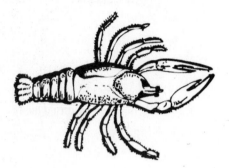

These look like miniature shrimp and are a relative. The largest producer in the world is the state of Louisiana. They produce over 22 million lbs. of these little "crawdads" a year.

The Secret to Removing the Meat from Crayfish

To begin with, crayfish are always cooked live, similar to lobsters and crabs. They have a much sweeter flavor and are affectionately known as "crawdads." All the meat is found in the tail of the crayfish. To easily remove the meat, gently twist the tail away from the body, then unwrap the first three sections of the shell to expose the meat. Next, you need to pinch the end of the meat while holding the tail in the other hand and pulling the meat out in one piece. If you wish, you can also suck out the flavorful juices from the head.

Eating it all!

The tails can be eaten as well as the orange fat, pancreas and even the liver. All parts are used in classic Cajun dishes.

LANGOSTINOS

Another relative of the shrimp, these small crustaceans are also called "rock shrimp." They can usually be found in the market frozen and are mainly used for salads, soups, or stews.

LOBSTER

The two most common species of lobster consumed in the U.S. are Maine and Spiny. Maine lobsters are the most prized and are mainly harvested off the northeastern seaboard. It is an excellent flavored lobster and the meat, when cooked, is a snow-white color. A smaller lobster but still a popular one is the Spiny lobster, which can be identified by the smaller claws. Never purchase a lobster, unless you see movement in the claws or if their tail turns under them when carefully touched.

Why are There Rubber Bands on Lobsters' Claws?

Rubber bands are placed on lobsters' claws to protect the lobsters from hurting each other. When lobsters are placed in close areas, they tend to fight and since they are very carnivorous, will eat each other.

Which is Best, Male or Female Lobsters?

Female lobsters have more meat than male lobsters and their meat is sweeter. Females also have the coral roe, which is sought after by many lobster lovers. To determine the sex of a lobster, just turn the lobster over and look between the juncture of the tail and the body. If the protrusions are soft, the lobster is a female, if they are rough it is a male.

Cuddle 'em

Before you start to tear a lobster apart, make sure you cover it with a towel so that the juices don't squirt out.

Lobsters May Be an Endangered Species

High tech lobster traps are getting so efficient that by 2005, lobsters may end up on the endangered species list. In Maine, 37 million lbs. of lobsters were captured and sent to market, the biggest season haul ever. This over-fishing may cause Maine to issue licenses that limit the number of lobsters a person can catch in a season.

Use the Microwave

Lobster should be added to dishes just before serving in order to retain their flavor. Overcooking is the biggest problem in retaining the taste of lobster.

Keeping the Tail Straight

Lobster tails have the tendency to curl up when they are cooked. To avoid this problem, just place a bamboo skewer through the back of the tail and out the front. When the skewer is removed, the tail will stay straight.

What Does the Newburg Mean in Lobster Newburg?

The "Newburg" is any seafood dish means that the recipe contains a special cream sauce that includes sherry. The name "Newburg" refers to a Scottish fishing village called "Newburg." The dish was first introduced in the early 1900s in the U.S. and has remained a popular way of serving lobster. Most restaurants tend to purchase the Spiny lobster for these types of dishes, since they are the least expensive.

A Left-Handed Lobster

Believe it or not, Maine lobsters may be either right or left-handed. They are not symmetrical with identical sides. The two claws are different and are used differently, one is larger with very coarse teeth for crushing, and the other has fine teeth for ripping or tearing. Depending on which side the larger, coarse-teethed claw is on will determine whether the lobster is right or left-handed. However, the flesh found in the smaller, fine-toothed claw is sweeter and more tender.

Can a Lobster Be Microwaved?

Microwave lobster is actually the preferred method in many of the better restaurants. The taste and texture are far superior to boiled or steamed lobster. Microwave allows all the natural juices to be retained. The color of the lobster is better as well. The problem some restaurants have is that it takes too many microwave ovens to handle a large volume of business. To microwave a lobster, you need to place the lobster in a large microwave plastic bag and knot it loosely. A $1^1/_2$-lb. lobster should take about 5-6 minutes on high power, providing you have a 600-to-700 watt oven. If you have a lower wattage oven, allow about 8 minutes. To be sure that the lobster is fully cooked, just separate the tail from the body and if the tomalley (mushy stuff in cavity) has turned green, the lobster is fully cooked.

Lobster must still be cooked live due to the enzymatic breakdown action problem, which occurs immediately upon their death. If you are bothered by the lobster's movements when cooking, which is just reflex, then place the lobster in the freezer for 10 minutes to dull its senses and it will only have a reflex reaction for about 20 seconds.

Why Lobsters Turn Red When Boiled

The red coloring was always there. However, it is not visible until the lobster is boiled. The lobster, along with other shellfish and some insects, have an external skeleton, which is made up of "chitin." Chitin contains a bright red pigment called "astaxanthin," which is bonded to several proteins. While the chitin is bonded, it remains a brownish-red color; however, when the protein is heated by the boiling water, the bonds are broken, releasing the astaxanthin and the exo-skeleton turns a bright red color.

Lobster Liver, a Delicacy?

Shellfish lovers seem to think that a special treat is to consume the green "tomalley" or liver found in lobsters or the "mustard" found in crabs. These organs are similar to our livers and are involved in deto-xifying and filtering toxins out of the shellfish. Many of these organs do retain a percentage of the toxins and possibly even some PCB's or heavy metal contaminants. Since in most instances, you are not aware of the areas these crustaceans are found, you should never eat these organs. However, the roe (coral) found in female lobsters is safe to eat. Lobster roe (eggs) are a delicacy in many countries.

Staying Alive!

To keep a lobster alive for up to 1 week, just soak a few pieces of newspaper in cool water, then wrap the lobster up by rolling it in the newspaper. Make sure that the lobster is completely enclosed and refrigerate it.

Bitter Lobster

Lobsters and crabs have very potent digestive enzymes, which will immediately start to decompose their flesh when they die. Both should be kept alive until they are to be cooked. The complexity and location of their diges-tive organs make it too difficult to remove them. If you are uncertain as to whether a lobster is alive or dead, just pick it up and if the tail curls under the lobster, it's alive. Lobsters should never be placed into boiling water as a method of killing them. The best way is to sever the spinal cord at the base of the neck with the end of a knife; then place them into the water. In some restaurants, the lobster will be placed into a pot filled with beer for a few minutes to get them drunk before placing them into the boiling water.

MUSSELS

Rope me a Mussel

Aquaculture mussel farming has become big business in the U. S. Mussels are raised on rope ladders, which keep them away from any debris on the bottom. This produces a cleaner, healthier mussel, and reduces the likelihood of disease. When grown in this manner, they are also much larger. Be sure that the mussels are alive when purchased. Try tapping their shell, if they are open, the shell should snap closed; if not, they're probably a goner. When mussels are shucked, the liquid that comes out should be clear.

Open Wide
When you are cooking mussels, they will be done when their shell opens. If the shells remain closed, they should not be forced open and eaten.

Billi-Bl Soup from France
Prepared from mussels, white wine and cream and named for a regular patron of Maxim's Restaurant.

Double Decker
Live mussels, covered with a damp towel, may be stored for about 2-3 days on a tray in the refrigerator. Never place one on top of the other.

Cut off Their Beard and They Die
Mussels are a common shellfish that are enclosed in a bluish shell and are for the most part aquafarm-raised. They should always be purchased live and should be cleaned with a stiff brush under cold water. The visible "beard" needs to be removed; however, once they are de-bearded they will die.

OYSTERS

Oysters are considered a delicacy worldwide. Consumption is over 97 million lbs. annually with almost 60% produced by aquaculture farming methods. Oysters will have a distinct flavor and texture that will vary, depending on what part of the world they were harvested from.

Is an Oyster Safe to Eat in the Months Without an "R"?

This may have been true decades ago before refrigeration; however, there is really no medical evidence that shows it to be dangerous to eat oysters in any month of the year. However, oysters tend to be less flavorful and less meaty during the summer months, which do not have an "R" because it is the time of the year that they spawn.

Oysters Will Be Under Pressure

You will never have to wonder again if that oyster you just ate was safe to eat raw. A new processing system for fresh oysters is available that will use high pressure (45,000 psi) for one minute to zap any bacteria that might make you sick. The high-pressure treatment will also make them easier to shuck.

New Oyster-Breeding Techniques

To help oyster breeders produce an oyster that has more meat and a thinner shell, breeders will be asking scientists to develop a genetic map of the oyster so that they will grow faster and produce more meat and improve the taste. This will speed up the traditional breeding methods, which may take years to produce the desirable attributes growers would like.

Not All It's Cracked up to Be

If you purchase an oyster and the shell is broken or cracked, discard it. It may be contaminated.

Oysters: A Shellfish Game

Be cautious of oysters that are harvested from the Gulf of Mexico during June, July and August. These summer months are months when the oysters may be contaminated with bacteria called "Vibro vulnificus." Cooking the oysters will kill the bacteria; however, raw oysters can be deadly to people who suffer from diabetes, liver disease, cancer and some gastrointestinal disorders. The bacteria kills about 20 people a year. The FDA may require that all Gulf Coast oysters caught in the summer months be shucked and bottled with a warning not to consume them raw.

Keep 'em Cool

Store live oysters in the refrigerator in a single layer with the larger shell down and covered with a damp towel. They should be consumed within 3 days.

Special Liqueur for Oysters

When preparing oysters Rockefeller, you need to use "Herbsaint Liqueur," which is made just for use in the dish. It is an anise-flavored liqueur made in New Orleans.

Don't Eat old Oysters!

Shucked oysters will stay fresh frozen for up to 3 months, if they are stored in their liquid and only 1-2 days under refrigeration. Oysters should be scrubbed with a hard plastic bristle brush under cold water before shucking them.

Tough Guy

If you are poaching oysters, only poach them until their edges start to curl. Oysters are easy to overcook and get tough.

Pop Goes the Oyster

Oysters are easy to remove from their shell, if you just soak them in unflavored club soda for 5-10 minutes or until they open their shell to see what kind of weird solution you placed them in.

Cleanest Oysters in America

If you want to be sure of the breeding and cleanliness of the oysters you eat, better call (206) 875-5494, The Ekone Oyster Company. These oysters are aquacultured on an 80 acre farm and can be shipped either fresh or try the world's greatest smoked oysters.

Oysters Found Infected with Parasite

Oysters harvested from six different rivers feeding the Chesapeake Bay were found to harbor the parasite, "Cryptosporidium parvum." Some oysters were found to have as many as 4,000 parasite eggs. The parasite eggs do not survive, if the oysters are heated to a temperature of 165°F., which means that if the oysters are boiled or fried they will not pose any health risk.

SCALLOPS

A member of the shellfish family that has a very short life span after it has been removed from the water. They tend to become tough very easily, if they are overcooked. The varieties seem almost endless with over 400 varieties presently identified. Two types of scallops are available: the sea scallop, which is about 2 in. wide, and the bay scallop which is about $^1/_2$ in. wide. Bay scallops are the more tender of the two. They should be sold moist, not dried out and should never have a strong odor.

You'll Never See Scallops on the Half-Shell

There is a major difference in this bivalve from clams, lobsters and mussels in that it cannot close its shell to protect itself in a closed liquid environment. The scallop does have two shells; however, these shells never close tightly. Because of this, when they are caught, they are unable to protect their juices, allowing the juices to be released. When this occurs, the process of deterioration and enzymatic breakdown begins very quickly and therefore once they are caught, they must be shucked on the boat, the viscera thrown away and the muscle preserved on ice.

SHRIMP

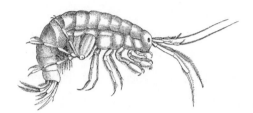

Shrimp are sold in a variety of sizes and will be classified on the package. Their size determines the number of shrimp per lb. The following is the size classification system used:

Extra Colossal	under 10 shrimp/lb.	Medium Large	36-40 shrimp/lb.
Colossal	under 15 shrimp/lb.	Medium	41-50 shrimp/lb.
Extra Jumbo	16-20 shrimp/lb.	Small	51-60 shrimp/lb.
Jumbo	21-25 shrimp/lb.	Extra Small	61-70 shrimp/lb.
Extra Large	26-30 shrimp/lb.	Tiny (bay shrimp)	Over 70 shrimp/lb.
Large	31-35 shrimp/lb.		

Shrimp have high water content and therefore will reduce down from 1 lb. to about $^3/_4$ of a lb. or less after cooking. Worldwide, there are over 250 species of shrimp of which the largest are called "prawns." Depending on where the shrimp feed and are caught, they may be found in a variety of colors from white, the more desirable color, to brown which mainly feed on algae and have a stronger flavor.

What is the Black Tube on a Shrimp's Back?

The intestinal tract of the shrimp can be found running the length of its back. It would be best to remove it, since it does harbor bacteria but is safe to eat if the shrimp is cooked, which will kill any bacteria. If you do eat it and you notice that the shrimp is somewhat gritty, it is because the intestinal tube remained intact, containing sand granules. De-veining the shrimp is relatively simple, all you have to do is run a small ice pick down the back and the tube will fall out.

De-Capitation a Must

Shrimp with heads are more perishable than those without heads. The head contains almost all its vital organs and the majority of the digestive system.

Is a Prawn a Shrimp or Is a Shrimp a Prawn?

Biologically, a prawn is different from a shrimp in that it has pincer claws similar to a lobster. A relative of the prawn is the scampi, both of which are considerably larger than the average shrimp. Restaurants in the U.S. rarely serve real prawns; they are just jumbo shrimp. Jumbo shrimp costs less than the giant prawns, but are not as tasty. If you do eat a "real" prawn, you will know the difference.

Good Advice

If shrimp develops a strong odor, it is probably ammonia, which means that the shrimp has started to deteriorate and if not cooked immediately, should be discarded. Shrimp cannot be re-frozen, and remember: almost all shrimp you buy has been frozen. This means that if you don't eat the shrimp that same day or possibly the next day, it should be thrown out.

Naughty, Naughty

A common problem with purchasing shrimp that has already been breaded is that a number of firms have been over-breading to increase the weight of the packages. The FDA has taken action against some companies for this practice.

Moderation is the Key

The cholesterol content of shrimp may be higher than most other fish; however, it is lower than any other type of meat product and does not contain a high level of saturated fat.

The Problem with Canning

If you purchase canned shrimp, always place the can into a pan of ice-cold water for about 1-2 hours before opening. This will usually eliminate the "off flavor" from the can. If canned taste still exists, try soaking the shrimp for 15 minutes in a mixture of lemon juice and cold water.

Tender Little Ones

Shrimp will always cook up nice and tender, if you cool them down before cooking them. Either place the shrimp into the freezer for 10-15 minutes or in a bowl of ice cubes and water for about 5 minutes. They should then be prepared by placing them into a warm pot (not over a hot burner), sprinkle with a small amount of sea salt, then pour boiling water over them and cover the pot. The larger shrimp cook in about 6 minutes, the average size ones are cooked in about 4 minutes and the small shrimp in about 2 minutes. The size of the shrimp should not affect their quality.

SQUID

Squid is a member of the shellfish family and may be sold as "calamari." It tends to become tough very easily when cooked and should only be cooked for 3 minutes for the best results. When adding squid to a cooked dish, it should be added toward the end of the cooking cycle when there is no more than 15 minutes left. Squid is the only shellfish that has more cholesterol than shrimp. The entire squid is edible. The squid has the largest eyes of any creature in the world.

"Yuk!"

The most unpopular foods among Americans are shark, squid and snails. Shark, however, is making a comeback, since people are finding out that it is a healthy, low-fat, good tasting fish.

Don't Overcook Shellfish

When you cook shellfish, try not and overdo it or they may become very tough. Clams, crab and lobster only need to be steamed for 5-10 minutes. Crayfish and mussels only need 4-8 minutes. Always remember to turn all shellfish except lobsters. Grilling an 8 ounce lobster tail only takes 10-12 minutes.

SALTWATER FISH

Anchovy

Anchovies are a popular poultry feed. Most of the over 200 million pounds caught annually are ground up and used for feed. Anchovies used for canning range in size from 3-5 inches. They are also used as a pizza topping and in "real" Caesar salad.

The Salt of the Sea

Anchovies can be desalted to some degree by soaking them in ice-water for about 15 minutes. They should then be placed into the refrigerator for another 45 minutes before adding them to a recipe.

- If you open a can of anchovies that are too salty, just rinse them in warm water before using them.
- Buy the best brands, since when it comes to anchovies, the lower the price, the lower the quality in all instances.
- Anchovies will last about 2 months under refrigeration after the can is opened and up to 1 year without refrigeration in a sealed can, due to their high salt content. Opened ones should be kept covered with olive oil.
- If you use anchovies in any dish, taste the dish before adding any further seasoning.

Pass the Paste

Anchovy paste is simply ground up anchovy fillets. They are then blended with salt and sugar and packaged in 2 oz. tubes.

Anglerfish (Lotte)

The angler species of fish may include several other unusual varieties, such as bellyfish, goosefish, sea devil, and monkfish. They have a relatively firm texture and are all low-fat. Monkfish are appearing on menus and are mainly used as a substitute for lobster, since the only part that is worth eating is the tail. Anglerfish can weigh from as little as 3 lbs. to as high as 25 lbs. They are more popular in France than in the U.S.

Barracuda

Weighs in at an average of 6.5 lbs. and is a moderately fat fish, usually caught in the Pacific Ocean. Most barracuda have very toxic flesh, due to their type of diet. The only edible variety is the Pacific barracuda.

Blue-Fish

This fish tends to deteriorate very rapidly and does not even freeze well. They usually weigh around 5 lbs. and have a thin strip of flesh running down its middle that should be removed before cooking or it may affect the flavor.

Cod

Cod is one of the lower-fat fishes with a very firm texture. Three varieties may be found in the fish market: Atlantic cod, Pacific cod and scrod. The scrod are the smallest of the cod family. As a substitute for cod, you might try the cuskfish, which is excellent for soups or chowders and has a taste similar to cod.

Croaker

All varieties are low fat except for the corvina. Croakers are a small fish, usually weighing in at around $\frac{1}{4}$ to $\frac{1}{2}$ lbs. and up to over 30 lbs., if you are lucky enough to catch a redfish. They are popular fish for making chowder.

Eel

Popular in Japan and in some European countries more than the U.S. It is a firm-textured tasty fish that resembles a snake and can grow to 3-4 feet long. The skin must be removed before cooking since it is very tough.

Flounder

This is the most popular fish sold in the markets and may appear as "sole." There are over 100 varieties and has a mild flavor and nice light texture. It is one of the low-fat fishes and weighs in anywhere from 1-10 lbs. Dover sole may be found on a menu and is imported from England. These are safer if they are aquacultured, since they are scavenger fish.

Grouper

These are also known as "sea bass" and can weigh up to 25 lbs. Before cooking, be sure and remove the skin. The skin is similar to the eel skin and is very tough. Grouper has a firm texture and is an easy fish to cook either baked or fried.

Haddock

Related to the cod and usually caught in the North Atlantic. A common smoked form of the fish is sold in markets and called "Finnan Haddie." The flesh of haddock will be somewhat softer than cod, which is a close relative.

Hake

An Atlantic Ocean fish that has a firm texture and is relatively low fat. It has a mild flavor and usually weighs in at about 3-7 lbs.

Halibut

Similar to a flounder with low fat, firm, texture. Normally weighs in at a healthy 15-20 lbs. and marketed as steaks or fillets. Can replace the more expensive salmon in most recipes.

Herring

Normally sold pickled or smoked, it is a high-fat fish with a very fine texture. When caught, they only weigh-in at around $^3/_4$ lb. Sardines are a member of the herring family. The best quality sardine is the Norwegian bristling. Norwegian sardines are the best source of omega-3 fatty acids, next to Chinook salmon. Their scales are pulverized and used in the cosmetic industry and they usually end up as an appetizer.

Mackerel

This high fat, relatively oily fish is similar to tuna. You may find it under a variety of names, such as Atlantic mackerel, Wahoo, Pacific Jack, Kingfish or Spanish Mackerel. It may be sold canned in a red meat variety and has an excellent level of omega-3 fatty acids. Best cooked in an acid marinade, using white vinegar.

Mahi Mahi

Even though it has been called the "dolphin fish," it is not related to the dolphin. There is a slight resemblance but the greenish color gives it its own unique look. These may weigh up to 40 lbs. and are one of the best eating fishes caught in Hawaiian and Florida waters. Usually sold as steaks or fillets.

Mullet

The majority of mullet is caught off the coast of Florida. It has an unusually firm texture and a relatively mild flavor. The flesh can be found in a variety of light and dark meats. It is somewhat oily and good for barbecuing.

Orange Roughy

Almost all orange roughy is imported from New Zealand and is a low-fat fish. The taste is slightly sweet and it has a texture similar to sole. May be cooked by any method and when imported normally comes in frozen fillets.

Perch

A true perch is only caught in freshwater; however, the ocean perch that is sold is really a rockfish. Perch is relatively low fat with a fairly firm texture. The majority of perch sold in the U.S. comes from the Great Lakes. Perch weigh-in at about 1-2 lbs. and are available fresh or frozen.

Pollack

Pollack is mainly used for fish sticks and surimi. It has a firm texture and a rich flavor. The darker layer of the flesh is not as mild as the lighter flesh. A very common fish used in chowders.

Pompano

Found mainly off the coast of Florida and has recently been affected by over-fishing, making it one of the more expensive fishes. It is an oily, firm textured fish, sometimes called a Boston bluefish, which it is not related to.

Sablefish

The sablefish is commonly called the "black cod." It has a high fat content, but a very light texture. Commonly found smoked, but can also be prepared by baking, poaching or frying.

Salmon

This is by far one of the tastiest fish you will ever eat. The fattest salmon is the Chinook (king salmon). The Coho salmon have less fat and are a smaller variety. The lower quality are the Sockeye and Pink salmon. Coho salmon deposit about 2,500 eggs during their 5 days of spawning.

White Lox

More and more salmon are being farm-raised, which may mean that the color of salmon may someday be white, instead of salmon-colored. The farm-raised salmon are not exposed to the same food supply in a pen that they are in the wild. Fish farmers are now adding synthetic pigments to the farm-raised salmon's food supply to make the color salmon.

Smoked Salmon or Lox and Parasites?

Good news for bagel and lox lovers! Smoked salmon, Lox, or Nova that are commercially processed should pose no health threat. When processed, Lox is heavily salted. Nova is salmon that originally came from Nova Scotia and is not as heavily salted. According to researchers at the Center for Disease Control and the FDA, no cases of parasitic contamination, has ever been reported in Lox or Nova. Occasionally, parasites are found in wild salmon but almost all the Lox sold in the U.S. is aquacultured. Cold-smoked salmon is always kept frozen, which will kill any parasites.

Salmon (Russian) Roulette

If you are a sushi lover and eat salmon, be aware that raw salmon has a 10% chance of being contaminated with the parasite roundworm "anisakis." This information comes from a FDA report, regarding samples taken from over 30 sushi bars.

Sardines

Sardines are an excellent source of calcium. In only $3^{1}/_{2}$ oz., they contain more calcium than an 8 oz. glass of milk. Milk has vitamin D added to help metabolize the calcium, while the sardines also supply vitamin D and phosphorus. Ounce for ounce, sardines can also supply you with more protein than a steak.

Sea Trout

These trout are usually caught off the shores of Georgia and the Carolina's. They are somewhat fatty, but have a good solid texture and are good for baking or broiling.

Shad

One of the fattier fishes and excellent for barbecuing. It is usually cooked whole with just the entrails removed, since it is very hard to fillet. The roe (fish eggs) is one of the more highly prized caviar.

Shark

The whale shark is the largest fish in the ocean. Sharks have intelligence and can learn equal to that of rats and birds. Sharks have been around for over 350 million years, which is 100 million years before the dinosaurs. Sharks have no bones and their skeletal structure is made up of cartilage, which is softer than bone. Shark flesh is becoming more and more popular everyday, since it is a tasty, low-fat fish with an excellent level of nutrients. There are 368 species of shark that have been identified to date.

If the Sharks Wink, Look Out
The shark is the only fish that has the ability to blink with both eyes.

Mmmm, Mmmmmm, Good
If you go to China, you will find shark fin soup a popular menu item at around $59 per bowl. In Hong Kong, herb shops sell dried shark fins for up to $66 per lb. At the rate sharks are being fished, they may become an endangered species within the next 20 years. In 2002, over 126 million sharks were caught.

Better Ger a Bigger Net
The largest shark in the world is the whale shark at about 60 ft. long.

Skate
A relative of the shark family, it has rays or wings, which are the most edible part of the fish. The taste is similar to scallops and the meat looks like crab meat because of the striations. Try to buy skate that does not have an odor of ammonia.

Swordfish
Has been found to contain high levels of mercury in its flesh and is not recommended as one of the safer fish to eat, unless you know that they have been caught well off shore. Usually sold in boneless loins and is excellent for barbecuing. It has a good flavor and fairly firm texture.

Three Cheers for the Chefs
Since swordfish are close to becoming extinct, many chefs all over America are now refusing to prepare swordfish until it is more readily available and the over-fishing stops.

Tuna
When purchasing tuna, make sure you purchase the best grade, which is the "albacore white." The other classes of tuna are darker in color and have a stronger flavor and aroma. They may be labeled light, dark or blended. These tuna are also very oily and usually higher in calories even if water-packed. Some brands use other types of fish in a related family and sell them as just "tuna." These fish include bonita, bluefin tuna and skipjack. Bluefin tuna may weigh up to 1,000 lbs. When tuna is packed in oil, it is sometimes called "Tonno Tuna."

Never Buy Fresh Tuna Packed On Ice
Contact with ice tends to bleed out the color, nutrients and the flavor. Frozen tuna is fine and is usually frozen when it is caught retaining the flavor. Yellowfin is best!

There's a Catch to This Fish Story

You probably think that if you purchase tuna in water, it will have fewer calories than the type that is packed in oil. Well, the truth is that albacore tuna may have a fat content that will vary by as much as 500%. Tuna manufacturers always try to use low-fat tuna in their product with about 1-gram of fat per serving. However, when the demand for the product gets extremely high, they have to resort to packaging the higher fat albacore, which contains 4-5 grams of fat per serving. Best to check the label.

Pack it in

Solid-pack is tuna composed of the loins with the addition of a few flakes. Chunk tuna may have parts of the tougher muscle structure, while flake tuna has mostly muscle structure and smaller bits all under $^1/_2$ in. Grated tuna is as close to a paste product as you can buy. If the chemical "pyrophosphate" (a preservative) appears on the label, it would be best not to buy the tuna.

Saving Flipper

Choosing tuna for tuna salad is more a matter of taste than the type of tuna. If you have noticed that tuna in cans is darker than it used to be, you're right. The reason is that smaller nets are being used so that the porpoises won't be netted. This means that the larger tuna won't be netted either. The smaller tuna has the darker meat.

Numero Uno

In 2004, Tuna was still ranked as the most popular fish sold in the U.S. Shrimp came in an easy second, while cod was third and Alaskan pollack next, due to its use in imitation shrimp and crabmeat. Americans consume about 4 lbs. of tuna per person annually.

Is Canned Tuna Safe to Eat?

A study performed in 1992 and reported in Consumer Reports stated that tuna, for the most part, is safe to eat. Only a few insect parts were found and the level of mercury was too low to be a health threat. However, in 1997 sulfides were reported in white albacore tuna and a warning was issued for persons allergic to sulfides not to consume that type of tuna. In 2002, tuna was declared to be one of the safest canned fish products, when compared to other fish canned products.

FRESHWATER FISH

Buffalo Fish

A common fish caught in the Mississippi River and the Great Lakes region of the U.S. It has a fairly firm texture and has enough fat that it can be barbecued. The average weight is around 4-6 lbs.

Carp

Used to make "Gefilte fish." It is a scavenger fish that may carry a degree of contamination. They should only be purchased if the label says that they are raised on a fish farm. Extremely difficult to skin and should be purchased as a fillet.

Catfish

Catfish is one of the more popular and tasty fish. Since they are scavengers, 85% are presently aquacultured in the U.S.

- They are low-fat fish with a relatively firm texture and not that good for barbecuing.
- If catfish smells "fishy" it is best not to buy it.
- The flesh should be white with no signs of blood sores.
- Since catfish has no connective tissue, it does not have to be cooked long to be tender.
- Catfish will dry out very easily if cooked too long.
- Catfish will only last 2-3 days in the refrigerator.

Pike

If you can find a Walleyed Pike, it is an excellent eating fish. They have literally been fished out of existence and should be on the endangered list until they make a comeback.

Smelt

One of the smallest fish, it is usually eaten whole with just the entrails removed. Best prepared pan-fried. They are high-fat fish with a firm texture.

Sturgeon

Sturgeon caviar (roe) is one of the finest. These fish can weigh up to 1,500 lbs. and are the largest of all freshwater fish. They are high fat and excellent for barbecuing. About 65% of the calories in sturgeon caviar are from fat.

Trout

Trout is one of the most common fish caught in the U.S. next to catfish. The most popular variety of trout is the rainbow trout, which is one of the tastiest fish. Almost all trout sold has been raised on fish farms.

Whitefish

A relative of the trout, it is also one of the best eating fish. It is high fat and best barbecued, broiled or baked. Commonly found in abundance in the Great Lakes. All fish purchased in supermarkets should be labeled Grade A.

CAVIAR

Beluga

Comes from the Beluga sturgeon from the Caspian Sea. The roe (eggs) range in size, but are usually pea-sized and silver-gray to black. This is the most popular in the U.S. There are two common varieties sold: Royal beluga, which has the best color, size and flavor and beluga.

Ossetra

Somewhat smaller than the Beluga, the color is a gray to brownish-gray. Derived from the smaller ossetra sturgeon. Has a nutty flavor and is somewhat saltier.

Sevruga

Even smaller than the ossetra, gray in color and has the smallest grain of the caviar. Has a strong flavor.

Caviar De Gironde

This caviar is from farm-raised French sturgeon from the Bordeaux region. The eggs are medium-sized and dark gray in color. The caviar has a delicate flavor and is not too salty.

Caviar D' Acquitaine

Caviar is from farm-raised sturgeon and similar to the ossetra, but with a very smooth finish and delicate flavor.

Tennessee Black

Caviar from a smaller sturgeon that is a relative of the Caspian Sea sturgeon and is smaller, ranging in color from gray to black with an excellent flavor.

Whitefish, Lumpfish and Salmon

This is the least expensive caviar, sometimes called "red caviar." Salmon roe is considered "sushi grade." It is low salt with a somewhat sweet flavor.

CAVIAR FACTS

Keep the Flavor

If you see the Russian word "malossol" on the caviar container, it means that only a small amount of salt was used to process it. This caviar will not have a long shelf life. Caviar loses much of its flavor and texture when cooked. Best to eat it cold. Caviar should be stored in the refrigerator and will last for 1 month if the temperature is about 28°F.

Very Expensive Cure

In many European countries, caviar has been used to treat hangovers due to its acetylcholine content.

The Right Utensils are a Must

Using the correct utensils helps to avoid damage to the delicate eggs. Never serve caviar on a metal platter.

What is "Pressed Caviar?"

Contains damaged and fragile eggs from a number of different fish, but is less expensive than caviar with all whole roe.

FISHY FACTS

Smells Fishy

Before handling fish, try washing your hands in plain cold water. Chances are you won't have a fish smell on them afterwards. A small amount of white vinegar placed into the pan you have fried fish in will eliminate the odor.

Sniff, Sniff, Smells Fishy

The seafood industry will be using an "electronic fish sniffer." The "sniffer" will sniff out bad seafood, before it is placed in the food case for sale. The accuracy is said to be almost 100% effective. The sensors in the "sniffer" will detect odor molecules. The "sniffer" will also be used to detect bacteria in wounds and to evaluate the quality of teas and coffee. These "electronic noses" will eventually replace almost all seafood inspectors. A digital visual inspection camera is also being researched. The University of Florida is doing this research.

The Deadly Fish (Arothronhispidus)
The "Death Puffer" is one of the most toxic fishes in the ocean. The stomach, liver and blood contain a poison that is deadly to humans, even the slightest trace of the poison will kill a person. However, the puffer fish is a delicacy in Japan and must be prepared by specially trained "Fugu" chefs who have learned the secret of preparation.

Cold Fish
When fish is frozen, it tends to lose some of its flavor. If you place the frozen fish in low-fat milk when it is thawing, some of the original flavor will return. It is recommended by chefs not to completely thaw a frozen fish before cooking, since the fish might become mushy. Frozen fish is easier to skin than a fresh one.

Taste Bud Treat
If you are going to bake fish, try wrapping it in aluminum foil with a sprig of dill and a small amount of chopped onion. Another method is to wrap the fish in a piece of well-oiled cheesecloth. This will make it easier to remove the fish from the pan.

Mild Acid to the Rescue
If you need to scale a fish, try rubbing white vinegar on the scales and then allow it to sit for about 10 minutes.

New Invention to Test Saltiness of Fish
A new machine has been invented that will accurately determine the level of salt in fish without killing the fish and analyzing the contents. The machine called a "near infrared spectrophotometer" has an optical-fiber probe that touches the scales of the fish and is capable of recording the volume of water and fat in the fish. From this information an accurate salt level is determined, which assists in the production of smoked fish and caviar.

Jack Frost Foiled By a Fish
Every year millions of dollars worth of valuable crops are destroyed by frost damage. Fish are able to tolerate extreme cold temperatures, which make genetic modification of fish genes that can be transferred into plants important. This will allow the plants to obtain a degree of protection against frost. While this should be possible by 2005, scientists are not sure if the public will accept mixing animal and plant genes.

Big Difference

Saturated fat only accounts for 10-25% of the total fat in seafood compared to an average of 42% in beef and pork.

Cooking Contaminants

Fish that feed on the bottom of lakes, such as Carp and Bass have a higher risk of becoming contaminated. However, cooking will neutralize most of the contaminants, which tend to be located in the skin and fat.

Have Your Rod and Reel Ready

If you are not sure if a fish is really fresh, place it in cold water. If it floats or swims away, it's fresh.

Aquafarms are Thriving

More fish will be raised on aquafarms than ever before. The latest fish to be hybrid and grown for food are salmon, striped bass and sturgeon. Trout and catfish are already being farmed. However, a problem is expected to arise in a few years. The waste from all these fish farms and the drugs used to keep the fish healthy may be polluting the areas around the farms and even the groundwater.

Carp to Be Aquacultured

Carp, which has been a popular eating fish in Asia for centuries, is coming to the U.S. in a big way. They will be aquacultured in the same ponds as catfish and will not compete with the catfish since they consume the algae and not the catfish food. The canned carp will start appearing in supermarkets and will be about the same price as canned tuna. The big head carp has lower fat content than white meat tuna packed in water with 40% of the fat as omega-3 fatty acids.

Fish from the Amazon

A number of new fish species that we are not used to will be showing up in trendy restaurants. These fish include tambacqui, filhote and caparari. These are firm-meat fish that can pass for pork when prepared properly. We are hoping by purchasing these fish, we can help the Amazonian economy and save a small amount of the rain forest.

Safety First

When marinating fish, it should always be done under refrigeration. Fish decomposes rapidly at temperatures above 60°F.

Firming up

If you would like to have a firmer texture to fillets, just soak the fillet in a bowl with 1 qt. water and 2 tbsp. white vinegar mixed in.

Fish and Shellfish Tenderizer

A number of fish and shellfish may need a bit of tenderizing, which can be done by soaking the seafood in 5 parts of vinegar to 1 part of water for about 8 hours. Salmon, oysters, lobster and abalone respond well to this method of mild-acid tenderizing. Make sure you rinse off the vinegar well before cooking.

The Steamy Side of Fish

When steaming fish, it should be wrapped in a piece of plain (no design) moistened paper towel. Place the fish in the microwave for 2-3 minutes on each side.

Dial the Fish Hotline 1(305) 361-4619

The majority of fish caught in the oceans are safe. However, in the warmer waters it would be best to call the fish hotline to be sure that the type of fish you are going to catch does not have a problem with "ciguatera." This is a cause of a number of cases of fish food poisoning.

Need a Big Freezer

Fish can be frozen in clean milk cartons full of water. When thawing, use the water as a fertilizer for your houseplants.

Preservation

Fish should always be cooked at a relatively low temperature to retain its moisture and provide a more, tender product. Fish dries out very quickly and should never be cooked at temperatures exceeding 350°F.

Pressure Test

To test a cooked fish to see if it is finished cooking, try pressing your finger on the side of the fish. No dent should remain; however, the fish may flake under the pressure.

Never Overcook

When cooking fish in a microwave, many manufacturers suggest that the fish be cooked at 50% power for more even cooking. Check your instruction manual for your particular microwave oven.

Moderation, if You're Pregnant

Studies state that pregnant women should not consume fish with high possible contamination problems. A number of tuna canneries tend to use Bonita in place of tuna in the less expensive brands. Bonita caught in the Pacific Ocean may contain PCB's. Another popular fish, white croakers, have also been found to contain PCB's as well as DDT. Eating fish twice a week is probably safe. However, if the fish are aquacultured there should be no problem. The healthiest and safest fish to eat are salmon, halibut, sole, skipjack tuna, and aquacultured catfish, trout and turbot.

To Sushi or not to Sushi

There is a risk of sushi containing the larva of a parasite called "anisakis," a roundworm. Violent pains set in about 12 hours after ingestion; however, some symptoms may not show up for at least a week. For safety sake, all fish prepared for use in sushi should be either cooked to an internal temperature of 140°F. or at least frozen for 3 days at -50°F. to kill any larva that might be present. Also, consuming raw fish too frequently may cause you to be deficient in a number of B vitamins. Raw fish contains an enzyme that tends to affect the absorption of these vitamins.

Contamination Possible?

The majority of all fish consumed in the U.S. is imported from over 100 foreign countries. Most of these countries have no inspection and poor sanitary conditions in the processing plants. When the fish enter the U.S., only 5-10% are ever inspected. In the U.S. we only have about 325 fish inspectors to inspect over 2,000 processing facilities and over 67,000 fishing vessels.

How Dry I am

If you are going to broil, barbecue or grill fish, be sure and purchase fish steaks that are at least 1 inch thick. Fish will dry out very quickly and the thicker the better, especially for barbecuing. The skin should be left on fillets when grilling, then remove it after cooking. When frying fish, make sure that the surface of the fish is dry.

Love me Tender.....

Fish only needs to be cooked for a very short time. Fish is naturally tender. However, if you overcook it, you will loose some of the flavor.

More Bounce to the Ounce

Saltwater fish have thicker, more dense bones than freshwater fish, which have thin, minuscule bones. The reason for this is that saltwater has more buoyancy. If you hate fighting the bones, purchase saltwater fish, such as cod and flounder.

What are Angels on Horseback?

"Angels on Horseback" are appetizers made by wrapping bacon around a shucked oyster, then cooking it. It is then served on toast and accompanied by a lemon wedge or hollandaise sauce.

Fishercise

Fish caught in rivers will have more flavor since they must swim against the currents, thus exercising more than lake fish. For this reason, trout are one of the best eating fishes. Cooler water fishes also have a higher fat content, which tends to make them more flavorful.

Red Spots are not Measles

If you see red spots on fish filets, it means that the fish has been bruised and has been handled roughly. This may occur from roughly throwing the fish around when it is caught or if it is poorly filleted. Too many bruises may affect the flavor of the fillet by causing deterioration of the surrounding flesh.

What About all Those Omegas?

Researchers at Harvard University tracked 45,000 men and their dietary habits in relation to eating fish. They found that the heart attack rates for men who ate fish six times per week was the same as those who ate fish approximately twice per month.

Tender Fish

Fish and shellfish do not have the extensive connective tissue that is found in land animals. Since the amount is small, it doesn't take a lot of cooking to gelatinize the connective tissue with moist heat. If you overcook fish, it will toughen the muscle fibers. A fish will be more tender when cooked, if you leave the head and tail on. This will cause more of the liquid to be retained during the cooking process.

Robot Sushi Chef

The Japanese have developed a robotic sushi chef that is capable of producing 1,200 pieces of sushi in one hour. The record of 200 pieces prepared in one hour is held by a Japanese sushi chef under ideal conditions. The sushi chef robot costs about $69,000.

What Fish are Aquacultured in the U.S.?

Aquaculture or fish farming originated in 2,000 B.C. in China. The first fish to be farmed was carp. China and Japan presently lead the world in aquacultured fish farms with the U.S. coming in fifth. At present, almost 94% of all trout sold in supermarkets and fish markets are aquacultured. In 2003, farmed fish will totaled over 2.1 billion lbs., about 20% of the nation's seafood. There are 3,723 fish farms in 28 states raising catfish, salmon, striped bass, sturgeon, tilapia and trout. Over 477 million pounds of catfish are marketed annually and 18 million lbs. of salmon.

Porcupine Fish - A Japanese Delicacy, or a Potent Poison?

This fish may go by a number of names, including Fugu fish, Pufferfish or Balloon fish. However, it may contain a very potent poison, "tetradotoxin," which is concentrated in the liver, ovaries, and testes. If the poison is eaten, the person may experience numbness of the lips, tongue, and fingertips with death following in a few hours. In Japan, chefs who prepare the fish must be licensed by the government and are trained to discard the poisonous organs.

Should Fresh Fish Be De-Gilled?

If the fish is caught fresh and prepared shortly afterwards, then it is not necessary to remove the gills. However, if the fish is more than 24 hours old, the gills should be removed. The gills tend to spoil faster than the rest of the fish and the overall flavor is affected.

Seafood Poisoning

Seafood is becoming more and more of a problem. The consumer hardly ever knows where the seafood is coming from and whether it is contaminated or not. Two types of poisoning are the most prevalent: "mytilotoxism," which is found in mollusks, clams and oysters, since these filter feeders may feed on microorganism that are toxic, and "ciguatera," which may be found in any type of seafood. Both types are serious enough to either make you very ill or kill you. Commercial fisherman have a better idea where the safe fishing beds are located. A person who is just out fishing in a river or lake and not aware of any contamination that may be present is at high risk in many areas of the U.S.

Fish Spoilage and Storage

The sooner a fish is gutted the better. The enzymes in a fish's gut tend to breakdown fish very quickly, if allowed to remain for too long a period. They are very aggressive and very powerful, which is one reason why fish is easier to digest than any other form of meat. When storing fish, you need to remember that the muscle tissue in fish is high in glycogen, which is their energy source. When the fish is killed, this carbohydrate is converted into lactic acid, which is usually an excellent preservative; however, the fish tends to use up too much of its energy source thrashing around when it is caught, trying to escape. Another problem with lengthy storage is that certain bacteria tend to be located outside of the digestive tract, unlike that of beef and will remain active even below the freezing point.

Never Flip Your Fillet

Fillets are so thin that they cook through in a very short period of time. The meat of the fillet is also so delicate that it has the tendency to flake apart when over cooked or if it is even turned. To avoid the fillet sticking to the pan, just use a liquid oil spray.

Adding an Acid, A Must When Poaching Fish

When poaching fish, the contents of the pot are usually somewhat on the alkali side and may react with a pigment in the flesh of the fish, known as "flavone." If this is allowed to occur, the flesh may become yellow, instead of the desired white color. If you add a small amount of wine, lemon juice, or other acid to the pot, it will neutralize the alkalinity and render the "flavone" harmless. If the mixture turns slightly acidic, it will actually whiten the meat more than it would normally be. Also, when poaching fish, keep the fish in single layers and be sure that the poaching liquid reaches the top of the fish.

How Can You Tell if a Fish is Fully Cooked?

The flesh of a fish is normally translucent. When it turns opaque and a solid white color, it means that the protein has coagulated and the fish is fully cooked. If you wish to be really sure, you will have to cut into the center at the thickest part with a fork. If the flesh flakes, it means that there was sufficient heat to gelatinize the collagen in the "myocommata" (fish connective tissue). Fish flesh contains very thin, parallel rows of muscle fibers that are held together by the connective tissue. It is these separate sheets of muscle fibers that flake.

Never Fish from a Bridge!

One of the more popular locations for people to fish is from a bridge near the highway. Fishermen in the know will never fish from a highway bridge because of the auto exhaust pollution, as well as the garbage that is thrown off the bridge by the passersby. Waters near bridges are polluted to such a degree that many are already posted with "No Fishing" signs. Fishermen think that the signs are posted to protect the fishermen from the passing cars, when it is actually to save them from becoming ill.

Hot Plate Special

Fish tends to cool very quickly and should be served on warm plates or on a warmed server.

SNAILS

Snails are considered a fair source of protein and are cultivated in the U.S. and Europe on snail farms. Fresh snails have been a gourmet treat for hundreds of years in Europe. If you have a recipe calling for snails, fresh snails must be trimmed and cooked before they can be used in a recipe to replace canned snails.

Yum, Yum

Fresh snails should always be cooked the day they are purchased and should be kept in the refrigerator until you prepare them.

Snail Stuffing

When purchasing snails in a gourmet shop, the shells will be separated from the snails. The shell should be cleaned before using them by boiling them for 30 minutes in a solution of 1 qt. water, 3 tbsp. baking soda, and 1 tbsp. sea salt. Make sure that you dry the insides of the shell before using them, with a hair dryer if necessary. Commercially purchased snail shells may be reused as long as they are boiled (as instructed) after each use and again, before adding the new snails.

Secret Breading Formula for Oven-Fried Fish

1 cup self-rising cornmeal
1/2 cup self-rising flour
3/4 tsp. table salt
1/2 tsp. powdered white pepper
1/3 tsp. cayenne pepper (optional)

1/4 tsp. garlic salt
2 tbsp. peanut oil
1 large egg
1 tsp. cool tap water

Use a small bowl and prepare an egg wash by mixing 1 large egg with 1 tsp. water. In another bowl, place the cornmeal, flour, salt, pepper, cayenne pepper and garlic salt and blend well. This breading recipe will bread about 2 lbs. of fillets. Rinse the fillets and pat dry, then place them into the refrigerator for about 30 minutes. Next, place the fillets in the egg wash, then the breading mix before placing them on the prepared cookie sheet. Prepare the cookie sheet by spreading the peanut oil evenly on the sheet. The oven should be pre-heated to 375°F. Cook the fillets 5 minutes on each side.

Chef's Secrets

- Placing the fillets in the refrigerator helps the breading adhere better.
- Peanut oil tends to bring out the flavor of fish and not overpower it.
- Powdered pepper will not cause the breading to crack.
- Make sure the egg wash coats the fish well or the coating may separate.
- For even cooking, never crowd the fillets on the cookie sheet.
- Use cookie sheet with at least 1 in. sides for even heat reflection.

Fat reduction tips: Spray pan with oil lightly. Use egg substitute.

Sodium reduction tips: Use salt-substitute or onion powder. Use garlic powder instead of the garlic salt.

Recommended fish: Perch and trout

The fisherman's formula for catfish fillets

First the breading: then the cooking.
1 large egg
1 cup buttermilk
1/2 cup self-rising flour
1 1/2 cups cornmeal
1/2 tsp. sea salt
1/2 tsp. finely ground black pepper
1/2 tsp. cayenne pepper
2 1/2 cups canola oil (high smoke point oil for frying)

The breading will be enough for about 3 lbs. catfish. Wash the fish and pat dry before starting. Place the lightly beaten egg in a medium-sized bowl and whisk in the buttermilk. In the second bowl, mix the flour, sea salt, black pepper and cayenne pepper together, then place the cornmeal in a third bowl. The fish should be dipped in the egg mixture first, then into the flour and seasonings, then into the cornmeal last. Use a heavy iron skillet with high sides and make sure that the oil is 360°F. before adding the fillets. Frying should only take about 6-7 minutes.

Chef's Secrets

- Be sure not to allow the temperature of the oil to drop below 325°F.
- Always use self-rising flour.
- Cajun seasoning mix may be substituted for the cayenne and black pepper.
- Real buttermilk is best, but hard to find unless you have a dairy nearby.
- Make sure the cornmeal is very fresh for the best flavor in the breading.

Fat reduction tips: Use a Teflon-coated pan and spray with liquid oil. Do not use dairy buttermilk, just supermarket buttermilk. Use egg substitute.

Sodium reduction tips: Use salt substitute.

Recommended fish: Catfish

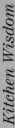

GENERAL FISH FRYING SECRETS

Always use the three-container method. The first one should contain regular flour, the second container, egg that has been whisked with milk, and the third with seasoned flour or cornmeal. The peanut oil should be between 350°F. and 360°F. and no more than 3 in. deep. When the temperature is this high, the cold fish will not cause the temperature to drop below 325°F. When the oil gets below 325°F., the breading has the tendency to absorb too much oil. When the fish is golden brown, remove it and place it on a piece of paper towel, patting both sides for a few seconds only, then place the fish on a wire rack or serve immediately. If the fish is not eaten or placed on the rack, it will begin to steam enough to cause the fish to become soggy.

How Sweet
IT IS!

General Information

American sugar intake per person in 1822 was 8.9 lbs. annually: presently it is 16 times that amount. The average daily refined sugar consumption per person in the U.S. is over 42 tsp. or 149 lbs. per year. For Valentine's Day 2002, over $704 million was spent on candy. It is hard to believe that we could eat so much sugar in a day, but sugar is hidden in many foods besides the sugar bowl. It can be found in thousands of foods. including soft drinks, candy, baked goods, toothpaste, cereals, etc. If you read the labels on foods, you will be surprised at the foods that contain one form of sugar or another.

Consuming excessive amounts of sugar can be a health hazard since sugar requires B vitamins and minerals to enable the body to metabolize it into glucose, yet it contains none of these. Therefore, it must steal nutrients away from other sites where the nutrients may be needed more. Sugar may also increase the rate at which we excrete the mineral calcium, making bones more fragile, as well as weakening the heart action. Sugar also requires chromium, which is crucial for the regulation of blood sugar levels.

COMMON SWEETENERS

Corn Syrup

Corn syrup is one of the most common liquid sweeteners due to its low production cost. It's produced from a mixture of starch granules derived from corn, which are then processed with acids or enzymes to convert it into heavy sweet syrup. The corn syrup is then artificially flavored and used for literally thousands of products, including pancake syrups, candy making, ice creams, etc. The fact that corn syrup tends to retard crystallization makes it a good choice for candy, preserves and frostings. Corn syrup does not store well and should be used by the date on the label.

Honey

Honey was first mentioned in the old writing of the Sumerians, Babylonians, the Hittite code, the sacred writings of India and the writings of the Egyptians. Palestine is often called the "land of milk and honey." During the 4th century B.C., the Egyptians used honey as a sweetener. By the 11th century A.D., the Germans were sweetening their beer with honey and honey was introduced to the American Colonies in 1638. The highest quality honey will be labeled "100% pure unfiltered," "raw," or "uncooked." This honey will not be nutrient-depleted by the heat processing.

Honey is a unique sugar in that it will not grow bacteria. It is the only food that has this unique quality; however, when using, it is twice as sweet as granulated sugar. Crystallized honey can be liquefied by just placing it into the microwave for about 1 minute, depending on the size of the jar and the wattage of the microwave. Never allow honey to boil or get too hot, since it will break down and must be discarded. 1 lb. of honey = 1 $\frac{1}{3}$ cups.

The Remarkable Honey Story

Bees gather honey by drawing the flower nectar into their proboscis (tube extending from their head). The nectar then passes through their esophagus into a honey sac (storage pod) located just before the intestine. The nectar is stored until the bee arrives back at the hive. While the nectar is in the sac, enzymes are secreted that begin to breakdown the starch into simple sugars and fructose. The bees' system also acts as a biologic filter and removes almost all traces of environmental toxins, such as exhaust emissions, pesticides, etc. This helps keep pollutants from entering the hive. The hive contains 1 mature queen, about 100 male drones, and 20,000 female workers. The bees utilize 8 lbs. of honey for daily activities for every one-lb. that reaches the market.

Bees must forage an equivalent of 3 times around the earth to provide sufficient nectar to make 1 lb. of honey, utilizing only 1 oz. for the trip. For 1 bee to fly around the world, it would only require 1 oz. of honey. Bees need to tap 2 million flowers and 55,000 miles to make just 1 lb. of honey. One honeybee will visit about 75 flowers every trip they make from the hive. For every gal. of honey the bee consumes, it travels 7 million miles, or 7 million miles to the gal., if you prefer. When the workers reach the hive, they pump and mix the nectar in and out of their proboscis until the carbohydrate concentration is about 50-60%, then it is deposited into the honeycomb. We consume about 1 lb. of honey per person annually in the U.S.

Types of Honey

Whole Comb- This is an unprocessed form, which comes directly from the hive. It can be purchased with the large waxy pieces floating in raw honey. The comb contains many unopened honey cells. The raw honey is from cells that were broken open when harvested.

Raw Honey- This is honey that has not been heat-processed and is in the original form harvested from the honeycomb. This product may contain insect parts and debris from the hive.

Filtered Honey- This is actually raw honey that has been heated just enough to allow the honey to pass through filters to remove the debris impurities. The heat is low enough to allow the honey to retain almost all of its nutrient values.

Liquid Honey- Liquid honey is heated to higher temperatures than any other processed honey so that it can be easily filtered. It is usually a lighter color and the flavor is somewhat milder than other types of honey. Because of the heat processing, the honey does not crystallize as easily as most other types of honey. Nutrients are for the most part lost in the processing of liquid honey.

Spun Honey (Crystallized)- This type of honey is not only heat-processed, but has a good percentage of its moisture removed to make it creamy and easy to spread. This honey lacks most nutrients that are associated with honey. It is just a sweet treat.

Creamed Honey- Honey that is produced by the crystallization of liquid honey under controlled conditions.

Pasteurized Honey- This honey has been high-heat processed to destroy yeasts, which can cause honey to ferment as well as melt the dextrose crystals that cause honey to granulate.

Dark Honey Better Than Light Honey

The University of Illinois has released information regarding the antioxidant levels in honey, which may surprise everyone who consumes honey. The honeybees' diet and where they forage for honey has importance as to the level of antioxidants and the color of honey. The darker the honey, the higher the antioxidant level in most cases. The lighter the honey, the lower the antioxidant level in almost all instances. Nectar collected from Illinois buckwheat flowers had 20 times more antioxidant power than bees that forage on California clover.

Honey is a Sap

Honey is actually a flower or plant sap that is released from the plant to regulate the plant fluids. A human releases fluids through the kidneys in a similar fashion. Honey nectars all vary somewhat in their nutritional makeup. Some have more vitamins and minerals, while some are higher in sugar. Honey can vary in its sugar content, as well as the type of sugars it contains. The sugars commonly found in honey are sucrose, glucose and fructose.

Bacteria Hates Honey

When the honey reaches the hive, the bee has diluted it and the honey must then be concentrated to resist bacteria and molds. The honey goes through a processing in the hive that returns the honey to its original level of concentration. The sugar concentration is so high that it kills any microbe that tries to eat it by drawing the moisture from its cells.

Honey-Colored

The color of honey is determined by the floral source the bees choose. There are three main colors:

- **White Honey** is gathered from clover or basswood. This is the mildest honey and the most desired by honey connoisseurs.
- **Golden Honey** is gathered from goldenrod and other flowers that grow in the fall. Golden honey has a stronger flavor than white honey.

- **Amber Darker-Colored Honey** is usually gathered from buckwheat flowers. It is the darkest and strongest honey and not one of the more desired unless you acquire a taste for it.

Mysteries of Honey

There are still scientific investigations that are ongoing, regarding honey. While over 200 different substances have been identified, there are still more that have not been found, especially the substances (enzymes) that are responsible for synthesizing long-chain sugars.

Baking with Honey

The best honey for baking is the mildest-flavored, which is the white or golden honey. When honey is added to a batter, it should be added in a slow stream with continuous stirring. Remember, if you use honey in baked goods, they will brown faster and you may want to reduce the oven heat by about 25°F. (-3.9°C.). The addition of honey will also produce baked goods that will remain moist for a longer period of time.

A Grrreat Substitute

When preparing jams and jellies, honey can be substituted for sugar. If the recipe calls for 4 cups sugar, just use 2 cups honey and cook the jelly just a little longer. Always use liquid honey and powdered pectin for the best results.

Read the Label

The highest quality honey will be labeled "100% pure unfiltered," "raw," or "uncooked" and will not be heat-processed.

Storing Honey

Honey should be stored in as airtight a container as possible, since the sugars are "moisture attracting" and will absorb moisture from the air, especially if the humidity is above 60%. If the water content of honey goes above 17%, the honey and the yeast will activate, the honey will ferment and the sugars will change the honey to alcohol and carbon dioxide.

Certain Honey Can Be Dangerous

Honey that is produced from certain geological areas may contain substances that are harmful to the human body. Farmers call this honey "mad honey." Bees that obtain nectar from flowers such as the rhododendron, azalea and laurel family may cause symptoms of numbness in the extremities, vomiting and muscle weakness. These are rarely fatal but will cause a bit of discomfort for a few days. Honey should never be given to babies since their digestive system is too immature to handle the botulism bacillus, if it is present and they tend to develop a form of infant botulism. Use only pasteurized honey, never honey that has not been pasteurized for children under 1 year of age.

Whoooops

If you coat a measuring spoon with vegetable oil before measuring honey, the honey will slide right off.

Africanized Honey Bees

The sting from just one of these bees is no worse than a sting from any other honeybee. However, they tend to protect their hives by having a swarm of bees chase the intruder away, which is dangerous.

Bees Can Detect Land Mines

Bees have the ability to retain minute amounts of certain chemicals from the air in areas that they forage for honey. Land mines give off a small amount of TNT, which can be found in honeybees. The University of Greenwich has developed a miniature antenna that can be attached to the bees and tracked by radar.

Making the Grade

Most honey sold in supermarkets is a blend of several different types of honey. The best types to purchase are U.S. GRADE A or U.S. FANCY when buying in retail outlets. If honey is labeled "pure," then it must be all honey without the addition of sweeteners. Use care when buying honey that states organic, uncooked, unfiltered or raw. These may contain debris or contaminants and need to be heated and filtered. These honeys may also contain traces of drugs that have used to treat bee ailments. Best to buy the U.S. grades in a pure state.

Honey as a Healer

In ancient times, honey was used externally as a dressing for minor wounds to speed up the healing process and reduce inflammation. Pure honey contains a substance called, "inhibine," which tends to prevent infections from getting a foothold. Honey was also used to desensitize people to pollens and other allergens.

A Problem with Honey

Raw honey may contain spores of the bacteria, Clostridium Botulinum. Honey is not recommended for young children and older adults who may not have a strong enough immune system to fight the bacteria. Botulism can be serious in these age groups and even the heat-processing may not kill the spores. Infant deaths have been reported from consuming raw honey. Most physicians recommend that children, especially up the age of 1, not consume any honey at all. Researchers are even looking for a link between infant sudden death syndrome and botulism. Honey should never be added to infant formula as a sweetener.

MAPLE SUGAR

Run Sap, Run

The "sap run" is one of the more interesting mysteries that nature has recently shared with us. Pure maple syrup is the product of the rock maple tree, which is the only tree that produces high quality syrup. The sap is only collected in the spring, providing ideal conditions exist. The amount of syrup available is dependent on the leaves converting the right proportions of sunlight, water, and carbon dioxide into sugar. Sap is only collected from the first major spring thaw until the leaf buds begin to burst. If the sap collection is not discontinued at this point, the syrup will have a bitter flavor.

Conditions must be near perfect to have a good "sap run." The winter must be severe enough to freeze the trees roots, the snow cover must extend to the spring to keep the roots very cold, the temperature must be extreme from day to night, and the tree must have excellent exposure to adequate sunlight. To produce sap, the tree needs to have stored sugar from the previous season in the trunk, especially in specialized cells known as "xylem" cells. Transport tubes are formed in the tree from both live and dead cells in which the xylem normally carries water and nutrients from the trees and root system to the leaves and trunk.

In early spring, when the rock maple tree thaws, the xylem cells tend to pump sugar into specialized xylem vessels, the transport tubes are now activated and the increase in sugar content in the xylem vessels creates a pressure that draws water into the vessels, increasing the water pressure. As the pressure increases, the xylem cells become more active and start to release waste products and carbon dioxide. The carbon dioxide gas level in the water tends to decrease with the rise in spring temperature, the trunk of the tree warms, causing the gas pressure and water to build up in the xylem tissues, forcing the sap to run and be collected.

Maple tree sap is about 3% sucrose with one tree averaging about 10-12 gal. of sap per spring season. To produce 1 gal. of "pure maple syrup," it requires 35 gal. of sap. The final syrup is composed of 62% sucrose, 35% water, 1% glucose and fructose, and 1% malic acid. The more the syrup is boiled during processing, the darker the syrup becomes due to a reaction between the sugars and proteins.

Very Limited Supply

The finest maple syrup in the U.S. is made by Everett and Kathryn Palmer of Waisfield, VT. The supply is always limited and you have to order ahead to buy this purest of the pure product. Just call (802) 496-3696.

Making a Maple Candy Treat

This treat goes back hundreds of years, except our great grandmothers didn't have the convenience of a microwave oven. The following ingredients will be needed:

Maple Candy Treat

3 cups Crushed ice
1/2 cup Real" maple syrup (imitation only if you must)

Place the maple syrup into a microwave-safe bowl and cook on high power for 4-6 minutes, depending on the wattage. The syrup must be at a hard stage and very hot (be careful) when it is removed. Place the crushed ice in about a 6 x 8 shallow glass dish and using a wooden spoon, spoon the syrup over the crushed ice. When the hot syrup comes into contact with the crushed ice, it will turn into hard strands of maple sugar, linking all the sugar molecules together. Remove the strands (with a fork), which will be fairly hard, allow them to cool, then place them into individual pieces of plastic wrap.

The Real Thing

When a product is labeled "maple sugar," it must contain a minimum of 35% "real" maple syrup. Try to find a product where the color is very light. The lighter the color, the higher the quality. Maple syrup is best stored in the refrigerator after it is opened to retain its flavor and retard the growth of mold. If it granulates, just warm it up slightly. It should last about 1 year and is best used at room temperature or slightly heated. Read the label well! Make sure it doesn't say: "maple flavored," "maple-blended," or use the word "imitation." The real thing is rare and does contain an excellent blend of natural nutrients, especially iron and calcium. The typical pancake syrup is almost pure corn syrup and artificial maple flavoring.

MOLASSES

Another Form of Sugar

Made from sugar cane by going through a complex processing which removes all nutrients, resulting in a white sugar. It is basically the by-product of the refining of sugar. The residue that remains after processing is the actual blackstrap molasses. Unsulfured molasses is actually produced to make molasses, and not the results of the processing to make sugar. Unsulfured molasses has a lighter, cleaner flavor than sulfured. Blackstrap molasses is collected from the top layer and is higher in nutrients than any other type of molasses. It is an excellent source of iron, calcium, and potassium. If a recipe calls for dark molasses, you can use light molasses without a problem. When you bake with molasses, be sure and reduce the heat about 25°F. or the food may over-brown.

Cane syrup may be confused with molasses, but is really cane juice that has been boiled down to make the syrup. Treacle is another sweetener that is similar to, but slightly different from molasses and is a paler, golden brown color. The key nutrients are iron, calcium and potassium. When a recipe calls for dark molasses, you can substitute light molasses without any noticeable differences in the flavor, only the color will be somewhat lighter.

Acidity of molasses can be reduced by adding 1 tsp. baking soda to the dry ingredients for every cup of molasses used. If you need to measure molasses for a recipe, try coating the measuring utensil with a spray vegetable oil and it will flow better with a more accurate measurement. Molasses has a degree of acidity that can be neutralized by adding 1 tsp. baking soda to the dry ingredients for every cup of molasses the recipe calls for. Molasses is best used in gingerbread and baked beans because of its robust flavor.

The Great Molasses Flood

On a very unseasonably warm day in January 1919, a large tank of molasses burst open in the North End of Boston, Massachusetts. Over 2 million gal. of sticky molasses syrup flowed down city streets at a speed of 35-40 miles per hour, carrying everything in its path along with it. Pedestrians, horses and buggies were not spared and slid along with the tide of molasses.

Sorghum

Sorghum is sometimes classified with molasses; however, there is distinct difference between the two. Molasses is produced from the juice of the sugarcane stalk and sorghum is produced from a different variety of sugarcane, called the sweet sorghum cane and is normally used for animal feed. While molasses is usually darker and slightly bitter since most of its sugar is refined out, sorghum tends to retain most of its sugar and has a higher nutrient value. Sorghum contains more calcium, iron and potassium than, honey, molasses or any other commercial syrup.

Raw Sugar (Turbinado)

Still a refined sugar and almost exactly like refined white sugar, except with the addition of molasses for color. Has no advantage over normal refined sugar except the price is higher. As with all sugar, it can be labeled "natural" to make you think that it is better for you.

ARTIFICIAL SWEETENERS

Acesulfame K

Anon-caloric sweetener, which is sold under, two brand names, "Sunette" or "Sweet-ne." It will provide sweetening and cannot be metabolized by the body, but passes through and is excreted. It has an advantage over Equal in that it can be used for high temperature baking and cooking. It is about 200 times sweeter than sugar and commonly used commercially in chewing gums, beverage mixers, candies, puddings and custards. Received FDA approval in 1989 and is in use worldwide.

Alitame

Sweetener that is produced from two amino acids (proteins) and has 2,000 times the sweetness of sugar. Alitame is metabolized by the body with almost no caloric value. It is a good, all-around sweetener that may be used in most recipes and baked goods.

Aspartame (Nutrasweet, Equal)

This approved sweetener is produced from phenylalanine, aspartic acid (two amino acids) and methanol. It has been implicated in animal laboratory testing related to nerve disease; however, testing is not conclusive and the studies were being conducted using high dosages, which may skew the outcome. Aspartame may also lower the acidity level of the urine, causing a reduction in the susceptibility to disease. The latest findings are that NutraSweet may cause an over-stimulation of brain neurons, leading to a reduction in memory function. The guilty party seems to be aspartic acid, which is an amino acid and part of NutraSweet. Recommendations are to reduce your diet soda intake to no more than 3-4 per week.

When soda containing NutraSweet is left at room temperature for 3-4 months, which it may be when stored before being sold, a chemical conversion may take place allowing the formation of formaldehyde, which is a toxic chemical that has been implicated in cancer and birth defects in laboratory animals. Caution must be taken when Aspartame is heated since a percentage may turn into methyl alcohol. It is not recommended for use in baked goods and any drink that requires a liquid being brought to the boiling point. Recent negative study results by leading universities and the Arizona Department of Health Sciences were regarded by the FDA as "unfounded fears."

Symptoms are becoming more frequently reported relating to Equal consumption and include sleep disorders, headaches, vision problems, dizziness and neural disorders. A double-blind study of diabetics using the products reported more adverse symptoms in the groups consuming Equal. The study was conducted using a measured quantity of Equal that was equivalent to 14 diet drinks per day. However, even if you don't consume that many diet drinks, Equal is now found in hundreds of other products.

When Equal was approved in 1980, the FDA set a maximum recommended amount of 34 mg. per Kg. of body weight per day. This equates to a 140-pound person drinking 12 diet drinks per day or the equivalent in foods containing Equal, NutraSweet or Aspartame. The World Health Organization recommended a maximum of 40 mg. per Kg. of body weight for adults. A child in an average day consuming an assortment of cereals, gum, candy, puddings, ades, soft drinks, etc. could easily exceed the adult maximum amounts. Future testing may prove very interesting.

In 2002, complaints were still being received, regarding symptoms that may be related to over-use of Equal and Nutrasweet. However, in moderation there still does not seem to be any concrete evidence that the sweetener should be removed from products.

Cyclamates

May be found again in baked goods and other products. The FDA reversed a decision and is now allowing the use of this artificial sweetener. However, it would still be best to read the label and try to avoid most artificial sweeteners.

L-Sugars

Artificial sweetener that contains no calories or aftertaste and is available to replace a number of other sweeteners. Can be substituted cup for cup for granulated sugar in recipes and may be available shortly.

Saccharin

This sweetener has been around since 1879 and is 300 times sweeter than sugar. It is used in many common products, such as mouthwashes and lipsticks. Presently, it is under additional testing by the FDA. Products that do contain saccharin must have a warning label, stating that saccharin may be hazardous to your health.

STEVIA

Is the new Sweetener Stevia Safe to Use?

This sweetener is new to the U.S. but has been used in South America and Japan for a number of years as a calorie-free sweetener. Stevia is an herbal extract from a member of the chrysanthemum family that is being sold in health food stores as a "dietary supplement." Since it is a natural herbal product, the Dietary Supplement Act of 1994 applies and the product was allowed into the country. However, the FDA is still not sure of any potential problems that might arise since testing is not conclusive at present. However, research from Japan says it is safe and may even prevent yeast infections, act to boost energy levels, and doesn't promote tooth decay. The extract is concentrated and is 200-300 times sweeter than table sugar. It is being used for cooking and may leave a licorice-flavored aftertaste.

Sycralose

Refined from common table sugar but has been concentrated to where it is 600 times sweeter with no calories. Sucralose is a very stable product in foods and carbonated beverages sold in Canada under the brand name "Splenda." Splenda can be used for high temperature cooking and will retain its sweet taste.

Substituting Sweeteners for Sugar

SWEETENER COMPARISON	SUGGESTED USE:
Equal® (Nutrasweet®)	1 pkt. = 2 tsp. sugar
Sucaryl®	Liquid 1/3rd tsp. = 1 tsp. sugar
Sugar Twins®	1 tsp. = 1 tsp. sugar
Sweet & Low®	1 tsp. = 1/4 cup sugar
Fructose	1 pkt. = 1 tsp. sugar
Sweetone™	1 pkt. = 2 tsp. sugar

SWEET FACTS

A Good Sweetener

Fruit is high in the sugar, "fructose." However, all studies show that there is no risk factor involved with this sugar, providing it is derived from fresh fruit. Consumption does not have to be limited and fructose breaks down slower than most sugars, giving the body more time to utilize it before it is completely broken down to glucose.

Too Much of a Good Thing May be Bad

Fructose is produced in a crystalline form for commercial products and is used extensively by the food industry. It can be found in baked goods, canned fruits, jellies, jams, carbonated beverages and even dairy products. Current research is showing, however, that when rats are fed crystalline fructose, they tend to age faster. High fructose consumption may also be related to glucose intolerance.

We're Supposed to Be Smarter

Over 50% of all chocolate sold in the U.S. is purchased by adults. The most popular chocolate is dark (semi-sweet) chocolate. Fry & Sons invented the chocolate bar in 1847 in England. To be able to use the term "milk chocolate," the chocolate must contain at least 10% chocolate liqueur and a minimum of 12% milk solids. To be called "dark chocolate" (semi-sweet), it must contain at least 15% chocolate liqueur and no more than 12% milk solids.

Dentists Retirement Food

Sucking on hard candy or lollypops causes a greater risk of tooth decay than consuming large quantities of cake, ice cream or doughnuts. Hard candy dissolves slower and may surround each tooth with a coating of sugar for a longer period of time. A study reported that fluid movement around teeth is slowed to a crawl by a high intake of sugar and sweetened foods.

Off to the Gym

Americans are consuming about 259,000 calories of sweeteners annually. These many calories will increase a person's weight by about 78 lbs. during their lifetime.

Boy, is Hershey Smiling

Americans consumed about $4.7 billion worth of candy products in 2004 and over 2.4 billion lbs. of chocolate candy bars. Over $670 million was spent on advertising junk foods in 2004.

Chocoholics Beware

The chemical, "theobromine," found in chocolate may reduce the amount of available protein that is absorbed through the intestinal wall. Sugar also reduces the body's ability to destroy bacteria. Oxalates, another chemical found in chocolate, may unite with available calcium, carrying it through the intestine as an insoluble compound, rendering it unusable.

HOT COCOA FACTS

Help! I'm Suspended

Cocoa does not mix well with water and tends to remain in suspension for only a short period of time. The heat from the water will cause the particles to remain in suspension only as long as the drink is hot. As the drink cools, a percentage of the particles will fall to the bottom of the cup. When mixed with hot milk, however, the fat in the milk tends to hold the chocolate better in suspension.

This Chiller Won't Scare You

A great drink in the summer is to take a cup of ice, a cup of whole milk and 3 tbsp. of a quality cocoa, and place it into a blender until the ice cubes are gone. Makes a great chocolate chiller. Ice can be added in place of the milk, if you prefer.

Don't Cook with Mixes

Mixes should only be used to prepare hot chocolate drinks. They contain milk or cream powder and sugar or a substitute. Only pure cocoa or "real" chocolate should be used when recipes call for cocoa powder or chocolate.

What is Dutched Cocoa Powder?

The actual process of dutching the cocoa powder involves adding an alkali to the powder, which mellows the taste. Dutching will improve the color and flavor of the cocoa powder.

What's new in Hot Chocolate Mixes?

There are new chemicals being added to some cocoas used for hot drinks. These new ingredients are called texturing agents and are tapioca-based products that will help keep the cocoa powder in suspension better, providing you with a smoother, more enjoyable drink. The new product is called Textra™ and is manufactured by National Starch Company and it actually gives the product a "mouth-feel" similar to that of fat, without the fat calories.

May Still Keep You Awake

Hot chocolate does have caffeine; however, it only has about 1/10th the amount found in a cup of regular coffee.

How Sweet I am

The better grades of powder are sweetened with sugar; however, there is a sugar-free hot chocolate available that uses Nutrasweet™. The amount of sugar is low in a hot chocolate and the real sugar is preferred to an artificial sweetener.

The Difference in European Cocoa

Most European cocoas are less sweet than the American varieties. Europeans prefer a cocoa that does not have the sweet taste so that they can enjoy the flavor of the chocolate more.

What is White Hot Chocolate?

White hot chocolate is hot chocolate without the "chocolate liquor," which make real chocolate "real." It does have a smooth, creamy flavor and is a favorite of many hot chocolate connoisseurs.

How Do Pop Rocks Work?

Pop Rocks are one of the few patented candies. Pop Rocks are produced by heating sugar and mixing the sugar with carbon dioxide gas at 600 psi. The gas then forms very small bubbles, which remain when the candy breaks apart and cools during processing. When you eat the candy, it melts and the tiny carbon dioxide bubbles burst, making a loud POP!

How Long Will Cocoa Powder Last?

If you purchase one of the better brands of cocoa powder, such as Mont Blanc, it should last for at least a year and be fresh.

Beat me, Beat me

If you want to eliminate the skin forming on top of your hot chocolate, just beat the drink for a few seconds until it gets frothy.

A Definite Improvement

Try mixing a tsp. cornstarch and a pinch of salt in a small amount of water and adding it to the pot of hot chocolate to improve the taste and texture.

Shaking Sugar

In Europe, confectioners' sugar is called "icing sugar." Most recipes call for confectioners' sugar to be sifted. It is also used frequently for "dusting" and some should always be kept handy in a shaker.

Just a Teaspoon of Vinegar..........

If you have added too much sugar to a dish, try adding a tsp. of apple cider vinegar to neutralize the sweet taste.

Overworking your Liver

Most candies, especially if they are multicolored, contain a number of additives that may be a hazard to your health. These include Red Dye #3 and #40, Green Dye #3, Blue Dye #2 and #12, Yellow Dye #5, and glycerides. Check out your favorite candy for any of these additives. Remember, your liver is the organ that must cleanse these potentially toxic chemicals from the body.

Precision Counts

If you're making candy, be sure and follow directions to the letter. Candy recipes are very exacting and variances can cause a poor quality product. Candy must be cooked at the temperature that is recommended; never try and speed up the process by increasing the heat. The lower the final temperature of the candy after it is cooked, will determine the softness of the final product. In fact, if the humidity in the kitchen is over 60%, it will adversely affect the final product.

It's Coming Alive, Looks a bit Shaky, it's Jelloman

In 1993, an EEG (brain wave machine) technician at St. Jerome Hospital in Batavia, New York hooked up the electrodes to a bowl of lime Jell-O. The wiggling bowl of Jell-O was found to have identical "brain wave" patterns to that of an adult human. Dr. Adrian Upton confirmed the EEG findings. Cranberry Jell-O is the only Jell-O flavor that actually is produced from "real" fruit. All the rest utilize artificial flavorings.

Beat me, Beat me

Fudge should be stirred or beaten with a wooden spoon. Beating the fudge is one of the most important techniques. Beat the fudge from its glossy, thin consistency to a slightly thick consistency. This is when you will need to add raisins or nuts and place into a pan to cool. Also, next time you prepare fudge, try adding a tsp. cornstarch when you first begin mixing the ingredients. This will make the fudge set up better.

Crystal Clear

When adding water to a candy recipe, always add very hot water for the best results and a clearer candy. Most freshly made candy will remain fresh for 2-3 weeks.

Don't Take a Beeting

Cane sugar should always be used for candies. Beet sugar tends to cause more foam.

Foods That Contain Sugar May Surprise You

Cough Drops	Rolls	Ketchup	Salt
Vitamins	Bacon	Waffle Mixes	Lipstick
Relish	Canned Fish	Laxatives	Pickles
Peanut Butter	Lip Gloss	Canned Beans	Licorice
Breath Mints	Soup Mixes	Eggnog	Baby Foods
Tooth Paste	Breads	Crackers	Soy Sauce
Stamp Adhesives	Gravies	Tenderizer	Processed Snails

Puff, Puff, Drink, Drink

Smokers frequently consume more sugar than non-smokers, probably due to the fact that smokers drink more sweetened coffee.

Sugar Disaster

Freezing has a negative effect on a number of candies, which never taste the same afterwards, and may lose their consistency. Hard candies may crumble, jellies become granular, cereal products and popcorn candy become mushy, and the rest lose their original consistencies due to the expansion of the liquid in their cells.

New Candy Bar

Russell Stover Candies will introduce a new candy bar that will be a peanut butter-and-jelly cup. The two-pack will consist of two chocolate cups that are filled with peanut butter and grape jelly. The candy will be sold in two size cups, large and small. A survey of consumers showed that 90% of people polled would purchase the new candy treat.

Protein to Be Used as Sweeteners

A new advance in biotechnology is creating interest in finding new natural sweeteners. Researchers will be utilizing proteins to modify foods and increase their sweetness. Taste-modifying proteins (TMP) are able to function as natural sweeteners and flavor enhancers. The most popular proteins that produce good results are "thaumatin," "monellin" and "miraculin." Thaumatin is derived from a fruit found in Western Africa and is the most popular. Monellin is also derived from a fruit found in West Africa and miraculin is derived from the Miracle fruit.

Chocolate and Licorice Bar, a Big Hit

The Cadbury Candy Company has introduced a new candy bar in New Zealand. The bar is a chocolate bar with twists of licorice running through it.

Oat Extract to ProvIde New Sweetener

A new extract from oats will provide sweetness to a number of products. The extract "beta-glucans" will be used in puddings, frozen desserts, snacks and nutrition bars. The product was developed by Crompton & Knowles Ingredient Technology Corp. and will be available in liquid or dry forms. The oat extract provides a source of natural sweetness and soluble fiber (beta-glucans).

Chocolate Bar That Will not Melt

A new method of producing chocolate will be used to produce a chocolate bar that will never melt in your hand. The bar is produced utilizing a new type of freeze-dried process that was used by NASA and creates a very low-density chocolate that only melts in your mouth.

Making Candy, Cool it!

If you are making candy and the weather is hot and humid, don't try and make chocolates unless the room is well air-conditioned. The best temperature to make chocolates, divinity, hard candy and fudge is between 62°F. and 68°F. with low humidity. These candies absorb moisture from the air very easily.

Fresh 'n Fruity

Jams and jellies are now being produced from a number of artificial ingredients. Best to read the label and make sure that the product you purchase is made from the "real fruit." If they are, and are labeled "lite," that would be even better since the sugar content has been reduced.

What is a Marshmallow?

Basically, it is a candy that has been produced since about 1850 when early settlers used sap from the marshmallow plant in the recipe. Marshmallow can also be made from corn syrup, albumen, granulated sugar and gelatin that have been beaten into a soft spongy consistency.

Non-Sticky Marshmallow

If you run your hands under very cold water before pressing marshmallow treats in a pan, your fingers will not stick to the marshmallow.

Snip, Snip

Marshmallows will store for a longer period of time if they are stored in the freezer. Just cut them with a scissors that has been dipped in very hot water to get them apart.

Moisturize me

Adding a slice of very fresh white bread or half an apple to a bag of marshmallows to soften them up works great. Just leave them alone for 1-2 days until they absorb the moisture.

De-Lumping your Sugar

Brown sugar has a tendency to lose moisture rather quickly and develop lumps. To soften brown sugar, try placing the sugar in the microwave with a slice of fresh white bread or $^1/_2$ an apple, then cover the dish tightly and heat for about 15 seconds. The moisture from the bread or apple will produce just enough steam to soften the sugar without melting it. If you store brown sugar in the freezer, it won't develop lumps.

Zap it!

To remove hardened brown sugar from a box, wrap it tightly in a towel and hit it on the counter a few good whacks. If that doesn't do it, just add a few drops of water to the box and microwave on full power for a few seconds. If neither one works, run over it with your car or throw it out and buy some more. Other than a touch of molasses, brown sugar is chemically identical to white sugar.

Don't Rain on my Preserves

Remember, never make preserves or jelly, if the humidity is over 50% or if it is a rainy day.

That's a Few Extra Calories

Ice cream sales in the U.S. in 2001 were approximately $3.4 billion. We averaged almost 16 qts. of ice cream per person.

What Causes an Ice Cream Headache?

The roof of your mouth is very sensitive and when something as cold as ice cream touches it, it causes a reaction. The nerves in the area respond to the cold by causing the blood vessels to dilate, thus making your brain respond to the cold by trying to warm the area which, in turn, causes a painful sensation for about 30 seconds.

Candy Chef's Secret

To successfully defrost candy, the temperature should be raised gradually. Place the candy to be thawed, still in the original wrapper, in a brown paper bag lined with a paper towel. This will absorb any moisture that may collect during defrosting.

Well Excuuuuse me!

Bloatiness and flatulence may be caused by frequent swallowing when people chew gum and suck on hard candy. The salivary glands produce saliva at a higher rate than normal, thus causing the frequent swallowing.

You Won't Believe it Until You Try it

Try using a small amount of vegetable oil on the threads of a syrup bottle. It will stop the syrup from running down the sides of the bottle.

The Percentage of Sugar in Some Common Foods

Jell-O	82.0%
Breakfast cereals	up to 68.0%
Candy Corn	59.5%
Milky Way	40.3%
Oreo Cookie	40.1%
Ketchup	29.0%
Hamburger Helper	24.0%

Heat Kills

If you think that a fruit jam or jelly will have vitamin C, think again! The processing kills almost all the vitamin C.

The Nose Knows

Candies stored in the refrigerator can pick up foreign odors and should be stored properly in a closed container.

It's Not the Real Thing

To be called chocolate, you must use chocolate liqueur in the product. White chocolate doesn't use the liqueur and is not really chocolate. It is produced from sugar, milk powder and cocoa butter. Cocoa butter is produced from chocolate liqueur and loses its chocolate flavor during the processing.

Free Flowing

Sugar will never cake-up, if you just place a few salt-free crackers in the canister to absorb the moisture. Crackers should be replaced every week.

Bubble, Bubble, Toil and Trouble

If you have a problem with candy boil-over, just place a wooden spoon over the pan to break the bubbles.

No Candy for Daddy

Adults are just as prone to hyperactivity as children from high sugar intakes. However, new studies are showing that there may not be much validity to this assumption.

Just a Spoonful of Sugar Makes the Medicine Go Down

The chemicals used to produce cough drops are so bitter, the sugar content can be as high as 50%. In fact, approximately 30% of all cough syrups and drops are at least 25% sugar.

Pop a Cube, but Not Too Often

If you must satisfy a sugar craving and don't want the calories, try eating a sugar cube. They only contain 12 calories each and contain no fat or preservatives.

A Vacation at Your Expense

When you consume too much sugar, it reduces the effectiveness of the body's healing mechanism, causing a prolongation in the healing time. Normally, white blood cells, which aid in the healing process, go to the site of the injury and assist the body by removing debris and starting the healing process. However, when there is an overabundance of sugar circulating in the bloodstream, they tend to get lazy and don't want to go to work. This increases the healing time.

Food Additives

Almost 98% (by actual weight) of food additives are corn syrup, pepper, mustard, baking soda, baking powder, citric acid, salt or a natural or artificial coloring agent.

How Sweet it is

In a recent study by Dr. Andrew Waterhouse at the University of California at Davis, chocolate was found to contain an antioxidant called "phenols." This is the same compound found in red wine that was thought to lower the risk of heart disease in France. The study found that cocoa powder prevented the oxidation or breakdown of LDLs (bad cholesterol). When LDLs are broken down, they tend to convert into fatty plaque forming particles that may contribute to the clogging of healthy arteries, thus becoming a risk factor for heart disease. A 12-oz. chocolate bar has the same amount of "phenols" as a 5-oz. glass of red wine. Additional studies are also showing that chocolate contains flavonoids, which act as an antioxidant that may have the ability to slow down the deposition of plaque on the walls of the arteries.

The Greatest Chocolate-Covered Marshmallow

This is by far one of the finest candies you will even taste. The Schwartz family has been making the candy since 1939, keeping its original logo and box all through the years. The marshmallow is light and airy and no comparison to the ones you buy at the store. They are covered with dark semi-sweet chocolate and if you really want a delicacy, try the ones with a caramel bottom. All ingredients are the finest possible and they can be ordered by calling (800) 358-0940.

The Birth of the Lollypop

In 1909, an employee named George Smith made a new confection on a stick while employed by a Connecticut candy maker. He was an avid race fan and named the confection after one of the most popular racehorses of that time, "Lolly Pop."

Can Babies Detect Sweet Tastes?

Babies who are only 1 day old can detect the taste of sweet; however, it will take them 6 weeks to respond to the taste of salt. Taste buds are able to detect sweetness in a food. if the food has only 1-part sweetness in 200. Saltiness can be detected if the food only has 1 part in 400.

What is a Goo-Goo Cluster?

This has been one of the favorite candies of the South since 1912, when Howell H. Campbell went into the candy business. He prepared the candy from chocolate, marshmallow, caramel and peanuts. The candy is occasionally found in some of the better stores in major cities around the country. The candy was named by a Nashville woman who suggested that Campbell name the bar after the only two words his infant son could utter, "goo-goo." The Goo-Goo Cluster was the first combination candy bar produced in the United States. To order, some of the bars call (615) 889-6360.

Eliminate a Sweet Craving

There are two ways to eliminate the craving for sweets: first, place a small amount of salt on your tongue; second, dissolve about 1 tsp. baking soda in a glass of warm tap water, then rinse your mouth out and don't swallow the water. The salt or baking soda tends to stimulate the hypothalamus gland, causing the papillae to become active and secrete saliva, which will eliminate the craving for sweets.

Gourmet Chocolate

For years wine has been labeled from a particular vineyard or region and many connoisseurs will only drink wines from that particular vintage or region. Wine tasters can tell you by sipping a wine the complete history of that wine and its level of quality. Well, chocolate has finally come of age and the latest craze is to purchase chocolates from a particular Epicurean grower and from a particular variety of the cocoa bean.

What is Chocolate Plastic?

Is actually a pliable decorating paste, prepared from a mixture of chocolate and corn syrup and has a texture similar to marzipan. It is used to wrap around the outside of cakes to make a ribbon, ruffles, decorative flowers or any other complex design. It can be rolled out to make a thin layer with a rolling pin.

Was the Baby Ruth Candy Bar Named After Babe Ruth?

Many people think that the Baby Ruth candy bar was named after the famous baseball player, especially since he did wish to produce a candy bar with his name on it. The candy bar was actually named after the daughter of then President Grover Cleveland, after she was born in the White House to honor her. Ruth did take the matter to court and lost.

Does Your Chocolate Stiffen Too Soon?

When you are melting chocolate, water droplets, excess condensation and high temperatures may cause the chocolate to stiffen prematurely (seize up). To alleviate this problem, add a tsp. of corn oil to the pan and stir. More oil can be added if needed to assure the proper consistency.

Cooking with Chocolate

- Never store chocolate in the refrigerator or the freezer or when you thaw it out condensation will form and affect its ability to melt smoothly.
- When you melt chocolate, make sure that not even a drop of water gets into the pot or the chocolate may sieve. If this happens, add a small amount of vegetable oil.
- The higher quality chocolate, the better.
- Make sure that the chocolate does not have a white film on it.
- Be sure that the chocolate snaps when broken.

It's Just Divine

Divinity fudge cannot be made on humid days. The air must be relatively dry, since the ingredients used and the type of preparation tends to attract moisture and will ruin the fudge.

The Candy Man Can

Hershey kisses obtained their name because the machine that produces them resembles someone kissing the conveyer belt. The Hershey Candy Company produces 2,250,000 Kisses everyday. However, the Dutch outdo us when it comes to candy consumption. They consume 65 lbs. of candy per person annually, while Americans only consume about 23 lbs.

Origin of Chewing Gum

A variety of gums, resins and plant latex have been chewed for thousands of years. The first recorded history of mixing a gum with sugar can be traced to the Arab sugar traders who mixed the sugar with acacia, known as "Gum Arabic." A number of gums were even used in early days as carriers for a variety of medications, which allowed the medicine to be released gradually. Commercially, the Curtis family with only mediocre results, as we know it today, first produced chewing gum in Bangor, Maine in 1850. However, in 1859 a New Yorker by the name of Thomas Adams used "chicle," the dried latex material of the sapodilla tree of Central America.

In 1871, a patent was issued to Adams for "chicle gum." Then, in 1885, William J. White of Cleveland further refined and improved the gum by adding corn syrup and flavoring the gum with peppermint, which was very successful. In 1893, William Wrigley invented Juicy Fruit and Spearmint gums and in 1900, Frank Fleer of Philadelphia placed a hard shell on the gum and called it Chiclets. Bubble gum was invented in 1928 by Fleer. The gums of today are produced from synthetic polymers, mostly styrene-butadiene rubbers and polyvinyl acetate. The final product is composed of 60% sugar, 20% corn syrup and only 20% actual gum material.

A Trick to Stop Syrup from Crystallizing

When boiling syrup, one of the more frequent and annoying problems is that of the syrup crystallizing when you are cooking it. The easiest method of avoiding this problem is to put a pinch of baking soda in the syrup while it is cooking. This will prevent the syrup from crystallizing by adding just a small amount of acidity.

The Jellybean Rule

Jellybeans have zero fat, no cholesterol and no nutritional value at all. The FDA has a new rule for advertisers of worthless foods to follow so that they will not be able to label food, such as jellybeans as a "healthy" food. This rule is actually called the "jelly bean rule." For a food to be called "healthy," a food must contain a minimum of 10% of the Daily Values for any one of several key nutrients. The food must also be low fat, low saturated fat and be low in sodium and cholesterol.

The Difference in Cane, Beet, White and Brown Sugar

Basically, all table sugar is sucrose, a simple carbohydrate that breaks down in the body to glucose in a short period of time. Both cane and beet sugars are not noticeably different in appearance or taste. Brown sugar still contains traces of molasses, which is a by-product of the sugar refining process. The nutritional difference between white and brown sugar is so insignificant it is not worth purchasing brown over white, unless it is called for in a recipe.

What is Sugar Cane?

A tall, cylindrically shaped plant that resembles a cane. It matures in 11-18 months and is ready to be harvested. Most sugar cane is still harvested by hand and is then processed utilizing a small amount of water to assist in the separation of the juices. The juice is clarified, using of lime and the decantation of impurities. The juice is then evaporated into syrup and centrifuged to extract the sugar crystals and eliminate the molasses. The sugar that results is brown and can be decolorized by passing the sugar through carbon filters and re-crystallizing by centrigation.

What is Sorghum?

Sorghum is usually thought of as just another type of molasses, however, there is a difference and it is really a unique product. While molasses is produced from the juice of the sugarcane stalk, sorghum is made from the juice of a different breed of sugar cane stalk called the sweet-sorghum cane, which is normally grown for animal feed. Molasses is usually darker and may be a slight bit bitter, since much of the sugar is refined out. Sorghum retains its sugar and is sweeter, as well as containing more nutritional value. Sorghum has more calcium, iron and potassium than honey, molasses or any other commercial syrup. The finest sorghum in the U.S. is made by Golden Mill Sorghum (316) 226-3368.

What is Chocolate Liqueur?

Real chocolate is made from chocolate liqueur, which is produced from cocoa pods. It is not really liquor in the sense most of us think of liquor, but the name given to the processed product obtained from the fruit of the cocoa tree. The cocoa tree is a member of the evergreen family and can only be found in equatorial climates. The tree grows to about 20 ft. and the pods that contain the cocoa bean are about 8-10 in. long with each pod averaging 30 beans each. In 2001, the cocoa bean crop was about 2.1 million tons most of which came from West Africa. The first step in the processing is actually in the field with the pods being opened and the beans allowed to sit in the sun.

This exposure causes a number of microbes to multiply, killing the seeds' embryo as well as producing changes in the structure of the cells. The cell walls deteriorate, releasing substances that mix together, resulting in the bitter "phenolic" compounds binding to each other and reducing the degree of bitter taste. The beans are then cleaned and dried and shipped to other countries. The bean now must be processed into the chocolate liqueur. They are roasted for about 1 hour at 250°F, which finally gives them the chocolate flavor. This involves approximately 300 different chemicals and results in the "browning reaction" and the color of chocolate. After they are browned, they are cracked open and the "nibs" (kernels) separated from the shells. The nibs are then ground up to release the cocoa butter, carbohydrates and proteins, which are all in the thick liquid oil called "chocolate liqueur." The refining process continues until the mixture ends up as a coarse chocolate or a powder.

Why Does Carob Powder Burn Instead of Melting?

When you heat cocoa powder used in "real" chocolate it contains fat, which allows it to melt. Carob does not contain any fat, therefore it will not melt, only burn. When carob flour is heated with water, the starch granules absorb moisture and rupture. This releases a gum that is used as a stabilizer and thickener in processed foods. If you use carob flour in a cake recipe, it will act like any other flour.

What is Blown-Sugar?

This is sugar that has been cooked to a point just below the hard crack stage. It is then poured onto an oiled marble slab and worked with a metal spatula until it has cooled enough to be worked by hand. The sugar is "satinized" by pulling it back and forth, until it has a glossy, smooth sheen. It is then formed into a ball and an air hose attached to a pump is inserted into the ball of sugar, and air is gently blown in. As it expands, the sugar is gently formed into sugar animals or other shapes, similar to glass blowing. The finished objects are then painted with a food coloring and used for display or consumed. They will last for months at room temperature, if stored in an airtight container.

Why all the XXXXXXX's on Sugar Bags?

The "X" symbol on sugar bags pertains to the fineness of the sugar. The more X's, the finer the grade of sugar you are purchasing. It actually indicates the number of holes per in. in the screening material used to form the size of the sugar crystals. If the package has four X's, then there were four holes per in. in the screen. A ten "X" sugar is usually a confectioners' sugar.

Carob, No Better Than Chocolate

Carob in its pure form does contain less fat than chocolate. Carob powder that is used to make carob confections is less than 1% fat, but has up to 48% sugar. Cocoa powder used in the manufacture of chocolate bars is 23% fat and only 5% sugar. However, when either one is processed into candy or chocolate bars, the differences are for the most part erased. In fact, some carob bars contain a higher level of saturated fat than a Hershey bar and more sugar than a scoop of regular ice cream. Carob does not, however, contain caffeine, which is found in chocolate.

Sugarless Gum, Friend or Foe?

Sugarless products that contain sorbitol or mannitol as the artificial sweetening agent may now be suspect of causing tooth decay just as much as regular gum. Neither one of these sweeteners actually cause tooth decay, however, they tend to provide nourishment for a bacteria that is influential in causing tooth decay. The bacteria in question are "Streptococcus mutan," which has the tendency to stick to your teeth and is relatively harmless until it obtains sweets. The bacteria seems to thrive on sorbitol and mannitol, just as they do with real sugars.

Coke Buys More Sugar than any Company Worldwide

Coca-Cola is consumed over 190 million times every 24 hours in more than 35 countries speaking 80 languages. Colas have a higher physiological dependency than smoking and drinking and find it harder to give up. The Coca-Cola Company is the world's largest purchaser of sugar and vanilla. The vanilla is mainly supplied by Madagascar, which was placed into a panic situation when Coke switched to the "New Coke," which had no vanilla. Lucky for Madagascar, the New Coke was rejected and Coke had to place the vanilla back in the product. Americans consume about 520 bottles/cans or 50 gallons of soft drinks annually per person.

A Serious Investigation

M&M's were originally produced for the military so that they would not get their hands sticky. The Mars company actually does continuing research to determine the colors and the number of each color that will be found in their packages of M&M's.

How Many Pounds of Candy Are You Eating?

In 1980, Americans were consuming 16.1 lbs. of candy per person annually and by 1993, the figure was up to 20 lbs. The candy industry had set their sights on a goal of "25 by '95." They were hoping that they could reach that goal but failed. The current estimates are that they did reach their goal by 2002. For the companies to reach their goal, you ate the equivalent of 195 candy bars per year.

Aging vs. Taste Buds

The tongue contains a number of clusters of specialized cells that form "taste buds." Each taste bud contains about 50 of these cells attached to a small projection, which adheres to the upper surface of the tongue. Most adults have a few thousand of these taste buds; however, some adults have only a few hundred. Most of our taste buds are concentrated on the back of the tongue; however, the taste of sweet and salt are located in the front of the tongue and sour on either side. Children have considerably more taste buds than adults, with locations on the back of the throat, the tongue, even the inner surfaces of the cheeks. Taste buds gradually decrease with age, especially after the age of 50. The cells that compose the taste bud only have a life of about 10 days, which is just as well if we burn our tongue regularly.

SYRUPS AND ICINGS

Putting on a Coat

A common coating for desserts and confections is a "glaze." A glaze is usually brushed or poured on and is prepared by combining a jam or jelly with a liquid, such as water or liqueur. The mixture is then strained to remove any pulp and warmed before being used. One of the more common glazes is a chocolate glaze, which is prepared from melted chocolate, cream, butter and corn syrup. Confectioner's sugar glaze is prepared by mixing confectioner's sugar with liquid, such as lemon juice or even water.

Heat me, Heat me

A commonly use icing is called "boiled icing." The icing is prepared by cooking sugar with whipped egg whites, then beating the mixture until it is smooth, syrupy and glossy. It may also be called Italian meringue.

Caramel

Caramel sauce is prepared from sugar and water. The mixture is cooked until it is a dark brown color. Caramel candy is prepared from sugar, milk or cream, honey or corn syrup and butter. Additional ingredients can also be added, such as nuts and chocolate bits.

Corn Syrup

Corn syrup has been produced in the U.S. since the mid-1800s and is made by extracting starch granules from the kernels. The starch is then treated with an acid, bacterial or malt enzyme, which turns it into sweet syrup. Corn syrup is important commercially because of its unique sweetness properties. Even though it is sweet, it can be changed into a sweet substance that does not register on our sweet taste buds. When using corn syrup, remember that there are two colors, dark and light, that can be used interchangeably. The dark, however, will impart a dark color to your food.

Sugar is Attractive

When using sugar to prepare syrups, remember that sugar has the tendency to attract moisture from the air and thus keeps foods moist. Cakes are lighter because the sugar slows the gluten from becoming stiff. It has the tendency to lower the freezing point of most liquids, which keeps ice cream in a state of a semi-solid. When used on meats, it will help retain the natural moisture. Sugar syrups are easy to prepare and very popular.

Easy to Prepare Sugar Syrups

Thin sugar syrup- One cup granulated sugar added to 2 cups water.

Medium sugar syrup- One cup granulated sugar added to 1cup water.

Heavy sugar syrup- One cup granulated sugar added to 3/4 cup water.

Thick sugar syrup- One cup granulated sugar added to 1/2 cup water.

In a small saucepan, add the sugar to the water and stir gently over low heat. Do not allow the mixture to boil until the sugar is completely dissolved. When boiling begins, stop stirring and continue to boil (uncovered) for about 1 minute. Flavorings can be added either before or after cooking. If you overcook the syrup, just add $^1/_4$ cup of boiling water and cook again.

Stages of sugar syrup- The thread stage is used to determine the actual temperature of the sugary syrup. In order for the candy to set up, it must crystallize into sugary syrup. Cook the syrup in a small saucepan over medium heat until it reaches the desired temperature. If you do not have a thermometer, the following will be useful:

Thread Stage 230^0-234^0F.(110-112.2^0C.): Syrup will form a soft light thread.

Soft Ball 234^0-240^0F.(112.2^0-115.6^0C.): Syrup will form a small ball that will flatten out by itself when removed.

Firm Ball 244^0-248^0F.(117.8^0-120^0C.): Syrup will form a firm ball that tends to flatten out when pressed between your fingers.

Hard Ball 250^0-265^0F.(121.1^0-129.4^0C.): Syrup will form a hard ball that has just a little give to it when squeezed.

Soft Crack 270^0-290^0F.(132.2^0-143.3^0C.): Syrup tends to separate into hard threads that are bendable.

Hard Crack 300^0-310^0F.(148.9^0-154.4^0C.): Syrup will separate into threads, which are hard and very brittle.

Caramelized Sugar 310^0-338^0F.(154.4^0-170^0C.): Syrup will become a golden color.

NOTE: When sugar is cooked above 350^0F. (176.7^0C.) will turn black and burn.

Bubble, Bubble, Toil and Trouble

When preparing sugar syrup, always watch the bubbles. Bubbles tend to get smaller as the sugar syrup thickens. If the syrup bubbles get too small, it's time to start over.

I'll Have Some Orgeat on my Ice Cream, Please

If you like the taste of almonds, try syrup called "orgeat," which is prepared from almonds and rosewater. Orgeat is also used in Mai-Tais and Scorpions.

SWEET FACTS

Beat me, Please!

Fudge should be stirred or beaten with a wooden spoon. Beating is important to produce a slightly thick, glossy consistency. The fudge will set up better, if you add 1 tsp. cornstarch when you begin mixing in the ingredients.

How Clear I am

When adding water to a candy recipe, always add very hot water for a crystal clear candy. Cold water may contain contaminants that cause cloudiness. Freshly prepared candy will keep for about 2-3 weeks.

How About Gritty Jelly

Jellies should never be placed in the freezer. They tend to lose their consistency and turn very granular.

Humidity, a Jelly Killer

Always remember to never prepare jellies or preserves on a day when the humidity is over 50%. High humidity causes the gelatin or pectin to absorb excess moisture leaving the product too watery.

Give Jelly a Squeeze

If you place jelly in a plastic squeeze bottle, it will be easier to use.

Small Batches Are Best

It is always best to prepare jellies in small batches. Large batches use large quantities of juices and it is necessary to boil it longer, resulting in a loss of flavor. The jelly may also darken and become somewhat tough.

Come on Slowpoke, Boil me Fast

Always boil jelly rapidly and as fast as possible. When jellies are boiled slowly, the pectin in the fruit juice may be destroyed.

Hic, my Jellied Fruit Fermented

Jellied fruit may ferment because yeast is allowed to multiply. This usually occurs only when the product is poorly processed and the jar poorly sealed. It may also occur if the sugar content is too low. If this occurs, don't try and save the batch. Best to throw it away.

Look, There's Beautiful Crystals in my Jelly

There are a number of reasons why crystals form in jellies. The following are four of the more common reasons:

- The crystals may form if too much sugar is used. Test the fruit juice with a Jelmeter (sweetness tester) to be sure that you have the proper proportions of sugar.
- Crystals can form if there is sugar that has not been dissolved and is stuck to the sides of the saucepan. Make sure you wipe the sides of the pan clean and free of crystals with a damp rag, before you fill the jars.
- The grape juice you are using may have tartrate crystals in it. To resolve this, just extract the grape juice and allow the tartrate crystals to settle down, which can be done by refrigerating the juice overnight and then straining the juice to remove the crystals.
- Crystals can also form from cooking the mixture too slowly or too long. The juice should be cooked at a rapid boil, when it reaches the jellying point, remove it from the heat immediately.

Doth your Syrup Run Over?

If you place a small amount of vegetable oil on the threads of a syrup bottle top, it will stop the syrup from running down the sides of the bottle.

Bubble, Bubble, Toil and Trouble

When jelly is poured into the jars from the pot, the pot must be close to the top of the jar or, if the jelly is poured slowly, air becomes trapped in the hot jelly and bubbles will form. Always hold the pot close to the top of the jars and pour the jelly as fast as you can. Bubbles may also indicate that the jelly has spoiled. When there are bubbles that move, throw out the jelly.

Just an old Softee

One of the most common problems when preparing jelly is that of the jelly being too soft. There are a number of reasons for this problem. The following are six of the most common ones:

- One of the more common problems is overcooking the fruit to extract the juice. Overcooking tends to lower the pectin level and thus reducing the capacity of the jelly to thicken properly.
- The use of too much water when extracting the juice will produce a jelly that is too runny. Follow instructions as to the proper amount to be used.
- The wrong proportions of sugar and juice will also cause the jelly to be too soft.
- When the jelly is undercooked, it tends to be soft due to insufficient concentrations.
- Too little acid can cause the jelly to become soft. If the fruit is low in acid, try adding a small amount of lemon juice.
- Making too large a batch can also cause the jelly to have difficulty setting up properly. Never use any more than 4-6 cups of juice for each batch.

Help, It's Getting Dark in Here

When you overcook jelly, some of the sugar and juice tend to burn and cause a darker color than you may be used to. Boiling too long is usually the cause of the darkness and making too large a batch. Also, if the jelly is stored for too long a period at too high a temperature, it may also cause darkening to occur.

My Jelly is Weeping, Poor Jelly

There are a number of reasons that cause jelly to "weep." Too much acid will cause a tear or two, or the pectin used is unstable and old. Proper acidity levels is very important if the jelly is stored in too warm a location, or if the temperature fluctuates too much, it may shed a tear as well. Jelly should always be stored in a dry, cool location.

Cloudy Jelly, Not too Appetizing

If the fruit you are using is green or not ripe enough, the jelly may be cloudy. Other reasons for cloudiness may be poor straining, which means that you may have forced the fruit through the strainer, instead of allowing it to drip naturally or not allowing the juice to stand before it was poured into the jars.

Too Tough Jelly

The reason that jellies tend to get tough and stiff is usually caused by overcooking. Jelly should be cooked to a temperature that is 80°F. (-13.3°C.) higher than the boiling point of water or until it flows from a spoon in a "sheet." Too much pectin or too little sugar in the juice will also contribute to the problem. When pectin is added, you should only use $^3/_4$ cup sugar to every 1 cup juice for the majority of the fruits.

Caffeine in Chocolate

The average chocolate candy bar has about 30 mg. of caffeine.

Sweetie, Your Candy is Boiling Over

If you have a problem with candy boiling over, try placing a wooden spoon across the top of the pot to break the bubbles.

Naughty, Naughty Fake Chocolate

To be called chocolate, the product must contain chocolate liqueur. White chocolate does not contain chocolate liquor and is not "real" chocolate. It is produced from sugar, milk powder and cocoa butter. Cocoa butter is derived from chocolate liqueur but loses its chocolate flavor during processing.

Help! My Syrup is Crystallizing

When boiling syrup, the most frequent problem is that of the syrup crystallizing. The easiest method of avoiding this problem is to just place a pinch of baking soda in the syrup while it is cooking.

11

Substitutions and
MORE

If you're using a cookbook and it was published in England, the following information will be very useful since many of the common cooking ingredients are called by different names.

BRITISH FOOD	AMERICAN FOOD
Plain Flour	All-Purpose Flour
Wholemeal Flour	Whole Wheat Flour
Strong Flour	Bread Flour
Single Cream	Light Cream
Double Cream	Whipping Cream
Castor Sugar	Granulated Sugar (10X)
Demerara Sugar	Brown Sugar
Treacle Sugar	Molasses
Dark Chocolate	Semi-Sweet Chocolate
Sultanas	White Raisins
Courgettes	Zucchini
Swedes	Turnips
Gammon	Ham

Active Dry Yeast (one package)
> 1 cake compressed yeast

Agar-Agar
> Use gelatin

Allspice
> $\frac{1}{4}$ tsp. cinnamon & $\frac{1}{2}$ tsp. ground cloves or
> $\frac{1}{4}$ tsp. nutmeg for baking only or Black pepper other than baking

Anise (use equivalent amount)
> Fennel, dill or cumin

Apples
> One cup of firm chopped pears and one tbsp. lemon juice.
> 1 lb. of apples = 4 small, 3 medium, or 2 large, or $2\frac{3}{4}$ cups sliced, or 2 cups chopped

Arrowroot
> Flour, just enough to thicken. Should take a few tbsp.

Baking Powder (one tsp., double - acting)
> $\frac{1}{2}$ tsp. cream, of tartar plus $\frac{1}{4}$ tsp. baking soda or,
> $\frac{1}{4}$ tsp. baking soda; plus $\frac{1}{2}$ cup of sour milk, cream, or buttermilk (must take the place of other liquid) or,
> 4 tsp. quick-cooking tapioca

Baking Powder (1 tsp., single - acting)
> $\frac{3}{4}$ tsp. double-acting baking powder

Basil (dried)
> Tarragon, or Summer savory, of equal amounts, or Thyme, or Oregano

Bay Leaf
> Thyme of equal amounts

Black Pepper
> Allspice in cooking, providing salt is also used in the dish

Borage
> Cucumber

Brandy
> Cognac or rum

Bread Crumbs (1/4 cup, dry)
> $\frac{1}{4}$ cup cracker crumbs or,
> $\frac{1}{2}$ slice of bread, may be toasted or crumbled or,
> $\frac{1}{4}$ cup rolled oats or,
> $\frac{1}{4}$ cup matzo meal or,
> $\frac{1}{4}$ cup sifted flour or,
> $\frac{1}{4}$ cup corn flakes

Bulgur
> Use equal amounts of: cracked wheat, kasha, brown rice, couscous, millet, quinoa

Butter (in baking)
> Hard margarine or shortening

Do Not Use Oil in Baked Products
>1 lb. = 2 cups
>1 cup = 2 sticks
>2 tbsp.= $^{1}/_{4}$ stick or 1 oz.
>4 tbsp. = $^{1}/_{2}$ stick or 2 oz.
>8 tbsp. = 1 stick or 4 oz.

Buttermilk
>One cup of milk plus 1$^{3}/_{4}$ tbsp. of cream of tartar or equivalent of sour cream

Cake Flour
>Use 1 cup of all-purpose flour minus 2 tbsp.

Capers
>Chopped green olives

Caraway Seed
>Fennel seed or cumin seed

Cardamom
>Cinnamon or mace

Cayenne Pepper
>Ground hot red pepper or chili powder

Chervil
>Parsley or tarragon (use less), or anise (use less)

Chives
>Onion powder (small amount), leeks or shallots (small amount)

Chocolate, Baking, Unsweetened (1 oz. or square)
>3 tbsp. unsweetened cocoa & 1 tbsp. butter or
>3 tbsp. carob powder & 2 tbsp. water

Chocolate, Baking, Unsweetened (1 oz. pre-melted)
>3 tbsp. unsweetened cocoa & 1 tbsp. corn oil or melted Crisco

Chocolate, Semi-Sweet (6 oz. chips or squares)
>Nine tbsp. cocoa, 7 tbsp. sugar & 3 tbsp. butter

Cilantro
>Parsley and lemon juice or orange peel and a small amount of sage
>or lemon grass with a small amount of mint

Cinnamon
>Allspice (use a small amount) or cardamom

Cloves (ground)
>Allspice or nutmeg or mace

Club Soda
>Mineral water or seltzer

Cornmeal
>Grits (corn) or polenta

Cornstarch
>Flour, a few tbsp. for thickening, usually no more than 2 tbsp.

Corn Syrup (one cup, light)
>1$^{1}/_{4}$ cups granulated sugar or,
>1 cup granulated sugar plus $^{1}/_{4}$ cup of liquid

Cream Cheese

Cottage cheese mixed with cream or cream with a small amount of butter or milk

Creme Fraiche

Sour cream in a recipe or $\frac{1}{2}$ sour cream and $\frac{1}{2}$ heavy cream in sauces

Cumin

$\frac{1}{3}$ anise plus $\frac{2}{3}$ caraway or fennel

Dill Seed

Caraway or celery seed

Edible Flowers (garnish)

Bachelor buttons, blue borage, calendula petals, chive blossoms, mini carnations, nasturtiums, pansies, rose petals, snap dragon or violets.

Eggs, Whole (1)

2 tbsp. water, 2 tbsp. flour, $\frac{1}{2}$ tbsp. Crisco & $\frac{1}{2}$ tsp. baking powder or,

2 yolks & 1 tbsp. water or,

2 tbsp. corn oil & 1 tbsp. water or,

1 tsp. cornstarch plus 3 tbsp. water if part of a recipe or;

1 banana (best for cakes and pancakes) or;

2 tbsp. of cornstarch or arrowroot starch or,

$\frac{1}{4}$ cup tofu (blend with liquid ingredients before adding to any dry ingredients)

Evaporated Milk

Light cream or half and half or heavy cream.

Flour (thickeners, use up to 2-3 tbsp. only)

Bisquick, tapioca (quick cooking), cornstarch, arrowroot (use small amount), potato starch, mashed potato flakes, or pancake mix

Garlic (equivalent of 1 clove)

$\frac{1}{4}$ tsp. minced, dried garlic or,

$\frac{1}{3}$ tsp. garlic powder or,

$\frac{1}{4}$ tsp. garlic juice or

$\frac{1}{2}$ tsp. garlic salt (omit $\frac{1}{2}$ tsp. salt from recipe)

Ghee

Clarified butter

Honey (one cup in baked goods)

$1\frac{1}{4}$ cups granulated sugar & $\frac{1}{4}$ cup water

Juniper Berries

A small amount of gin

Lemongrass

Lemon or lemon rind or verbena or lime rind

Lemon Juice

Use $\frac{1}{2}$ tsp. white vinegar for each tsp. lemon juice, unless the flavor is required.

Lovage

Celery leaves

Marjam

Oregano (use small amount), thyme or savory

Masa Harina

Corn flour

Mascarpone

    Cream cheese, whipped with a small amount of butter

Meat

    Tempeh (cultured soybeans provides a chewy texture)

    Tofu (after it has been frozen)

    Wheat gluten

Milk, Evaporated

    Light cream or half and half or heavy cream

Milk (in baked goods)

    Fruit juice & $\frac{1}{2}$ tsp. baking soda mixed in with the flour

Milk (one cup)

    $\frac{1}{2}$ cup evaporated milk & $\frac{1}{2}$ cup of water or,

    3 tbsp. powdered milk & 1 cup of water.

    If whole milk is called for, add 2 tbsp. butter

Molasses (one cup)

    1 cup of honey

Nutmeg

    Allspice or cloves or mace

Nuts (in baked goods only)

    Bran

Oregano

    Marjoram, rosemary, or thyme (fresh only)

Pancetta

    Lean bacon (cooked) or very thin sliced ham

Parsley

    Chervil or cilantro

Polenta

    Cornmeal or grits (corn)

Poultry Seasoning

    Sage & a blend of any of these: thyme, marjoram, savory, black pepper, rosemary

Rosemary

    Thyme, tarragon, or savory

Saffron ($\frac{1}{8}$ tsp.)

    1 tsp. dried yellow marigold petals or,

    1 tsp. azafran or,

    1 tsp. safflower or,

    $\frac{1}{2}$ to 1 tsp. turmeric (adds color)

Sage

    Poultry seasoning, savory, marjoram or rosemary

Self-Rising Flour (1 cup)

    1 cup all-purpose flour & 1 tsp. baking powder, $\frac{1}{2}$ tsp. salt, and $\frac{1}{4}$ tsp. baking soda

Shallots

    Small green onions, leeks, standard onions (use small amount) or,

    scallions (use more than is called for)

Shortening (one cup in baked goods only)

    1 cup butter or

    1 cup hard margarine

Sour Cream (1 cup)

    1 tbsp. white vinega & sufficient milk to make 1 cup. Allow the mixture to stand for 5 minutes before using or,

    1 tbsp. lemon juice & enough evaporated milk to make 1 cup or,

    1 cup of plain yogurt if it is being used in a dip or cold soup or,

    6 oz. cream cheese plus 3 tbsp. milk or,

    $\frac{1}{3}$ cup of melted butter & $\frac{3}{4}$ cup of sour milk for baked goods

Tahini

    Finely ground sesame seeds

Tarragon

    Anise (use small amount), chervil (use larger amount), parsley (use larger amount), or a dash of fennel seed

Tomato Paste (1 tbsp.)

    1 tbsp. ketchup or,

    $\frac{1}{2}$ cup of tomato sauce, providing you reduce some of the other liquid

Turmeric

    Mustard powder

Vanilla Extract (in baked goods only)

    Almond extract or other extracts that will alter the flavor

Vinegar

    Lemon juice in cooking and salads only, or grapefruit juice in salads, wine, and marinades

Yogurt

    Sour cream, creme fraiche, buttermilk, heavy cream or mayonnaise (use in small amounts)

COMMON LIQUID SUBSTITUTIONS

The following substitution may be used for liquids that are not available at the time the recipe is being prepared. However, it is always better to use the ingredients called for in the recipe for the best results.

INGREDIENT	ADEQUATE SUBSTITUTION
1 cup barbecue sauce	1 cup ketchup & 2 tsp. Worcestershire sauce
1 cup broth	1 bouillon cube dissolved in 1 cup of water
1 cup butter	1 cup vegetable shortening & 2 tbsp. water
1 cup buttermilk	1 tbsp. lemon juice & balance of cup in milk, then allow to stand for 5 minutes before using or add 1 tbsp. of vinegar to 1 cup evaporated milk and allow to stand for 5 minutes before using.
1 cup chili sauce	1 cup tomato sauce & $\frac{1}{2}$ cup sugar & 2 tbsp. vinegar
1 cup corn syrup	$\frac{3}{4}$ cup sugar & $\frac{1}{4}$ cup water
1 cup creme fraiche	$\frac{1}{2}$ cup sour cream & $\frac{1}{2}$ cup heavy cream
1 egg	1 banana or 2 tbsp. cornstarch or arrowroot starch or $\frac{1}{4}$ cup tofu blended into liquid ingredients well
1 cup evaporated milk	Equal amount of light or cream or half and half
1 cup heavy cream	$\frac{3}{4}$ cup whole milk & $\frac{1}{3}$ cup of butter
1 cup light cream	1 cup milk & 3 tbsp. butter
1 cup ketchup	1 cup tomato sauce & 4 tbsp. sugar & 2 tbsp. vinegar & $\frac{1}{4}$ tsp. ground cloves
1 cup honey	1 $\frac{1}{4}$ cups granulated sugar & $\frac{1}{4}$ cup water
1 tsp. lemon juice	1 tsp. of vinegar
1 cup molasses	1 cup honey
1 cup whole milk	4 tbsp. dry whole milk & 1 cup water or 1 cup buttermilk & $\frac{1}{2}$ tsp. baking soda
1 cup non-fat milk (skim)	4 tbsp. nonfat dry milk & 1 cup water
1 cup sour milk	1 tbsp. lemon juice or vinegar & additional milk to fill 1 cup, allow it to stand for 5 minutes
2 drops hot pepper sauce	Dash of cayenne or red pepper
2 tsp. tapioca	1 tbsp. all-purpose flour (more if desired)
1 cup tomato juice	$\frac{1}{2}$ cup tomato sauce & $\frac{1}{2}$ cup water
1 tbsp. tomato paste	1 tbsp. tomato ketchup
1 cup tomato puree	6 oz. can tomato paste & 6 oz. water
1 cup wine	1 cup apple juice or apple cider or 1 part vinegar, diluted in 3 parts of water
1 cup yogurt	1 cup buttermilk or sour cream

Extracts and Essences

INGREDIENT	ADEQUATE SUBSTITUTION
Angostura Bitters	Orange Bitters or Worcestershire sauce
Anise Extract	Anise Oil (only use 50%)
Cinnamon Extract	Cinnamon Oil (only 1/4 as much)
Ginger Juice	Place minced ginger in cheesecloth and squeeze out the juice.
Oil of Bitter Almonds	Almond Extract (use 50% more)
Peppermint Extract	Peppermint Oil (use 1/4 as much)
Rose Water	Rose Syrup (2-3 drops)

Oils and Cooking Sprays

Almond Oil	Walnut Oil or Extra Virgin Olive Oil
Canola Oil	Corn Oil or Safflower Oil
Clarified Butter	Butter (foods may overbrown)
Coconut Oil	Canola Oil or Corn Oil
Corn Oil	Canola Oil or Soybean Oil
Ghee	Clarified Butter or Canola Oil
Grapeseed Oil	Avocado Oil (very high smoke point)
Peanut Oil	Corn Oil 0r Canola Oil
Schmaltz	No known substitute when prepared right
Soybean Oil	Corn Oil

Vinegar Substitutes

Apple Cider Vinegar	Wine Vinegar
Balsamic Vinegar	Sherry Vinegar
Champagne Vinegar	Apple Cider Vinegar
Raspberry Vinegar	Red Wine Vinegar
Red Wine Vinegar	Balsamic Vinegar
Rice Vinegar	Apple Cider Vinegar
White Vinegar	Apple Cider Vinegar (canning with at least 5% acidity)

I Can See a Rainbow, See a Rainbow......

Liquid food colorings are sold in small bottles since a little goes a long way. Food coloring is composed of water, propylene glycol and artificial colors, many of which are suspect in relation to laboratory studies pertaining to cancer in mice. However, the small amount that is used should pose no health risk. A new addition to the colorings is decorative gels, which are composed of corn syrup, water, modified corn starch, salt, carrageenan gum, citric acid, preservatives and, of course, those artificial dyes. Liquid food colorings have a safe shelf life of about 4 years if stored in a cool, dry location.

Measurements

These Liquids Do Measure up

60 drops	=	5 ml. or 1 tsp.
3 tsp.	=	1 tbsp.
2 tbsp.	=	30 ml. or 1 fl. oz.
8 tbsp.	=	$\frac{1}{2}$ cup
5 large eggs	=	1 cup
2 tbsp. butter	=	1 oz.
1 oz.	=	30 grams
Juice of 1 orange	=	5-6 tsp.
8 fluid oz.	=	1 cup
16 fluid oz.	=	2 cups (1 pt.)
32 fluid oz.	=	4 cups (1 qt.)
4 qt.	=	6 cups (1 gal.)

Grandmother's
PERSONAL CARE SECRETS

GROOMING AND SUCH

This Will Really Give your Shampoo a Lift
If you want your hair to be shiny, just add a small amount of vodka to the shampoo bottle.

Slippery when Wet?
For inexpensive bath oil, try using sunflower oil and either lavender or rose petal herb.

A Revival
Hairbrushes and combs may be revived by soaking them in a pot of warm water and 1 tbsp. baking soda or ammonia.

Reflecting

If you lose a contact lens, turn the lights off and use a flashlight. The lens will reflect the light.

Squeaky Clean

If you want your hair to really sparkle, try adding a tsp. of white vinegar to your final rinse.

Ring Around the Finger

If you are unable to remove a ring, try placing your hand in a bowl of very cold water for a few seconds.

Or Just Wear Gloves

If you would like to keep dirt from getting under your nails when you are working in the garden, just rub your nails over a bar of soap before starting work.

A Cleaner-Upper

Laundry detergent makes an excellent hand cleaner for very hard to clean hands.

A Cup of Joe

If you have red hair or are a brunette, try rinsing your hair with black coffee, then clear water to add luster.

Feet Ade

If you want to freshen your feet, try using a few fresh lemon slices. Just rub it in.

This Will Snap You Awake Instantly

The life of pantyhose can be extended if they are placed in the freezer for the first night only. It will strengthen the fibers, but make sure you thaw them out before wearing then, unless you are having trouble waking up in the morning.

Tastes Good, too

An inexpensive facial treatment is as follows: for normal to somewhat oily skin, use 1 cup yogurt, 1 tsp. fresh lemon juice, 1 tsp. fresh orange juice and 1 tsp. carrot juice. Blend all ingredients well and apply to your face for 10-15 minutes, then rinse with warm water.

New Use for Breakfast Food

For a great facial scrub, try using a paste of oatmeal and water. Apply the paste, then allow it to dry until your skin feels tight. Then remove it with your fingers with a back and forth motion to remove the dead skin.

Ode De Refrigerator

Perfume should be stored in the refrigerator if you're not going to use it up over a reasonable period of time, approximately 30 days.

Great Treat for Halloween

Mashing $1/2$ avocado and spreading it thickly on your face can make a great facial. Wait 20 minutes, then wash off with warm water. Don't let your husband see you.

Why Didn't I Think of That?

Place a small amount of vegetable oil on the threads of nail polish bottles and the lid won't stick.

Yuk!

To make your own deodorant, mix 2 tsp. baking soda, 2 tsp. petroleum jelly, and 2 tsp. talcum powder.

Fruit-Paste

To remove the yellow from your teeth, try using mashed fresh strawberries to brush with.

A Little Dab Will Do you

Many types of toothpaste are now adding baking soda to their formula. However, you could just use a small amount of baking soda to brush your teeth. Just dampen your brush and sprinkle it on.

A Pasty

For bad sunburn, try making a paste of baking soda and water. Works almost as good as the white vinegar.

How Dry I am

If you want to make a bar of soap last longer, try unwrapping it before you use it and allow it to dry out.

Shampoo Away

To add shine to your hair and to remove shampoo buildup, try adding 2 tbsp. apple cider vinegar to the rinse water.

A Little Acid Goes a Long Way

Before polishing your nails, try applying a small amount of white vinegar to your nails. They will stay shiny longer and it will clean them. Bleaching your fingernails is easy. All you have to do is soak them in lemon or lime juice. The mild citric acid will do the job.

Baby Yourself

Baby oil will do the same job as a fancy cleansing cream at about a third of the price.

The Eyes Have it

For puffy eyes, place slices of cucumber on your eyes. There is a chemical in cucumber that acts as an anti-inflammatory.

Perfume Holder

If you want your perfume to last longer, try applying a small amount of petroleum jelly first on the area.

Skinade

Skin blemishes can be cleared up quickly by dabbing them with lemon juice 4-6 times per day.

Balancing Act

If you want to restore the natural acid balance to your skin, try using $\frac{1}{2}$ cup of apple cider vinegar in a basin of water. Splash it on your face, then allow it to dry before removing with a towel.

Being Thrifty

To make an inexpensive shampoo, mix $\frac{1}{2}$ cup white vinegar, $\frac{1}{2}$ cup dish detergent, $\frac{1}{4}$ cup water with 2 tsp. mayonnaise (not low-cal).

Sweet Grit

To remove garden stains from your hands, try placing about $\frac{1}{2}$ tsp. sugar with the soap lather when you wash your hands. You will be amazed how easily the stains are removed.

The Mad Scientist

The formula for good liquid hand soap is a 4 oz. bar of soap, preferably one that has a moisturizing cream, and 3 cups of water. Grate the soap as fine as possible, then add the water. Microwave on high till dissolved, stirring every few minutes, then allow it to cool before using.

A Little Squirt

If you want your makeup to last longer, try spraying your face first with mineral water and allowing it to dry.

Hot and Cold

If you break your lipstick, try heating the broken ends over a matchstick until they are soft, then place them together and place in the freezer.

No Hanging Around Anymore

If hangnails are bothersome, try rubbing vitamin E oil around the cuticles.

Shades of Lawrence Welk

To make your own bubble bath liquid, try placing soap slivers in a porous drawstring bag. Attach the bag to the tap while the water is filling the tub, and instant bubble bath! Place herbs in the bag for a pleasant fragrance.

13

Getting Out
THE STAINS

GENERAL RULES FOR STAIN REMOVAL

- Never rub too hard to remove a stain since this will cause damage to the fabric, which can never be repaired.
- Never wash any fabric before attempting to remove the stain, Washing in a detergent may actually set the stain and make it impossible to remove later.
- Stains on washable fabrics should be treated as soon as possible.
- Remember, fresh stains will come out more easily than old ones.
- Non-washable items that normally go to the cleaners should be taken as soon as possible. Identify the stain for the dry cleaner. If you know what the stain is, be sure and tell him/her.

Remove Mildew from Clothes
Just moisten the mildew area with salt and lemon juice, then place it in the sunlight to bleach out the stain.

Pouring Salt on an Open Spill
If you ever spill red wine on your carpet, try pouring salt on the area as soon as possible and watch the wine being absorbed almost instantly. Then wait until it dries, and vacuum it up. Salt tends to provide a special capillary action that will attract most liquids.

Lights on
When trying to remove stains at home, make sure you do it on a clean, well-lighted work surface. Always use fresh clean rags or a towel.

Rust Removal
Rust stains can be removed by wetting the areas with lemon juice, then sprinkle with a small amount of salt and allow to sit in direct sunlight for 30-45 minutes.

Chrome Cleaner Works Great
Automotive chrome cleaner will clean many kitchen appliances.

That Burning Sensation
A scorch can be removed by rubbing a raw onion on the scorched area and allowing the juice to soak in thoroughly for at least 2-3 hours before washing.

Make Sure it's Chilled
Bloodstains may be cleaned with club soda.

A Shining Example
To shine chrome fixture, try rubbing them with newspaper while they are still damp. Baby oil and a soft cloth works well. Aluminum foil will also do the job.

A Word to the Wise
If you are going to use a commercial stain removal substance, be sure and follow directions carefully.

Testing, One, Two
Always test a stain remover on an area of the fabric that will not show to be sure of the colorfastness of the fabric. Allow the product to stand on the area for at least 3-5 minutes before rinsing off. If there are any changes in the fabric color, do not use.

Hide That Spot

When treating a spot, it should be placed face down on paper towel, then apply the stain remover to the underside of the garment, allowing the stain to be forced to the surface and not back through the fabric. The paper towel should be replaced a number of times, if it is a tough stain to remove.

Where Art Thou Color?

If you are going to use a bleach product, never use it on a colored garment. It is necessary to bleach the whole garment to avoid uneven color removal. If there is a change in color, it will at least be uniform.

Residues be gone

As soon as the stain is removed, launder immediately with your favorite laundry detergent. This will also remove the residues from the stain remover. wwwtextileaffairs.com/stains.htm

Stain Removal Products

Prompt treatment is the key to stain removal, and it would be wise to have the supplies on hand at all times. The following is a list of some of the more common ingredients needed for most stain removal. However, more natural stain and general cleaning preparations are recommended.

BLEACHES
Chlorine bleach
Fabric color remover
Non-chlorine, all fabric, bleach

MISCELLANEOUS REMOVERS
Ammonia
Rust stain remover
White vinegar

DETERGENTS
Enzyme detergent
Enzyme presoaker
Liquid detergent

SOLVENTS
Dry cleaner spot remover
Nail polish remover
Rubbing alcohol
Turpentine

SOAPS
Laundry detergent
White bar soap

SUPPLIES
Clean white cloths
Paper towels

**Any of the above products that cannot be found at the supermarket
will be available at any drug store.**

Caution:

Some stain removal materials are flammable, while others are poison or toxic. Store them safely and use with care.

Chemical Alert

Keep stain removal supplies out of reach of children. They should be stored in closed containers with childproof lids and in a cool, dry location away from any food products.

Smells Nice, Too

Lemon extract will remove black scuff marks from shoes and luggage.

Hard One to Get out

Stains from ballpoint pens can be removed with hair spray or milk.

Reading the Writing

Read the labels on cleaning products and follow directions. Heed all label warnings and always try to store them in their original containers.

Container Smarts

Empty and wash all containers immediately after using them. It is best to store stain removal supplies in glass or un-chipped porcelain containers. Solvents will ruin plastic containers. Rusty containers should never be used

Be careful. Never allow chemicals near your face and especially your eyes. Wash any spilled chemicals off your hands as soon as possible.

Wear a Gas Mask

Use chemicals that give off vapors in a well-ventilated location, preferably outside. Try not to breathe the vapors.

Poooof

Never use a solvent near an open fire or an electrical outlet.

Yum, Yum Fabric

Never add solvents directly into the washing machine. Always allow a solvent-treated fabric to dry before washing or placing it into the dryer.

A Witches' Brew

Never mix stain removal materials with each other, especially ammonia and chlorine bleach. If it's necessary to use both, make sure one is thoroughly rinsed out, before adding the other.

RECIPES FOR SAFE CLEANING PRODUCTS

The following recipes are safe when mixed in the quantities indicated below. The mixing of other household chemicals may be dangerous.

All-Purpose Household Cleaner- Add 1 tsp. liquid soap and 1 tsp. trisodium phosphate (TSP) to 1 qt. of warm water. This is a very effective cleaner for many cleaning jobs, including countertops and walls. However, try an area of the wall that will not show before using, in case your walls are painted with a poor quality water-based flat paint.

Chlorine Bleach- Best to use hydrogen peroxide-based bleach.

Degreaser (engines, etc.)- Best to use a water-based cleaner that is well diluted instead of kerosene, turpentine, or a commercial engine degreaser. These are available in paint stores and the label should read "nonflammable," "non-toxic," or "store at temperatures above freezing." These will be water-based products and will do the job.

Degreaser (kitchen, grill)- Add 2 tbsp. or TSP to 1 gal. hot water or use a non-chlorinated scouring cleanser with a scouring or steel wool pad.

Fabric Softener- Fabrics produced from natural fibers do not need fabric softeners, only synthetics.

Floor Cleaner- For vinyl floors, use ½ cup white vinegar to 1 gal. warm water. Wood floors may be damp-mopped with a mild liquid soap.

Furniture Polish- Mineral oil may be used; however, most wood surfaces may be cleaned with a damp cloth.

Oven Cleaner- Mix 2 tbsp. baking soda or TSP in 1 gal. warm water and scrub with a very fine steel wool pad (0000). Rubber gloves should be worn and the area rinsed well. For difficult baked-on areas, try scrubbing with a pumice stone. If the above fails, try using an oven cleaner that states "no caustic fumes" on the label.

Glass Cleaner- Use 2-3 cup spray bottle with ½ tsp. liquid soap, 3 tbsp. white vinegar and 2 cups of water. If the windows are very dirty, try using more liquid soap.

Laundry Detergent- Use laundry soap in place of the detergents. Washing soda may be used in place of a softener. An alternate would be to use detergents with no added bleaches or softeners. Bleach should be used in moderation when needed.

Mildew Remover- Scrub the area with baking soda or if very stubborn with TSP.

Scouring Powder- Baking soda will work well in most instances.

Toilet Bowl Cleaner- Use a non-chlorinated scouring powder and a stiff brush. To remove hard water deposits, pour white vinegar or a commercial citric acid-based toilet bowl cleaner into the toilet and allow it to sit for several hours or overnight before scrubbing.

NOTE: Washing soda and TSP are caustic and should be kept out of the reach of children.

Fabric Advice

It is best to know the fiber content in clothing items. If sewn-in labels are to be removed, a note should be made as to which item it was removed from. Any durable press or polyester fabric, such as Dacron holds soil very well and especially stains. A dry cleaning solvent will work the best. If the stain remains after the first treatment, try once more. If the fabric has been washed or has been placed in a dryer, the stain may never come out.

- Never use chlorine bleach on silk, wool, or Spandex.
- Never remove a stain from leather: take it to the dry cleaners or send to an expert.

STAIN REMOVAL FROM WASHABLE FABRICS

A number of stains can be removed right in your washing machine. Laundry detergents that state that they contain enzymes will provide the best cleaning and stain removal. Enzyme presoak products provide extra cleaning and stain removal for fabrics that may have a more difficult stain. An enzyme detergent or enzyme presoak product should be able to remove the following common stains:

Blood	Gravy	Body soils	Egg
Fruits	Milk	Chocolate	Grass
Cream soups	Baby formula	Puddings	Vegetables
Baby foods	Ice cream	Most food soils	

I Wonder Where the Yellow Went?

Yellowed fabrics can be restored and even old unknown stains may be removed by first soaking in an enzyme presoak product (Proctor & Gamble has excellent ones), such as Biz and then laundering.

Can't Perform Magic

Remember, even the best enzyme detergent or enzyme presoak product is not capable of removing all types of stains. A number of grease soils and highly colored stains may require special pretreatment before laundering. Since many stains require a variety of different soil removal treatments and techniques, it is important to identify a stain before trying to remove it. A number of stains may actually be set if the wrong method is used.

Stains Usually Removed and their Recommended Methods

Beverage- Sponge the area with cold water or soak, then sponge again. Launder with oxygen bleach and the hottest water that is safe for the fabric.

Blood- Soak the fabric in cold water as soon as possible. If the stain persists, soak in warm water with a presoak product before laundering. Try club soda.

Candle Wax- The surface wax should be removed with a dull knife. The item should then be placed stain-face-down on paper towels, then sponge the remaining stain with dry cleaning solvent. Allow it to dry, then launder. If traces of color from the wax remain, try soaking it in Biz or oxygen bleach before laundering again. If the color is still present, try laundering again using chlorine bleach, if the fabric is chlorine bleach-safe.

Catsup\Tomato Products- Remove excess with a dull knife, then soak in cold water and launder, using the hottest water the fabric will stand.

Chewing Gum/Adhesive Tape/Rubber Cement- First: apply ice to the stain to harden it. Remove excess stain material with a dull knife. Place the item face down on paper towels and sponge with a dry cleaning solvent.

Chocolate\Cocoa- Soak in cold water, then launder with oxygen bleach, using the hottest water the fabric will stand.

Coffee/Tea- Best to soak in Biz or oxygen bleach, using the hottest water that is safe for the stained fabric, then launder. If the stain persists, try laundering again using chlorine bleach, if it is safe to do so.

Cosmetics- Dampen stain and rub gently with a white bar soap, then rinse well and launder.

Crayon- If there are only a few spots, they can be treated the same as candle wax. If there are many items that are stained, first wash the items with hot water and laundry soap (e.g. Ivory Snow) and 1 cup baking soda. If the spots remain, have the clothes dry cleaned.

Deodorants And Anti-Perspirants- Apply white vinegar, then rub and rinse. If the stain remains, try saturating the area with rubbing alcohol, rinse, then soak in Biz or an oxygen bleach and launder. If the stain remains, wash in chlorine bleach if safe for fabric.

Dye Transfer- If; you have white fabrics that have picked up dye from a colored garment that "bled," try restoring the white by using a fabric color remover. Launder if any of the dye remains, using chlorine bleach if it is safe for the fabric.

Egg/Meat Juice- Remove excess with a dull knife, then soak in cold water. Launder in oxygen bleach in very hot water.

Fabric Softeners- These stains usually result from accidental spills and can be removed by rubbing the area with a piece of cloth, moistened with bar soap, then launder.

Formula- Soak in warm water, then launder with oxygen bleach and the hottest water that is safe for the fabric.

Fruit\Fruit Juices- Soak in cold water before laundering.

Grass- The green area should be sponged with denatured alcohol before washing in very hot water and oxygen bleach.

Grease Stains- The stained area should be placed face down on paper towels. Dry cleaning solvent should be placed on the backside of the stain and then brushed from the center of the stain to the outer edges, using a clean white cloth. Moisten the stain with warm water and rub with bar soap or a mild liquid detergent, then rinse and launder.

Gum- Rub with ice and carefully remove the gum with a dull knife before laundering.

Ink Stains- For removal of ballpoint stains, place the stain face down on paper towels and sponge the back of the stain with dry cleaning solvent. If there is some ink left, try rubbing the area with a moistened bar soap, rinse and then launder. For any other type of ink stains, just try and remove the stain with a dampened cloth and bar soap, rinse and soak in Biz or an oxygen bleach using very hot water. If the stain won't come out, try using chlorine bleach, if the fabric is safe. Some permanent ink may never be removed.

Ink Felt Tip- Rub the area with Fantastic or Mr. Clean, rinse and repeat if necessary. May be impossible to remove.

Iodine- Rinse the fabric from the underside with cool water, then soak in a solution of fabric color remover, rinse and then launder.

Lipstick- The stain should be placed face down on paper towels and then sponged with dry cleaning solvent, replacing the paper towels frequently while the color is being removed. Moisten the stain with cool water and then rub with bar soap, rinse and launder.

Mildew- Fabric should be laundered, using chlorine bleach if it is safe for the fabric. If not, try soaking it in oxygen bleach and then launder.

Milk- The fabric should be rinsed in cold water as soon as possible, and then washed in cold water, using a liquid detergent.

Mustard- Moisten stain with cool water then rub with bar soap, rinse and launder using chlorine bleach, if it is safe for the fabric. If not, soak in Biz or an oxygen detergent using very hot water, then launder. It may take several treatments to remove all of the stain.

Nail Polish- The fabric stain should be placed face down on paper towels, then sponge the back of the stain frequently and repeat until the stain disappears and launder. Never use nail polish remover on fabric, best to have them dry cleaned.

Paint- Try to treat the stain while it is still wet. Latex, acrylic and water-based paints cannot be removed once they have dried. While they are wet: rinse in warm water to flush the paint out, then launder. Oil-based paints can be removed with solvent that is recommended on the paint can. If it does not give this information, try using turpentine. then rinse and rub with bar soap, and launder.

Perspiration- Moisten the stain and rub with bar soap. Be gentle as perspiration may weaken some fibers, especially silk. Most fabrics should be presoaked in Biz or an enzyme detergent and then laundered in hot water and chlorine bleach, if the fabric is safe. Another method is to mix 4 tbsp. salt to 1 qt. hot water and sponge on the fabric until the stain disappears.

Perfume - same as beverages

Rust- Never use chlorine bleach on rust, apply a rust stain remover, rinse then launder. You can also use a fabric color remover and then launder, or if the stain is really stubborn, try using 1 oz. oxalic acid crystals (or straight warm rhubarb juice) dissolved in 1 gal. water, mixed in a plastic container, then rinse and launder.

Scorch- Soak the fabric in a strong solution of Biz and oxygen bleach, using very hot water if safe for the fabric, then launder. If the scorch remains, it will be necessary to repeat the procedure using chlorine bleach, if the fabric will take it.

Shoe Polish- Try applying a mixture of 1 part rubbing alcohol and 2 parts water for colored fabrics and only the straight alcohol for whites.

Suede- Rain spots can be removed by lightly rubbing the area with an emery board. If there are grease spots, try using white vinegar or club soda, then blot out the stain. Afterwards, brush with a suede brush.

Tar- The area should be rubbed with kerosene until all the tar is dissolved, then wash as usual. Test a small area first to be sure it is colorfast.

Tobacco- Moisten the stain and rub with bar soap rinse, then launder. If the stain persists, try soaking it in Biz or an oxygen detergent, then launder. As a last resort, use chlorine bleach if the fabric is safe.

Urine, Vomit, Mucous- Soak the fabric in Biz or an enzyme detergent. Launder using chlorine bleach, if safe for the fabric. If not, use oxygen bleach with detergent.

Wine/Soft Drinks- Soak the fabric with Biz or oxygen bleach using very hot water, then launder. Use chlorine bleach if needed and if the fabric is safe.

NATURAL METHODS STAIN REMOVAL

Totally Thrifty

If you wish to use less detergent and save money, try using slivers of old soaps placed in a sock with the neck tied. Place the sock into the washer and you will use less detergent.

Setting It Permanently

To colorfast a possible problem garment, try soaking the colored garment in cold, salty water for 30 minutes before laundering.

Don't Get Stung

After washing a piece of clothing with a zipper that has given you problems, try rubbing beeswax on the zipper to resolve the problem and remove any grime that has accumulated.

The Old Bubble Machine

Placing too much soap in the washing machine can cause problems. If this happens, just pour 2 tbsp. white vinegar or a capful of fabric softener into the machine to neutralize some of the soap.

Begone, Old Soap

When washing clothes, to be sure that all the soap has been removed, try adding 1 cup white vinegar to the rinse cycle. The vinegar will dissolve the alkalinity in detergents, as well as giving the clothes a pleasant fragrance.

The Green, Green Grass of Home

Grass stains will be easily removed with toothpaste, scrub in with a toothbrush before washing. Another method is to rub the stain with molasses and allow it to stand overnight, then wash with regular dish soap by itself. If all else fails, try methyl alcohol, but be sure the color is set. Best to try an area that won't show first.

Greaseless

Spic and Span placed in the washer is a great grease remover, $\frac{1}{4}$ cup is all that is needed.

Wrinkle Remover

To avoid ironing many different types of clothes, just remove them from the dryer the second it stops and fold or hang up immediately.

Catch that Color

Washing colored material for the first time may be risky, unless you wash it in Epsom salts. One gal. water to 1 tsp. is all that is needed. The material will not run.

The Disappearing Act

An excellent spot remover can be made using 2 parts of water to 1 part rubbing alcohol.

A Dirty Job

To remove difficult dirt, such as collars, mix $\frac{1}{3}$ cup of water with $\frac{1}{3}$ cup of liquid detergent and $\frac{1}{3}$ cup of ammonia. Place the ingredients in a spray bottle. Rubbing shampoo into the area may also work.

Lint Magnet

To keep corduroy garments from retaining lint, turn them inside out when washing.

Hairballs

To avoid hairballs on acrylic sweaters, turn them inside out when washing them.

One of the Toughest

Iodine stains can be removed using a mixture of baking soda and water. Allow it to remain on for about 30 minutes, then rub with mild action.

Use Only the Unsalted

Butter or margarine will remove tar from clothing, just rub until it's gone. The butter is easily removed with any type of spray and wash product.

Inka-Ka-Dinka-Doo

Rubbing alcohol or hair spray may remove a number of ink pen stains.

Beware of a Tight Fit

If you wash slipcovers, be sure and replace them when they are still damp. They will fit better and will not need to be ironed.

Blowdrying

If sweater cuffs are stretched, dip them in hot water and dry with a hairdryer.

A Spot of Tea, Perhaps

Tea stains on tablecloths can be removed with glycerin. Try letting it sit overnight in the solution before washing.

Into the Freezer

Candle wax on tablecloths can be removed by freezing with ice cubes.

Yuk

Lace doilies should be hand-washed in sour milk for the best results.

Hold the Shaving Cream

If you have a problem with small burrs on sweaters, try using a disposable razor to remove them.

Easy Does It

If you are washing a wool garment, be careful not to pull on it. Wool is very weak when wet. Lay the garment on a towel, roll it up and squeeze the excess water out.

Neutralizer

If you have a difficult bloodstain, try making a paste of meat tenderizer and cold water. Sponge on the area and allow it to stand for 20-30 minutes. Rinse in cold water, then wash. Hydrogen peroxide may also work.

Bathing Stuffed Animals

To clean stuffed animals that cannot be placed in the washer, just place them in a cloth bag, add baking soda, then shake.

Powder me

White flour will clean white gloves, just rub.

A Slippery Subject

Lipstick stains will clean out of clothes by using Vaseline.

A Revival

If you shrink a woolen garment, try soaking it in a hair cream rinse. This will usually make them easy to stretch back into the original size. Another method is to dissolve 1 oz. Borax in 1 tsp. hot water, then add it to 1 gal. warm water. Place the garment in, stretch back to shape, then rinse it in 1 gal. warm water with 2 tbsp. white vinegar added.

Be Stingy, Be Smart

When you are doing a small wash load, tear the fabric-softening sheet in half for the same results.

A Solid Fact

To make your own spray starch, purchase 1 bottle of liquid starch concentrate and mix one part of liquid starch to 1 part of water. Use a spray bottle.

Button, Button, Who's Got the Button

If you lose buttons regularly on children's clothing, try sewing them on with dental floss.

True Grit

If your iron is sticking, try running it over a piece of paper with sprinkled salt on it.

Well-Seasoned Curtains

Water-stained fabrics should be placed in salt water and soaked until the stain is gone.

Bring in the Sub

If you prefer not to use bleach, try substituting 3 tbsp. hydrogen peroxide to the wash load.

Save the Buttons

Always remove buttons before discarding a garment. They may come in handy at a later date.

Attractive Salt

Cleaning silk flowers is easy if you place them in a plastic bag with 2 tbsp. salt and shake vigorously while holding on to the stems. Salt tends to attract the dust.

Ironing Smarts

When ironing, always iron the fabrics that require a cool temperature first as the iron heats up.

Dew Tell

Mildew on shower curtains can be removed with a mixture of $\frac{1}{2}$ cup bleach, $\frac{1}{2}$ cup powdered detergent, and 1 gal. water. To prolong the life of shower curtains, add 1 cup of white vinegar to the final rinse.

Making Colors Fast

To prevent jeans from fading (if you want to), soak the jeans in $\frac{1}{2}$ cup of white vinegar and 2 qt. water for 1 hour before you wash them for the first time.

Jean Smarts

Blue jeans should only be washed in cold water, then placed in a moderate heat dryer for only 10 minutes. Then they should be placed on a wooden hanger to continue drying.

Dollar Saver

If you would like to save dollars on dry cleaning of wool blankets, try washing them in a mild dishwasher soap on a very gentle cycle, then air fluff to dry.

No One Will Ever Know

If you scorch a garment, try removing the scorch with cloth that has been dampened with vinegar. Only use a warm iron, not too hot. Cotton scorch marks tend to respond better to peroxide.

Insulation

A sheet of aluminum foil placed underneath the ironing board cover will allow the heat to be retained for a longer period of time.

Button, Button....

Always remember to place a small amount of clear nail polish in the center of every button on a new garment. This seals the threads and they will last longer.

A Shocking Situation

A pipe cleaner dipped in white vinegar should be used to clean the holes in the iron after it is completely cool. Make sure it is unplugged.

If You're in a Spot

Glass cleaner sometimes makes an excellent spot remover, if you need something in a hurry. Make sure the fabric is colorfast.

Brighten-up

If you want to whiten your whites, try adding a cup of dishwasher detergent to the washer. Even whitens sweat socks.

Any Pencil Will Do

A sticky zipper will respond to a rubbing with a lead pencil. Does an excellent job of lubricating it.

A Temporary Solution

If a button comes off, try reattaching it with the wire from a twist tie.

Don't Suck your Thumb

If you use a thimble to sew or sort papers, try wetting your finger before you place the thimble on. This creates suction and holds the thimble on.

A Sealer

When you wash your sneakers, spray them with a spray starch to help them resist becoming soiled.

Dirty Bottom

If the bottom of the iron gets dirty, just clean it with a steel wool soap pad. If you want to make it shiny again, just run a piece of waxed paper over it.

Rustade

Rust marks on clothing can be removed with lemon juice and a small amount of salt easily rubbed in, then allowed to sit in the sun for 2 hours.

And Away We Go

To dry the insides of shoes or sneakers, try placing the blower end of the vacuum hose inside.

A Tripper-Upper

If you have problems with your shoelaces becoming undone, just dampen them before tying them.

A Word of Caution

Silk clothing should be hand washed using cool water with Ivory liquid soap. When you rinse, try adding a small amount of lanolin to help preserve the material. Always drip dry, never place the garment in the dryer. Then, iron using a soft piece of cloth over the garment.

Shape-up, and Don't Lose your Color

Cold water should always be used in the rinse cycle to help the clothes retain their shape and color.

Kitchen
PROBLEMS & SOLUTIONS

CABINETS

Problems/Questions:

1. Hinges squeak when opening the doors.
2. Using the wrong method when preparing to re-paint cabinets.
3. Cleaning the cabinets with the wrong materials.
4. Cabinet hinge is loose.
5. Cabinet door does not close properly.
6. The cabinet door keeps banging when closing.
7. Cabinet doors are not level.
8. Cabinet drawers are sticking.
9. Scratch or small dent in door.
10. Cabinet is swelling from moisture.

Solutions/Answers:

1. Squeaky door and cabinet hinges, as well as sticky locks, can be sprayed with a non-stick vegetable spray, such as PamTM or a silicon spray. Do not use WD-40 in a lock since it contains petroleum distillates and will collect dust.

2. When refinishing and painting kitchen cabinets, there is no need to sand them first. Just use a degreaser, paint it on then wipe it off as per manufacturer's directions. It will remove the grease and the grime.

3. Never use abrasive cleaners, such as scouring pads or powdered cleansers. Use liquid dish soap and water. Never use aerosols sprays that contain silicones or paste waxes. Be careful not to allow oven cleaners to touch the cabinets.

4. If you have a loose cabinet hinge, you will have to drill out a larger hole and be sure you don't go all the way through the cabinet. Glue in a hardwood peg, usually a $\frac{1}{4}$" dowel rod. When the glue dries, sand off the top making it flush with the surface of the door and then re-drill your hole.

5. The door hinge is out of alignment and needs to be adjusted.

6. The bumper pads are either worn out or gone and need replacement.

7. This could be a screw that is attaching hinge to frame and is loose. Loosen all screws, align and retighten.

8. The drawer gliders are out of alignment or you have debris in the track. Spray with a silicone spray.

9. Use colored putty to fill in.

10. This is usually caused by putting wet dishes away.

CABINET TIPS:

Musty Odor Begone

If you have a musty odor in your cabinets, just sprinkle some baking soda around and allow it to remain for 1-2 days.

Fire Hazard!

Follow directions for self-cleaning ovens, especially if there are cabinets over them.

COUNTERS

Problems/Questions:

1. How can I clean a laminate countertop?
2. What can I use to refinish an old wood countertop?
3. What kind of paint should I use to paint over a Formica counter?
4. How to clean Corian®?
5. Will hot pots damage the Corian® surface?
6. The counter has separated from the wall.
7. Countertop is chipped.
8. There are gaps in caulking at seams or around the sink.
9. Small scratches in cultured marble tops.
10. How can I seal a new butcher block counter?
11. The curling iron has left a yellow burn mark on the Formica counter.
12. What are the disadvantages of a Formica countertop?
13. What are the advantages of buying a Corian counter?
14. What are the problems with Corian counters?
15. What are the advantages of a wood block counter?
16. Are there problems with wood block counters?
17. What are the problems with ceramic tile counters?
18. What is the best surface for a kitchen counter?

Solutions/Answers:

1. Use a liquid detergent or a very mild abrasive cleaner and a very light touch. If the stain is bad, try using full-strength Pine-Sol.
2. After you sand the bad areas, refinish with polyurethane and use three coats for the best results.
3. Sand lightly then apply Kilz paint and allow to full dry. Then three colors of gray light, medium and dark and marbleize them together. Allow it to dry then apply five coats of polyurethane. Remember this will not be a food-safe surface.
4. Gentle abrasive powder bleach on a damp surface will do the trick. Allow it to remain for 5 minutes before sponging it off. Rinse well and dry.
5. Cast iron and aluminum pots should never be placed on Corian® if they are hot. If the bottom of the pot is wet, it may also leave a mark on the surface.
6. This is usually caused by settlement and can be corrected by caulking between the countertop and the wall.
7. Best to call professional company for repair.
8. This is usually caused by shrinkage and can be repaired by re-caulking or using seam filler.

9.   These can be polished or buffed out.

10.   Use boiled linseed oil and apply with a paintbrush. Allow it to dry for 24 hours before applying a second coat, then wait another 24 hours. Wipe the second coat off by rubbing with a clean cloth.

11.   If the burn is not too deep, it can be removed with a scouring cleanser. If it is deep, there is not much you can do about it.

12.   Abrasive cleaners will scratch and dull the surface. Sharp knives will leave scratch marks as well. Hot pots will actually melt the finish and warping can occur if the area is wet for too long a period. The seams are too easily seen and depending on the quality, some will fade in time.

13.   They are fairly stain resistant and easy to clean and most scratches can be repaired.

14.   They scratch easily and hot pots will melt the surface finish.

15.   Very durable if cared for and cleans easily. Scratches can be removed by sanding.

16.   If you allow large amounts of water to remain on them, they may turn black and require sanding and re-sealing, which is expensive. Keep them dry and clean.

17.   If the grout is not kept clean, it will become discolored and mildewed. Tile tends to chip and is not easy to replace. If you break a tile you need to drill holes and remove the tile, clean the area and replace with a new tile.

18.   Granite is the best counter. It does require proper sealing but is scratch resistant, hot plates can be placed on it and it is the best looking counter.

COUNTER TIPS:

Spit Shine?

If you would like a quick shine on your countertop, just wipe it down with white vinegar.

Is Your Laminate Dull?

You can brighten a dull laminate countertop by applying a coating of quality car wax. If you buff it off really good, very little of the wax will remain and you will retain the shine. It is safe to place food on the counter afterwards.

CUTLERY

General Information:

One of the most important utensils in a kitchen is your knife. There are a number of different materials used in knife blades, many of which are relatively new and need to be evaluated as to which will suit you best. Make sure the handle is secured with at least three rivets. It should feel comfortable and always avoid plastic grips. When cutting foods, the best surface would be a soft wooden cutting board. Hardwoods and plastic boards tend to dull the blade faster and also reduce the life of the knife.

CARBON STEEL

This is, by far, the best for taking the sharpest edge and is the preferred knife for the serious chef. However, if the blade is not constantly kept dry, it will rust. Acids in foods may also take their toll and turn the blade black, which can be imparted back to foods.

Super-Stainless Steel- This is not one of the better quality blades. Once it dulls and loses its original well-honed sharpness, it is almost impossible to restore to a decent level of sharpness. However, it does resist rust and staining.

Stainless Steel- Has the ability to resist rust and the acid effects from foods. Will take a sharper edge than the super stainless steel, but will dull and does not really take a very sharp edge.

High-Carbon Stainless Steel- This is the most expensive of the four types mentioned here and will not rust nor stain. It does not have to be washed and dried continually when in use. Can be sharpened to a sharper edge than either of the other stainless steel knives.

Problems/Questions:

1. How do you sharpen a knife?
2. What is the proper way to store a knife?
3. What should I look for when buying a knife?

Solutions/Answers:

1. The one method that should never be used on a good kitchen knife is that of allowing a coarse grinding wheel to be used. The blade will only last a few years and will become thinner and thinner. Rotating steel disks are not recommended either. The preferred method is a "butcher's steel."

This is just a rough-surfaced, hard metal rod with a protective handle. If the butcher's steel is used frequently, it will keep the edge on the knife. If you have a problem keeping the edge, it may mean that you are not using the sharpener as frequently as you should and you may have to use a "whetstone" to return the edge. The whetstone is made of silicon carbide (carborundum).

2. One of the best ways to store a quality knife is to keep it in a wooden countertop knife holder that was made for the knife. However, not all wooden holders are quality ones and the holder should not have a hard surface for the blade to lie on. The higher quality holders will have a protective liner that allows the edge of the blade to rest free. When a knife is stored in a drawer with other utensils, it will end up with small nicks on the blade that will eventually ruin a high quality knife.

3.   Purchasing a knife is an investment that you need to make. It is a kitchen tool that is indispensable and unless you buy a quality knife, you will not have it very long and will not be very satisfied with the results. Purchase either carbon-steel or high-carbon steel knives. The manufacturer should be a recognized name, such as Triden, Wusthof or Heckles. The blade and handle should all be one piece and the handle should not be attached to the blade. If the knife has a plastic hilt, it is not recommended.

DISHWASHER

General Information:

Dishwashers have at least one motor that is attached to a pump that forces the water up into sprayer arms. When it is in the drain cycle, it pushes the water and debris out of the dishwasher and into the sink that has the garbage disposer. Any larger food particles then wait for the next time you run the dishwasher to be reduced into minute particles that will go down the drain. Most European dishwashers have two motors, one for washing and the other for draining.

The latest dishwashers now have a soil-sensor, which checks the water to see if it is still containing debris from the dishes. If the water is clean, the dishwasher will advance to the next cycle. This is a recommended feature when purchasing a new dishwasher.

Problems/Questions:

1.   Odors from a garbage disposer side sink are occurring frequently.
2.   The dishwasher will not run.
3.   The dishwasher is overfilling.
4.   The soap dish is still full after the dishwasher has completed running.
5.   Dishwasher did not turn off when the door was opened when it was operating.
6.   The dishes are not drying completely.
7.   The dishwasher is making a funny noise.
8.   There is water in the dishwasher in the morning when the dishwasher is empty.
9.   My glasses are spotted.
10.   The dishes are not coming out clean.

Solutions/Answers:

1. Always run the garbage disposal unit after the dishwasher has finished running for a few seconds.

2. There are a number of reasons for the dishwasher not running. If water has seeped into the electronics, it will burn out the timer or one of the other six control switches. Call a repairman!

3. If the dishwasher is overfilling, then the float switch has gone bad and stopped functioning and needs to be replaced.

4. When the soap dish or the rinse-aid dispenser does not empty, it means that the timer switch has not sent a signal to the bi-metal switch that opens it and needs to be replaced.

5. The door switches may eventually get damaged or get debris in them and not function. This needs a service call to fix.

6. If the dishes are not drying, the drying fan has stopped functioning or is not functioning efficiently to do the job and needs to be replaced. It is usually found in the back right corner.

7. Sometimes funny noises can be eliminated by checking to see if a small object or a pit has fallen into the pump assembly.

8. If you find water in the dishwasher when there shouldn't be any, this is called "weeping water" and is usually caused by a faulty fill valve, which will need to be replaced.

9. Spotted glasses may be caused by a lack of water flow or from hard water. If the glasses are getting a rainbow hue, then it is probably from using too much detergent. This can also be caused by water not being hot enough. Try running the sink faucet until hot water starts running out. Also, opening the dishwasher too soon after it has finished will cause this problem.

10. This is usually caused by obstructed water flow caused by poor loading of the dishes.

DISHWASHER TIPS:

A Heated Solution
If the dishes are not coming out clean, trying running the sink's hot water tap until it gets warm, before you start the dishwasher. This will help the first cycle to have hotter water. If this doesn't work, you need new nozzles.

Granules or Gels
Most dishwasher manufacturers recommend that you use powders or granules and not gels. Gels tend not to perform as well.

Appliances That Don't Like Each Other
To extend the lifetime of the dishwasher, never have it next to the refrigerator, since both emit heat unless you place an insulation panel between them.

Are Rusty Racks your Problem?

If your dishwasher racks are getting rusty, purchase a bottle of rack touch-up at any appliance parts department. New tine ends are also available.

Tang You Very Much

If your dishwasher is looking dingy and has deposits on the walls, just add 1 cup of TangTM to the dishwasher and run it through a cycle. It will clean the interior and refresh the inside.

Bubble, Bubble, Here Comes Trouble

If your dishwasher is full of soapsuds and bubbles, you used the wrong detergent or tablet. Place 2 tbsp. vegetable oil into the soapy water to break up the suds and sprinkle salt on the suds to disperse them. Placing ice cubes on the suds will also help to alleviate the problem.

Getting Mold in here..............Help!

If you use your dishwasher at least twice a week, you should have no problem with mold from the moisture. Residual water on the bottom will cause mold growth, if the dishwasher is not used regularly and should be cleaned.

Dishes Getting Bored, What's the Problem?

Some dishwashers put cold water into the dishwasher and the dishwasher must heat the water before it will start. This can take up to 30 minutes.

In-Depth Cleaning

For a thorough cleaning, place a bowl with 3 cups of white vinegar on the bottom rack and leave all racks in place. Do not place dishes in the dishwasher. Run the dishwasher through the wash and rinse cycle ONLY. Make sure that you turn the machine off before it goes into the drying cycle.

EXHAUST HOOD (RANGE HOOD)

General Information:

Many range exhaust hoods really do not do a good job of eliminating steam, grease, smoke and food odors. Some hoods only re-circulate the air through a filter and return the air to the kitchen. A range hood has to be vented to the outside to really be effective. Most re-circulating air vents can be converted to one that exhausts outside without too much trouble.

Problems/Questions:

1. How can I recharge a charcoal filter and clean a range hood?
2. Motor is overheating.

3.   Can a dirty light bulb be cleaned?

4.   How do you clean the greasy parts?

5.   Flapping noise heard in the hood.

Solutions/Answers:

1.   If you have a charcoal filter in your range-hood, it can be recharged by placing it in a 450°F. oven for 30 minutes (after completely cleaning the frame). If there is any grease left on the frame, it may catch on fire or smoke up the house. Many activated charcoal filters cannot be cleaned and should be replaced once a year.

2.   Clean the fan blades with just soap and water. Dirty fan blades will restrict airflow and may cause the motor to overheat and catch on fire.

3.   Light bulbs in vents need to be removed and very gently cleaned with cool water and soap.

4.   If parts are real greasy, use ammonia and water to clean them. Never use abrasive pads or scouring powder on the vent parts. Metal grids need to be soaked once a month in ammonia and water.

5.   This is caused by the outside wind moving the damper and is a normal sound when it is windy.

EXHAUST HOOD TIP:

Fire, Fire, Leave the Hood Alone

If a fire starts on the range top, never turn the fan on over the range or you may pull the flames into the hood and into the house attic or ductwork.

FLOORING

General Information:

There are several types of kitchen flooring for you to choose from. The following are some of the more popular types:

- Earthen Tiles - These come in two forms, glazed and unglazed. You can even buy handmade ones with custom details. Most of the tiles are made from fine-grained clay and are machine-shaped and pressed. Glazed tiles are very resistant to stains and moisture; however, be sure and treat the grout with a liquid silicone sealer. Colored grout works best. These tiles cost $5 to $25 per square ft. with installation costing $3 to $5 per square ft. If you are going to install it over a deck, be sure and use $1/2$" concrete backing board nailed over the deck and cement the tile to it. Use only grade 3 for kitchen floors.

- Hardwood Floors - This is normally $3/4$-inch tongue-and-groove planking. It has a warming affect on a room and will compliment the cabinets and counters. The cost is about $6 to $8 per square ft. and can be refinished when it becomes worn. Be sure and seal the floor with three coats of urethane. The floor does not do well if water is allowed to remain and will buckle.

- Kitchen Carpeting - This thin, tough carpeting used to be very popular. However, it has not been used very much anymore, since it does not handle spills well and doesn't really fit in with today's kitchen styling. It is rubber-backed and does provide a soft, underfoot feel. It is very affordable and does come in stain-resistant.

- Plastic Laminate Flooring - This is a wood-grain plastic laminate, which contains silica sand and is harder than countertop laminates or hardwoods. It is bonded to plywood planks or squares. It simulates wood and is a tough floor.

- Pre-finished Veneers - These are pre-finished tongue-and-groove plywood planks and squares topped with hardwood veneers. Most of these are installed as floating floors. The planks are glued together along the tongue-and-groove joints and then laid over a foam pad. Urethane finished veneers cost about $3 to $6 per square ft. installed. The top of the line, however, has a super-hard acrylic-plastic sealant forced deep into the veneer, making it more resistant to scratches and dents.

- Resilient Flooring - This comes in either vinyl-sheet goods or tiles and is very affordable. The prices range from $6 to $40 per square ft. with installation running from $4 to $8 per square ft. There are two types of this flooring: layered and full-depth. The layered has a printed vinyl fused to white, fibrous or foam liner. The second type is inlaid, which has colored composition particles extending the full depth of the flooring.

The recommended is the inlaid since there is no surface layer that can be punctured, snagged or will tear more easily. The price is dependent on the thickness of the wear layer. If you plan to place this type of flooring over existing flooring, it would be best to have a professional do the job.

- Stone Flooring - These are permanent floors and are marble, slate or granite. They are susceptible to scratching, especially marble. Granite is the most durable and stone floors and runs from $12 to $30 per square ft. plus installation.

KITCHEN CARPETING

Problems/Questions:

1.   The seam is coming apart where the carpet was joined.

Solutions/Answers:

1.   Best to handle this problem as soon as it appears and before the edges start fraying. There are two ways to correct the problem depending on the location: if the problem is in a high traffic area, pull back the area that has come loose and use carpet glue on the part that has come up. Be careful not to get the glue on the carpet, so don't use too much. If you use too much and it seeps through when you place a medium weight on the area to hold it down until it dries, you may ruin the carpet. If the problem is at the wall, just use double-sided carpet tape.

LINOLEUM

Problems/Questions:

1.   What can I do with leftover linoleum?
2.   How can tar be removed from the floor?
3.   Can't remove old linoleum flooring.
4.   How can I fix a gouge in the flooring?

Solutions/Answers:

1.   You can use leftover linoleum to line pantry and cabinet shelves. It will make cleaning the shelves easier.
2.   To remove tar, just place some dry ice on the tar and wait for it to harden, then scrape it off.
3.   The easiest method of removing old flooring is with a heat gun. It will still be a messy job, but it will get done. If you are working to remove tiles, a hair dryer will work just as well.
4.   A gouge can be fixed using almond-colored kitchen and sink caulking and using a small amount of food coloring to try and match the floor color. It won't remove the gouge, but it won't be very noticeable.

LINOLEUM TIPS:

Don't Use Rubber Backing
Never use a foam or rubber-backed mat or rug on a linoleum floor or it will cause permanent discoloration.

Curling Tiles?
If one of the tiles has started curling on the edges, use a blow dryer on high heat and warm the tile, just enough to soften it. Raise it and place fresh glue down, then press it back into place and place a heavy weight on it till it dries. Be sure that there is no glue seeping out or whatever you place on it to hold it in place will be there permanently.

FREEZER CHEST

General Information:
All modern day freezers are now automatic defrost freezers that do not need to be turned off and defrosted. When frost builds up in the freezer, it automatically melts. The more food you have in the freezer, the more efficient the freezer energy usage. It will take more energy to keep a half empty freezer cold than a full one. The automatic defrost freezers have a timer that turns off the freezer every 6-8 hours and turns on the defrost heater.

Some models also have a timer that can be set to run the defroster at a specific time of the day.

The water from the defrosting then goes into a pan under the freezer and is evaporated by either fan blowing warm air over it or by the heat of the compressor.

Problems/Questions:
1. Frost is building up in the freezer and is not defrosting.
2. Freezer is not getting cold enough.
3. The freezer is not freezing properly.

Solutions/Answers:
1. If the frost is building up, the timer is not working to send a signal to the heater motor or the heater motor is not working. One of the two will need replacement. The condenser coils may also be dirty and need cleaning.
2. If the freezer is not getting cold enough or is not freezing, it may be due to a number of different problems. The compression is not functioning, you may have a refrigerant leak or the timer is

not working properly. Need a repairman.

3.   If the freezer is running and not freezing properly or developing frost near the top, check the door seal and be sure that they are sealing the door properly. In time, these will need to be replaced. Depending on the climate, the rubber seal will deteriorate and cause abnormal leakage. The magnetic strip may also become loose and not hold the door shut tight.

FREEZER TIPS:

Ouch! I Got Freezer-Burned

Freezer burn is actually dehydration that is caused by the food being exposed to the air in the freezer. Food in supermarket wrappings are not airtight and if frozen for more than a few days, the foods need to be re-wrapped in as airtight a wrapping as possible.

Frosty, the Freezer......

When frost builds up on the walls of a freezer that is not frost-free, it needs to be thawed out if it reaches about 1-in. thick.

How Cold is Cold?

Your freezer should maintain a temperature of 0° to 8°F. If you immediately turn the freezer on and fill it with food, it will take about 24 hours to reach this temperature. Best to leave a new freezer on for 24 hours before placing food in it.

To Fill or not to Fill

It is best to keep your freezer at least half-full to maintain a constant temperature.

Freezing Foods

- Foil containers are best for freezing if you are going to go from the freezer to the oven.
- Only freeze baked goods that are low in moisture. Breads must be wrapped very tightly.
- Foods that contain spices will not freeze well and retain the flavor of the spice.
- Vegetables must be blanched before freezing.
- Frozen fruits do not retain their flavor.
- Remove fat from meats and they will freeze for a longer period of time.
- Remove all poultry innards before freezing.
- Low fat fish freeze better.
- The higher the fat content of dairy products, the better they will freeze.
- Cheese will freeze well.
- Most sauces freeze well.

GARBAGE DISPOSAL

General Information:

The disposer works by using a small motor, which powers a flywheel that throws the garbage into a shredder, producing a pulp that will easily flush down the drain. There are two major types of garbage disposal units. They are the batch feed, which is activated by turning a stopper and the continuous feed operated by turning on a wall switch.

Problems/Questions:

1.   When you turn on the switch, the disposer does not run.
2.   If the disposer just hums and does not perform, it usually means that there is a clog or jam.
3.   Are there any foods that will cause a jam?
4.   The disposal is not draining.
5.   Food is flying out.

Solutions/Answers:

1.   If the problem is electrical, try pushing the small red button on the bottom of the disposer. Sometimes a jam will cause the unit not to work at all and it may appear to be an electrical problem. However, removing the jam and pressing the red button usually works.
2.   If you look down the sink into the unit with a flashlight and see a foreign object, use a needle-nosed pliers to remove it. If the object is jammed into the blade, use the "L" shaped metal tool (Allen wrench) found under the sink. Place the small wrench into the hole on the bottom of the disposer and turn it to release a jam before removing the foreign object. The small wrenches are available at any hardware store.
3.   There are a number of foods that will cause a jam and stop the disposer. These include garlic skins, celery strings, corn husks and tea bag strings.
4.   If the disposal is not draining, try a plunger and be sure it is seated well before trying to push it down a few times. If this does not work, you will have to remove the curved trap under the sink and clean it out.
5.   If food is flying out of the disposer, you have not placed the rubber stopper over the hole. The stopper should have small holes in it to allow water in.

DISPOSER TIPS:

Cold Solution

To sharpen the blades of a garbage disposer, just place 3-4 ice cubes into the disposer and run it for a few seconds. This should be done once a month if the disposer is used regularly. To freshen it, grind lemon peels in it.

A Little Bit Will Do Ya

Never place any type of chemical drain cleaner into a garbage disposal. If you need to get rid of odors, use a small amount of white vinegar.

Seasoning the Disposer

Just pour $1/2$ cup of table salt in the garbage disposal, then run with water as usual. This will clean and freshen up the disposal. However, if you prefer, you could pour $1/2$ cup of baking soda in the drain and flush it with very hot water.

Run Water, During and After

Most people are aware that you should run water while running the disposal. However, you should also run the water for 30 seconds after it has finished running to be sure that all the garbage has cleared the pipes.

Ouch, Ouch, That's too Hot

Always use cold water when running the garbage disposal.

Never place your hand into a garbage disposal. Always use a needle-nosed pliers kept under the skin to remove foreign objects.

HOT WATER DISPENSER

General Information:

This unit works with a control valve that is on top of the sink and dispenses hot water. The heating element is under the sink and heats the water to a temperature that is set by the factory. If the heating element goes bad, it is best to replace the entire unit, since a service call and repair will usually cost more than a new unit.

Problem/Questions:

1.   The water is just trickling out.
2.   The water is not getting hot enough.
3.   Not getting enough hot water from a sink unit.
4.   What is the temperature of the water?

Solution/Answers:

1.   If you are not getting enough water from the tap then the line is partially clogged and will need to be removed and flushed out. There may also be a leak in the line, so check under the sink for water spillage.

2.   If the water is not getting as hot as you would like, then you will need to read your manual and reset the temperature control, which was set by the factory. If a plumber is installing a new unit, be sure he/she adjusts the temperature control to the desired temperature before leaving.

3.   These under the sink units can only supply a few cups of water at a time.

4.   The temperature of water coming out of a unit is 190°F, which is enough to give you a nice burn.

ICE CUBE MAKER

General Information:

The ice cube maker is a small appliance that is in the freezer compartment of the refrigerator and continually makes ice cubes. The icemaker works by signaling the water-fill valve to send water to it, filling the tray. When the water thermostat signals the water-fill unit that the tray is full, it stops sending water. When the ice cubes reach a certain temperature, there is a signal sent and the tray empties.

Problems/Questions:

1.   Ice cubes taste and smell bad.

2.   The icemaker won't make ice.

3.   How often should you change the filter?

4.   Is it possible to get clear ice cubes?

Solutions/Answers:

1.   If your ice cubes have an off taste or smell bad, then they have probably picked up refrigerator odors and have been in the icemaker too long. Even if the water is filtered, this will still occur.

2.   First check and see if it has accidentally been turned off. There is a thin, coat-hanger metal bar on the right side of your icemaker and when the bar is up, the icemaker is off. If the bar is down, the icemaker is on. If the bar is up, slowly lower it and the icemaker should work.
        A common icemaker problem is freeze-ups. Next time this happens, just use the hair dryer to defrost the problem. This problem won't occur, if you release a few ice cubes every few days.

3.   If you start detecting a bad taste, it may be from an old worn-out filter and should be changed. These filters should be changed every 6 months.

4.   Cloudiness in ice cubes is caused by entrapped air bubbles. If you want clear ice cubes, boil the water first and make them in an ice cube tray.

KITCHEN SINK

Problems/Questions:

1.   Sink is scratched and chipped.

2.   Why is it taking too long to get hot water?

3.   Leaky faucet.

4.   Can't get rid of an odor in the sink.

Solutions/Answers:

1.   If your sink is scratched and chipped, it can be resurfaced for about $300, however it is only guaranteed for about a year. A spry-on epoxy coating is applied and this only holds up well for bathroom sinks and bathtubs, since they are not used as much as the kitchen sink. Buy a new sink! However, most hardware stores have a do-it-yourself kit that works great.

2.   Waiting for hot water at the kitchen sink can waste thousands of gal. of water every year. The solution is to purchase a Chilipepper™ hot water appliance. It is a small pump that speeds up water from the hot water heater to the sink. www.chilipepperapp.com/ksink.htm.

3.   Leaky faucets can be expensive when you start to figure that one drip per second over the course of a year will consume about 400 gal.of water. It only takes a few minutes to replace a washer or tighten the faucet insert.

4.   Odors in the sink can usually be eliminated by running very hot water down the drain or placing 2 tbsp. of baking soda in the drain and allow it to remain for a few minutes before running the hot water. If this fails, place 1 cup of white vinegar in the drain and allow it to remain for 20 minutes before flushing with hot water.

KITCHEN SINK TIP:

Glub, Glub

After trying a "plumber's helper" with no success, try the following method. Remove all standing water so that you are able to pour the ingredients into the drain. First, pour 1 cup baking soda, 1 cup table salt, and $1/2$ cup white vinegar into the clogged drain. These will start dissolving any organic matter and grease away immediately. Allow to stand for 5 minutes, then flush 1-2 qts. of boiling water down the drain.

MICROWAVE

General Information:

The microwave contains a small transmitting antenna similar to one a TV station might use. The microwave oven converts the house current into an extremely high voltage, which feeds the "magnetron." The magnetron converts the current into radio waves, which cause the liquid molecules in the food to vibrate at a fast rate, causing friction and generating heat for cooking.

Some foods are not meant to be placed in a microwave, such as breads since their internal structure is composed of many air pockets. The structure breaks down easily in the microwave and the bread becomes tough.

Problems/Solutions:

1. Microwave shuts off periodically when running.
2. You hear a loud "humming noise" and the microwave is not cooking the food.
3. Microwave is running but is not cooking the food.
4. The microwave display is counting down and the food is not cooking.
5. Microwave goes completely dead when the door is opened.
6. The fan is not running.
7. I burnt food and now the microwave is dead.

Solutions/Answers:

1. If the microwave shuts off periodically, check to see if the fan is running. If the fan is not running when it shuts down, there may be a short in the wiring. Another reason may be that the air intake grill is plugged up with dirt. Use an old toothbrush to clean the grill.
2. If you hear a hum, the magnetron is probably bad or you have a bad high voltage diode.
3. If all seems normal and the food is not being cooked, it may be a loose high voltage wire, a bad solder joint on the board, magnetron problem or a power relay problem.
4. The display counting down and no cooking taking place is usually a bad door switch or a faulty relay.
5. If the microwave goes dead, it is usually a faulty door switch that has blown the inferior fuse.
6. If the fan does not run, the microwave needs to be taken in for service since the fan is needed to cool the magnetron.
7. The fuse will sometimes blow, if the sensor sense overcooked burned food.

MICROWAVE TIPS:

Fill 'er up

Used microwave food containers should be saved and used for leftovers; just fill, freeze and re-heat. It is always wise to check and see if a dish is microwave safe and will not melt. Just place the container next to a $\frac{1}{2}$ full cup of water and turn the microwave on high for about 1-$\frac{1}{2}$ minutes or until the water is boiling. If the dish is hot when you touch it, you will be able to cook with it.

Don't Get Zapped

Microwave doors may become misaligned, especially if you tend to lean on them occasionally. They will leak radiation and should be checked periodically with a small, inexpensive detector that can be purchased in any hardware store.

Neatness Counts

If you don't clean up the microwave regularly, the spills will cook onto the surface. To remove them easily, just place a sponge dipped in water or a small dish with $\frac{1}{2}$ cup of water in the microwave and cook on high for about 2 minutes then wipe up.

Why the Glass Tray?

Glass trays are placed in the bottom of all microwave ovens to catch spills and raise the food up off the floor of the unit, allowing the microwave energy to hit the bottom of the food.

Exploding Foods

Certain foods will explode in a microwave, especially if they have skins that will not allow the water that is expanding to be released. These include eggs, potatoes, squash and any food that has a shell or tight skin.

OVENS

Problems/Questions:

1. Oven will not come on.
2. The oven bake light comes on but the oven will not heat up.
3. Oven is cooking too fast.
4. The bake time is not working.
5. The self-clean option is not working.
6. Oven door is getting too hot.
7. Problem: trying to clean oven racks.

8.   There is a red glow in my oven but it won't light.

9.   The surface burners are working but my oven and broiler will not work.

10.   There are sparks coming from the oven.

Solutions/Answers:

1.   If the oven does not come on it may be due to loss of electrical power, clock may not be set to manual, a burned wire connection, bad selector switch, fuse blown, circuit breaker kicked off or a defective thermostat.

2.   If the oven is not heating up, it may be from a defective bake element, a bad thermostat or a burned wire connector. Usually, it is the bake element and will need to be replaced.

3.   Cooking at a higher temperature may mean that the thermometer is not calibrated, has a defective thermostat, the selector switch is bad or the bake/broil switch has gone bad.

4.   Bad clock, defective selector switch, bad wire connection or you don't know how to operate the unit.

5.   The panel cover for door glass is not in the right position, the door was not locked, clock improperly set, defective thermostat, the self-clean switch is not closing or a defective clock.

6.   If the door is getting too hot, it may be due to defective door seals, poor insulation or the door hinges are out of alignment.

7.   Oven racks can be easily cleaned with a pumice stone, as well as smooth porcelain surfaces in the oven.

8.   The red glow in the oven is the "glow-bar" which glows red-hot and when it reaches a specified temperature, the gas jets will open. If the igniter is faulty, it will not reach the proper temperature and the gas will not be released.

9.   When the range burners work and the oven won't work, it is usually due to the clock being set wrong.

10.   If you ever see sparks coming from the oven, unplug the oven from the wall immediately. After you unplug the unit, see if you can tell where the sparks came from so that you can replace the part or call a serviceman.

OVEN TIPS:

Help! I'm Cooking

If you have ever wondered why you can place your hand into a hot oven and not be burned, the answer is simple, air does not conduct heat well. However, if you leave it in there long enough, it will come out medium-well. Water conducts heat more efficiently and will easily burn you.

Cleaning-up

The majority of aerosol oven cleaners contain sodium hydroxide (lye), which is also found in drain cleaners. When lye is sprayed on burnt fats and carbohydrates, it converts them into soap that is easily wiped off with a damp cloth. It would be best to switch to any one of a number of the newer products that use organic salts and are less dangerous.

Remember to Turn it off

If you have an oven that is not equipped with a self-cleaning feature, then just preheat the oven to 200°F., then turn it off. Place a small bowl with $1/2$ cup of ammonia on the center shelf, then close the oven and allow it to stand overnight. The next day, open the oven and allow it to air for 30 minutes in a well, ventilated kitchen, then wipe up the mess with a warm, damp paper towel.

Don't Use Oven-Cleaner

Oven cleaners should never be used in self-cleaning ovens.

My Broiler is Sick

If you are having problems with the broiler not broiling, the broiler element has burned out and needs replacement.

POTS AND PANS

General Information:

There are a number of materials that are used to manufacture pots and pans, many of which do not really do the job adequately. Remember, the thicker the gauge of the metal, the more uniformly it tends to distribute the heat. The finish on the metal will also affect the efficiency of the cookware.

Problems/Questions:

1. Oil fires in a non-stick pan.
2. Stainless steel is streaked.

3. Cleaning non-stick pots and pans.

4. The lid broke on a pot.

5. Food is stuck to a pot.

6. How can I clean a discolored aluminum pan?

Solutions/Answers:

1. There is only a 50-50 chance of saving a non-stick pan that has had an oil fire in it. However, there is 1 possible solution: try making a paste from baking soda and water and apply it to the pot, then allow it to remain overnight. Apply mild pressure the next day and hope for the best.

2. If your stainless steel is streaked, just clean with olive oil or club soda.

3. For the most part, these plastic-coated pots are easy to keep clean. However, they do stain and may, over time, develop a buildup of grease and oil. If this occurs, it will adversely affect the efficiency of the non-stick surface. To clean the surface, just mix 2 tbsp. baking soda with $\frac{1}{2}$ cup white vinegar in 1 cup water. Place the ingredients into the pot, set the pot on the range and boil it for about 10 minutes. Wash the pot, then rub vegetable oil on the surface of the plastic coating to re-season it.

4. If you lose a top knob to a saucepan lid, try placing a screw with the thread side up into the hole, then attaching a cork on it.

5. Fill the pan with warm water and place a fabric softener sheet in the water, then allow the pan to soak overnight.

6. Fill the pan with water and add 1 tbsp. cream of tartar and boil for about 20 minutes.

TIPS ON POTS:

Copper

These will not react with any food and are safe to cook in. Copper is one of the best heat conductors and is preferred by many chefs. Copper pans, however, should only be purchased if they have a liner of tin or stainless steel to be safe, otherwise they may leach metals into the food. When you cook in glass, remember to reduce the oven temperature by 25°F. One of the worst types of cookware is the thin stamped, stainless steel pots with a thin copper-coated bottom. The copper coating is approximately 1/50th of an inch in thickness and too thin to distribute the heat efficiently and uniformly.

The "real" copper cookware provides excellent heat distribution on the bottom, as well as the sides of the pan. The copper, however, needs to be kept clean and if black carbon deposits form to any degree, it will affect the heat distribution significantly. These pots are usually lined with tin, which must be replaced if it wears out, otherwise excess copper may leach into the food causing a health risk. Foods that are high in acid will increase the release of copper. The metal ions in copper will also react with vitamin C and reduce the amount available.

Shine that Copper

A great cleaner for copper can be made from a paste prepared from white vinegar, salt and all-purpose flour. Another method is to spread catsup on the copper and allow it to remain for 10 minutes before wiping it off.

Enameled Cookware

While the enamel does resist corrosion, it is still metal coated with a thin layer of enamel. The coating is produced by fusing powdered glass into the metal surface, which is, in most instances, cast iron. The cookware can chip easily, if hit against another object and can even shatter, if placed from a very hot range into cold water.

Glass Cookware

Rapid temperature changes may cause the glass to crack or break in many brands. Glass has a very low "heat-flow" efficiency rating and when boiling water is poured into the glass cookware, the actual heat that is transferred from the boiling water to the bottom of the cookware will travel slowly back to the top of the pot. Because of this, the bottom of the pot will swell and the top of the pot does not expand, creating a structural type of stress and a crack is very possible. Corningware® and Pyrex™ in that order would be the only choices for glass cookware, since both will resist most stresses.

Aluminum

The majority of cookware sold in the U.S. in 2002 was aluminum, which is an excellent heat conductor. Current studies report that there is no risk from using this type of cookware, unless you are deep-scraping the sides and bottoms of the pots continually, allowing aluminum to be released into the food. Rarely does anyone do this. Excessive intake of aluminum may lead to Alzheimer's disease. Aluminum cookware stains very easily, especially if you are using hard water to cook with. Certain foods, such as potatoes, will also cause the pans to stain easily. If you cook a high-acid content food, such as tomatoes, onions, wine, or if lemon juice is used in aluminum, it will probably remove some of the stain. If a pan is already stained when the acidic foods are cooked, it may transfer the stain to the food, possibly turning your foods a brownish color.

Aluminum pans also tend to warp, if they are subjected to rapid temperature changes, especially if they are made of thin gauge aluminum. If they are made of a thick gauge, they will have excellent heat-flow efficiency and will not rust, thus making the thick pan the best pan for use as cookware. Water and cream of tartar will clean aluminum. Just fill the pan with water and add 1 tbsp. cream of tartar, then boil for 15 minutes before washing. Lime-soaked pickles should never be made in an aluminum pot, even though the instructions state that aluminum is recommended. A chemical reaction takes place, which is not healthy.

Cast Iron/Carbon Steel

A Cast Iron/Carbon Steel pot may only supply a small amount of iron in elemental form to your diet, but not enough to be much use nutritionally. Certain acidic foods, such as tomato sauce or citrus fruit, may absorb some iron but not enough to supply you with adequate daily supplemental levels. Iron does, however, conduct heat fairly well. These are both non-stainless steel, iron-based metals that have a somewhat porous, jagged surface. These pots need to be "seasoned." To accomplish this, you need to rub the cooking surfaces with canola oil and heat it at 300°F, for about 40-50 minutes in the oven, then allow it to cool to room temperature before using. The oil has the ability to cool and seal the pores and even provide a somewhat nonstick surface. Another factor is that when the oil is in the pores, water cannot enter and possibly cause the formation of rust.

These pots should be washed daily using a mild soap and dried immediately. Never use salt to clean the pot, since this may cause rusting. If a cleaner is needed, be sure it is a mild one. Iron pots tend to release metal ions that react with vitamin C and reduce its potency. Cast iron pots can be cleaned by just filling the pot with warm water and dropping in 3 denture-cleaning tablets, then allow the pot to sit for 1 hour. This method will not affect the seasoning. To remove rust, just use sand and vegetable oil and rub lightly.

Cast Iron Pots

To clean burned-on food from a cast iron pot, just mix sand and vegetable oil in the pot and scrub with steel wool. Be sure and re-season afterwards.

Non-Stick

These include Teflon™ and Silverstone™ and are made of a type of fluorocarbon resin that may be capable of reacting with acidic foods. For 2002, there were a few minor improvements but basically, stay with the top brands. If you do chip off a small piece and it gets into the food, don't be concerned. It will just pass harmlessly through the body. Never allow any brand of "non-stick" surface pan to heat to a high temperature dry. The pan may release toxic fumes if heated above 400°F. for more than 20 minutes. This could be a serious problem for small pets and birds. Proper vegetable oil seasoning on most pots will produce a non-stick surface without the risk and last for months. These non-stick surfaces are the result of a chemically inert fluorocarbon plastic material being baked on the surface of the cookware or other type of cooking utensil. Silverstone™ is the highest quality of these non-stick items.

The food is actually cooked on jagged peaks that protrude from the bottom, which will not allow food a chance to stick to a smooth surface. The surface is commercially "seasoned," producing the final slick surface. The major contribution of a non-stick surface is that of allowing you to cook without the use of fats, thus reducing the calories of foods that would ordinarily be cooked with fats. The less expensive non-stick cookware usually has a very thin coating and will not last very long with everyday use. With heavy usage and continual cleaning, the coating will eventually wear thin.

Stainless Steel

To be a good heat conductor, they need to have a copper or aluminum bottom. High acid foods cooked in stainless steel may leach out a number of metals into the food, which may include chlorine, iron and nickel.

Multi-Ply Pans

The bottoms of these pans usually have three layers. They are constructed with a layer of aluminum between two layers of stainless steel. Stainless steel does not have the hot spot problem and the heat will be more evenly diffused by the aluminum.

Clay Pots

Remember to always immerse both the top and bottom in lukewarm water for at least 15 minutes prior to using. Always start to cook in a cold oven and adjust the heat after the cookware is placed into the oven. If sudden changes occur, the cookware may be cracked. Never place a clay cooker on top of the range directly on the heat.

RANGE TOP

General Information:

Electric range tops have visible coil burners or may be a "smooth top" that has the burners integrated into the glass surface top. The range tops have a coiled wire beneath the burner area, which conducts electricity heating up the burner or surface area.

Problems/Questions:

1. Burners will not light or take too much time lighting.
2. Ovens will not light.
3. The surface element will not lower down and remains on high heat.
4. One of the burners will only work intermittently.

Solutions/Answers:

1. If burners don't light, chances are the small holes for the gas to go through are plugged and need to be cleaned out with a very fine piece of wire.
2. If the ovens will not light, it may be due to a circuit breaker problem, or the oven fuse, if it has any, blew, or clock settings were touched by someone not familiar with the oven, or there's a short in the wiring.
3. If the burner will not lower and stays on high heat, the switch control is bad and will have to be replaced.
4. If only one of the burner elements works intermittently you have a worn or bad contact in the receptacle that the element plugs into.

RANGE TIPS:

Never Clean These with a Harsh Cleaner

The burner top is usually aluminum and should never be cleaned with an oven cleaner.

Not very Attractive

If you wipe down your walls with a mild solution of white vinegar and water occasionally, the walls will not attract grease.

Put a Lid on it

A fire in a pan can easily be put out by just placing a lid over the fire, thus cutting off the oxygen supply.

Gasping for Oxygen

One of the best fire extinguishers is baking soda. The oxygen supply is cut off and the flame goes right out. Always keep an open box in the cupboard next to the range. However, with any type of oven cleaner, make sure that there is good ventilation or they may burn the lining of you mouth and throat.

Don't Use an Electric Buffer

To make cleaning up easier, just rub the top of the stove with a car wax occasionally, and it will stop the grease from sticking to the top.

REFRIGERATOR

General Information:

The refrigerator is one of the most complex appliances in the kitchen. There are a number of thermostatic controls, ice and water dispensers, automatic defrosters, compressors, condensers, metering devices, evaporators and lighting. In normal operation, very little ever goes wrong with a refrigerator, However, the more electronics we are presently placing in them, the more problems are occurring.

Problems/Questions:

1.   The refrigerator is not automatically defrosting and frost is showing up.
2.   The refrigerator is not cooling.
3.   Water is running down the back of the refrigerator.
4.   Water dispenser is dripping.
5.   The refrigerator shocked you when you touched it.
6.   The refrigerator is cold and the freezer is not working or visa versa.

Solutions/Answers:

1.   The defrost heater, which is located just underneath the cooling coils behind the back panel, has stopped working and probably needs replacement.

2.   If the refrigerator is not cooling, this is one of the more serious problems and you may have to replace either the compressor, the condenser, or the capillary tubes have plugged up and is now allowing the refrigerator to flow. Another solution to the lack of cooling may be that the thermostat has gone bad, interrupting the electricity flow to the compressor, which stops the cooling process.

3.   If water is running down the back of your refrigerator, it means that the drain tube is blocked and the water is unable to get to the tray to be evaporated and needs to be cleaned out. You will have to remove the drain tube and blow air into it to clean it out.

4.   If you have a leaky water dispenser, you will need to replace the water valve. The water pressure may also be too high.

5.   If you were shocked when touching the refrigerator, there is a bare wire touching somewhere and it needs to be found and fixed.

6.   If one side is cold and the other is not, it means that one of the temperature gauges is stuck or broken.

REFRIGERATOR TIPS

Stop Racks from Rusting

Because of the moisture in a refrigerator, the racks may rust. To prevent this, just coat the racks with floor wax.

Cover up

To cover a scratch on your refrigerator or freezer, try using the same color enamel paint. This really works great and will last a long time.

Clean Living

If you have a problem with mildew forming in your refrigerator, just spray the inside with vegetable oil. Spray the freezer after it has been defrosted and next time, it will be easier to defrost.

Slick Idea

If you have a problem with ice cube trays sticking to the bottom of the shelf, try placing a piece of waxed paper under the tray. Freezing temperatures do not affect waxed paper.

Keep your Fizzle in

The refrigerator is a good place to store many chemicals, such as hydrogen peroxide. It will stay active for a longer period of time. Nail polish is another chemical that likes the cold and will go on smoother.

How Sweet it is!

To eliminate refrigerator odors, just leave $\frac{1}{2}$ a lemon in the refrigerator. Old coffee grounds in a cup or a few charcoal briquettes works great, too. You can also place a few drops of "real" vanilla on a cotton ball and place it into the refrigerator.

A Clean Oil is a Healthy Coil

If you clean the coils underneath or on the back of the refrigerator, you will have a substantial energy saving. Purchase an inexpensive condenser cleaning brush and be sure to clean the front plate. The backing, which is usually cardboard, is very important to the running of the refrigerator and keeps air being pulled over the hot condenser, keeping it cool. If this cover is gone, the compressor will eventually burn out.

Testing the Door for Leakage

The door gasket will wear out eventually and cause cold air to leak out. To test the gasket, place a dollar bill between the door and the gasket and close the door. If you can't remove the bill, the gasket is OK.

I'm Getting Dizzy

Best not to move a refrigerator on its side unless you really have to. The oil may come out of the compressor and run up the cooling lines.

Can I Place a Refrigerator in the Garage?

Not a problem unless it is a self-defrosting and the garage temperature drops below 50°F. When this occurs, the oil may become too thick and cause a compressor failure.

It's Getting Crowded in Here!

Best not to pack your refrigerator too full or it will restrict air circulation and give you poor cooling conditions. Freezers, however, can be packed full with no problem.

Produce Drawer Secret

If you have a 2 produce drawer refrigerator, keep 1 drawer with $\frac{1}{2}$ in. water in the bottom and keep your green, leafy produce in this drawer. It will not hurt the workings of the refrigerator and will keep the greens crispy longer.

Small Electrical Appliances

BREADMAKERS

Problems/Questions:

1. The motor is laboring.
2. Breads all have a crack around the top and sides.
3. The bread has a burned crust.

Solutions/Answers:

1. If you hear the motor laboring too much when you are sending something through the machine, allow the machine to rest for 20 seconds before continuing.
2. The dough is probably too dry. Try adding 1-2 tbsp. liquid. If the machine is programmable, increase the rising time.
3. Set the crust control to light or choose the sweet bread setting. You can also remove the bread from the machine 5-10 minutes before the bread cycle ends. Reducing the amount of sugar sometimes helps as well.

CAN OPENER

De-Gunker

To clean your can opener, try running a piece of paper towel through it. This will pick up the grease and some of the gunk.

COFFEE MAKER

The Cleaner the Coffee Maker, the Better Tasting the Coffee
Never use soap in a coffee maker. Always clean it with a solution of 50% white vinegar and 50% water. Allow it to run through a complete cycle, then refill it with cold water and let it run through another cycle.

FOOD PROCESSOR

Zap it with Soap
To keep your food processor clean, try running a small amount of liquid dishwasher soap through it, then rinsing thoroughly.

IRON

Clogged Iron your Problem?
When your steam iron stops steaming, it is probably clogged with mineral deposits. The best way to remove the deposits is to place white vinegar in the water reservoir, then place the iron flat on an oven rack and plug it in. Set the steam setting and by the time the steam starts coming out, the mineral deposits will have dissolved.

Seasoning your Iron
If your iron is leaving small black marks on the clothes, sprinkle a small amount of salt on a piece of paper, then run the warm iron over the salt to clean the bottom. This will also eliminate starch buildup on the bottom of an iron. Toothpaste will also remove starch.

Can't Steam, All Gummed up
If the holes in your iron are all clogged up with hard water deposits, just mix a solution of $\frac{1}{3}$ cup white vinegar and 1 tbsp. baking soda and blend well. Pour the solution into the iron and heat the iron just until

it starts steaming. Turn it off and empty it, then fill it with warm water to rinse very well. Empty and rinse a few more times. Then run the steam on a piece of old rag to remove any residue.

MIXMASTER/BLENDER

Clean me or Lose me
To keep your blender and mixer working great, be sure and lubricate all moving parts with a very light coating of mineral oil (not vegetable oil). This should be done every 3 months. Before you use a measuring cup to measure a sticky liquid, try spraying the inside with vegetable oil and the liquid will flow more freely.

TOASTER OVEN

Yuk! Melted Plastic
When plastic melts on your toaster oven, you need to handle the problem immediately. Turn the oven off and allow it to cool, then remove the plastic with acetone (nail polish remover). Make sure that the area is well ventilated, since the fumes may be hazardous.

WATER PURIFIER

General Information:
There are numerous methods of home water purification systems. If you decide to purchase a system, be sure to investigate the different types and the availability of service for that particular system. A number of units only produce a minimal quantity of pure water, which would not be sufficient for many families, while other units do not provide the level of desired filtration. The most common unit for a home is the reverse-osmosis filter system.

This is one of the most popular units sold in the U.S. and utilizes a duel sediment filter system. The system is effective in removing up to 90% of the minerals and inorganic matter. The system works by forcing water through a thin membrane, which removes the inorganic metals. Most units only produce a few qts. of water a day.

Problems/Questions:
1.   Is the water really filtered?
2.   How often should the filter cartridge be replaced?

Solutions/Answers:

1.   The only way to be sure is to purchase a test kit from a hardware store or check with your local water company.

2.   The cartridge filters should be replaced twice a year for the average home.

NOTE: Never hook a reverse-osmosis unit to an icemaker, since it does not generate enough water pressure to operate the water inlet valve properly.

OTHER TYPES OF WATER FILTRATION:

Activated Charcoal Filtration Units

A number of the more popular units filter the water through activated charcoal filters. This method is very efficient in filtering out insecticides, pesticides, chlorine and organic matter. However, this type of tiler is not very effective in filtering out bacteria and un-dissolved metals, such as lead, copper, iron and manganese. Filters need to be checked regularly and changed or the system will be useless. If you do choose this type of unit, be sure it does not contain silver to neutralize bacteria. Silver is not that effective and a percentage may end up in your drinking water.

Chlorination

Systems that utilize chlorine to kill bacteria usually produce water with a somewhat off-taste and odor to the water. The system must be functioning properly at all times or there is the possibility of the chlorine forming a dangerous element.

Multi-Stage Filtration

These units are one of the most effective and usually recommended above most other units. They utilize a number of filtration methods, such as a pre-filter, which will remove iron, rust, dirt particles and sediments as small as 5 microns. They also have a lead-activated carbon filter, which removes lead and chlorine, as well as a carbon block filter to remove chlorine, improve taste, remove odors and most organic impurities.

Micro-strainers

A good method of filtration; however, it is not able to remove most nitrates and nitrites. It will remove almost all chemicals and bacteria.

Distillation

Distillation is one of the most effective methods of filtration. Water is boiled producing steam, which is then cooled to produce water vapor, which is then trapped. However, certain gasses are not removed through this method. The more efficient distillers utilize activated charcoal filters as an additional organic material remover. Be sure and de-scale your distiller regularly or the efficiency will be greatly reduced.

Aeration

Radon gas is a continuing water contamination problem, especially in the Midwest U.S. An aeration filter is the most effective type of filter to resolve this problem. A survey conducted by the Environmental Protection Agency estimated that over 8 million people are at risk from radon contamination.

Ultraviolet Radiation Purifiers

These types of filters are very effective in filtering out bacteria and are normally installed on wells in conjunction with other types of filtration units. This system does require a constant electrical line voltage. It does not remove cyst contamination.

Ozonators

These filters are being used more extensively than ever before and are frequently found on swimming pools built after 1992. They utilize activated oxygen that is capable of purifying and removing bacteria without chlorination. Recommended more for swimming pools rather than drinking water since the system may produce bromate, which may be related to tumors of the kidney.

Carbon Filters

These filters utilize carbon to attract the contaminants, which then adhere to the carbon. They are useful in removing odors, improving the taste of water, and eliminating organic chemical compounds. Their drawback is that they do not remove heavy metals.

Magnetic Water Conditioners

Since all home appliances or equipment that use water builds up scale over a period of time, these conditioners are a must for homeowner who wish to protect their investment with a minimum of repairs from water scale damage. These systems do not affect water purity; however, they condition the water, magnetically altering the physical characteristics of water-borne minerals. The mineral will no longer be able to cling to the insides of the water pipes and no scale can be formed.

TRASH COMPACTOR

General Information:

When you place trash into a compactor and close the door and then press the start button, the motor will start and causes a set of reduction gears or operates a belt-pulley system that lowers the ram. The ram exerts high pressure on the trash and flattens it. As soon as the ram reaches the set point, the motor reverses and raises the ram back up to the top.

Problems/Questions:

1.   The compactor will not work at all.

2.   The ram is stuck.

3.   The ram goes down and does not come all the way back up and the door opens.

4.   The drawer is hard to open.

5.   Can I place glass or jars in the compactor?

Solutions/Answers:

1.   If the compactor does not work, check the wall socket first, then the ground fault interrupter (GFI) and the switches, which include the door, key or micro switches. Try plugging some other appliance into the socket to be sure it is working.

2.   If the ram gets stuck or has gone down and won't come back up, there may be a broken drive belt, chain or one of the gears has broken.

3.   If the ram partially comes back up and the door opens making a vibrating noise, the garbage is not being rammed down evenly and you have a large object that is not being crushed or broken up.

4.   When the drawer is hard to open, it means that there is food or an object stuck and needs cleaning out. If damage has been done, then you may have to replace the tracks or rollers.

5.   You can put any type of garbage into the compactor that you would normally throw into your trashcan in the home.

TRASH COMPACTOR TIPS:

Kill Those Bugs

Use a good bacteria-killing cleaner or a de-greaser to regularly clean the compactor, especially the surface head of the ram. Compactors are breeding grounds for bacteria.

UTENSILS

Great Grater Tip

Cleaning the grater will never be a problem, if you use a small piece of raw potato before trying to wash it out. Sometimes a toothbrush comes in handy, too.

MISCELLANEOUS KITCHEN TIPS

Easy Does it

A nick on the rim of a glass can be easily removed with an emery board. Don't use a nail file or sandpaper. They are too coarse and will scratch the glass and ruin it.

Soap Works as Well

If you are having problems with sticky drawers, try rubbing a candle along the tops of the runners.

Odor Eaters

A number of foods are capable of removing odors. Vanilla extract placed in a bottle top in the refrigerator will remove odors, while dry mustard is commonly used to eliminate onion odors from hands and cutting boards. Other solutions include leaving a small cup of used coffee grounds on 2 shelves.

An excellent method of removing odors from the kitchen is to keep a few washed charcoal briquettes in a shallow dish on top of the refrigerator. Frying a small amount of cinnamon will chase all odors from the home.

Getting in Shape

Butcher blocks will not only harbor bacteria deep down in the cracks, but are also difficult to clean. They need to be washed with a mild detergent, then dried thoroughly and covered with a light layer of salt to draw any moisture that may have gotten into the crevices. The wood can then be treated with a very light coating of mineral oil. Make sure it is only a light coating since mineral oil may affect the potency of a number of vitamins in fruits and vegetables.

Time Saver

Keeping a grater clean so that you can continue to work and still grate a number of different foods is an old chef's secret. A chef will always grate the softest items first, then grate the firmer ones.

Not a Crack up

A trick used by antique dealers to remove hairline cracks on china plates or cups is to simmer the cup in milk for 45 minutes. Depending on the size of the crack, the protein (casein) in the milk will fill in the crack.

Not a Fashion Statement

A great idea used by professional cooks worldwide is to keep a small plastic baggie handy, in case you have both hands in a food dish or dough and need to answer the telephone.

Glue Remover

The glue on any type of contact paper will easily melt by running a warm iron over it or using a hair dryer on high heat.

Measuring up

If you want to use the fewest utensils possible, first measure out all the dry ingredients, then the wet ingredients. By doing this, you can use the measuring spoons or cups for double-duty.

Slippery Subject

When preparing a pan that needs to be greased, try saving your salt-free butter wrappers or use a fresh piece of bread. Remember, salt butter wrappers may cause foods to stick.

One for the Gripper

If your glasses are slick, try placing a wide rubber band on them so that the children will get a better grip.

Handle me Carefully

Refrigerator handles are a prime source of bacteria lurking and waiting to cause a problem. Best to clean the handle everyday (at least once).

Keep it a Bit Chilly

Check the temperature in the refrigerator at least every other month to be sure that it is holding 40°F. and the freezer is at 0°F. Best to be safe than sorry!

Move Over, Give me Room to Breathe

Remember, for your refrigerator to be efficient, the food you store has to have room to breathe. Cool air must be able to circulate around the food freely.

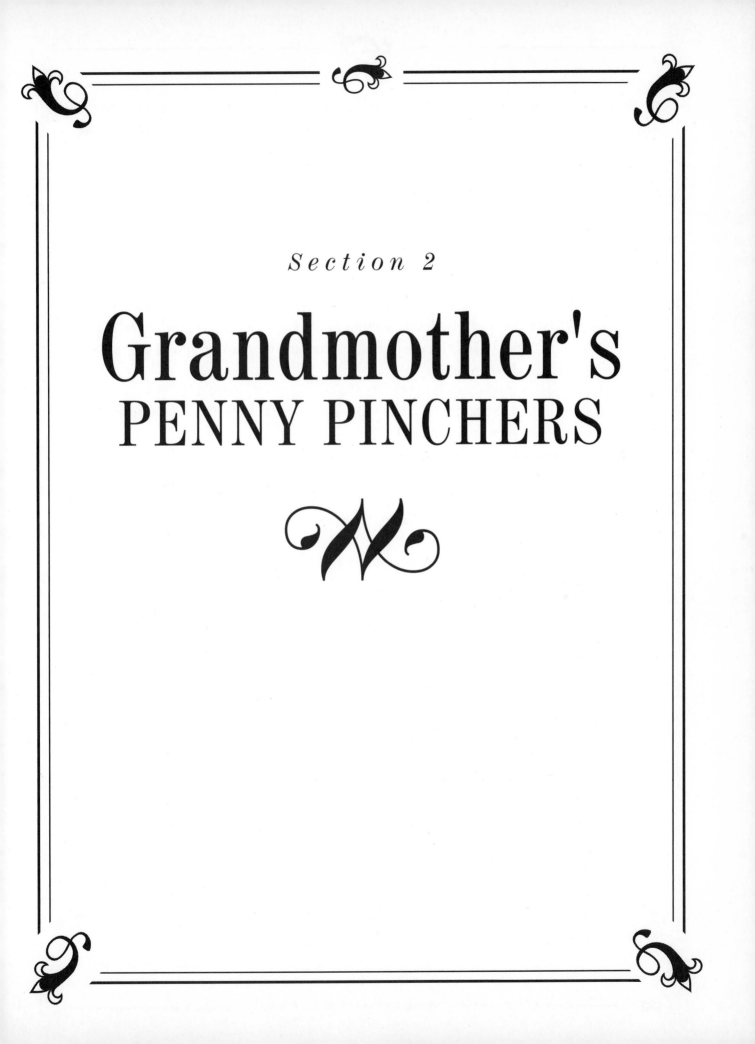

Section 2

Grandmother's
PENNY PINCHERS

The formulas in this section have been tried and tested through the years and only the most common ones have been included. To obtain the best results, follow directions closely and use caution in handling any chemicals.

If you are going to make a number of different formulas, it will be necessary to obtain certain graduated measuring cups, spoons, glass bottles with caps and a set of scales. Many formulas, however, do not require any special items and can easily be prepared with items found in almost any kitchen. Containers should be enameled ware, hard earthenware or porcelain, unless another type of container is specified. Children's formulas and many of the craft formulas can be prepared in a glass or plastic container.

Additional equipment to keep handy includes a mortar and pestle for powdering, a good Fahrenheit thermometer, funnel, mixing utensils, rotary mixer, brushes, molds, cheesecloth, filter paper, assorted bottles and cans that seal. A double boiler is used quite a bit and for some formulas, an alcohol lamp and stand with a piece of asbestos may be required.

When a formula calls for 1 or 2 parts of a substance, be sure to substitute with an appropriate liquid or solid. Don't mix them up. It should always be 1 to 2 ounces, if it's 1 to 2 parts of a liquid or 1 to 2 cups, if it is a powder. Don't mix liquids with powders unless the formula advises to do so.

When asked to filter or strain a solution, use a piece of fine cloth, muslin or cheesecloth. Fine filtering can also be done by purchasing fine filter paper and making it into a cone-shape before placing it in the funnel.

The formulas in this section are offered as information only. The author or publisher is not responsible for mishaps associated with the handling and use of some of the chemicals. Chemicals are all very dangerous when not handled properly; even everyday home cleaning products purchased at the supermarket can cause severe illness and/or injury. There are over 1,000 products that can easily be purchased in supermarkets and drugstores by almost anyone that are either poisonous or dangerous when misused.

Many of the formulas were revised from ones that were hundreds of years old. Many chemicals used then are not available today and substitutions were made to provide you with up-to-date information that is environmentally safe when applicable.

Children should always be supervised by an adult when mixing any formula.

Please note that any remedies included in this section do not take the place of your physician's advice or prescribed medications, but are provided as another source of information regarding a number of illnesses and how they were treated before modern medicine came of age.

Before attempting to produce any of the formulas, the reader should read the instructions fully. When heating chemicals, always be sure the area is well ventilated and/or to have an exhaust fan on.

15

Savings
FROM YOUR BEEF DOLLAR

There are many different cuts of meat and it would be wise to get to know some of the less expensive cuts. It is true that the less expensive cuts are usually tougher than the other more expensive ones; however, when prepared properly it would be hard to tell the difference. Varying your meat cuts will save you money as well as add variety to your dishes. Markets usually vary the cuts of meat that they place on sale and you need to take advantage of their sales. There are over 225 cuts of meat to choose from at the supermarket meat department.

The method of cooking a particular type of meat is very important to preserve the flavor and to reduce shrinkage. You don't want to dehydrate a piece of meat to the point of losing servings.

BEEF

U. S. Government Meat Grades

Beef	Fat Calories	Veal	Lamb	Pork
Prime	50%	Prime	Prime	No. 1
Choice	39%	Choice	Choice	No. 2
Good	30%	Good	Good	No. 3
Standard	Standard	Utility	No. 4	
Commercial	Utility	Cull	Utility	

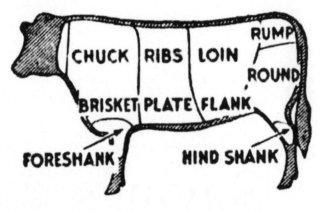

MAJOR CUTS OF BEEF

There are eight major cuts of beef butchered in the United States: they are called; shank, flank, brisket, chuck, round, rib, plate and loin. The eight cuts are given a number of additional names, which will be more recognizable to the consumer. These include names such as sirloin, porterhouse, top round, eye of the round, New York, T-bone, etc. These explain the way the eight major cuts are actually cut up. The tenderness of beef will depend on the location of the cut and the method of cutting. Some cuts are tougher than other cuts: these include, pot roasts (chuck roasts), which are cut from the neck area of the cow and will be the least expensive.

Brisket Cuts- The brisket is cut from behind a cow's front leg or may be cut from the leg itself. Normally, a tough cut of beef needs to be cooked in liquid for about 2-3 hours. If you wish to get the best results when preparing a brisket, rotate the roast $^1/_4$ turn every 25 minutes. The brisket is fully cooked when you see the fat just starting to roll off. However, if the fat can easily be removed with your fingers, the brisket is overdone.

Chuck Cuts (Roasts)- These are the toughest cuts and should be cooked in a small amount of liquid and may need to be tenderized.

Flank and Plate Cuts (Skirt)- Most of the time, if USDA Good grade is purchased, it will need tenderizing. Prime and Choice are much better choices for these cuts. They are usually cut in strips and used for stir-frying. London broil is made from flank steak. Best if marinated.

Cooking Beef

Beef is mainly composed of protein (in the form of muscle tissue), fat and water. If you remove the fat, beef is actually about 60% water. Beef muscle fibers are supported by small bands of connective tissue: either collagen or elastin. The cuts of meat from a muscle that gets a lot of exercise has more connective tissue, resulting in a tougher cut of meat. Since the connective tissue in these areas usually have a fat layer surrounding the connective tissue, melting it away with heat and liquid (such as stew) allows the meat to become tender. This tenderizing process actually turns the collagen into gelatin.

The other type of connective tissue, elastin, can only be broken down by slicing the meat into small strips or pounding the beef with a tenderizing hammer. Another method of tenderizing beef is to marinate the beef in an acidic solution, which softens the collagen. Marinating for too long a period may, however, cause the meat to lose moisture when it is cooked and lose juices. When any cut of cooked beef cools, the meat may become tough since the collagen, which has turned to liquid, turns back into a solid.

MONEY-SAVING MEATS

Beef for Beef Stew

Stew meat (can be from shank, chuck, neck, brisket or heel of round), brisket (from corned beef when cured), heart, sweetbreads, tongue and kidney. All should be braised first except tongue. The sweetbreads can then be baked, fried and diced.

- A good money-saver is to purchase a lower grade of beef; however, the less tender the cut of beef used, the longer it will take to cook it and make it tender.
- Large beef bones should be saved to provide a greater flavor for stews.
- White fat around the beef indicates a more, tender cut. Yellow fat indicates a tougher cut.
- Plan on 1-2 cups of stew per person.
- Beef chuck is the most common meat for stew and has an excellent flavor and is low in cost.
- Liquids should only be partially covering the food.
- Before adding the stew beef, roll the pieces in all-purpose flour that has been seasoned with your favorite seasonings. After lightly breading the beef pieces, place them in the refrigerator

for 45 minutes so that the bread will adhere better.

- Best to place the pieces of meat into a frying pan with about $\frac{1}{4}$ inch of oil and brown the meat before placing the meat into the stew pot. The meat will not brown nicely in a stew pot.

- Always remove all visible fat from the meat. Chuck has enough fat laced throughout the meat to add flavor.

- If you don't have a pot big enough to brown the stew meat in one layer, brown the meat in small batches.

Never add hot water when additional water is needed. Always add cold water to stew. Studies show that adding hot water makes the meat tough.

Hamburger Meat

- If the meat is ground twice through the butcher's meat grinder, the meat will be more dry. When coarsely ground, the meat will be more moist and will not lose as much fat.

- To keep your hamburger patties uniform in size, just scoop up the meat with an ice cream scoop.

- Chuck meat (about 30% fat) is the typical hamburger meat sold in supermarkets. It will be more flavorful since the area of the cow that it is cut from is a more exercised area.

- When thawing hamburger meat, try and slow-thaw it in the refrigerator. Microwave thawing is faster but removes too much moisture from the meat.

- Low-fat burgers will usually have about a 15% fat content. These burgers will have poor flavor unless seasoned.

- When preparing patties from standard burger meat, make them a little larger to make up for shrinkage due to the higher fat content.

If you over-mix hamburger meat, the burgers will be very heavy. Over-mixing is a mistake most people make when making hamburgers.

- To save money and for a great taste, try reducing the amount of fat and meat, and using some ground potatoes or soy meal as a replacement.

- Don't squeeze the meat too hard when forming the burger or it will be too dense and take a long time to cook.

- To make your burgers cook up crispy, just sprinkle a small amount of cornstarch on top just before you place them on the grill.

- Always start burgers on a very hot grill for the best results and don't overcook or they will dry out.

Try not to press down hard on the burgers while cooking or it will remove too much of the juices. This is a common practice since people are in a hurry and believe that this will speed up the cooking time. It will, but you get a dry burger.

A Real Money-Saver

When hamburger meat is on sale, try buying 5-pound packages. Add chopped onions, some garlic seasoning and celery. Cook the meat until it is well done and drain well before placing the meat into a food processor to break it up into small pieces. Bag the meat into 1-2 pound packages and freeze for later use in sloppy Joes, spaghetti sauce, tacos, etc.

Meatloaf

- Low fat ground meat is healthiest for meatloaf but lacks flavor.
- Ground round is usually the choice of chefs. However, many chefs prefer ground chuck, which is 22-30% fat for the flavor.
- When adding breadcrumbs, be sure they are moist not dry to obtain the best results.
- To reduce the amount of meat, just use a grated potato as a partial replacement.
- Finely diced and sautéed onions and celery add a great touch to meatloaf.
- Never place aluminum foil on top of tomato sauce or it will eat away the aluminum and put excess aluminum in the meatloaf, which is not very healthy.
- Meatloaf can be mixed in a large plastic bag to avoid the mess.
- Try icing the entire meatloaf after it is finished cooking with hot mashed potatoes.
- Allow the steam to dissipate for about 10 minutes before slicing the meatloaf and it won't fall apart.

Roasts

- Chuck roasts will be the toughest roast and should be cooked in a small amount of liquid. Try and buy "choice" chuck if possible.
- Round roasts will be tender and be cooked any number of ways.
- Briskets are tough and usually take 2-3 hours in a liquid to tenderize them.
- If the surface of a roast becomes dark after 2-3 days under refrigeration, smell it. It should still be good, but you need to use it immediately.
- When storing a roast, always place it back into its own juices.
- Never rapid thaw a roast or you will lose too much moisture.

- Roasts can be aged to improve the flavor, if you have purchased "good" grade beef instead of "choice" or "prime."
- To age a roast, just place it in the refrigerator on a broiling rack (with paper towels under it) so that air can circulate around it. The roast should be unwrapped and in the back of the refrigerator for 3 days before you cook it.
- To easily remove fat from a fatty roast, refrigerate the roast after it has been partially cooked. The fat solidifies and is more easily removed.
- A roast should be left at room temperature for a short period of time before placing it in the oven. Roasts will cook more evenly if they are somewhat warm to start instead of cold.
- Start a roast in a pre-heated oven to help retain the juices.
- If you prefer moisture in the pan, try using de-fatted broth or V-8 juice. Tomato juice works well and acts as a meat tenderizer.

If your roast has high fat content sprinkle the top with dry mustard to reduce the excess fat from entering the roast.

- Basting a roast with a de-fatted broth will keep the roast moist without the added fat.
- Never use a seasoning that has salt until the roast is almost finished cooking or it will draw moisture from the roast.

To retain more juices start a roast at a high temperature, then reduce the temperature after about 20 minutes.

- If you roast in a covered pan, lower the temperature by 250F.
- If you must cook a frozen roast, increase the cooking time by about 50%.
- Do not slow-cook a roast or it may dry it out. Cooking roasts in the oven provides a dry-heat cooking method, which tends to dry out the meat. Large cuts of meat do well and hold their moisture better than small cuts.
- When a roast is finished cooking, let the roast rest for 10 minutes and allow the moisture that has gone to the center to dissipate back to the edges of the roast before slicing. Keep the roast covered while it is resting either with the roasting lid or a piece of aluminum foil (providing it does not have tomato sauce on top).
- Remove a roast when it is about 100 below the required temperature and it will continue cooking while it is resting for 10-15 minutes. The roast should be at the correct temperature when you get ready to serve it.
- A roast will shrink due to water loss. The cells lose their ability to retain water the more the meat is cooked.

Rib Roast

- If you want the most tender and flavorful rib roast, ask your butcher to cut the rib roast from the "small end." The small end is between the 9th and 12th ribs. Or just ask for the "first-cut."
- Have the butcher remove the short ribs and the shinbone to make carving the roast easier.
- Another trick is to have the butcher loosen the ribs and then tie the roast back together for you.

Pot Roast

- The best cut of meat for pot roast is the first-cut or flat-cut brisket. This cut will have just the right amount of fat for a good pot roast.
- Always slice pot roast across the grain to avoid shredding the meat.

Swiss Steak

- The best Swiss steak is made from bottom round.
- Best to use a very heavy skillet with a tight-fitting lid.
- Chefs will pound flour into the steak with the side of a meat cleaver until almost all the flour has been absorbed by the meat. For 2 pounds of steak, they use 4-5 tablespoons of flour.
- After the flour is pounded in, the meat should be allowed to rest for 10 minutes.
- The flour in the Swiss steak will provide body and thicken the sauce as the steak cooks.

Skirt Steak

- Cut from the pad of muscle that runs from the ribs to the loin.
- Be sure that the butcher has removed the silvery membrane.
- Usually sold in pieces that are about 12 ounces each.
- Use high-moisture meat that should be allowed to reach room temperature before you cook the steak.
- Cook over high heat to sear, then cook very quickly.
- The steak should be allowed to rest for 5 minutes before serving to allow the juices to return to the surface.
- Slice the steak on the bias to allow for a larger, thinner slice.

Sweetbreads

- The best quality will be from young animals. Calves' sweetbreads (thymus gland) are more tender since they are from young animals.
- Calves' sweetbreads will be white.
- Sweetbreads tend to become more reddish as the animal ages.
- Best to use the same day they are purchased since they only have a refrigerator life of 1 day.

Cooking Sweetbreads

1. Soak the sweetbreads in a solution of 1 quart cold tap water mixed with 3 tablespoons of pure lemon juice for 1 hour to draw out residual blood.
2. If you are concerned about the sweetbread retaining their shape when cooked, slice into strips and place on a flat plate or cookie sheet, then place a very heavy weight on top and refrigerate for 2-3 hours before you cook them.
3. Blanch for 5 minutes; then place into a bowl of cold water, which will firm them.
4. After they have been firmed and cooled, remove the outer membrane and connective tissue.
5. Best when grilled or sautéed.

Broiling Meats

The following meats are best broiled: T-bone, sirloin, porterhouse, club, round steak, rump roast, hamburgers and flank steak on a pre-heated broiler pan and as close to the heat source as possible and only to sear. A flank steak should be cut into thin diagonal slices for the best results.

- Lower heat is used for large, thick meats.

Always place meats under the broiler as dry as possible.

- Meat and fish will brown more evenly if they are at room temperature instead of directly from the refrigerator.
- Always heat the broiler and the pan before placing any meat in.
- Higher heat for thinner cuts and for meat that are to be cooked rare.
- Fat around meat may have the tendency to catch fire if it gets too hot or if it is too close to the flame or element.
- If the meat you are cooking is thin, it should be cooked close to the flame or element so that it will cook faster and retain its moisture.
- If you are going to baste the meat, be sure and use a warm solution. If the solution is cool or cold, it will slow down the cooking time.
- To reduce the risk of flare-ups. Place a few slices of bread on the bottom of the pan to soak up excess fat drippings.
- Only turn meats once when broiling.

Broiler Temperatures

Cut of Meat	Thickness	Rare	Medium	Well Done
		minutes per side		
Beef	1 in.	5 min.	6 min.	7 min.
(all steaks)	1½ in.	9 min.	10 min.	12 min.
	2 in.	16 min.	18 min.	20 min.
Lamb	1 in.	N/A	6 min.	7 min.
(loin, rib or chops)	1½ in.	N/A	9 min.	11 min.
	2 in	N/A	15 min.	17 min.
Pork				
(ham shoulder slice)				
Raw	1 in.			10 min.
Pre-Cooked				5 min.

Roasting

- The cut of meat to be roasted should be large enough so that it will retain enough moisture through this dry-cooking method.

- For the best flavor, purchase a roast with the bone in to increase the flavor and to act as a heat conductor shortening the cooking time.

- Allow a roast to remain out of the refrigerator for about 1-2 hours before cooking.

Always start a roast in a pre-heated oven to help retain the juices.

- Never use any seasoning that contains salt on a roast or it may draw moisture from the meat.

- If you marinated the roast, the olive oil massage is even more important to help retain the moisture.

- Placing vegetable juice in the bottom of the pan will provide more flavor than using water.

- Use a roasting pan that has a very heavy lid, the heavier the better to keep the steam in so that it will re-circulate into the cooking liquid.
- Searing a roast contributes to drying out the roast and is not recommended by most chefs.

If the roast has high fat content and thick fat covering, just sprinkle the surface with a small amount of dry mustard to neutralize the fattiness.

- If the roast has a fat layer or if you are barding it, cook the roast fat-side up to naturally baste the roast.
- If you slow-cook a roast it will retain more moisture and will not shrink as much; however, it will not be browned very well.
- A fast method of cooking a pot roast is to tightly wrap the roast in heavy-weight aluminum foil after sprinkling 2 packages of dry onion mix over the roast. Cook in a pre-heated 300°F. oven for 3 hours. Vegetables can be added to the pot after 2 hours of cooking time has elapsed.
- If you want a nicely browned roast to retain the moisture and not have too much shrinkage, then place the roast in a very hot oven for the first 20-25 minutes then reduce the heat back to the recommended setting.
- If the roast does not have a fat layer on top, then the roast should be turned once or twice and basted with the juices for the best results.

Allow the roast to rest for about 15 minutes after you remove it from the oven. The juices tend to go toward the center during cooking and will return closed to the surface after the roast is allowed to rest.

- While the roast is resting, cover the roast with tin foil.

Braising

Money-saving cuts that can be braised are rump or chuck roast, which can be made as pot roast, short ribs, liver (beef), chuck steak, round steak and flank steak.

- Braising may be done either on the range or in the oven. This method is preferred for certain foods since the heat surrounds the pot.
- A heavy pot with a lid that closes tight is recommended.
- The liquid used for braising is always used as either all or part of the sauce.
- Braising (browning) is almost always the initial step in the cooking process of any meat on which a brown crust is desired.
- Pan-frying is the typical method of braising.
- When braising, the food is never completely covered by the liquid.

- Braising can be used for many cuts of meat. The meat is first browned in a very small amount of oil or butter. The pan is then covered as tightly as possible while the meat continues to cook.
- If you oven-braise, you can do it at 325°F. and it will braise more evenly.

Sprinkling a small amount of flour on the meat during cooking will help it to brown.

- Make sure that there is only a very small amount of liquid or the steam generated will poach the meat.
- The liquid in the pot should only be simmering, not boiling.
- Occasionally blot the top of the meat with a paper towel to eliminate excess moisture for the best results.

VEAL

The cuts of veal that can be roasted and will save you money are rib roast, rump roast, round roast or a stuffed, rolled shoulder roast. If you want to broil in either a pan or oven the best bets are loin steak, round steak, loin chop, rib chops. Shoulder chops are best pan-broiled or braised. Simmering veal is best done with stewing veal meat (can be from shank, neck, breast), or shoulder skillet steak.

- Be sure that the fat on veal is very white and not yellow.
- Veal is very delicate meat and should be cooked similar to chicken.
- Cook veal within 1-2 days after purchase for the best flavor.
- Veal is best when cooked using a moist-cooking method and should be cooked slowly.
- Veal is low fat meat and if you cook a veal roast, it would be best if it were barded. Your butcher can do this for you if you have never done it before.
- Ground veal is rarely used in meat loaf or hamburger since it requires added fat.
- Veal will easily turn tough if overcooked. Since many dishes call for thin slices of veal, such as veal scaloppini, it is easy to overcook veal.
- The best seasonings for veal are sage, thyme, tarragon and basil.
- Veal should never be aged.

Veal Breast
- Breast of veal is the least expensive cut and is best stuffed and cooked very slowly.
- The breast is cooked, stuffed for 20-25 minutes per pound at 350°F. to an internal temperature of 170°F.

Veal Roast
- Chefs tend to rub butter on the roast and then sprinkle paprika on top to give the roast a nice

brown color.

- Allow the roast to sit still in a warm environment, covered for about 30 minutes before attempting to slice it or it will fall apart.
- Many chefs cover a veal roast with a layer of fat since it is so lean and may cook somewhat dry.
- Boneless veal roasts are also frequently rolled in breadcrumbs to protect the delicate skin before being placed in the roasting pan. The best method is to place the breadcrumbs on a piece of wax paper and hold the edges with one hand, while you roll the roast back and forth with the other hand.

LAMB

Most lamb is expensive compared to other types of meat. The following are a few types that are not too expensive and can provide a tasty alternative to beef.

Chops
- The blade-end or shoulder chops have a higher fat content than loin-end chops, but are lower in cost.
- A thin layer of fat is desirable on lamb chops.
- The darker the meat, the stronger the taste and the older the animal.
- Cuts of lamb that have the bone in will be more flavorful.
- Should be served hot or cold, never just warm for the best flavor.
- The normal serving size is two chops.

Irish Lamb Stew

If you add one cup of black coffee to lamb stew, it will improve the flavor and darken the meat.

- To maintain good flavor, cook the vegetables before adding them to the stew.

Shish Kebob

- The lamb should be prepared the day before by cutting it up into cubes and placing it in a marinade overnight.
- Portions should be 6 ounces per person.
- Place the lamb cubes on the skewers and grill or broil separately from the vegetables.
- The most common vegetables are mushrooms, onions, tomato and green pepper.
- Broil or barbecue the vegetables separate and place them between the lamb cubes just before serving.
- When the vegetables are placed on the skewers and cooked at the same time, the steam from the released liquid makes the lamb too moist.

Broiling- The following lamb is best broiled: Loin chop, rib chop, leg steak.

Roasting- Any leg roast, loin end of leg, breast roast, rolled shoulder (rolled) or crown roast.

Braising- Shoulder, neck or leg.

Simmering- Stewing lamb meat (can be from shank or neck). Both can also be used for broth.

PORK

Make sure that all cuts of pork are cooked well and there are no signs of pink. Fresh cuts should be firm and fine-grained with a grayish-pink tone and should have some fat marbling on the outside.

Ham (Leg of Pork)

- The ham bone is excellent for soups.
- The flavor of a ham can be improved by heating even if it doesn't require it on the label.

If you purchase a "country ham," it will have been smoked and aged through a special curing process. Unfortunately this process tends to make these hams relatively salty. These hams may need to be skinned, soaked for a period and simmered.

- If you need to store the ham, check the wrapper for specific instructions.
- Many canned hams go through a special sterilization process and can be stored at room temperature for a prolonged period.
- When you purchase a cured ham, be sure that it has the U.S. inspection seal on it. This assures

you that the meat was cooked properly.

- If you ask a butcher (real nice), they will remove the bone from the ham for you.
- To remove a canned ham, just immerse it in hot tap water for 2 minutes to loosen the gel.
- The rind can easily be removed if you slice it lengthwise straight down the center before baking. The ham should be cooked slit-side down and the rind removed as soon as the ham is removed from the oven while the rind is still hot.
- When using ham for soups, use a number of small pieces instead of large chunks to intensify the flavor.

If you are going to glaze a ham, it is best to remove about $^1/_4$ inch of the fat before glazing.

- To caramelize the exterior of a ham, use light brown sugar.
- A glaze can be made by combining 1 cup of brown sugar, $^3/_4$ cup of unsweetened pineapple juice and 1 teaspoon of dried mustard.
- If ham slices are too salty, place them in a container of low fat milk for 20 minutes, rinse and dry before cooking.
- If you think that you have a ham that is too salty, just cook it for half the cooking time, then remove it from the oven and pour a small bottle or can of ginger ale over it. This will de-salt it about 30%.
- If you want to de-salt a ham further, rub salt on the outside of the ham after pouring the ginger ale on and it will drain more salt water out of the ham and de-salt it about 60%.
- Pre-cooked ham slices dry out very easily and only need to be browned on each side.
- If you cook ham slices too fast, they may become tough.

Pork Chops

- Cook loin pork chops in a greased skillet adding a small amount of water to the pan, then cover and cook for about 30-40 minutes or until tender. The water will create just enough steam to keep the chops moist.
- When purchasing raw pork, be sure that the meat is a nice pale pink color. The darker the meat the older the animal.
- Check the color of the fat: it should be white on pork and beef, which indicates more tender meat. If the fat is yellow, the meat may be somewhat tough.
- Just to be safe, even though there is rarely a health problem with rare pork, cook it to an internal temperature of 155^0-165^0F.
- Pork chops should be purchased about 1 in. thick to maintain the juices when they are cooked.
- If you prefer thin pork chops, cook them with the lid on the pan for a short period of time since

they dry out very quickly.

- Pork chops that are to be stuffed should be at least $1^1/_2$ in. thick and should be rib or loin chops.
- Always cut the pork chops to be stuffed from the fat side and make the slit almost to the bone. After you stuff the chop use small metal skewers to close the opening while they are cooking.
- Pork should never be left at room temperature for more than 1 hour before being refrigerated.

The juices should be clear when the pork chop is done.

- When cooking pork chops, the excess fat should be removed.
- Pork chops do well on the grill, but be sure they are at least 1" thick for the best results.
- For juicier pork chops, allow them to stand for 10 minutes after they are cooked. Keep them warm and covered and they will be juicy all the way through.

Roasting- Any fresh shoulder butt, picnic shoulder, smoked butt, loin roast, fresh ham, spareribs and whole tenderloin.

Braising- Rib chops, loin chops, shoulder steak, tenderloin (whole or filet) and spareribs.

Simmering- Boneless boned butt, pig's feet, spareribs, smoked ham and ham hocks.

Top Ten Pointers for Meat Storage

1. Bacteria vs. Fresh Meat - Meat is very perishable, will spoil easily and can be a home for a number of bacteria. Refrigerate meat as soon as you bring it home. You can wipe the meat off but do not wash the meat. The meat should be re-wrapped loosely in a market paper, plastic wrap or waxed paper. Airtight coverings are not recommended since the meat should be allowed to have air circulating around it. Store in the coldest part of the refrigerator if the meat will not be used immediately. If the meat is tightly packaged by the market, it may be best to loosen the wrappings a little.

2. Steaks & Roasts - Small cuts of meat tend to go bad faster and should be used as soon as possible. If not frozen, three days is usually the maximum time in the refrigerator after bringing the meat home from the market. Steaks and chops should be cooked within 2-3 days of purchase; however, roasts can be stored for 3-4 days. Frozen steaks can be cooked (broiled) without defrosting them under low heat.

3. Freezing Tips - Small cuts of meat are best frozen if you plan on keeping them for more than 2-3 days. Always use special freezer paper if you plan on freezing meats for more than 1 week. For 1-2 weeks, you can wrap the meat in waxed paper and then over-wrap them with aluminum foil. Best to wrap each steak or chop separately. The freezer should be turned to the highest position until the meat is fully frozen, then you can reduce the position.

Use plastic liner bags from cereal boxes to store meats in the freezer.

4. Leftover Fowl - Chicken and turkey should not be allowed to remain at room temperature for more than 30-40 minutes before being refrigerated.

5. Special Cuts of Meat - Certain cuts of meats are very sensitive to spoilage. Some of these include liver, sweetbreads, kidney, stew meat that has been cut into small chunks and any cubed meat.

6. Cooked Meats - Cooked meats need refrigeration after 30-40 minutes at room temperature depending on the internal temperature of the final product. If the steak is prepared rare and not fully consumed, it should be stored within 20-30 minutes at the most.

7. Game Meats - Meats such as venison will keep for about 8-10 months if wrapped properly and stored at 0^0F.

8. Smoked Meats - These meats should be handled and stored the same as any other meat. If the meat comes in a re-sealable wrapper, it can be left in it providing the seal can be closed tightly. If the package is not well sealed, the odor from the meat may spread to other products in the refrigerator. All smoked bacon and hams should be consumed within a week of purchasing them.

9. Canned Meats - Always refrigerate any canned meat to be 100% safe. This is especially important for the larger sizes of canned meats. The smaller sizes of meats such as a canned ham is better protected by the small can and is less likely to go bad as fast.

10. Keeping Meats Frozen - If you store meat in a special moisture-proof material, they will last for quite a while. Most meats can be stored safely for at least 12 months at 0^0F. Cured foods, such as smoked ham are best not frozen because of the high salt content. Never refreeze any meat unless it has been cooked thoroughly.

Fowl
SAVINGS

Chicken is an excellent source of protein and considerably less expensive than most meat. Most supermarkets do not process chicken on weekends and rely on chicken that has been placed in the coolers during the week to last through the weekend. Therefore, it is usually best to purchase chicken Tuesday through Saturday for the freshest chicken. Chickens should be purchased as whole chickens to get the best buy since it is labor intensive for the market to cut the chicken in pieces, as well as the additional cost of packaging material.

There are two types of chickens you can purchase: chickens that are either "dressed" or "ready-to-cook." If you purchase a "dressed" chicken, it will be a whole chicken with its head, feet and all the entrails still inside. This not a good buy since you are paying for a lot of waste, which can equal as much as 25% of the total cost. The "ready-to-cook" chickens are what most people purchase. These chickens are inspected and are tagged with the weight and brand for identification.

Turkey, however, is usually a better buy than most chicken because of its larger size and less waste. Turkeys have less waste because they have less bone in relationship to the amount of meat. Farmers have now developed broad-breasted birds that are an excellent buy. A four-to-nine pound turkey will feed a family of 4-6 people at an excellent price per serving.

BAKED

- Always bake chicken at medium heat, since a high heat setting will result in a drier, stringier piece of chicken or turkey.
- Only bake chicken to 180°F. Any higher or lower and the fowl will be either underdone or dried out.
- If you remove the white hard tendon running lengthwise in the chicken breast, it will reduce shrinkage when the breast is cooked.

Since the majority of the fat content in both chicken and turkey is found in the skin, removing the skin is recommended in almost all instances when preparing the fowl. The quality of the fowl you are purchasing is important and freshness is one of the most important factors, which will make the dish more flavorful and appealing. If you can purchase a bird that is fresh and has never been frozen, you will probably notice the difference in taste. A kosher chicken will even taste better and will be a cleaner bird.

Boiled
- If you are going to use chicken or turkey in a casserole or pot pie, just boil the chicken until it is about ³/₄ cooked and allow it to remain in its own liquid for about one hour under refrigeration before using in the dish.
- Partial boiling for dishes produces a juicier piece of chicken.

Roasted

A roaster chicken is between is between 2-6 months old when slaughtered and a fryer or broiler is only 6-8 weeks old.

- A free-range chicken will be tastier if roasted.
- Roasting chickens have more fat than broilers.
- Roasters should weigh at least 3 pounds.
- Place very thin lemon slices under the skin to tenderize the chicken if you use an old bird.
- The roasting should be done in a 350°F. oven for 1-1½ hours and only baste once after 1 hour of cooking time.
- To deep-brown the chicken, just make a basting solution of some of the drippings and add a small amount of butter and corn syrup. Baste during the last 10 minutes of cooking time and raise the heat somewhat.

Stewing

- Never allow stewing chicken to come to a full boil. You will lose the flavor of the base in the chicken.
- Stewing should always be done on top of the stove or in the oven.
- Somewhat fatty chickens are best for stewing. Fat hens are the best and usually weigh about 4-5 pounds.

Whole Chicken

- If you are going to stuff a chicken, figure ³/₄ cups of stuffing per pound.
- The chicken will be cooked through when the leg feels loose.
- A 3-4 pound stewing chicken will take 1-2 hours to cook.
- It will take about 1 cup of stuffing to stuff the little bird.
- Serve adequate side dishes.

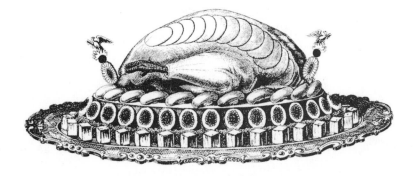

Quality is Important

Make sure the chickens you purchase are plump and look fresh whether you purchase them dressed or ready-to-cook. If the thigh looks thin and the bones heavy or if the chicken has a long, scrawny neck, don't buy it. The skin should be yellow not white or have a bluish tint to it.

Size Counts

The larger chickens are called fowl hens or stewing chickens. Their meat is not as tender as the smaller birds, but they have an excellent flavor when slow cooked in a moisture environment. They are excellent for stews, chicken pot pies, fricassee, chicken and dumplings and chicken a la king.

One of the best poultry buys you can make is to purchase a large turkey, which will provide 2-3 meals depending on the size of the family. Turkeys will freeze well and can be frozen for up to 12 months and retain their quality.

Watch Out for Food Poisoning

- Never stuff any fowl the night before. Stuff the bird just before placing it in the oven.
- Remove all stuffing as soon as you start carving the bird and refrigerate as soon as possible.

- Never allow warm gravy to remain at room temperature for more than 20-30 minutes before refrigerating.
- Never partially cook any fowl and leave the balance to be cooked the next day.

Frozen Poultry

All parts of poultry can be purchased frozen with good quality. There are several rules for freezing or thawing poultry:

- Leave the poultry in its original container and place it into the food-saver compartment of the refrigerator. Allow about 5 hours for every pound to thaw. The average chicken takes overnight, while a large turkey can take 2-3 days.
- If you wish to quick-thaw the poultry, just place it into a sink with cool running water until you can work with the poultry. This will take 1-3 hours, but make sure that you do not allow the bird to remain under the water after it has thawed.
- If you are thawing parts, place the opened package contents on a rack or tray and thaw until the pieces can be separated. If you want to speed up the process, place a small fan directed at the parts.
- Fried chicken is one of the only foods that can be fried and then frozen. You can thaw the chicken out and take it on a picnic.
- Always buy chicken and turkey when they are on sale and freeze for up to 1 year. During Thanksgiving, many markets will offer a buy-1, get-1 free promotion. This is an excellent way to save a lot of money and get many turkey dinners.

More Money-Saving Tips

1. If you purchase a bird with pinfeathers, use a cigarette lighter to singe the feathers. This will not cause any smudging of the skin. Never freeze chicken or turkey with pinfeathers.

2. To keep the meat moist, place a cored apple into the chicken instead of stuffing it.

3. Allow $^3/_4$ of a pound per person when purchasing chicken.

4. Chicken will only last for 3 days in the refrigerator after being cooked or it will pick up refrigerator odors. Must be wrapped tightly.

5. Always double-wrap chicken for the best results when storing in the refrigerator or freezing.

Lemon as a Tenderizer

Lemon is a natural tenderizer for chicken and gives chicken a unique flavor. You might also try basting it with a small amount of Zinfandel. Remember, a low-to-moderate cooking temperature will produce a juicier chicken, since more fat and moisture are retained.

17

Saving
THE SEAFOOD DOLLAR

The popularity of fish has risen since the 1980's and more varieties of fish have become available. Consumption of fish in 2002 averaged 24.1 pounds per person. More fish than ever are now raised in aquaculture fish farms. The fats in fish are high in polyunsaturates and contain the omega-3 fatty acids that may protect us from heart attacks by keeping the blood from coagulating too easily. Studies show that even canned or frozen fish retain most of their omega-3 fatty acids. However, many fish and shellfish may still harbor certain bacteria and parasites. Cooking is a must for fish and shellfish since they should never be eaten raw. Also, never consume the skin or visible fat on fish as most of the contaminants, if present, will be located there.

Be a Skillful Buyer
There are many varieties of fish sold in the United States: the most common are flounder, mackerel, haddock, halibut, ocean perch, cod and whiting.

Choosing Fresh Fish in the Supermarket

Skin- The skin should always have a shiny look to it and when finger pressure is applied, it should easily spring back to its original shape. The meat should be firm to the touch with no visible blemishes. Never buy fish if the skin has any dark discoloration.

Eyes- When you look into the eyes, they should be bulging and not sunken into the head, which is a sign of a dried-out fish. The eyes should also be clear and not cloudy. If the fish winks at you, this is a very good sign.

Scales- The scales should not be falling off. If you notice loose scales, don't buy the fish. The scales should also have a healthy, bright and shiny appearance.

Gills- The gills must look clean with no sign of any slime. Their healthy color is a reddish- pink. Gray gills are a sign of an old fish that has seen better days.

Odor- A fresh fish never smells "fishy." If the fish does have a strong odor about it, it is probably from the flesh decomposing and releasing the chemical compound, "trimethylamine." Seafood should be as fresh as possible, usually no more than 2-3 days out of the water.

Choosing Frozen Fish in the Supermarket

Odor- If frozen fish has an odor, it has probably thawed and been re-frozen. When it is thawed, it should have hardly any odor.

Skin- Be sure that the skin and flesh are frozen solid and that there is no discoloration or soft spots. The skin should be totally intact with no areas missing.

Wrappings- The wrapping should be intact with no tears or ice crystals. Be sure that the fish is frozen solid.

Common Forms of Supermarket Fish

Whole Fish- Complete with entrails, needs to be sold shortly after it is caught.

Drawn Fish- Whole fish with only the entrails removed.

Dressed Fish- Totally cleaned up with entrails removed and ready to party or cook.

Fish Fillets/Steaks- Large pieces of fish with the bones removed. When both sides are removed, they are sometimes called butterfly fillets.

Cured Fish- These are usually sold as smoked, pickled or salted fish. If the fish is sold as "cold smoked," it was only partially dried and will have a very short shelf life. If the label reads, "hot smoked," the fish was not fully cooked and should be kept frozen until used.

Dried Fish- Fish that has been processed using dry heat, then salted to preserve it.

Salted Fish- These fish are used mainly for pickling in a brine solution.

A Word to the Wise

If you see a seafood product with "USG INSPECTED" on the label, report it to authorities: this is not a legal designation. The label should read "Packed Under Federal Inspection" or (PUFI). This means that it was packed in the presence of, or at least inspected by a Federal Inspector.

SHELLFISH

Pollution and Shellfish Still a Problem

Presently, about 34% of all shellfish beds in the United States have been officially closed because of pollution. All coastal waters worldwide are in jeopardy of also being closed to fishing. One of the world's b e t t e r known seaports, Boston Harbor is so polluted that fisherman are advised not to fish there anymore. Mutant fish are being caught in Boston Harbor with tumors and bacterial infections. The sewage problem is so bad in the Gulf States of Louisiana and Florida that 67% of the oyster beds have been closed to fishing. In Europe about 90% of the sewage is still dumped into coastal waters.

Fish and Shellfish Tenderizer

A number of fish and shellfish may need a bit of tenderizing, which can be done by soaking the seafood in 5 parts vinegar to 1 part water for about 8 hours. Salmon, oysters, lobster and abalone respond well to this method of mild-acid tenderizing. Make sure you rinse off the vinegar well before cooking.

Cooking Fish and Shellfish

The best advice when it comes to purchasing fish and shellfish is to know your market fish department and be sure that the fish and shellfish are from safe fishing grounds. The problem with contaminants being found in both fish and shellfish is reaching serious levels. Many fish and shellfish are now being grown in aquafarms that have control of what the fish are consuming.

FISH

- Preparing a fish with its head and tail on will allow more of the juices to remain in the meat and produce a juicier, more moist dish. Make sure, however, that the fish has been scaled and gutted.
- When freezing all fresh fish, they should be frozen in water.

De-Boning Fillet
- An easy trick used by chefs to de-bone fillet is to use a vegetable peeler and just lightly run it over the fillet, allowing the tiny bones to catch in between the blade. Then they just give a slight twist and the bones come out.

Game fish
- Game fish should not be frozen for more than 1 month for the best results when preparing.

When freezing game fish, be sure and remove the gills or the fish will be bitter.

- All scales must be removed before freezing.
- The head can be left on if desired.
- If the fish is over 2 pounds, place a double sheet of aluminum foil or plastic wrap inside, which will make a big difference when defrosting the fish.
- The fish should be wrapped in plastic wrap, then aluminum foil. After it is frozen, pack the fish in freezer paper.
- To defrost the game fish, place it into a sink of cold water and allow it to remain until it is has reached the temperature of the water and is thawed and flexible.

COOKING METHODS

Baking Fish (general information)
- Pre-heat the oven to 425^0F.
- Rinse the fish well under cold running water and pat dry with paper towel.
- If you are going to bake a whole fish, make sure that you dry the inside as well.

Broiling Fish (general information)
- The best cuts of fish to broil are fillets and steaks that are $1/4$ to $1\frac{1}{2}$-inches thick.
- The fish should be rinsed well under running cold water and dried on paper towels.
- Pre-heat the broiler pan.

- It is not necessary to add any additional oil or butter.
- The broiler pan should be sprayed with vegetable oil before placing the fish on it.

If you are broiling a whole fish, be sure and slash the skin on both sides a few times to avoid curling.

- The fish will retain good moisture if you don't overcook it, which is easy to do under a broiler.
- Lean fish, such as bass and pike should be basted to prevent drying out.
- Turn the whole fish only once, halfway through the broiling.
- Fillets do not have to be turned and should be skin-side down.
- The pan should be placed 4-5 inches from the heat source.
- Broil for 6-10 minutes per inch of thickness or until the flash is opaque.
- If you are going to broil frozen fish, double the cooking time and turn the fish halfway through the cooking time.

Frying Fish (general information)
- Basically, all you need is peanut oil and a crispy coating.
- The typical batter contains beer, flour and eggs.
- The fish can also be coated with just cornmeal and flour.
- The seasonings that are added are up to your taste.
- The three-container method is normally used. The first contains flour; the second contains egg that has been whisked with milk and the third with your special blend of seasoned flour.
- Press the fish into the flour; shake off well, then dip into the milk mixture and very gently into the seasoned flour.
- When batter-frying fish, the batter should be cold to prevent too much oil from being soaked up into the fish.
- The oil should be 350°-360°F.

Grilling Fish (general information)
- Make sure that the fish is rinsed well under cold water.
- Best to marinade the fish for 1-2 hours under refrigeration.
- One of the best marinades is a combination of olive oil, cloves, chili peppers (mild), orange and lime, juices. Salt and pepper to taste.

Grilling should be done over direct high heat for 6-10 minutes per inch of thickness.

- Grilling times are dependent on the thickness, type of fire source (wood, charcoal, gas or electric), the distance the fish is from the heat source and whether the grill is open or closed.

- Make sure that the fish is cooked until the insides are opaque.
- The fish should only be turned once for the best results.
- Grilling covered imparts a great smoky flavor to the fish.

Microwave Fish Cooking (general information)
- All fish needs to be defrosted before placing in the microwave.
- Generally to microwave a fish takes 3-6 minutes per pound in a 600-700 watt oven on high power.
- The skin side should be placed down and a few slashes made into the skin to avoid curling.
- Thicker pieces of fish should be placed along the outer edges so that it will cook more evenly.

Never salt fish when microwave cooking or the salt on top of the fish may cause the fish to cook unevenly.

- The fish should not be totally opaque since it will continue cooking for a few minutes after you remove it. Allow it to sit for about 5 minutes, covered, before serving.

Poaching Seafood (general information)
- This entails cooking the fish in gently simmering liquid, usually lightly salted lemon water, fish or vegetable stock or a mild wine.
- Do not poach tuna, swordfish or shark.
- Poaching should never overpower the flavor of the fish, but should complement it.

The fish should first be rinsed well under cold water and wrapped in cheesecloth, leaving enough room so that the ends can be twisted and knotted.

- The skin can be removed before serving if you wish.
- When preparing fish in this manner the ends can be used as handles, if you have to raise or lower the fish.
- Use a deep pan and place your liquid in the bottom, then bring it to a boil, reduce the heat to a slight simmer and add the fish in single layers with enough liquid to cover the fish by about 1 inch.
- The fish should be cooked gently for 6-12 minutes per inch of thickness or until it is opaque all the way through.
- Fish do not have to be turned when poaching.
- To save money, poaching liquid can be served as a broth if you wish.
- Poaching liquid can also be frozen and used as the liquid of choice when poaching again.

Sautéing (general information)
- This method is best for thinner fillets or very small whole fish if they are 1" thick or less.

- If you can't fit the whole fish in a 10" skillet, forget about pan-frying the fish.
- Rinse the fish or fillet under cold water and pat dry with paper towels.
- If you would like to seal in the juices, lightly flour the fish before placing it in the pan or heavy-duty skillet, which is preferred.
- Sauté in 1-2 tablespoons of butter (clarified is OK) and 1-2 tablespoons of vegetable oil. Do not use olive oil unless you are using clarified butter.
- Heat over medium-high heat, then add fish to the heated oil and be sure and not crowd the fish. They need their space or they will get soggy.
- Fry for about 6-12 minutes per inch of thickness or until the flesh is opaque.

The fish should be turned over halfway through the cooking time.

- If the fish is very thick or you are frying a whole fish, reduce the heat to medium and cook for a few minutes longer.
- Make sure that you place the fish on paper towels to remove the excess oil before placing on a platter to serve.

Haddock
- Best when stuffed, poached or baked.
- Can be substituted for cod; however, the flesh will be slightly softer.
- Smoked haddock is known as "finnan haddie."

Hake (Whiting)
- Tend to be softer and more moist than cod, which hake is commonly compared to.
- Whole dressed fish as well as fillets are usually available in supermarkets and fish markets.
- The fish is best poached, steamed, baked or pan-fried.
- Small whiting are usually floured and fried whole.
- Very versatile and inexpensive fish.

After the fish is cooked, the bones are easy to remove.

Halibut
- Usually prepared as steaks, fillets or poached.
- Can be sautéed similar to salmon with good results.
- White-flesh halibut can be substituted for sole in most recipes.

Catfish

- Best if baked, broiled, deep-fried or poached.
- Catfish should never smell fishy when cooked.
- The skin is very tough and can be hard to remove.
- Best to purchase catfish fillets.
- When buying catfish, make sure that the flesh is not spongy or dry.
- If the catfish has a strong "fishy" smell, don't buy it.
- When buying frozen catfish, be sure that the package has no partial thawing.
- If you purchase catfish that has been skinned, be sure that the meat is white with no sign of blood sores.
- Catfish must be cooked or refrigerated immediately after purchasing.
- Frozen catfish cannot be kept for more than 6 months.

Never refreeze catfish.

- Catfish should be cooked to an internal temperature of 140^0F.
- Catfish has almost no connective tissue and cooks very quickly.

Mackerel

- Mackerel is best cooked in an acid medium for the best flavor. Citrus juices are one of the best marinades for mackerel.
- Very oily fish that is related to tuna.
- The outer layers of meat are red and the inner layers are lighter.
- Light, mild-flavored meat.
- Very perishable and needs to be purchased fresh and used that day.
- Sold as whole fish, skin-on fillets and steaks.

Mackerel must be kept well, iced from the moment it is caught to the time it is being prepared for cooking.

- Can be pan-fried, baked or broiled.

Stretching
THE EGG AND DAIRY DOLLAR

All dairy products are very perishable and contain tens of millions of bacteria. The optimal refrigeration is actually just over 32^0F. ; however, few refrigerators are ever set that low or will hold that low temperature. Most home refrigerators remain around 40^0F., which goes higher every time the door is opened.

SAVING MONEY ON MILK

Milk can be purchased in larger quantities, if the price is right and frozen for up to 2 weeks if left in the original container. However, be sure and pour out a little to allow 2 inches for expansion.

Curds and whey are two proteins found in milk and milk products. The curd is actually "casein" and tends to form into a solid. The whey may be composed of several proteins, the most predominant being "lacto-globulin" and all are suspended in liquid. The liquid that you see on the top of yogurt or sour cream and other natural dairy products is the protein whey, not water, and should be stirred back into the product. Before you boil milk, be sure and rinse the pan in cold water to stop the milk from sticking to the pan.

Milk will last longer and remain fresher if it stored at about 34^0F. (1.1^0C.). However, the average refrigerator temperature is about 40^0F. (4.4^0C.) providing the door does not get opened too frequently.

Milk should never be purchased in see-through plastic containers. When light hits the milk, it can lose up to 44% of its vitamin A content in low fat or skim milk. Markets are now placing these containers under light shields. Many manufacturers are now tinting the containers, which does help.

Light cream can be whipped, if you add 1 tablespoon of unflavored gelatin that has been dissolved in 1 tablespoon of hot water to 2 cups of cream. After you whip it, refrigerate it for 2 hours. Heavy cream will set up faster, if you add 7 drops of lemon juice to each pint of cream.

If a recipe calls for buttermilk and you don't have any, try using slightly soured milk. Soured milk may be used in many baking recipes. Buttermilk may be substituted for whole milk in most recipes, but you will need to add $^1/_2$ teaspoon of baking soda to the dry ingredients for each cup of buttermilk you use. To make soured milk, just place 1 tablespoon of white vinegar into one cup of milk and allow it to stand for 10-15 minutes. If you are in a hurry, just place the cup in a microwave for about 30 seconds. There are a number of dry milks available at the supermarket, which can be used for several types of cooking purposes, as well as drinking and in your cereal. Remember that after you reconstitute the milk, allow it to age for 4 hours in the refrigerator for the best taste. After dry milk is reconstituted, it will last for about 3 days in the refrigerator. All dry milk products should be fortified with vitamins A and D. If the label reads "Extra Grade," the product will be of the highest grade. Grade A is not the highest grade of dry milk. Powdered milk has a tendency to absorb odors and moisture from the air. Try and purchase small packages unless you use a large amount. When powdered milk is canned with nitrogen or carbon dioxide, it will last for long periods of time.

Skim and non-fat powdered milk is the same product and is just milk that has been dehydrated to a powder form. There are two types of non-fat milk, regular and instant. A special spray-drying process is used. However, the instant is processed further so that it will dissolve faster. The regular non-fat milk is mainly used in the baking industry. To prepare a cup of milk, you will need to add 3 tablespoons of the instant to 8 ounces of water. Shaking the milk before you drink it will also add some air to the milk and make it more palatable. The powder can be added to most dishes to increase the calcium level in foods. Can last for 6 months without refrigeration. Flavored non-fat is now appearing in supermarkets, especially in chocolate flavored drinks, such as cocoa and malted milk.

Dry whole milk contains 100% of its fat content and has a shorter shelf life than non-fat dry milk. This milk is usually found in camping stores for hikers. Requires refrigeration to have a better shelf life.

Dry buttermilk can be used in a recipe that calls for buttermilk and has a slightly higher fat content than non-fat milk. The shelf life is shorter than non-fat milk.

Milk can retain its freshness if it's not contaminated by drinking from the carton for up to one week after the expiration date.

Evaporated milk is now available in whole low-fat, and nonfat, and is only sold in cans. It is heat-sterilized and will store at room temperature for 5-6 months. Partially frozen evaporated low-fat milk can be whipped and will make a low-fat whipped topping. If you need higher peaks, try adding a small amount of gelatin.

Every $\frac{1}{2}$ gallon of Grade A pasteurized milk contains over 50 million bacteria and if not refrigerated, will sour in a matter of hours. Milk should really be stored at 34^0F. instead of the average refrigerator temperature of 40^0F. Milk should never be stored in light as the flavor and vitamin A are affected in 4 hours by a process known as "autoxidation." The light actually energizes an oxygen atom that invades the carbon and hydrogen atoms in the fat. Powdered non-fat dry milk is dehydrated, thus losing its water content. The milk still contains about 35% protein (casein) and about 50% sugar (lactose). When you add water to

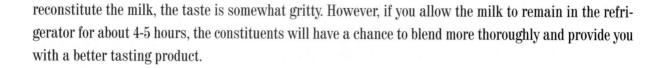

reconstitute the milk, the taste is somewhat gritty. However, if you allow the milk to remain in the refrigerator for about 4-5 hours, the constituents will have a chance to blend more thoroughly and provide you with a better tasting product.

When purchasing milk, be sure and buy it in a container that is not clear plastic. If the milk is exposed to the ultraviolet rays emitted from florescent lights for 4 hours in the supermarket, the milk will lose 45% of the vitamin A content in 1% low-fat milk and 32% in 2% low-fat milk. Manufacturers are now starting to sell milk in yellow-tinted containers.

If you want your milk to have a longer shelf life, just add a pinch of baking soda to the carton. If you place a small amount of baking soda in milk, it will reduce the acidity level just enough to add a few more days to the expiration date. However, milk will normally last for a week after the expiration date and still be useable if stored properly and no one drinks out of the carton. Another method is to transfer the milk from a carton to a screw-top glass jar, to reduce the effects of oxidation.

SAVING MONEY ON CREAM, YOGURT AND ICE CREAM

Cream has the tendency to curdle when poured over acidic fruits. To eliminate this problem, try adding a small amount of baking soda to the cream, then mixing it well before pouring it over the fruit. Baking soda is capable of reducing the acidity level in fruits.

Sour cream is easily made by adding 4 drops of pure lemon juice to $^3/_4$ cup of heavy cream. Allow the mixture to stand at room temperature for about 40 minutes.

Some of the higher quality ice creams now come with a thin plastic covering that can be placed over the exposed surface of the ice cream to provide a degree of protection from odors. If your brand does not have the plastic sheet, just use a doubled sheet of plastic wrap to cover the ice cream.

If you have ever opened up yogurt or cottage cheese and noticed a liquid that looked like water and thought that it was seepage, you were wrong. The liquid that has separated is "whey," which is a good protein that has problems remaining in suspension after the air gets in the package. Stir the whey back in, it's good for you.

When cream is having a somewhat off-odor and you need to use it, try mixing in 1/3rd teaspoon of baking soda. The baking soda will neutralize the lactic acid in the cream that is causing the souring. Before you use the cream, however, make sure the flavor is within normal boundaries.

Icicles or ice crystals in ice cream are usually formed from opening the door to the freezer too often. It doesn't take very much of a temperature drop to force the water molecules out of some of the ice cream cells and form the ice crystals. If the ice cream is stored for a prolonged period of time at 0^0F. (-17.8^0C.), the crystals will change their form again. Just scrape the crystals away since they are harmless.

SAVING MONEY ON CHEESES

Mold can be scraped off cheeses as long as you scrape off enough so that you are sure to have a clean area.

The wax coating on cheeses will protect it. If there is an exposed edge, try covering it with butter to keep the area moist and fresh.

Buttermilk can be used to soften dry cheese. Place the cheese in a shallow, covered dish with a one-inch layer of buttermilk and refrigerate overnight.

Cottage cheese will last 7-10 days longer if you store it upside down. When you open cottage cheese, spores enter from the air and live on the oxygen layer. When you turn cottage cheese upside down and allow it to fall to the top, you eliminate a percentage of the oxygen layer. Many of the remaining spores then suffocate and the ones that remain cannot grow as fast, allowing the cottage cheese to last about 7-10 days longer.

Vinegar to the Rescue

If you want to keep cottage cheese fresh, another method is to add 1 teaspoon of vinegar to the carton and stir it in well. This will really keep it fresh for a long period of time.

- The wax coating on cheeses will protect it. If there is an exposed edge, try covering it with butter to keep the area moist and fresh.

- To keep cheese longer without mold forming, place a piece of paper towel that has been dampened with white vinegar in the bottom of a plastic container that has a good seal before adding the cheese. Also, add 5-6 small sugar cubes for any mold that does get in to go to for food.
- Soft cheeses can be grated using a metal colander and a potato masher.
- Cheeses that have dried out may still be used for dishes that require grated cheese.

If you want to store cheese for a longer period of time, to avoid the cheese becoming moldy, just place the cheese brick into a well sealed plastic container with a piece of paper towel on the bottom that has been lightly soaked with vinegar, then add 3-4 sugar cubes. If any mold spores are lurking around after you seal it, they will be killed by the vinegar or go to the sugar cube.

Be sure and cook milk and cheeses at a low temperature so that they will not be ruined.

SAVING MONEY ON BUTTER

When butter and cheese are produced, the fermentation process is controlled by "lactic acid." When lactic acid is genetically altered, it will cause the dairy product to possess higher levels of "diacetyl," which is the flavoring component. The taste will be more satisfying and the product will have a longer shelf life. The new strain of lactic acid will be able to produce 3-4 times more "diacetyl."

When storing butter, it will be more important where you store it than how long it will last. Butter tends to absorb odors more efficiently than any other food. If you store it near onions, it will have an onion smell. If it's around fish, it will smell fishy, etc. If butter is refrigerated, it will retain its flavor for about 3 weeks, then it starts losing it rather fast. If you desire a rich butter flavor, it would be wise to date your butter package. Butter will freeze if you double-wrap it in plastic, then foil to keep it from absorbing freezer odors. It will last for 9 months if fresh when frozen and must be kept at 0^0F.

Oxidation will take its toll on butter just like any other fat. It tends to react with the unsaturated fats and causes rancidity. This reaction can be slowed down to a crawl if the butter is either under refrigeration or placed into the freezer. Butter should always be kept tightly wrapped.

If you allow butter to soften at room temperature then cream it with a mixer, it will go further and have fewer calories per pat serving.

Spreading Frozen Butter

Use a potato or vegetable peeler to shave frozen butter.

Make butter at home! It's really not as hard as might think. Using a food processor, place the bowl and metal blade unit in the freezer for 20 minutes. Measure 2 cups of cold heavy whipping cream (never use ultra-pasteurized) into the ice-cold bowl and metal blade and process for 3-5 minutes, scrapping down the sides to make sure that it all gets processed. Be sure to continue processing until all the solids are separated from the liquid. Then pour off the liquid, which is a protein substance called "whey." The solids (butter) need to be refrigerated and used within 3-4 days. This will make about 6-7 ounces of butter.

SAVING MONEY ON EGGS

If you keep all your eggs in one location, be sure and place a pencil mark on the older eggs so that they can be used up first.

If you need to buy a large quantity when they are on sale, just rub a small amount of vegetable oil on the egg to seal it up and it will last for weeks.

Never freeze any product with hardboiled eggs, since the egg whites will get rubbery.

Weight of 1 Dozen Eggs

Jumbo	=	30 ounces
Extra Large	=	27 ounces
Large	=	24 ounces
Medium	=	21 ounces
Small	=	18 ounce
Pee Wee (bakery eggs)	=	15 ounces

Calories

1 Large egg	=	80 calories
1 Egg white	=	20 calories
1 Egg yolk	=	60 calories

Measuring Eggs

1 Large egg (2oz)	=	$\frac{1}{4}$ cup
1 Med. egg ($1\frac{3}{4}$ oz)	=	$\frac{1}{3}$ cup
1 Small egg ($1\frac{1}{2}$ oz)	=	$\frac{1}{6}$ cup

If an egg cracks when being boiled, just remove it from the water and while it is still wet, pour a generous amount of salt over it, let it stand for 20 seconds, wrap it in tin foil, twirl the ends and replace it in the boiling water.

There are three grades of eggs: U.S. Grade AA, U.S. Grade A, and U.S. Grade B. Grade B eggs are usually used by bakeries and commercial food processors. All egg cartons that are marked "A" or "AA" are not officially graded. Egg cartons must have the USDA shield, as well as the letter grade.

If you want to increase the volume of beaten eggs, try using a bowl with a small rounded bottom. This reduces the work area and creates the larger volume.

The refrigerator shelf life of an egg is approximately 2-4 weeks depending on storage methods. Always store eggs in a closed container or the original carton for longer life and to avoid the egg absorbing refrigerator odors. If they are stored with the large end up they will last longer and the yolk will stay centered. Also, try rubbing a small amount of vegetable oil on the shell to seal it.

If you plan on using egg white powder, use 2 level tbsp. of powdered egg white plus 2 tbsp. of warm water to equal 1 egg.

- Powdered egg whites are easy to use and you don't have to separate the yolk
- Any recipe that calls for just egg whites, just use egg white powder
- You don't have to wait until the egg whites come to room temperature
- They are pasteurized and safe
- Long shelf life
- Helps reduce fat and cholesterol in dishes

If you have used the egg whites for a recipe and want to save the yolks for a day or two, try storing them in a bowl of water in the refrigerator.

If you have problems with poached eggs breaking up, you may have salted the water. Salt tends to cause the protein to break apart.

HARD BOILED FACTS

- You can prevent boiled eggs from cracking by rubbing a cut lemon on the shell before cooking.
- Boiled eggs should be cooled at room temperature before refrigerating them in an open bowl.
- To make the eggs easier to peel, just add a small amount of salt to the water to toughen the shell, then rinse them immediately in cold water.
- Another trick is to add a teaspoon of white vinegar to the water the eggs are being boiled in; this may also help prevent cracking. The vinegar tends to soften the shell allowing more expansion. However, they may not be as easy to peel. To remove the shell from a hard-boiled egg, roll it around on the counter with gentle pressure then insert a teaspoon between the shell and the egg white and rotate it.

- Always cool a hard-boiled egg before you try and slice it, it will slice easier and not fall apart.
- After you make hard-boiled eggs, never place them in cool water once they are peeled.
- Hard-boiled eggs will last under refrigeration for 1 week.
- Eggs have a thin protective membrane that, if removed or damaged and placed in water or a sealed container, may allow bacteria to grow.
- Hard boiled eggs should never be frozen since egg white changes: texture and becomes tough. When freezing fresh eggs, always break the yolk. The whites can be frozen alone and the yolks can be frozen alone unless you plan on using them at the same time.

When preparing scrambled eggs, allow 3 eggs per person. Most people eat more eggs when they are scrambled. If other ingredients are added, such as cheese or vegetables, then 2 eggs per person is sufficient.

You can substitute 2 egg yolks for 1 whole egg when making custards, cream pie filling, and salad dressings. You can also substitute 2 egg yolks plus 1 tsp. of water for 1 whole egg in yeast dough or cookie batter. If you come up one egg short when baking a cake, substitute 2 tbsp. of mayonnaise. This will only work for one egg.

EGG SIZE SUBSTITUTIONS

Substitute

Extra	Large	Medium	Small
1 Large	1	1	not recommended
2 Large	2	2	3
3 Large	3	4	4
4 Large	3	5	6
5 Large	4	6	7
6 Large	5	7	8

You can use egg substitutes for most recipes. Two that you can't use them for are cream puffs and popovers. You can substitute $^1/_4$ cup of an egg substitute for 1 large egg or 2 tablespoons = 1 large egg yolk.

Commercial food producers dispose of over 120,000 tons of eggshells every year. A new process has been invented that removes the egg membrane from the eggshells making both products usable. The shells are used as a calcium supplement and the membranes can be used in medical research as a source of raw collagen. The shells will now be worth $100 per ton and the membranes $1,000 per gram.

EGG DISHES

MAKE YOUR OWN MAYONNAISE

Mayonnaise must contain at least 65% oil by weight. If it has any less, it must be called salad dressing. Most fat-free mayonnaise contains more sodium than "real" mayonnaise. A tablespoon of "real" mayonnaise contains only 5-10 mg. of cholesterol, since very little egg yolk is really used and most mayonnaise has a soy base.

Formula for Standard Mayonnaise

The following ingredients will be needed:

1 Large egg	*1 1/2 Tsp. white wine vinegar*
1/2 Tsp. table salt	*1 Cup corn oil*
1 Tsp. mustard (optional)	*1 1/2 Tsp. lemon juice*
1/4 Tsp. ground white pepper	

Place the egg, salt, mustard, pepper and vinegar in a blender and blend for 6 seconds, then place the mixture in a food processor and process for 15 seconds while adding the oil a small stream at a time (very slowly). As soon as all the oil has been added, stop the processor and add the lemon juice to taste. If the mayonnaise is too thick, add a small amount of water and if too thin, process for a little longer.

19

Getting Smart
WITH VEGETABLES

Avoid using baking soda around fruits and vegetables. Baking soda is a base and many fruits and vegetables are somewhat acidic. When you mix a base and an acid, you may end up with a salt, and also a significant loss of taste.

PROPER STORAGE SAVES DOLLARS

Certain vegetables, such as peas, corn in the husk and any bean in their pod should be stored without removing them from their original container. This also preserves their food value for a longer period of time.

If you want to preserve corn for an extra day or two, just cut a small piece off the stem and place the ear in a pan with about 1 inch of water. Be sure and allow the outside leaves to remain on.

Always remove the tops from carrots, turnips, beets and parsnips, since they tend to draw moisture from the vegetable.

It is always a good idea to line your refrigerator produce drawers with a piece of paper towel to absorb excess moisture. Mold spores love moisture. If you also add a small amount of white vinegar to the paper towel, it will help.

Parsley should always be stored in a sealed jar in the refrigerator.

Try placing a few sponges in your vegetable drawer to absorb moisture.

Wrap all produce loosely, as air must be allowed to circulate around them to reduce spoilage.

If you want to speed up the soaking time for beans, just pour boiling water over them and allow them to soak for 1 hour.

Pinto beans are a dried bean that is an excellent source of protein. They should have a bright uniform color; fading is a sign of aging or long storage periods. When preparing pinto beans, try and purchase ones of uniform size; the smaller ones may become mushy before the larger ones are cooked. If you feel that this may be a problem, try adding a small amount of baking soda to the water while they are cooking.

If legumes are kept in a dry, cool location below 70^0F., they will last for up to 1 year and retain most of their nutrient content. They may be stored in their original bag or container, or transferred to a sealed glass jar. Never mix old beans with new beans, as they will not cook evenly. It is not necessary to freeze dried beans; it will not help to retain their nutrient content any longer. Beans in cooked dishes may be frozen, however, they may be somewhat mushy when thawed but can last for up to 6 months. Pinto beans contain about 22% protein, while beef has only 18%, and eggs 13%.

Broccoli should be stored in a plastic bag in the refrigerator. It will keep for only 3-5 days before the florets start opening and a loss of nutrients occur. To freeze broccoli, the leaves need to be removed and the stalks peeled. The broccoli should be cut into small lengthwise strips and blanched for 5 minutes, chilled and drained well, then placed in a sealed plastic bag. May be frozen for 10-12 months at 0^0F. A recent study at the University of Kentucky compared the vitamin C content of whole broccoli and plastic wrapped broccoli. Broccoli that was left out in the air lost 30% of its vitamin C content in four days while the broccoli that was wrapped in plastic only lost 17% and retained its color better. The respiration rate of the broccoli was slowed down conserving the nutrients.

Cabbage will last longer if stored in the refrigerator sealed tightly in a plastic bag. It should stay for about 2 weeks. Cabbage is 91% water.

Grandmother's Trick

If you add a small piece of horseradish to the pickle jar, it will keep the vinegar active while keeping the pickles from becoming soft.

When carrots are stored in a sealed plastic bag, a chemical is released called "terpenoid" that will reduce the sweetness and make the carrot somewhat bitter. Also, if carrots are stored with apples, melons, avocados, peaches, pears or green tomatoes they will develop terpenoids faster. Those fruits and vegetables tend to give off more ethylene gas as they ripen.

Carrot greens are high in vitamin K and E, which are lacking in the carrot.

- Celery will only store in the refrigerator for 7-10 days and should not be placed in water.
- Don't discard the celery leaves. Dry them, then rub the leaves through a sieve turning them into a powder that can be used to flavor soups, stews, and salad dressings. This can also be made into celery salt.
- Celery, carrots and lettuce will crisp up quickly if placed into a pan of cold water with a few slices of raw potato.
- To prevent celery from turning brown, soak in lemon juice and cold water before refrigerating for only a few minutes.

When you purchase celery, purchase the greenest you can find, it will be the healthiest and have the most flavor.

One of the best methods of storing celery for a prolonged period of time (2-3 weeks) is to wrap the celery tightly in aluminum foil.

Corn is one vegetable that is always better if eaten when it is fresh, preferably the same day you purchase it. As soon as corn is picked, it immediately starts to convert the sugars to starch. The milky liquid in the kernel that makes corn sweet will turn pulpy and bland in only 2-3 days. Corn loses 25% or more of its sweetness in less than 25 hours after harvesting.

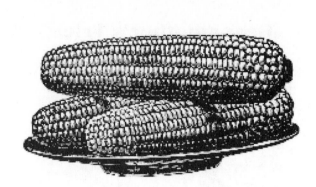

This is the reason that many people add sugar to the water when cooking corn. This guarantees the taste, which was probably lost after a few days in storage. Leftover fresh corn should be cooked for a few minutes just to inactivate the enzymes and store the ears in a sealed plastic bag for 1-2 days before using. If you plan on freezing corn, it needs to be cleaned and blanched for 4 minutes in boiling water. First allow the water to drain, tray-freeze keeping room between the ears so that the kernels will retain their shape and not be crushed when sealed in plastic bags. Frozen corn will freeze for 1 year.

Cucumbers tend to shrink during shipping and storage. The wax coating is to prevent the shrinkage and is edible. The skin should never be removed until you are ready to eat the cucumber or it will lose most of its vitamin C content. The cucumber is capable of holding 30 times its weight in water and is a member of the "gourd family." If you can remember back to the 1930's, "cucumber" was a slang word for a one-dollar bill.

Before you store your lettuce, you should remove the core by hitting the core once against a hard surface, then twist the core out.

All types of lettuce love the cold and the closer the temperature gets to 32^0F. without going below that, the longer it will last and the crispier the lettuce will be. Most refrigerators range between 35^0-40^0F., which is good but not the ideal temperature for lettuce. The lettuce should be stored without washing in a sealed plastic bag with a small hole or two for ventilation. Lettuce will turn brown easily if allowed to remain near most other fruits or vegetables due to the level of ethylene gas given off by most fruits and vegetables.

If you are only going to need half an onion, use the top half since the root half will store longer in the refrigerator.

Onions should be stored ideally in hanging bags, which will allow the air to circulate around them. Never purchase an onion if it has the slightest hint of decay since it will spread rapidly to healthy onions. The location should be cool and dry. If the weather is hot and humid, it will cut the storage time in half otherwise they should last about 2-3 weeks.

- If you refrigerate onions, they will last for about 2 months but may pass their aroma on to other foods in the refrigerator, even eggs.
- Sprouted onions are still good to use, as well as the sprouts. To freeze onions, just slice then (do not blanch them) and place them into a sealed plastic bag.
- They will freeze well for about 1 year.
- The smell of onions can be removed with a strong solution of salt water or a small amount of white vinegar.
- Chives need to be refrigerated and used within 3-4 days after purchase for the best flavor. If frozen, they can be added to any dish while still frozen. Chives can be stored in the refrigerator wrapped in paper towels in a plastic bag. They should last for about 1 week.

Onions: should only be purchased hard and dry; avoid onions with wet necks, this indicates decay. Also, avoid onions that have sprouted. They can easily be stored at room temperature or refrigerated.

A chemical in sweet potatoes is activated by temperatures below 40^0F. and tend to make a sweet potato taste bitter. Best not to refrigerate that poor sweet potato.

Sweet potatoes, yams, and white potatoes are actually an enlarged stem called a "tuber" that extends from the plant underground and is the storage depot for the plants excess carbohydrates. The potato plant bears a vegetable similar to a small mini-tomato and is not that good to eat. If potatoes are stored below 40^0F., they tend to release more sugar and turn sweet. Potatoes will last longer and remain solid longer, if they are stored in a cool, dry location, preferably at 45^0-50^0F. Air must be allowed to circulate around potatoes since moisture will cause them to decay. Potatoes do not freeze well, since a large majority of the cells tend to burst, causing the potato to become mushy and watery when thawed. Commercially processed potatoes will freeze.

White potatoes should be stored at room temperature in a dark area and not refrigerated. Refrigeration tends to turn potato starch to sugar. However, if the potato is removed from the refrigerator and left at room temperature, the sugar will convert back to starch.

It is best to purchase potatoes in bulk bins and not in bags. It is too difficult to determine which ones are bruised. If ginger root is stored with potatoes, it will help them stay fresh longer. If half an apple is stored with potatoes, it will stop the sprouting by absorbing any moisture before the potato does.

The only potato that can be stored in the refrigerator is the new potato. They will retain a good quality for 7-10 days.

The Anti-Sprouting Apple
If you place an apple in a bag of potatoes, the potatoes will not sprout.

Onions should never be stored with potatoes in the same bag. Onions tends to release gases that will alter the flavor of a potato. Cooking the two together is not a problem unless you overdo the quantity of onions and it takes over the flavor and aroma of the potato.

SAVING VEGETABLES

Many markets will sell partially wilted vegetables, which can easily be revived by placing them into a bowl of ice water in the refrigerator for 45 minutes.

When the potato chip bag is left open and they become stale and lose their crispiness, just place the bag in the microwave for 45 seconds on high and then allow to stand for 2 minutes.

Baked potatoes that are leftover can be re-baked if you dip them in water and bake them in a 350^0F. oven for 15-20 minutes.

To re-harden potatoes, try placing soft raw potatoes in ice water for $^1/_2$ hour or until they become hard. Brown areas on potatoes are the result of oxidation and vitamin C losses.

Place some sponges on the bottom of the vegetable drawer to absorb moisture and the vegetables will last longer.

To revive frozen vegetables, just pour boiling water over them, which will rinse away all traces of the stale frozen water.

You can revive wilted lettuce by placing the lettuce in a bowl of cold water and add a few slices of raw potato. Place in the refrigerator for about 45 minutes.

To remove the bitterness from a standard cucumber, not the long skinny English variety, cut about one inch off the end and then rub the two exposed areas together in a circular motion while occasionally pulling them apart. This will cause enough suction to release a substance that causes some cucumbers to have a bitter taste. Then discard the small end you used to release the bitterness.

Making the Grade
Fruits and vegetables are sold in three grades: U.S. Grade A Fancy, U.S. Grade B Choice or Extra

Standard, and U.S. Grade C Standard. Grades B and C are just as nutritious but have more blemishes. The grades refer to all canned, frozen or dried products.

To keep white vegetables white, try adding a small amount of cream of tartar to the water when they are cooking.

Fresh fruits and vegetables can also be found in three grades: U.S. Fancy, U.S. Fancy #1, and U.S. Fancy #2. These grades are determined by the product's size, color, shape, maturity and the number of visible defects.

The major component in the cell wall of fruits and vegetables is a complex carbohydrate called "cellulose." The higher the cellulose content, the firmer the fruit or vegetable. To tenderize the cellulose, heat and moisture are used. However, certain vegetables have different levels of cellulose in their various parts. Stems have more than tips, which is why it is necessary to remove the outer covering with a vegetable peeler before cooking broccoli or asparagus, otherwise the tips will be mushy and the stalks, tender. When heat or moisture is applied to the vegetable, it tends to destroy the cells' capability to retain and release moisture, which causes a structural breakdown resulting in tenderness. It also dissolves some of the pectin, which is active in holding the cells walls together.

When you choose lettuce in the supermarket, be sure and look at the bottom. If there is any rust color on the core, the lettuce will not last as long. Fresh lettuce has a white core on the bottom.

Salads
You will never have another soggy salad, if you just place an inverted saucer in the bottom of a salad bowl. The excess water; left after washing the vegetables and greens, will drain off under the saucer and leave the salad greens high and dry.

After you tear or chop up your lettuce, place a pinch of salt in the bowl and shake it. This will keep the lettuce crisp and prevent pre-mature wilting.

Cooking Vegetables
Salting the water when cooking any fruit or vegetable will draw a percentage of the liquid out. This may change the desired consistency and they may not cook evenly.

Placing vegetables in boiling water or exposing them to steam for 2-5 minutes was the accepted method of blanching for hundreds of years. The heat would inactivate the enzymes that tend to destroy the vegetable in a short period of time and allow them to be stored for longer periods. Science has now found that if you microwave the vegetables in a 700-watt microwave for 4 minutes with a few tsp. of water, seal them in a plastic bag and freeze them, it will work better than the boiling water or steam. The microwave provides just enough heat to inactivate the enzymes and retain the vitamin C content.

Next time you cook a fibrous vegetable, such as cabbage, celery or beets, try adding 2 tsp. of white vinegar to the cooking water. Vinegar is a mild acid and is able to breakdown the cellulose, which makes the vegetables stringy and somewhat tough.

Use a well-greased muffin tin to bake tomatoes, apples, or bell peppers. This will keep them in shape.

When you are cooking dried beans, make sure you add 3 tsp. of a pure vegetable boil to the water; this will help prevent boil over.

To tell whether a bean is fully cooked, squeeze the bean. You should never feel a hard core. If you are cooking the beans in an acid medium, such as with tomatoes, this will slow down the cooking time and testing the tenderness of the beans is a must. The taste of beans can be improved by adding a small amount of brown sugar or molasses.

Many people worry about the loss of nutrients due to the long cooking and soaking times for beans and other legumes. Studies performed by the USDA, however, have proved that legumes, even if they require 1-1$\frac{1}{2}$ hours of cooking time, will still retain from 70-90 percent of their vitamin content and almost 95 percent of their mineral content. The most affected were the B vitamins of which about 45-50 percent are lost.

When corn is cooked, the protein goes through a chemical change called "denaturization" which simply means that the chains of amino acids (proteins) are broken apart and reformed into a network of protein molecules that squeeze the moisture out of the kernel turning the corn rubbery. The heat also causes the starch granules to absorb water and swell up and rupture the kernel, thereby releasing the nutrients. Corn should be cooked just long enough to cause the kernels to barely rupture, which allows the protein to remain tender and not tough. When corn is boiled in water, 50% of the vitamin C is destroyed, however, if you cook it in a microwave without water almost all of the vitamin C is retained. Worldwide there are 200 varieties of corn; however, corn ranks as a vegetable low on the overall nutritional scale.

VEGETABLE THICKENERS SAVE MONEY

Cornstarch is a thick, powdery flour that is made from the corn's endosperm. It is an excellent thickener for sauces but tends to form lumps easily unless it is mixed slowly into a cold liquid and then added to a hot liquid. Stir the cornstarch until it mixes thoroughly, then boil it for a few minutes to thicken the sauce or stew. When you are thickening a stew or soup, be sure and remove as much fat as possible before adding the cornstarch.

Okra is actually a vegetable that consists of numerous unripe seed capsules. It is a very high carbohydrate food that is high in fiber and starch and contains a good amount of pectin and gums. The combination of these food elements; provide an excellent thickener for soups and stews. As okra is heated the starch granules absorb water and increase in size. The starch granules soon rupture and release "amylose" and "amylopectin" molecules: as well as some of its gums and pectin. These then attract additional water molecules and increase the volume, thus thickening the food.

FREEZING VEGETABLES

Best not to freeze lettuce, celery, fresh tomatoes or carrots. They don't freeze well and the quality is lost.

Blanching is a must! When vegetables are frozen, enzymes may still remain active and cause changes in the color, texture, and taste in the vegetable even if they have been previously stored under refrigeration. Freezing will slow the changes down; however, it will not totally inactivate the enzymes. If vegetables are blanched by either boiling them in water that has boiled for 2 minutes first (to release oxygen) or steaming them for 3-4 minutes, it will not cook them but will inactivate the enzymes and the vegetables will retain their color, texture, and taste. Of course, the enzymes are important to good nutrition and it would be more desirable to only purchase enough for a few days at a time.

If you choose to blanch in a microwave, I suggest you read up on the procedure in your manual. It is not as efficient as boiling water blanching and cold spots are possible, which will not kill the enzymes that must be destroyed.

Vegetables that are frozen and not blanched are still good to eat; however, the quality, color, texture and flavor will be considerably lower than those that have been blanched before freezing.

Corn must be handled just right or it will not be very edible. Corn should be blanched according to directions and chilled immediately in a bowl of ice water until the cobs are completely cooled down. Before you cook the ears, allow them to partially thaw at room temperature and place a small amount of sugar in the water.

Vegetables should be cooked right from the freezer for the best results. The only exception is corn-on-the-cob and leafy greens.

Other than most vegetables that normally will pack loose, most foods should have a small air space to allow for expansion.

What Are the Top 20 Nutritious Vegetables?

The following list of vegetables start with the most nutritious calculated from their nutrient levels of 10 of the most important nutrients. They must contain all 10, which include protein, iron, calcium, niacin, vitamins A & C, potassium, phosphorus, thiamin, and riboflavin.

1. Collard Greens
2. Lima Beans
3. Peas
4. Spinach
5. Sweet Potatoes
6. Turnip Greens
7. Winter Squash
8. Broccoli
9. Kale
10. Brussels Sprouts
11. Mustard Greens
12. Swiss Chard
13. Parsley
14. Tomatoes
15. Corn
16. Beet Greens
17. Pumpkin
18. Okra
19. Potatoes
20. Carrots

LEFTOVER VEGETABLES

Beet tops should not be discarded since they are high in nutrients and taste great when cooked up.

When you remove the peas from pods, save the pods and add them to soups for a great taste. The pods are eatable!

Leftover spinach can be finely chopped and added to many dishes even waffles.

20

Savings Tips
FOR FRUITS

When choosing fruits, it is always best to choose the healthiest looking and if possible, check the original box it came in to see if the fruit was graded "U.S. Grade No.1" or at least has a USDA stamp on the box or crate. To preserve the nutritional quality of fruits, leave them in their original packaging material if frozen. This will reduce the risk of exposure to air, which may result in a loss of flavor and cause discoloration. Brown areas on fruits mean that oxidation has taken place from exposure to the air of the more sensitive inner flesh, and that the vitamin C content has been lost. Brown discoloration can be reduced if you slice bananas, apples, plums, and peaches with a stainless steel knife, then either combine them with any citrus fruit or sprinkle them with lemon or pineapple juice. The citric acid from the lemon or pineapple neutralizes the effects of the oxidation.

The majority of fruits and vegetables are able to handle cold fairly well with the exception of tropical fruits whose cells are just not used to the cold. Bananas will suffer cell damage and release a skin-browning chemical and avocados will refuse to ripen in the cold when stored below 45°F. and oranges will develop a brown-spotted skin. The best temperature for squash, tomatoes, cucumbers, melons, green peppers, pineapple, and most other fruits and vegetables is actually at about 50⁰F. A few exceptions are: lettuce, carrots, and cabbage who prefer 32⁰F. The humidity is also a big factor and most fruits and vegetables need to be stored in the storage drawers, which will protect them from drying out.

The last thing a cook wants is mushy fruit. This frequently encountered problem can be resolved by just adding some sugar to the cooking syrup. This will strengthen the cell walls with an artificial sugar "cell" wall. The sugar will also have the effect of drawing some of the fluid back into the cell to slow down the drying out of the fruit and retaining the desired appealing consistency.

Order of the Nutritional Quality of Fruits

1. Fresh, if brought to market in a short period of time.
2. Dehydrated, if Grade A or No. 1.
3. Freeze Dried, if packaged at the site where grown.
4. Frozen, if packaged within 12 hours of harvest.
5. Canned.

Apples will ripen very quickly at room temperature. If you are not sure of their level of ripeness, just leave them out for 2-3 days before refrigerating them. Apples should be stored in the refrigerator, ideally at 36⁰-38⁰F. to stop the ripening process. They may be washed, dried and placed into a plastic bag. When refrigerated, apples will stay fresh for 2-4 weeks. Apples may also be stored in a cool, dry location in a b a r r e l that has sawdust in it. The apples should never touch each other and will last 4-6 months. To freeze apples, they need to be cored, peeled, washed and sliced. Spray them with a solution of 2 tsp. of ascorbic acid (vitamin C) in 12 tbsp. of cold water, then place them in a container leaving $^1/_2$ inch at the top.

Never store an apple near a banana unless you wish to ripen the banana in a very short period of time. Apples tend to give off more ethylene gas than most other fruits (except green tomatoes) and will hasten the ripening of many fruits and vegetables. Ethylene gas is a natural gas that is released by all fruits and vegetables as they ripen. Ethylene has been used for centuries to ripen fruits and vegetables. Fruits and vegetables may be gassed to ripen them as they are trucked to market. Ethylene increases the permeability of the cell membrane allowing the cell to respire more and use oxygen to produce carbon dioxide up to five times faster than it ordinarily would. This increased activity of the cell causes the fruit or vegetable to ripen faster.

If the apples are losing their moisture and taste, try slicing them up, placing them in a dish and pouring cold apple juice over them and refrigerating for 30 minutes.

As soon as a banana ripens at room temperature, they should be stored in the refrigerator to slow down the ripening process. The skin will turn black, however, this does not affect the flesh for a number of days.

- Bananas will freeze well for a short period of time; however, they will be a bit mushy when thawed and are better used in dishes.
- Frozen banana treats are eaten while the banana is still frozen solid which does not give them the thawing time to make them mushy.
- The new miniature bananas have more taste than many of the larger ones and can be consumed in the same manner.
- Excellent spices to use on bananas are cinnamon and nutmeg.
- Bananas are often sold as chips and should not be considered a healthy snack food since they are usually fried in saturated fat oil. It would be best to choose an air-dried chip if you can find one. Only one ounce of fried banana chips can contain 150 calories and up to 10 grams of fat, most of which is saturated.

Bananas will freeze for about 6-7 months if left in their skins. Ripe bananas can be mashed and frozen in one-cup portions and can be used for baking. If you peel the whole ripe banana, place it in a plastic bag and it can be frozen whole.

Strawberries that are not sweet enough can easily be sweetened by sprinkling powdered sugar on them and allowing them to stand for a short while. When the sugar is placed on the surface of the berry, it mixes with the moisture that is naturally being released producing a solution that is somewhat denser than the liquid inside the berry. Through osmosis, the liquid with the less density flows toward the liquid, which is more dense, placing the sugar inside the strawberry cells and sweetening the berry.

LEMON AND LIME FACTS

- Submerging a lemon or lime in hot water for 15 minutes before squeezing will produce almost twice the amount of juice.
- Warming the lemon or lime in the oven for a few minutes will help release the juice. This also works well for other citrus fruit.
- If you only need a few drops of juice, slightly puncture one end with a skewer before squeezing out the desired amount. Return the lemon to the refrigerator and the hole will seal up and the balance of the fruit will still be usable.
- Lemons and limes will keep longer in the refrigerator if you place them in a clean jar, cover them with cold water and seal the jar well.
- After using $1/2$ of the fruit, store the other half in the freezer in a plastic bag. This reduces the loss of moisture and retards bacterial growth.
- When lemon is used as a flavoring, it tends to mask the craving for the addition of salt.
- Lemon and lime peelings may cause skin irritation on susceptible people. They contain the oil "limonene."

Olives will retain most of their nutrient values and flavor for about 1 year if the can is unopened and they are stored in a cool location. Once opened, they will only last for 1 month if refrigerated. Best to store the opened olives in a well sealed glass jar with their original brine. Adding a thin layer of olive oil on top of the brine will also extend the refrigerator life by about 2-3 weeks. If you purchase bulk olives, they can be stored in a glass jar in olive oil for about 2 months. If a white scum develops, just remove it and wash the olives off. Discard any soft olives.

Poor Gelatin

Fresh pineapple contains the enzyme "bromelain" that will prevent gelatin from setting up. This enzyme may also be used as a meat tenderizer. Studies in the future may also show that bromelain may be effective in reducing the plaque in arterial walls.

21

Freezing & Refrigerating
FOODS

There is always an uncertainty in the public's mind regarding whether or not to freeze or refreeze a food and if it is frozen, how long it will retain its nutrient value, as well as its flavor and consistency. Many foods do not do well when frozen; some get tough, some develop ice crystals shortly after being placed in the freezer, while others get mushy when defrosted.

The longer a food is frozen, the higher the nutrient loss. Seal all freezer-stored foods as well as possible to retain the nutrient level and avoid freezer burn, as well as the formation of ice crystals. While ice crystals are not a serious problem, they can affect the quality of the food as it is being thawed and makes the food mushy.

When you freeze foods, you are actually freezing the water that is in the food cells. As the water freezes, it expands and a number of the cell walls rupture, releasing their liquid, which then freezes into ice crystals, thus resulting in the food becoming softer. These changes in texture are more noticeable in fruits and vegetables, since they have higher water content than most other foods.

Biologically, the process that occurs is referred to as "osmosis." Osmosis is the process by which a liquid passes through a semi-permeable membrane (cell wall) in order to equalize the pressure. When the food is frozen, the solids inside of the cell cause the water to become more concentrated, allowing the liquid from outside the cell to enter, form crystals, and eventually cause a number of the cells to burst. Since some of the flavor of the food is contained in each cell, a percentage of the flavor is also lost. Meats, fruits, and most seafood are more negatively affected than vegetables.

Certain vegetables, such as tomatoes, lettuce and celery are so high in water content they literally turn into mush when frozen. When cooked products are frozen, their cell walls are already softened, therefore they do not burst as easily. This is especially true when high starch vegetables, such as corn, lima beans and peas are included in dishes.

The damage to foods when freezing them can be controlled to some degree by freezing them as fast as possible. When foods are frozen more rapidly, the ice crystals that are formed are smaller and cause less cell wall rupture. If you know you will be freezing a number of items or a food that you really want to keep in good shape, try setting the freezer at the coldest setting a few hours before you place the food in. Some freezer manuals also will advise you which shelves are in the coldest area.

The temperature of your freezer should never fluctuate more than a few degrees to keep foods at their best. The temperature should be kept at least 0^0F. or below for the best results. Thawing and re-freezing is the worst thing you can do to foods. Every time the temperature drops in the freezer, some of those small ice crystals will convert to larger ice crystals and little by little, the dish will be ruined.

If you are going to try and freeze any dish that has alcohol in it, remember alcohol will not freeze like water and may need to be frozen at a lower temperature.

A good trick when you go away on vacation is to place a baggie with a few ice cubes in the freezer. If a power failure occurs while you are gone and the food thaws and re-freezes, it can affect the quality of the food as well as increase the bacterial growth. You need to be aware of this fact and discard the food.

- There are a number of foods that should never be refrigerated since the cold causes either loss of flavor, sprouting or the starch turning to sugar. These include garlic, onions, shallots, potatoes and tomatoes.
- Frozen sandwiches will thaw by lunchtime. If the bread is buttered prior to freezing, the bread will not become soggy and absorb any filling.

Freezer Temperature and Foods

Freezer Temperature	Quality Changes After
30°F.	5 Days
25°F.	10 Days
20°F.	3 Weeks
15°F.	6 Weeks
10°F.	4 Months
5°F.	6 Months
0°F.	1 Year

FOOD PRESERVATION SAVES MONEY

The preservation of food is possible only if some method is used to destroy or control the growth of microorganisms that cause spoilage. There are a number of methods, which include drying, dehydrating, salting, smoking, radiation, heating, freezing and the use of chemical agents (preservatives, etc.). The microorganisms that cause food spoilage can be found everywhere. They are in the water, air, counter surfaces, brought home on foods, and even in the product itself. In many cases the food is contaminated as a natural occurrence, such as salmonella being present in the chicken ovaries. Microorganisms can exist in two forms, either visible to the naked eye, such as in colonies or in small spores, which are for the most part invisible to the naked eye and carried by the air. There are three divisions of microorganisms, molds, yeast and bacteria.

Molds are usually airborne "spores" or "seeds" that may light on a food product and start to multiply. They may also send out "feelers" or "filaments" and grow in colonies, which may be seen in many colors, depending on their food source. Mold spores will move from one food to another, especially fruits, so it would be wise to check your foods when you bring them home to be sure that none has any mold on them. Foods with a high acid content, such as tomatoes, pickles and fruits are especially susceptible to the growth of mold.

Yeast is a small one-celled fungus that produce enzymes, which convert sugars to alcohol and carbon dioxide in a process called fermentation. It is also an excellent dietary source of folic acid. Yeast and molds can be destroyed by processing the foods at boiling temperature.

Bacteria need only a small amount of organic material and some moisture to grow and multiply. They grow by splitting their cells and may develop either acid or alkaline properties. Bacteria grow rapidly between 40 and 140°F. The longer the food is kept in this zone, the more the bacteria will multiply. High temperature cooking will destroy most bacteria. When there is no moisture or the available moisture is used up, growth in all of these microorganisms cease, dry up and become dormant until moisture is again introduced.

Freezing Baked Goods

Certain foods need care when freezing and also special preparation techniques after they have been removed from the freezer. The following foods are some of the more popular that most people freeze.

Biscuits- Prepare as per instructions, then freeze in a well-sealed bag. Should be heated unthawed at 350°F. for about 20 minutes.

Coffee Cake- Bake until the cake is a light brown only, then cool as quickly as possible and freeze. Thaw at room temperature in freezer wrapping. If the cake has been frozen in aluminum foil, heat at 400°F.

Muffins- Prepare as per package directions, then freeze. Thaw at room temperature, then heat at 300°F. for about 15-20 minutes.

Doughnuts- Prepare as usual and freeze. Remember that raised doughnuts will freeze better than the cake type. Glazed doughnuts do not freeze well. Thaw at room temperature for about 10 minutes before placing in a 400°F. oven to heat.

Bread (homemade)- Prepare as usual and allow the bread to cool before placing in freezer. Thaw at room temperature and if wrapped in aluminum foil, bake at 300°F. for about 10 minutes.

Sandwiches (closed)- If you are going to freeze sandwiches, use day-old bread and spread butter, margarine or salad dressing to the edges of the bread before adding any filling. Do not use crisp vegetables, cooked egg white, preserves, mayonnaise or tomatoes. Package in aluminum foil and freeze. Thaw at room temperature in original wrapping for about 3-4 hours or in a lunch pail.

MONEY-SAVING TIPS WHEN FREEZING FOODS

There are a number of important facts that should be adhered to, if you wish to freeze foods successfully:
- When preparing any vegetable for freezing, be sure and undercook it. Re-heating will complete the cooking.
- Freezing tends to intensify the flavor in spices, such as garlic, pepper, oregano, and cloves so you should use less, then add more before serving. Additional onions can be used since freezing tends to cause the flavor to be lost. Salt should be used in moderation or not at all. Salt tends to slow down the freezing process.

Penny Pinchers

- Never use quick-cooking rice in a dish that will be frozen, as it tends to become mushy. Use regular or converted rice.

- Artificial flavorings and sweeteners do not do well when frozen.

- Toppings should always be added before serving. Cheeses and bread, crumbs on foods do not do well.

- Freezing causes old potatoes to fall apart; always use new potatoes in dishes that are to be frozen.

- Gravies and sauces need to be made somewhat thicker than normal since they will usually separate.

- Cool foods first in the refrigerator before freezing.

- A freezer that is full will use less energy than a half-full freezer because frozen foods retain cold air for a long period. The freezer will run fewer hours per day and save considerable money in electricity.

Chest Freezer vs Upright Freezers, Can You Save $$$$$$$?

This debate has been around for a long time; however, the answer has always been a fairly simple one. The chest freezer, even though the door may be larger, will retain its cold setting longer when the door is opened. since cold air is heavier than hot air and tends to stay put. The upright freezer tends to release most of its cold air the minute the door is opened. Chest freezers will maintain and hold the preferred 0^0F. freezer level to maximize food storage times before spoilage.

New Storage Bags Save Dollars

A new plastic storage bag for fruits and vegetables is now on the market. The bag contains hundreds of microscopic holes that allow air to circulate around the produce. The bag is also impregnated with "oya," a natural substance that will absorb ethylene gas, released by the produce as it ripens and will help the produce ripen. Unfortunately, the more ethylene gas the produce expels and remains around the food, the faster the food ripens and spoils. The bags are tinted green to lessen the effects of light reducing the potency of the vitamins. The bag is marketed under the name "Evert-Fresh." Produce stored in these bags will last 10 times longer than standard plastic storage bags, and in tests over a 12-day period, 50% more of the vitamin C was retained.

Storing Margarine

Margarine will absorb odors from foods that are stored nearby very readily. It should be sealed as tightly as possible and should store for 4-6 months in the refrigerator. Margarine freezes well and will keep for 1 year if the temperature is kept at 0^0F.

Freezer Storage Times at Zero Degrees Fahrenheit

FOOD	MONTHS	FOOD	MONTHS
MEATS		**DAIRY PRODUCTS**	
Beef, Lamb	6-12	Milk	2 weeks
Chops, Cutlets, Beef Hamburger	3-5	Ice Cream	4 weeks
Ground Pork	1-3	Cream (40%)	3-4
Sausage	1-2	Eggs (not in shell)	7-10
Bacon (unsliced)	3-5	Margarine	2-4
Bacon (sliced)	1	Butter	2-4
Fish	3-6	Cheddar Cheese	5-6
Ham	3-4		
Liver	3-4	**FRUITS**	
Poultry	4-6	Apples (sliced)	10-12
Giblets	3	Apricots	10-12
Duck, Goose	5-6	Berries	11-12
Rabbit	9-12	Cherries (sour)	12
Shrimp or Shellfish (cooked)	2-3		
Turkey	6-8		
Hot Dogs	2-3		
Luncheon Meats (ready-to-eat)	0		

Storage Times for Refrigerated Dairy Products at 0°F.

PRODUCT	DAYS	MONTHS
Butter	45-90	7-8
Butter, Clarified	60-90	7-8
Buttermilk	7-14	3
Cream	3-5	3
Cream, Whipped		
Commercial	30	Do Not Freeze
Homemade	1	2
Eggs (in shell)	20	Do Not Freeze
Eggs (hard boiled)	7	Do Not Freeze

PRODUCT	DAYS	MONTHS
Eggs (yolks)	2-4	12
Eggnog	3-5	6
Half & Half	3-4	4
Ice Cream, Commercial	2-3	
Frozen Desserts	1-2	
Mayonnaise	60	Do Not Freeze
Margarine		
Regular & Soft	120	12
Diet	90	
Milk	3-7	3
Non-Dairy Creamer	21	12
Non-Dairy Toppings		
Container	7	12
Aerosol can	90	Do Not Freeze
Sour Cream	14	
Yogurt	14	2

Storage Times for Baking Staples

Product	Shelf Life
Arrowroot	1 Year
Baking Powder	3-6 Months
Baking Soda	18 Months
Cornstarch	1 Year
Cream of Tartar	1 Year
Extracts	1 Year
Gelatin, Boxed	1 Year
Salt	Forever if Kept Dry
Tapioca	1 Year
Vinegar	1 Year
Yeast	Date on Package

- Foods wrapped in aluminum foil may be subjected to two problems. The first is that since aluminum foil is such a great insulator, it tends to slow down the heat transfer and food will not freeze as fast as you may want it to. Bacteria may grow and not be killed when the food is re-heated. Secondly, when you crinkle the aluminum foil to place it around the food, micro-cracks develop which may allow air and moisture to penetrate the food. If you plan on storing food for more than 2-3 days in the refrigerator in aluminum foil, you should probably wrap the food in plastic wrap first. Aluminum foil will also react with foods that acidic or salty and may impart a strange taste to the food.

- If ice cream thaws, it should not be re-frozen. Jelly, salad dressing, and mayonnaise do not freeze well on bread products. The freezer in your refrigerator is not the same as a supermarket food freezer. It is best used for storing foods for short periods only. Foods should be frozen as quickly as possible and temperatures should be 0^0F. or below. Potatoes become mushy when frozen in stews or casseroles. Their cells have high water content and break easily when frozen. However, mashed potatoes freeze well. Any bakery item with a cream filling should not be frozen. They will become soggy. Custard and meringue pies do not freeze well. The custard tends to separate and the meringue becomes tough. Waffles and pancakes may be frozen, thawed and placed in the toaster.

22

Breads & Baked
PRODUCTS

Baking is a dry-heat method of cooking foods, which surrounds the food with heated air. Baking, for the most part, dries the food out and therefore, the need to control the amount of moisture lost is important. The more moisture lost, the less volume.

Save Wrappers
Save the bread bags from store-bought bread for use when you bake bread.

Waxed Paper Best
Fresh bread will not get moldy as fast if you wrap it in waxed paper and place it in the refrigerator.

Eat It Fast
French bread is made without fat. The fat content in bread tends to slow down the loss of moisture in

bread and keep it softer by reducing the percentage of gluten from forming too strong a structure. French bread may get stale after only 5-7 hours, which is why the French purchase their bread supplies at least twice a day.

Spud Water

The water from boiled potatoes contains just the right amount of starch to substitute for the water you might use in a bread recipe. It will also help keep the bread fresher for a longer period of time.

Very Absorbing

If you are going to freeze a loaf of bread, make sure you include a piece of paper towel in the package to absorb moisture. This will keep the bread from becoming mushy when it is thawed out.

Real Crummy

If you burn bread, try removing the burned area with a grater. If you don't want to eat it afterwards, just grate it up and save for use as breadcrumbs.

Make Buns into Sticks

Leftover hot dog buns can be sliced into sticks, then garlic-buttered and toasted in the oven. Serve them as bread sticks or cut into croutons.

Where Did my Moisture Go?

To replace lost moisture in a loaf of bread that has hardened, try wrapping it tightly in a damp towel for about 2-3 minutes, then place the bread in the oven at 350°F. for 15-20 minutes. Moisture can easily be replaced in French or Italian bread by just sprinkling the crust with cold water and placing the loaf in a 350°F. oven for 8-10 minutes.

Getting Older is no Fun at all

When the bread is baked, a large percentage of the water accumulates in the starch. As the bread ages, the water is released from the starch and the protein, allowing the texture of the bread to become more crumbly and firm. As the bread continues to age, the water content inside the bread is released and the water is absorbed by the crust, drying the crust and making it hard through evaporation of the moisture into the air.

Tie me up, but be Gentle

The best method of re-heating biscuits or rolls is to put them into a slightly dampened paper bag sealed with a tie. Place the bag into the oven at a very low temperature. Adding raisins to bread slows down the staling process, which is why raisin bread will last twice as long as regular bread at room temperature.

Whewwwwwww

When baking rye bread, do not place any containers with water to create steam. The steam will ruin the bread.

Bad Yeasties

Excess yeast will cause the bread to go stale quicker.

Do the Right Thing

When freezing bread, be sure and use freezer paper or freezer bags, not plastic wrap or aluminum foil.

Zapppppp

Brownie mixes are high in moisture and do well in the microwave.

Yukkkkkkk

Never wrap frosted cakes in aluminum foil. Always use plastic wrap.

Help! I've been Exposed

One of the best methods of keeping the insides of a cake from drying out is to place a piece of fresh white bread next to the exposed surface. The bread can be affixed with a short piece of spaghetti.

A Little Dip Will Do Ya

It really isn't worth the trouble, but if you want to revive a cake that has gone stale, just very quickly dip it in low-fat milk and place it in a 350^{0}F. oven for 10-15 minutes.

Hard to Chew

When preparing dough for baked goods, hard water may cause a problem since too high a mineral content may result in the gluten not being able to develop properly. If the gluten does not develop properly, the crust will be tough.

MONEY-SAVING TIPS

To purchase the highest quality white bread, make sure the list of ingredients reads, "unbleached flour" instead of "white flour" or just "flour."

Non-dairy creamer can be used to replace dry milk in your bread recipe.

If white bread is your bread of choice, only purchase the bread if it clearly says, "enriched" on the label; many do not.

The high mineral content of hard water may retard fermentation by causing the gluten to become tough. The minerals will prevent the protein from absorbing water the way it normally would. To counteract this problem, there are a number of methods you may wish to try, such as using bottled water, adding a small amount of vinegar to reduce the pH, or adding more yeast. Water that is too soft can cause the dough to be sticky.

Why purchase chocolate slivers, when all you have to do is use your potato peeler on a Hershey bar?

Save your used coffee cans: they make excellent containers to store cookies in. Use the original plastic lid or a piece of plastic wrap sealed with a rubber band.

If you have a problem with burning the bottoms of cookies when making a number of batches, all you have to do is to run the bottom of the pan under cool water before placing the next batch on the pan. When you start with too hot a surface, the cookies may burn their bottoms. The desired shape of the cookies may also change if placed on the hot pan.

Cookies tend to burn easily. One method of eliminating this problem is to remove them from the oven before they are completely done and allow the hot pan to finish the job.

To store cookie dough in the refrigerator, use an empty egg carton. Since they usually come waxed, they do not need any greasing.

Whipped butter, margarine or any other soft spread that is high in air and water-content should never be used in a cookie recipe.

Icing tends to become thick and difficult to work with after a short period of time. If this happens, just add 2-3 drops of lemon juice and re-mix the icing.
French toast, waffles and pancakes may be made and frozen. They can them be placed into the toaster for an easy breakfast.

If you are going to use frozen biscuits, heat them frozen at 350^0F. for 15-20 minutes. Frozen biscuits should not be kept for more than 2-3 months.

Club soda can be used to replace milk or water in the recipe for the lightest pancakes. Make sure that the club soda is at room temperature.

To prevent a soggy crust on a homemade pizza, just place the cheese on before the tomato sauce. Never use a microwave to bake a pie. The insides will cook long before the crust is done.

Breadcrumbs have the tendency to scatter when you grind stale bread for crumbs. Best to place a paper bag around the grinder outlet to catch the crumbs. Tie the bag with a piece of string or use a rubber band. Use an empty salt container to hold the breadcrumbs.

Biscuit mix can be used to make other foods, such as waffles, dumplings, cookies, date nut bread, Danish, etc.

Saving Money on Pies

Pumpkin mix can be expensive; however, you can substitute steamed squash and it will be hard to tell the difference. If you want to replace the egg, just use a tbsp. of cooked oatmeal beaten into the mixture to hold everything together.

Store pies in the refrigerator and to make them taste fresh, just reheat at 350°F. for 7-9 minutes before serving.

Saving Money on Pancakes

Pancakes have the tendency to stick to the grill and you will lose a number of them. But if you fill a small cheesecloth or muslin bag with table salt and rub the bag over the surface of the hot skillet before pouring on the batter, they won't stick. You also won't have to grease the flipper.

Saving Money on Cakes

Common Causes for Cake Failures

- Cake will fall if too little flour is used.
- Cake will rise too high in center and crack if too much flour is used.
- Cake will brown on top too much before it has risen enough if oven heat is too high.
- Cake will be soggy if too much shortening is used.
- Cake will be too heavy if too much sugar is used.
- Cake will have large holes and tunnels if you beat too much after flour is added

Flour has the tendency to pack down and sifting will save you money by only using the amount necessary.

Never press flour down in a measuring cup or shake it down.

Laundry & Stain
REMOVAL

Laundering Tips

Repair any torn or damaged garments before laundering or the laundering process may make the area worse.

Zippers should be closed before laundering since an open zipper may catch in a piece of clothing and cause damage.

If you use fresh cake soap, it is best to unwrap the soap and allow it to dry out for a week or so before you use it. This will extend the life of the soap.

Save leftover slivers or pieces of soap and keep them in a jar. If you add boiling water the soap will turn into a jelly-like mixture and can be used.

Cut a small pocket in a sponge and place the small slivers of leftover soap into the pocket. This will provide a soapy washing sponge.

Never allow a washing machine to agitate more than 15 minutes or the dirt that came out may be forced back into the clothing. Usually 5 minutes of agitation is enough for most clothing.

Using laundry starch will protect cottons and linens from soiling as well as restoring the original finish to a number of fabrics. This protects them from being washed too often and becoming damaged.

Never add solvents directly into the washing machine. Always allow a solvent-treated fabric to dry before washing or placing it into the dryer.

If you dry starched garments in a dryer, they should be dried by themselves and never with other non-starched items. The starch may also come off and end up on unstarched garments.

Be sure and wipe off the dryer cylinder after drying starched garments so that the starch will not end up on garments that you do not want starched.

Yellowed fabrics can be restored and even old unknown stains may be removed by first soaking in an enzyme presoak product (Proctor & Gamble has excellent ones), such as "Biz" and then laundering.

Remember, even the best enzyme detergent or enzyme presoak product is not capable of removing all types of stains. A number of grease soils and highly colored stains may require special pretreatment before laundering. Since many stains require a variety of different soil removal treatments and techniques, it is important to identify a stain before trying to remove it. A number of stains may actually be set if the wrong method is used.

General Stain Removal Rules
- Never rub too hard to remove a stain since this will cause damage to the fabric, which can never be repaired.
- Never wash any fabric before attempting to remove the stain. Washing in a detergent may actually set the stain and make it impossible to remove later.
- Stains on washable fabrics should be treated as soon as possible.
- Remember; fresh stains will come out more easily than old ones.
- Non-washable items that normally go to the cleaners should be taken to the cleaners as soon as possible. Identify the stain for the dry cleaner. If you know what the stain is, be sure and tell him.

GETTING RID OF COMMON STAINS

To remove mildew from clothing, just moisten the mildew area with salt and lemon juice and allow it to sit in the sunlight to bleach out the stain.

If you spill red wine on your carpet, try pouring salt on the area as soon as possible and watch the wine being absorbed almost instantly. Wait until it dries and vacuum it up. Salt tends to provide a special capillary action that will attract most liquids.

When trying to remove stains at home, make sure you do it on a clean, well-lighted work surface. Always use fresh clean rags or a towel.

Rust stains can be removed by wetting the area with lemon juice, sprinkling it with a small amount of salt, then placing the stained cloth in direct sunlight for 30-45 minutes.

A scorch can be removed by rubbing a raw onion on the scorched area and allowing the onion juice to soak in thoroughly for at least 2-3 hours before washing.

Blood stains may be cleaned with club soda.

If you are going to use a commercial stain removal substance, be sure and follow directions carefully.

Always test a stain remover on an area of the fabric that will not show to be sure of the colorfastness of the fabric. Allow the product to stand on the area for at least 3-5 minutes before rinsing off. If there are any changes in the fabric color, do not use.

When treating a spot, it should be placed face down on a paper towel. Then, apply the stain remover to the underside of the garment, which will force the stain to the surface (and not back through the fabric). The paper towel should be replaced a number of times, if it is a tough stain to remove.

Never use a bleach product on a colored garment. To avoid uneven color removal, it is necessary to bleach the whole garment. If there is a change in color, it will at least be uniform.

As soon as a stain is removed, launder immediately with your favorite laundry detergent. This will also remove the residues from the stain remover.

Prompt treatment is the key to stain removal, and it would be wise to have the supplies on hand at all times. The following is a list of some of the more common ingredients needed for most stain removal; however, more natural stain and general cleaning preparations are recommended.

Bleaches
Chlorine bleach
Fabric color remover
Non-chlorine, all fabric bleach

Miscellaneous Removers
Ammonia
Rust stain remover
White vinegar

Detergents
Enzyme detergent
Enzyme presoaker
Liquid detergent

Solvents
Dry cleaner spot remover
Nail polish remover
Rubbing alcohol
Turpentine

Soaps
Laundry detergent
White bar soap

Supplies
Clean white cloths
Paper towels

Any of the above products that cannot be found at the supermarket will be found at any drug store.

Caution:

Some stain removal materials are flammable, while others are poison or toxic. Store them safely and use with care.

Lemon extract will remove black scuff marks from shoes and luggage.

Stains from ballpoint pens can be removed with hair spray or milk.

Empty and wash all containers immediately after using them. It is best to store stain removal supplies in glass or unchipped porcelain containers. Solvents will ruin plastic containers. Rusty containers should never be used

Be careful: never allow chemicals near your face and especially your eyes. Wash any spilled chemicals off your hands as soon as possible.

Use chemicals that give off vapors in a well ventilated location, preferably outside. Try not to breathe the vapors.

Never use a solvent near an open fire or an electrical outlet.

Never mix stain removal materials with each other, especially ammonia and chlorine bleach. If it necessary to use both, make sure one is thoroughly rinsed out before adding the other.

RECIPES FOR SAFE CLEANING PRODUCTS

The following recipes are safe when mixed in the quantities indicated below. The mixing of other household chemicals may be dangerous.

All-Purpose Household Cleaner
> Add 1 tsp. of any liquid soap and 1 tsp. of trisodium phosphate (TSP) to 1 qt. of warm water.
> This is a very effective cleaner for many cleaning jobs, including countertops and walls. However, try an area of the wall that will not show before using, in case your walls are painted with a poor quality, water-based flat paint.

Chlorine Bleach
> Best to use hydrogen peroxide-based bleach.

Degreaser (engines, etc.)
> Best to use a water-based cleaner that is well diluted, instead of kerosene, turpentine or a commercial engine degreaser. These are available in part stores and the label should read "nonflammable," "non-toxic," or "store at temperatures above freezing." These will be water-based products and will do the job.

Degreaser (kitchen, grill)

Add 2 tbsp. of TSP to 1 gal. of hot water or use a non-chlorinated scouring cleanser with a scouring or steel wool pad.
Fabric Softener
Fabrics produced from natural fibers do not need fabric softeners, only synthetics.

Floor Cleaner

Vinyl floors: use ¹/₂ cup of white vinegar to 1 gal. of warm water.
Wood, floors: may be damp-moped with a mild liquid soap.

Furniture Polish

Mineral oil may be used. However, most wood surfaces may be cleaned with a damp cloth.

Oven Cleaner

Mix 2 tbsp. of baking soda or TSP in 1 gal. of warm water and scrub with a very fine steel wool pad (0000). Rubber gloves should be worn and the area rinsed well. For difficult baked-on areas, try scrubbing with a pumice stone.

If the above fails, try using an oven cleaner that states "no caustic fumes" on the label.

Glass Cleaner

Use a 2-3 cup spray-bottle with ¹/₂ tsp. of liquid soap, 3 tbsp. of white vinegar and 2 cups of water. If the windows are very dirty, try using more liquid soap.

Laundry Detergent

Use laundry soap in place of the detergents. Washing soda may be used in place of a softener. An alternate would be to use detergents with no added bleaches or softeners. Bleach should be used in moderation when needed.

Mildew Remover

Scrub the area with baking soda or, if very stubborn, with TSP.

Scouring Powder

Baking soda will work well in most instances.

Toilet Bowl Cleaner

Use a non-chlorinated scouring powder and a stiff brush. To remove hard water deposits, pour white vinegar or a commercial citric acid-based toilet bowl cleaner into the toilet and allow it to sit for several hours or overnight before scrubbing.

Note: Washing soda and TSP are caustic and should be kept out of the reach of children.

FABRIC ADVICE:

It is best to know the fiber content in clothing items. If sewn-in labels are to be removed, a note should be made as to which item it was removed from. Any durable press or polyester fabric, such as a Dacron, holds soil very well and especially stains. A dry cleaning solvent will work the best. If the stain remains after the first treatment, try once more. If the fabric has been washed or has been placed in a dryer, the stain may never come out.

- Never use chlorine bleach on silk, wool or Spandex.
- Never remove a stain from leather: take it to the dry cleaners to send to an expert.

STAIN REMOVAL FROM WASHABLE FABRICS:

A number of stains can be removed right in your washing machine. Laundry detergents that state that they contain enzymes will provide the best cleaning and stain removal. Enzyme presoak products provide extra cleaning and stain removal for fabrics that may have a more difficult stain. An enzyme detergent or enzyme presoak product should be able to remove the following common stains:

Blood	Gravy	Body soils	Egg
Fruits	Milk	Chocolate	Grass
Cream soups	Baby formula	Puddings	Vegetables
Baby foods	Ice cream	Most food soils	

The following stains will usually be removed with the following recommended methods:

Alcoholic Beverages

Rinse the area immediately with cold water. The alcohol is soluble in water and will come out easily.

Beverages

Sponge the area with cold water or soak, then sponge again. Launder with oxygen bleach and the hottest water that is safe for the fabric.

Blood

Soak the fabric in cold water as soon as possible. If the stain persists, soak in warm water with a
presoak product before laundering. Try club soda.

If you have a difficult bloodstain, try making a paste of meat tenderizer and cold water. Sponge on the area and allow it to stand for 20-30 minutes. Rinse in cold water, then wash. Hydrogen peroxide may also work.

Candle Wax

The surface wax should be removed with a dull knife. The item should then be placed stain face down on paper towels. Sponge the remaining stain with dry cleaning solvent. Allow it to dry and then launder. If traces of color from the wax remain, try soaking it in "Biz" or oxygen bleach before laundering again. If the color is still present, try laundering again using chlorine bleach if the fabric is chlorine bleach safe.

Candle wax on tablecloths can also be removed by freezing with ice cubes.

Candy

Since candy is usually made from sugar, it should come out easily using cold water on a sponge.

Catsup/Tomato Products

Remove excess with a dull knife, then soak in cold water and launder using the hottest water the fabric will stand.

Chewing Gum/Adhesive Tape/Rubber Cement

First, apply ice to the stain to harden it. Remove excess stain material with a dull knife. Place the item face down on paper towels and sponge with a dry cleaning solvent.

Chocolate/Cocoa

Soak in cold water, then launder with oxygen bleach using the hottest water the fabric will stand.

Coffee/Tea

Best to soak in "Biz" or oxygen bleach using the hottest water that is safe for the stained fabric, then launder. If the stain persists, try laundering again using chlorine bleach if it is safe to do so.

Cosmetics

Dampen stain and rub gently with a white bar soap. Then rinse well and launder.

Crayon

If there are only a few spots, they can be treated the same as candle wax. If there are many items that are stained, first wash the items with hot water and laundry soap (e.g. "Ivory Snow") and 1 cup baking soda. If the spots remain, have the clothes dry cleaned.
Deodorants and Anti-Perspirants
Apply white vinegar, then rub and rinse. If; the stain remains, try saturating the area with rubbing alcohol, rinse then soak in "Biz" or an oxygen bleach and launder. If the stain remains, wash in chlorine bleach if safe for fabric.

Dye Transfer

If you have white fabrics that have picked up dye from a colored garment that "bled," try restoring the white by using a fabric color remover. Launder if any of the dye remains using chlorine   bleach, if it is safe for the fabric.

Egg/Meat Juice

Remove excess with a dull knife, then soak in cold water. Launder in oxygen bleach in very hot water.

Fabric Softeners

These stains usually result from accidental spills and can be removed by rubbing the area with a piece of cloth moistened with bar soap, then launder.

Formula

Soak in warm water, then launder with oxygen bleach and the hottest water that is safe for the fabric.

Fruit/Fruit Juices

Soak in cold water before laundering.

Glue

Soak the area in lukewarm water and a neutral detergent.

Grass

The green area should be sponged with denatured alcohol before washing in very hot water and oxygen bleach.

Grease Stains

The stained area should be placed face down on paper towels. Dry cleaning solvent should be placed on the backside of the stain and then brushed from the center of the stain to the outer edges, using a clean white cloth. Moisten the stain with warm water and rub with bar soap or a mild liquid detergent, then rinse and launder.

Gum

Rub with ice and carefully remove the gum with a dull knife before laundering.

Ink Stains

For removal of ballpoint stains, place the stain face down on paper towels and sponge the back of the stain with dry cleaning solvent. If there is any ink left, try rubbing the area with moistened bar soap. Rinse, then launder. For any other type of ink stains, just try and remove the stain with a dampened cloth and bar soap, rinse and soak in "Biz" or an oxygen bleach, using very hot water. If the stain won't

come out, try using chlorine bleach, if the fabric is safe. Some permanent ink may never be removed.

Rubbing alcohol or hair spray may also remove a number of ink pen stains.

Ink, Felt Tip
Rub the area with "Fantastic" or "Mr. Clean," rinse and repeat if necessary. It may be impossible to remove.

Iodine
Rinse the fabric from the underside with cool water, then soak in a solution of fabric color remover, rinse and then launder.

Lead Pencil
You will need to work glycerin into the stain with a blunt-edged object, then apply a few drops of ammonia and gently work it into the stain. As the stain dissolves, use warm water to flush the area.

Lipstick
The stain should be placed face down on paper towels and then sponged with dry cleaning solvent, replacing the paper towels frequently while the color is being removed. Moisten the stain with cool water, then rub with bar soap, rinse and launder.

Lipstick stains will also clean out of clothes by using Vaseline.

Mildew
Fabric should be laundered using chlorine bleach if it is safe for the fabric. If not, try soaking it in
oxygen bleach and then launder.

Mildew on shower curtains can be removed with a mixture of $\frac{1}{2}$ cup bleach, $\frac{1}{2}$ cup powdered detergent, and 1 gal. of water. To prolong the life of shower curtains, add 1 cup of white vinegar to the final rinse.

Milk
The fabric should be rinsed in cold water as soon as possible, then washed in cold water using a liquid detergent.

Mud
Allow the mud to dry as much as possible, then dry brush the area lightly. Sponge the rest of the mud off with a solution of warm water and a mild detergent.

Mustard

Moisten stain with cool water; then rub with bar soap, rinse and launder using chlorine bleach, if it is safe for the fabric. If not, soak in "Biz" or an oxygen detergent, using very hot water, then launder. It may take several treatments to remove all of the stain.

Nail Polish

The fabric stain should be placed face down on paper towels, then sponge the back of the stain frequently and repeat until the stain disappears, and launder. Never use nail polish remover on fabric; best to have them dry cleaned.

Paint

Try to treat the stain while it is still wet. Latex, acrylic and water-based paints cannot be removed once they have dried. While they are wet, rinse in warm water to flush the paint out, then launder. Oil-based paints can be removed with solvent that is recommended on the paint can. If it does not give this information, try using turpentine, then rinse and rub with bar soap, and launder.

Perfume

Flush with a solution of water and a detergent as soon as possible, since perfume contains alcohol and may cause some garment to run.

Perspiration

Moisten the stain and rub with bar soap. Be gentle, as perspiration may weaken some fibers, especially silk. Most fabrics should be presoaked in "Biz" or an enzyme detergent, then laundered in hot water and chlorine bleach, if the fabric is safe.
Another method is to mix 4 tbsp. of salt to 1 qt. of hot water and sponge on the

fabric until the stain disappears.

Rust

Never use chlorine bleach on rust; apply a rust stain remover, rinse then launder. You can also use a fabric color remover, then launder or if the stain is really stubborn, try using 1 oz. of oxalic acid crystals (or straight warm rhubarb juice) dissolved in 1 gal of water mixed in a plastic container, then rinse and launder. Rust marks on clothing can also be removed with lemon juice and a small amount of salt; easily rubbed in, then allowed to sit in the sun for 2 hours.

Scorch

Soak the fabric in a strong solution of "Biz" and oxygen bleach using very hot water and. if safe for the fabric, then launder. If the scorch remains, it will be necessary to repeat the procedure using chlorine bleach, if the fabric will take it.

Shoe Polish

Try applying a mixture of 1 part rubbing alcohol and 2 parts water for colored fabrics, and for white garments only, straight alcohol.

Suede

Rain spots can be removed by lightly rubbing the area with an emery board. If there are grease spots, try using white vinegar or club soda, then blot out the stain. Afterwards, brush with a suede brush.

Stuffed Animals

To clean stuffed animals that cannot be placed in the washer, just place them in a cloth bag, add baking soda, then shake.

Tar

The area should be rubbed with kerosene until all the tar is dissolved, then wash as usual. Test a small area first to be sure it is colorfast. Butter or margarine will also remove tar from clothing, just rub until it's gone. The butter is easily removed with any type of spray-and-wash product.

Tea

Tea stains on tablecloths can be removed with glycerin. Try letting it sit overnight in the solution before washing.

Tobacco

Moisten the stain and rub with bar soap: rinse, then launder. If the stain persists, try soaking it in "Biz" or an oxygen detergent, then launder. As a last resort, use chlorine bleach, if the fabric is safe.

Urine, Vomit, Mucus

Soak the fabric in "Biz" or an enzyme detergent. Launder using chlorine bleach, if safe for the fabric. If not, use oxygen bleach with detergent.

Wine/Soft Drinks

Soak the fabric with "Biz" or oxygen bleach. using very hot water, then launder. Use chlorine bleach if needed and the fabric is safe.

24

Money-Saving Tips
FOR HOUSE CLEANING

Making your own cleaning products can save you hundreds of dollars every year. Many of the products that you purchase in the supermarket are prepared from a number of common ingredients that can be found around your home or are easily purchased and inexpensive.

This chapter will provide you with dozens of easy-to-prepare formulas and hints that will make your cleaning chores easier and save you money

If the vacuum cleaner bag gets too full, it places a load on the motor and causes excessive wear and tear. Using an overfull bag too often will burn the motor out, since it will have to work against back pressure.

Use a discarded wire brush to remove lint, hair, etc from vacuum cleaner or carpet cleaner brushes.

If you screw a small drawer knob or small handle into the back of a scrub brush, it won't slip out of your hands.

To make a dry mop, use old discarded athletic socks. Just place the sock on the holder of your mop and you have a new dry mop.

Household sponges will last longer, if you soak them in cold salt water occasionally and boil them or place them into the dishwasher once a week.

If a chamois gets hard and stiff, just soak it in warm tap water and add 1 tsp. of olive oil to the water. The chamois will look just as good as the day you bought it.

To clean your dust mop, just lay it on a piece of newspaper and vacuum it off.

If you paint clear shellac on your baseboards, they will be easier to clean.

Place wax on your windowsills and the rain and dirt will come off much easier.

If you paint the area around wall switches with a clear shellac, it will be easier to clean since this area gets dirty very easily.

Your floors will last longer and look better, if they are cleaned regularly. Clean the floor first, then wax to protect it. If you have a floor that does not need waxing, damp-mop the floor at least every 2-3 days.

Never clean a porcelain top on a range when it is hot. Wait for the porcelain to cool or it will not last long and will start showing micro cracks.

If you would like your sink to smell better, just place a handful of baking soda in the sink and allow it to remain overnight.

If any of your metal-ware shows rust, just allow it to sit in a pan of white vinegar overnight or longer if needed.

Rub furniture polish on brass fixtures to keep them in good condition.

Just drop 2-3 "Alka-Seltzer(tm)" tablets in your toilet and wait 20 minutes before scrubbing with a toilet brush. Between the citric acid and the bubbles, it will work great.
To clean your can opener, try running a piece of paper towel through it. This will pick up the grease and some of the gunk.

If you wipe down your walls with a mild solution of white vinegar and water occasionally, the walls will not attract grease.

Place some non-iodized salt on a sponge and clean away. Make sure that the salt is not iodized or no more fish.

If the sun is shining on your windows, try not to wash them until they are in the shade. When they dry too fast, they tend to show streaks.

Just pour $\frac{1}{2}$ cup of table salt in the garbage disposal, then run with water as usual. This will clean and freshen up the disposal.

Don't bother buying fancy dust cloths that are treated to attract dust, when all you have to do is to dip a piece of cheesecloth in a mixture of 2 cups water and $\frac{1}{4}$ cup lemon oil. Allow the cheesecloth to air dry and it will do just as good a job as the expensive: cloth.

Caution: Never mix chlorine bleach and household ammonia in any formula.

FLOOR CARE

MARBLE, THE TOUGHEST OF THE TOUGH, BUT BE GENTLE!

Marble, one of the toughest floor surfaces, is basically naturally compressed, crystallized limestone that can range from somewhat porous to very compact. It can be polished to a high shine and will remain that way with very little care almost forever. The following solutions will clean and keep the marble shining with a minimum of effort. Strong detergents and abrasives should never be used on marble since they will dull the shine and may cause deterioration of the marble.

Great Marble Cleaning Formula

Mix together the following ingredients in a small bucket to make a paste:

6% hydrogen peroxide

White all-purpose flour

The thick paste mixture needs to be placed on the complete marble floor area, not just a soiled spot or the balance of the marble or it will not have the same clean color. Place enough of the mixture to heavily coat the floor and place plastic sheeting over the mixture, taping down all around the edges. Allow the mixture to sit on the marble for 36 hours, then carefully remove it with a plastic spatula and rinse the marble thoroughly with cool water.

Powder for Cleaning Marble

The following ingredients will be needed:

3 Cups sodium sulfate

1 Cup sodium sulfite

Place the ingredients in a small bucket and mix well, then place some of the mixture on a damp sponge and rub on the marble to clean it. Wipe off the mixture with warm water on a clean cloth that has been rung out very well.

Basic Marble Cleaner

The following ingredients will be needed:

4 Parts soft soap

4 Parts whiting

1 Part sodium bicarbonate

2 Parts copper sulfate

Place all the ingredients into a container and mix well. Rub the mixture on the marble with a flannel cloth and allow it to remain for 24 hours, then wash it off with clear, cool water. Polish the marble with a clean flannel cloth.

If stains won't come off a marble tabletop, just rub the spots with a cotton ball dampened with lemon juice. Allow it to sit for 30 minutes, if the stain does not respond immediately.

Cleaner for Parquet Floors

The following ingredients will be needed:

2 1/4 Cups mineral oil	2 Tbsp. household ammonia
3/4 Cup oleic acid	4 1/2 Tbsp. turpentine

Place the mineral oil and the oleic acid in a bucket and mix well (wear rubber gloves), then add the ammonia and turpentine, while stirring well to mix completely. This is a concentrated solution and 1/2 cup of the solution needs to added to 1/2 gal. of warm tap water, then mop the floor. Store in a well-sealed container for future use.

WOOD FLOORS, A TOUCH OF THE OLDEN DAYS

The combination of wooden flooring and carpeting is becoming more common in the last 5 years and lends a bit of the olden days to your home. The care and cleaning of these floors, however, take more time since they must be cared for as if they were a fine piece of furniture. Wood floors are more expensive than most carpeting and should be vacuumed regularly or the dirt and grime will scratch the surface and the floor will need re-finishing after very few years.

If your floor has been sealed with a varnish or shellac, never clean them with a water-based product or even clear water. A turpentine product is recommended. In fact, most wood floors will be damaged if water is used since the water tends to raise the grain and permanently dull the wood. The only exception to the rule is if the floor has been water-sealed. If the wood has been oiled, it would be best to just clean the floor with a mild solution of dish soap and just damp mop it to remove the suds and any scum leftover.

General Cleaner for Wood Floors

The following ingredients will be needed:

2 1/4 Cups mineral oil	5 Tbsp. turpentine (toxic)
3/4 Cup oleic acid (from drug store)	2 Qt. cool tap water
2 Tbsp. household ammonia (toxic)	

Place the mineral oil and oleic acid in a container and mix, then add the ammonia and turpentine and mix well. Place 1 cup of the mixture into the water, then apply to floor with a sponge mop. Rinsing will not be necessary. **Keep out of reach of children.**

Basic Liquid Floor Wax

The following ingredients will be needed:

1/4 Lb. beeswax   1/2 Cup raw linseed oil

1 Lb. paraffin   3 Cups turpentine

Place the beeswax and paraffin in a double boiler and heat until melted. Remove from the heat and allow the wax to cool. After it has cooled for 5-10 minutes, stir in the linseed oil and the turpentine and mix thoroughly. A thin coat of the wax can be applied to the floor and then buffed with a mop buffer or electric polisher.

If you run out of floor wax, just use ¹/₂ cup vinegar and 2 tbsp. furniture polish in a gal. of warm water. You can also just add a tbsp. of skim milk to the wash water.

Wax Remover #1

The following ingredients will be needed:

5+ Cups washing soda

Warm water as required

Place the washing soda in a bucket and add just enough water to make a loose paste. Place the paste on the floor and allow it to dry. The wax should bubble up and flake off easily. The floor needs to be thoroughly rinsed until the wax and washing soda residue is removed. The longer the washing soda is left on and moist, the more wax will be removed.

Wax Remover #2

The following ingredients will be needed:

2 Cups household ammonia   4 Qt. warm tap water

1/2 Cup washing soda

Place all the ingredients into a bucket and mix well (wear rubber gloves). Using a sponge mop, place a good layer of the solution on the floor and allow it to sit for 5-10 minutes. Scrub the floor as you would normally and the old wax should be loosened and easily removed.

BE GENTLE, OR LINOLEUM WILL HAVE A CRACK-UP

Linoleum can be manufactured by using a mixture of resins, small particles of cork or wood fibers) and linseed oil that is adhered to a canvass, burlap or felt backing using high pressure. Never use a strong alkali-based cleaner on linoleum since they tend to ruin the linseed oil binder and may cause the floor to develop cracks, thus shortening the usable life of the flooring. Best to use a mild detergent solution and dry as soon as it's been cleaned. A linoleum formula should never be used on a wood or cork floor.

Linoleum floors should never be flooded with water and only a quality wax should be used on them.

If your linoleum gets faded and worn out, just buy a special paint that can be used on top of the linoleum.

Paste Wax for Linoleum #1

The following ingredients will be needed:

2 Cups carnauba wax	4 1/2 Cups mineral spirits
2 Cups ceresin wax	

Place the carnauba and ceresin wax in a double boiler and melt. Remove from the heat and allow the wax to cool, then very slowly add the mineral spirits stirring continually. When the mixture starts to harden around the edges, pour into a container and allow the mixture to harden.

Paste Wax for Linoleum #2

The following ingredients will be needed:

2 Tbsp. paraffin wax	4 Cups turpentine
4 Tbsp. yellow beeswax	

Place the waxes in a double boiler and heat until melted, then remove from the heat and add the turpentine, while continually mixing. Allow the mixture to cool and store in a sealed container.

Basic Linoleum Polish

The following ingredients will be needed:

    1 Part palm oil   4 Parts kerosene

    18 Parts paraffin

Place the paraffin in a double boiler and melt. Remove from the heat and add the oil and kerosene while mixing very well.

Basic Linoleum Cleaner

The following ingredients will be needed:

    5 Parts beeswax   5 Parts varnish

    11 Parts oil of turpentine

Place the beeswax in a saucepan and melt over low heat. Remove from the heat and very slowly stir in the oil of turpentine, then add the varnish and continue stirring until the mixture is well blended. Apply the cleaner after the floor has been washed with soap and water with a soft cloth mop.

Paste Wax for Wood Floors

The following ingredients will be needed:

    2 Tbsp. yellow beeswax   2 Cups mineral spirits

    5 Tbsp. ceresin wax   4 Tbsp. turpentine

    9 Tbsp. carnauba wax   3/4 Tbsp. pine oil

    3 Tbsp. montan wax

Place the waxes in a double boiler and heat until the waxes melt, then remove from heat. In another container, mix the turpentine, mineral spirits and pine oil together well and add this mixture to the wax and stir well. When the temperature of the wax mixture is at 135°F., pour it into a metal container and allow the wax to cool and set for 8-10 hours at room temperature.

A NON-RESILIENT FLOOR NEEDS TLC

This category of flooring includes ceramic tile, concrete, brick and all types of stone flooring material. Best to just clean stone and brick surfaces with a solution of vinegar and water (1 cup vinegar to 1 gal. water) whereas concrete needs to be cleaned with an all-purpose detergent or concrete cleaner. If tile is in bad shape and needs to be cleaned to remove ground in dirt and residues, the following formula will be needed. Otherwise, just use a mild soap solution.

Spanish Tile Cleaner and Conditioner

The following ingredients will be needed:

2 1/3 Oleic acid   3 Cups cool tap water

1 Tbsp. triethanolamine (from drug store)

Place the ingredients into a double boiler and just heat; do not allow boiling. Remove from heat and beat with an electric mixer until the mixture becomes milky. Apply the mixture to the tile floors with a sponge and allow it to dry for 8-10 hours before rubbing off with a dry bath towel.

FIRST AID FOR OLD WOOD FLOORS

The following bleach is very poisonous and needs to be used with extreme caution and not swallowed by children, adults or pets. However, it is the treatment of choice to remove all the old stains and even the ground-in-grime from years of abuse and poor cleaning methods. The old wood floor should be cleansed as best as possible first with a good wood floor cleanser.

Bleach for Wood Floors

The following ingredients will be needed:

      18 Cups sodium metasilicate (from drug store)

      2 Cups sodium perborate (from drug store) (POISON)

      1 Gal. very hot tap water

Place the two sodium ingredients into a bucket and mix well. In another bucket, place the gal. of very hot water, then add the sodium ingredients into the water, while mixing well. Then scrub the floor with a soap-and-water solution before using the bleach. Place the bleach on the floor with a sponge mop and allow it to remain for about 30 minutes before rinsing the floor with cool, clear water. If you still have spots that are not coming out, just re-do those spots.

Non-Slip Wax for Wood Floors

The following ingredients will be needed:

      2 Cups denatured alcohol (flammable)   2 Tbsp. acacia

      1 Cup orange shellac (flammable)   2 Tbsp. turpentine (flammable)

Place all the ingredients into a small bucket and blend well, then apply to the floor with a cloth sponge mop and allow the wax to dry for 45 minutes.

Floor Wax for Dance Floors

The following ingredients will be needed:

1/2 Lb. talc

1 Cup stearic acid

Place the ingredients into a glass container with a lid and mix well, then sprinkle a small amount around the floor

Dusting Magnet Mop Oil

The following ingredients will be needed:

1 Cup turpentine (flammable)

2 Cups mineral oil

Place the ingredients into a container and mix well. Place a small amount of the mixture on your dust mop and the dust will jump into the mop.

Dust with Softener Sheets

Fabric softener sheets that have been used in the dryer make excellent dust rags. They will attract the dust and make it easier to clean. Also the items you dust will not attract dust as easily.

Making Colorless Floor Shellac

The following ingredients will be needed:

1 Qt. denatured alcohol

12 Oz. pure flake shellac

Place all the ingredients into a sealed container and shake frequently until the shellac is fully dissolved in the alcohol. Do not use a metal container to store this solution, it will turn the shellac black. Shellac should be used as an undercoat before you varnish a wood floor. This will give you a hard long-lasting beautiful finish for many years.

Making Floor Varnish

The following ingredients will be needed:

    3 Parts Manila copal (spirit soluble)   3 Parts Venice turpentine

    15 1/2 Parts powdered ruby shellac   62 1/2 Parts alcohol (96%)

Place the alcohol in a large container and dissolve the other ingredients into the alcohol. The solution then needs to be filtered through a number of thicknesses of wire screening.

No-Wax Floor Cleaner

The following ingredients will be needed:

    1 Cup white vinegar   1 Tbsp. Castile soap (liquid)

    1/4 Cup washing soda   2 Gal. very hot tap water

Place all the ingredients into a bucket and blend well, then mop the floor as usual. This formula will eliminate any greasy condition.

BATHROOM CLEANING

Removing Mildew

While many people tend to use a formula containing chlorine bleach, which does work well, I prefer a somewhat milder chemical mixture that will not be as harsh to your lungs. Mix the following ingredients together in a medium plastic container:

    1/2 Cup Borax

    1 Gal. hot tap water

The solution will remove the mildew and then should be washed with the same solution and allowed to remain and not washed off for a lasting effect.

IT'S A DIRTY JOB, BUT SOMEBODY HAS TO DO IT

Toilets are made of either porcelain or ceramics and are acid-resistant, which is good since most of the commercial toilet cleaners contain either an acid or ingredients that turn into acid when they come into contact with water. Needless to say, if you swallow most commercial toilet cleaners it will most likely lead to your demise in very short order. If you use one of the following formulas and there is still a ring that persists, try using a pumice bar to remove the ring. Just dampen the bar and gently rub the surface to avoid scratching it. A "00" sandpaper will also do the trick.

Making Toilet Bowl Cleaner #1

The following ingredients will be needed:

    1 Cup hydrogen peroxide   2 Qt. warm tap water

    1 Tbsp. household ammonia

Place all the ingredients into a bucket and mix well. You will need about 1 qt. of the solution for each toilet. Pour the solution in the toilet and allow it to remain for about 30-40 minutes before you scrub and flush. If this is done weekly, residues and discoloration should not occur.

Toilet Bowl Cleaner #2

The following ingredients will be needed:

    3/4 Cup alum (powdered)   1 1/2 Cups caustic soda

    1/4 Cup table salt   (use with gloves and mask)

Place the ingredients in a container and mix well with a wooden spoon, then store in a well-sealed container in a cool, dry location. Caustic soda can cause burns if it comes into contact with the skin. When cleaning the toilet, wet the sides with your toilet brush, then sprinkle the mixture on the sides and allow it to remain for 10-15 minutes. Scrub and flush for a sanitary bowl you can show off to your neighbors.

Inexpensive Toilet Bowl Cleaner #1

The following ingredients will be needed:
    1 Cup white vinegar

Place the vinegar into the toilet and allow it to remain for 8-10 hours, then scrub.

Inexpensive Toilet Bowl Cleaner #2

The following ingredients will be needed:
    1 Cup Castile soap (liquid)   1/4 Cup baking soda
    1/4 Cup borax

Place all the ingredients into a container and mix well. Add a small amount of very warm water if you have a problem blending the ingredients. Pour into toilet and scrub with a brush.

Removing Soap Residue from Washcloths

Mix the following ingredients together in a small bowl:
    1 Tbsp. white vinegar
    2 Cups warm water

Soap residues tend to buildup in washcloths even after they have been laundered. If you would like a clean washcloth, just soak the washcloth in the mixture for 10 minutes and ring out before laundering. Lemon juice may be substituted for the white vinegar.

GERM ALERT! CALL OUT THE HEAVY ARTILLERY

The first thing to remember is that germs love moisture. If you keep surfaces dry, it will reduce the incidence of bacteria getting a foothold and causing odors and unhealthy conditions. Disinfectants will kill bacteria and almost all molds, but only for a short period of time. Therefore, it is necessary to clean the surfaces that are more susceptible to contamination more frequently than most other areas of your home.

Penny Pinchers

Bathroom Disinfectant Cleaner

The following ingredients will be needed:

1 Qt. very hot tap water	1 1/3 Cups pine oil (Pinesol®
1 1/3 Cups powdered household laundry detergent	will do fine)
	1 half gallon plastic container

Place the water and detergent in the 1/2 gallon plastic container and mix until the detergent is fully dissolved. Skim off any foam that develops, then gradually add the "Pinesol®" or pine oil as you continue stirring. To use the solution, add 1 part disinfectant to 1 part warm water. For toilets, use full strength. Store in well-sealed container and, as with all chemicals. store away from children.

Odorless Disinfectant

The following ingredients will be needed:

4 Parts ferric chloride	4 Parts calcium chloride
5 Parts zinc chloride	3 Parts manganese chloride
5 Parts aluminum chloride	69 Parts cool tap water

Place all the ingredients into a container and blend well.

Simple Household Disinfectant for Big Jobs

The following ingredients will be needed:

1/2 Cup borax
1 Gal. very hot tap water

Place the ingredients into a large container and mix well.

Simple Household Disinfectant

The following ingredients will be needed:

    2 Tbsp. borax   *1/4 Cup pure lemon juice*

    2 Cups very hot tap water

Place all the ingredients into a spray bottle and shake until well blended. This will be as effective as most standard brands.

Ceramic Tile Cleaner

The following ingredients will be needed:

    1/4 Cup white vinegar   *7 Cups warm tap water*

    1/3 Cup household ammonia   *1 Spray bottle*

    1/2 Cup baking soda

Place all the ingredients in a medium plastic bucket with a well-sealed cover and shake to mix thoroughly. Place the mixture in 2-3 jars, label and save. Never add chlorine bleach to this mixture. Use with rubber gloves to protect your delicate hands and spray on surface to be cleaned.

Super Tub and Tile Cleaner

The following ingredients will be needed:

    1 Tsp. borax   *3 1/4 Tbsp. white vinegar*

    1/2 Tsp. washing soda   *2 Cups very hot tap water*

    1/2 Tsp. liquid dish soap   *1 Spray bottle*

Place all the ingredients into a spray bottle and mix well. Spray the solution on the area to be cleaned and wipe with a dampened sponge. This is a good powerful solution.

Cleanser for Shower Nozzle Residue

The following ingredients will be needed:

1 Cup white vinegar   1 Cup very hot water

1 Tsp. lemon juice   1 Spray bottle

Place all the ingredients into a small bowl and mix well, then sponge on the showerhead and clean with an old toothbrush.

Bathroom Fixture Cleaner

The following ingredients will be needed:

1/2 Cup white vinegar   1/4 Cup baking soda (fresh)

1 Cup clear household ammonia   1 Gal. warm tap water

Place all the ingredients in a small bucket and mix well. Pour into a number of smaller jars for storage. Place a small amount into a spray bottle and use on fixtures and soap scum. Wipe clean with a warm soft cloth.

Herbal Disinfectant

The following ingredients will be needed:

1 Tsp. essential rosemary oil   1/2 Tsp. essential peppermint oil

1 Tsp. essential lavender oil   1/2 Tsp. essential rose oil

1 Tsp. essential lemon oil   1/8 Tsp. essential love bud oil

1 Tsp. essential eucalyptus oil   2 1/2 Oz. fresh distilled water

Place all the ingredients in a medium bowl and mix thoroughly. Store the solution in a well-sealed glass jar. Place a small amount in a spray bottle and keep in the bathroom to freshen it up.

General Bathroom Cleaning #1

The following ingredients will be needed:

3 Tbsp. baking soda (fresh)   2 Cups warm tap water

1/4 Cup household ammonia

Place all the ingredients in a spray bottle and shake to mix.

General Bathroom Cleaner #2

The following ingredients will be needed:

1 Lb. baking soda (fresh)   1 Cup warm tap water

4 Tbsp. liquid hand soap

Place all the ingredients in a spray bottle and shake to mix. This formula is not as harsh as the one with ammonia. It is also safer around children.

Porcelain Stain Remover #1

The following ingredients will be needed:

1 Bar naphtha soap (grated)   1 Gal. very hot water

1/2 Cup mineral spirits (from drug store)

Place the soap and water into a bucket and mix well, then add the mineral spirits. Scrub the stain with a small medium bristle brush, and then rinse well with cool water. Wear rubber gloves for this job and remember that mineral spirits are flammable, so use caution.

Scum and Mildew Buildup, Activate the Salt

Shower curtains will develop a layer of mildew and scum, especially over the course of a year. Most curtains can be washed in the washing machine, which should do the job. However, you may wish to use the following formula or at least soak the curtains in the bathtub in a strong solution of salt water before you hang them up after they get out of the washing machine. The salt bath should only be needed about once a year.

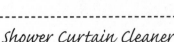

Shower Curtain Cleaner

The following ingredients will be needed:

1/2 Cup soap flakes *1 Cup white vinegar*

1/2 Cup baking soda (fresh) *Mineral oil*

Place warm water in the washing machine and add 2 large towels and the shower curtains. Add the soap flakes and baking soda and run the wash cycle. Add the vinegar and a few drops of mineral oil to soften the curtains in the rinse water.

GENERAL HOUSEHOLD CLEANING

First Remove the Pet Crumbs, Toys, and Coins

As a general rule, all types of upholstered furniture needs to be vacuumed regularly to avoid excessive wear from the grit acting like sandpaper in the fabric every time you sit down and squirm around. A foamy type of solution tends to work best on most upholstered furniture since it does not saturate the fabric and will dry in a short period of time. Before cleaning any type of fabric, it would be wise to test an area in an inconspicuous location before cleaning the soiled areas. However, foamy solutions should not be used on any type of velvet or similar fabric.

Dry Cleaner for Upholstered Furniture

The following ingredients will be needed:

1 Cup baking soda (fresh)

1 Cup cornstarch

Place the ingredients into a sifter and sift into a small bowl. Mix the powder with enough cool water to prepare a loose paste. Sponge on the fabric and allow it to stand for 20-30 minutes and dry before brushing off or vacuuming.

Basic Upholstery Cleaner

The following ingredients will be needed:

1 Oz. trisodium phosphate (TSP)

1 Gal. cool soft water

Place the ingredients into a container and mix well. Sponge the cleaner on the upholstery lightly, first making sure that the color will not be damaged. Try the solution in an area that will not be noticed. This should be safe for most fabrics.

Keep Chimney Soot-Free

The following ingredients will be needed:

1 Cup table salt

1 Cup zinc oxide (from pharmacy)

Place the ingredients in a medium container and mix well. Sprinkle on logs before igniting to make logs burn cleaner.

Indoor Stone and Brick Cleaner

The following ingredients will be needed:

1/2 Cup household ammonia   1/4 Cup baking soda (fresh)

1 Cup white vinegar

Place the ingredients into a container and mix thoroughly. Use with a soft bristle brush and rinse with warm water.

Cleaner for Fireplace Glass

The following ingredients will be needed:

1/2 Cup white vinegar   1 Gal. cold tap water

1 Tbsp. household ammonia   1 Spray bottle

Place all the ingredients in a small bucket and mix thoroughly. Place some of the solution in a spray bottle and spray on fireplace glass, then rinse with warm water and dry with a soft cloth.

DON'T WANT SANTA TO GET HIS SUIT DIRTY

There are very few good cleaners that will work on the creosote buildup that is left over from burning wood. If the buildup is not cleaned out at regular intervals, it will buildup to such a point that it may cause a fire. Soft woods, such as pine deposit more creosote than hard woods, such as oak. If you do burn more soft woods, then the chimney should be cleaned at least once a year.

Fireplace Cleaner

The following ingredients will be needed:

6 1/2 Oz. naphtha soap (grated)   3/4 Lb. pumice (powdered)

3 Pt. very hot tap water   3/4 Cup household ammonia

Place the water into a pot and add the naphtha soap. Place the pot on low heat and cook until the soap if fully melted. Then remove the mixture from the heat and allow it to cool. Stir in the pumice and household ammonia and mix thoroughly. Wear gloves and use a stiff brush to clean, then rinse with clear water.

Hi Ho Silver

The most common form of tarnish that occurs on silver is the result of the silver coming into contact with hydrogen sulfide found in the air. This causes a reaction to take place and forms a brownish coating of silver sulfide on the silver item. A number of common foods, such as eggs contain a sulfur compound that will also cause silver to become tarnished. Tarnish will not occur if the silver item is washed thoroughly after each use, dried well and wrapped as airtight as possible before being stored. Moisture has the ability to speed up the tarnishing of most silver items.

Silver Cleaner

The following ingredients will be needed:

1 Tsp. baking soda   1 Cup boiling water

1 Tsp. table salt

Place a piece of aluminum foil on the bottom of a glass pan and pour the boiling water in, then add the baking soda and the salt. Blend all the ingredients well, then place the silver-ware into the liquid, making sure each piece is touching the other. Tarnish will magically disappear. If the pieces are badly tarnished, additional soakings may be necessary.

Silver Paste Cleaner

The following ingredients will be needed:

3 Tbsp. cheap vodka   1/2 Tsp. liquid dish soap

1/2 Cup diatomaceous earth

Place all the ingredients into a small bowl and mix well, adding just enough water to prepare a thick paste. Best to store in a wide mouth jar. Use with a dampened sponge just as you would with the expensive spread from the market.

If your silverware becomes discolored from egg stains, just rub them with table salt before washing in soapy water.

All-Around Household Cleaner #1

The following ingredients will be needed:

8 Cups warm tap water   1/2 Cup household ammonia

1/2 Cup baking soda (fresh)

Place the baking soda, ammonia and one cup of warm water in a well-sealed 1/2 gal. plastic jug and mix thoroughly. Add the additional 7 cups of warm water and shake. To use the mixture, it is necessary to pour 1/2 cup into 1 gal. of hot tap water.

Caution:Always test a small hidden area before using a new chemical to be sure that the surface to be cleaned is colorfast to that chemical.

All-Around Household Cleaner #2

The following ingredients will be needed:

3   Tbsp. washing soda

1   Qt. warm tap water

Place the water in a bucket and add the washing soda. Stir until the washing soda is fully dissolved. This cleaner is also great for heavy dirt areas.

Multi-Action Cleaner

The following ingredients will be needed:

1/4 Cup baking soda

1/2 Cup white vinegar

1 Cup household ammonia

1 Gal. warm tap water

Place the water in a bucket, add the other ingredients and mix well. Store in a well-sealed bottle and use as a multi-purpose cleaner.

Spray Cleaner for Most Jobs

The following ingredients will be needed:

1 Tsp. borax

2 Tbsp. white vinegar

1/2 Tsp. washing soda

2 Cups very hot tap water

1/2 Tsp. liquid hand soap

1 Spray bottle

Place the vinegar, soap, borax and washing soda into the spray bottle and mix well. Add the hot water and mix, then use and wipe with clean sponge.

Grease Cutter #1

The following ingredients will be needed:

2 Tbsp. white vinegar

3 Cups very hot tap water

1/2 Tbsp. washing soda

1 Spray bottle

1/4 Tsp. liquid hand soap

Place all the ingredients into the spray bottle and mix well. To make this mixture even stronger, just add 1/2 tsp. borax to it.

Grease Cutter #2

The following ingredients will be needed:

    1/4 Cup baking soda (fresh)   3/4 Cup household ammonia

    2/3 Cup white vinegar   Very hot tap water

Place the baking soda, vinegar and ammonia into a bucket and mix well. Add the hot water up to 3/4 of the bucket and mix well. Excellent grease remover. Then rinse the area well with clean warm water. Best to use rubber gloves to protect your delicate hands.

Baseboard Cleaner

The following ingredients will be needed:

    1 Tbsp. cornstarch   2 Cups very hot tap water

    1/3 Cup white vinegar   1 Spray bottle

Place the cornstarch in the spray bottle with the hot tap water and mix. Add the vinegar, mix again and spray.

WINDOWS ARE A PANE

A good tip to remember is never to clean windows when the sun is shining on them, since they will dry too fast and streak. Newspaper tends to shine and clean the windows when combined with a good cleaner. A stronger solution is usually needed for the outside glass, especially if the glass is sprayed by hard water from sprinkler systems. The first solution will easily remove hard water spots.

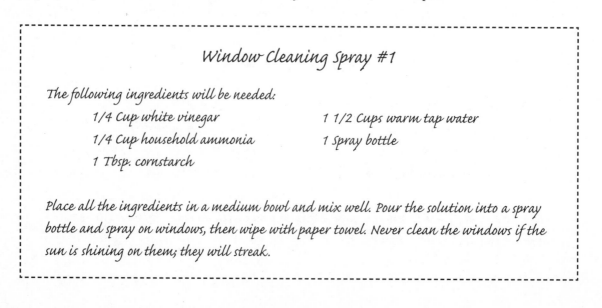

Window Cleaning Spray #1

The following ingredients will be needed:

    1/4 Cup white vinegar   1 1/2 Cups warm tap water

    1/4 Cup household ammonia   1 Spray bottle

    1 Tbsp. cornstarch

Place all the ingredients in a medium bowl and mix well. Pour the solution into a spray bottle and spray on windows, then wipe with paper towel. Never clean the windows if the sun is shining on them; they will streak.

Window Cleaning Spray #2

The following ingredients will be needed:

1 Cup isopropyl alcohol   1 Tbsp. of white vinegar
(flammable, use caution)

2 Cups cool tap water   2 Drops blue food coloring

Place the alcohol into the water in a medium bowl and mix well, then add the vinegar and food coloring and mix. This will look and clean just like the blue store brands of window cleaners.

Window Cleaner

The following ingredients will be needed:

2 Tbsp. white vinegar
1 Qt. cool tap water

Place the ingredients into a spray bottle and shake to mix.

Lemon Glass Cleaner

The following ingredients will be needed:

4 Tbsp. reconstituted lemon juice
1 Gal. cool tap water

Place the ingredients into a 1 gal. container and mix well. Place a portion into a spray bottle.

Heavy Duty Cleaner for Windows

The following ingredients will be needed:

1/4 Cup isopropyl alcohol (70%)   1 Tsp. liquid detergent

1/4 Cup household ammonia

Place the alcohol and the ammonia into a spray bottle and shake well to mix, then add the detergent and mix gently or it will cause too many suds.

Simple Window Cleaner

The following ingredients will be needed:

1/2 Cup pure lemon juice

2 Cups warm tap water

Place the ingredients into a spray bottle and shake well to blend.

Grease-Cutting Window Cleaner

The following ingredients will be needed:

1 Tbsp. deodorized kerosene

1 Qt. cool tap water

Place the ingredients into a container (wear gloves) and sponge on glass, then polish with a piece of newspaper.

No-Streak Window Cleaner

The following ingredients will be needed:

1 Tbsp. cornstarch   1 Qt. warm tap water

1/4 Cup white vinegar

Place all the ingredients into a small bucket and mix well. This mixture may be applied with a rag or sponge or placed into a spray bottle. Shake well before each use.

6

De-Icing Window Cleaner

The following ingredients will be needed:
- 1/2 Cup isopropyl alcohol
- 1 Qt. warm tap water

Place the ingredients into a small container and mix well, then sponge on windows and wipe off with paper towels.

Basic Wall Cleaner

The following ingredients will be needed:
- 1/4 Cup baking soda (fresh)
- 1/2 Cup white vinegar
- 1 Cup household ammonia
- 1 Gal. warm tap water

Place all the ingredients in a medium bucket and mix well. Sponge on the dirty area, and then rinse well.

I WONDER WHERE THE YELLOW WENT

Furniture made from natural materials should be cared for regularly or it tends to turn yellow and even crack. Bamboo, rattan and wicker furniture should all be vacuumed frequently and wiped off with a lightly dampened soft cloth. To prevent yellowing, clean gently with a stiff brush that has been dampened with a strong saltwater solution. Most manufacturers of this type of furniture recommend that the furniture be given a light coating of shellac about every 12-18 months.

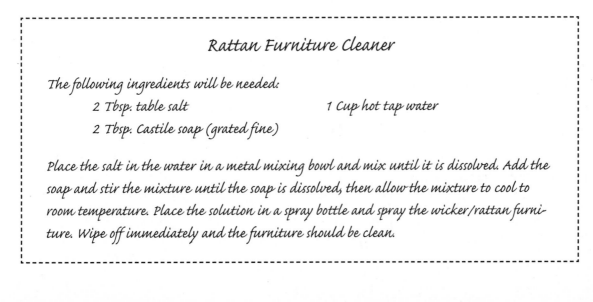

Rattan Furniture Cleaner

The following ingredients will be needed:
- 2 Tbsp. table salt
- 2 Tbsp. Castile soap (grated fine)
- 1 Cup hot tap water

Place the salt in the water in a metal mixing bowl and mix until it is dissolved. Add the soap and stir the mixture until the soap is dissolved, then allow the mixture to cool to room temperature. Place the solution in a spray bottle and spray the wicker/rattan furniture. Wipe off immediately and the furniture should be clean.

Basic Cleaning Powder

The following ingredients will be needed:

1/4 Cup soap flakes	2 1/4 Tsp. of borax
1 1/2 Cup boiling water	1/4 Cup whiting

Place the water in a bucket and dissolve the soap flakes and borax fully. Allow the mixture to cool to room temperature before adding the whiting, and then mix well. May be stored in a sealed plastic container. Mildly abrasive, but can be used on most fixtures without scratching them. Adding additional whiting can increase the abrasive qualities of the powder.

Computer Screen & Keyboard Cleaner

The following ingredients will be needed:

1/2 Cup rubbing alcohol	1/2 Cup cool tap water
1 Tbsp. baking soda (fresh)	

Place the ingredients into a small jar and use as needed on a soft cloth. Store in a well-sealed jar in a cool location.

WOOD FURNITURE

The Wonderful World of Natural Wood

Natural wood furniture provides warmth in your home that cannot be achieved by either metal or glass. Most wood furniture has a finish that utilizes a varnish, shellac or lacquer that is polished to a high shine and will retain that shine for many years providing the shined surface is cleaned with a quality wood cleaner and polished regularly with a soft dry cloth. Most commercial products contain a solvent that will remove previous layers of polish, however, and these should not be used on a natural wood surface that is only protected by a coating of wax. If using oils on wood, use only a small amount to prevent buildup and the surface becoming gummy.

Wood Polish and Cleaner

The following ingredients will be needed:

1/4 Cup lemon juice   1/8 Cup white vinegar

1/8 Cup quality linseed oil (food grade)

Place all the ingredients into a small glass jar with a lid and mix well. Apply with a soft dry cloth, then polish with another clean, dry cloth.

To remove a piece of paper that has become stuck to the furniture, just place a few drops of vegetable oil on the paper and allow it to sit for about 30 minutes or more, if needed.

Lemon Furniture Polish

The following ingredients will be needed:

1 Tbsp. lemon oil   1 Spray bottle

1 Qt. mineral oil

Place the ingredients into the spray bottle and mix well before each use. Wipe off the polish with a soft, dry cloth.

When you polish furniture, be sure and place a cloth around a small sandbag. This will provide weight, which will result in a smoother, more even waxing.

Furniture Polish and Cleaner

The following ingredients will be needed:

1/3 Cup white vinegar   2/3 Cup turpentine
1 Cup Linseed oil

Place all the ingredients into a large bowl or small bucket and mix well. The solution should be applied with a soft cloth to remove old polish and leave a nice shine. Store in a well-sealed jar.

Wax Furniture Polish #1

The following ingredients will be needed:

4 Parts yellow wax   2 Parts turpentine
1 Part rosin

Place the wax and rosin in a pot and heat until they are well blended, then remove from heat and stir in the turpentine during the cooling period.

Wax Furniture Polish #2

The following ingredients will be needed:

4 Parts yellow wax   1 Part turpentine
1 Part linseed oil

Place the wax and linseed oil in a pot and heat until they are well blended, stirring continuously. Remove from the heat, add the turpentine and mix well.

All new pieces of wood furniture should be polished with a wax polish every 2 weeks, rather than once a month to protect the wood from water or glass rings.

Oil Furniture Polish #1

The following ingredients will be needed:

1 Lb. cedar oil

1 Pt. turpentine

1 Pt. ammonia water

Small piece of dish soap

Place the turpentine into a container and dissolve the cedar oil completely in it, stirring well. Add the ammonia water and the dish soap to help prevent the solution from losing its emulsion and separating.

Oil Furniture Polish #2

The following ingredients will be needed:

1 Pt. paraffin oil

1 Pt. kerosene

8 Oz. acetic acid (vinegar)

Place all the ingredients into a container and mix well. Store in a well-sealed container and shake well before each use. This is a fast-drying polish that will not coat the furniture.

Furniture Polish and Woodworm Deterrent

The following ingredients will be needed:

5 Oz. linseed oil (food grade)

5 Oz. turpentine

2 Oz. rubbing alcohol

2 Oz. vinegar

Place all ingredients in a medium jar with a lid and shake well. Apply to wood furniture with a dry soft cloth.

If you newly varnish a piece of furniture, be sure and place it upside down so that dust can't settle on it.

Penny Pinchers

THE MAGIC OF SCRATCH REMOVAL

Most scratches can easily be removed if you have the right solution and a little know-how. Remember to always go with the grain of the wood when rubbing the area with scratch remover. Patience is important if you want the scratch to remain hidden for a long period of time. It is necessary to allow the solution or filler to remain for about 24 hours before attempting to remove any excess. Deep scratches can be filled with a crayon that can be obtained at most hardware stores to match the color of the wood, and then melted into the scratch. There are many different items that can be used to hide scratches, such as eyebrow pencils, permanent markers, crayons, shoe polish, iodine and nail polish to name just a few.

Hiding Scratches in Dark Wood

The following ingredients will be needed:
- 10 Drops white vinegar
- 4 Drops iodine

Using a small glass bowl, place the vinegar on the bottom and add the iodine a drop at a time until the color you wish is obtained. Mix and dab on scratch. Wipe off immediately with a soft cloth.

To restore a dulled finish to a piece of mahogany furniture, just use a soft cloth that has been lightly dampened with warm water and white vinegar. Be sure that the cloth is rung out well.

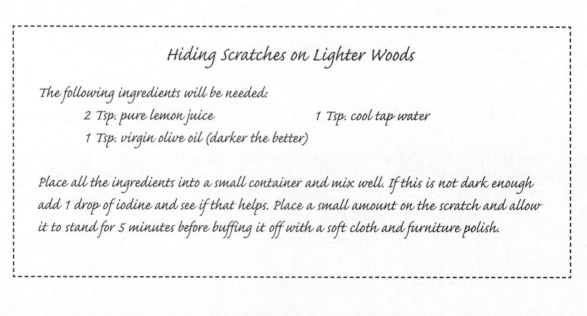

Hiding Scratches on Lighter Woods

The following ingredients will be needed:
- 2 Tsp. pure lemon juice
- 1 Tsp. virgin olive oil (darker the better)
- 1 Tsp. cool tap water

Place all the ingredients into a small container and mix well. If this is not dark enough add 1 drop of iodine and see if that helps. Place a small amount on the scratch and allow it to stand for 5 minutes before buffing it off with a soft cloth and furniture polish.

The Best Wood Wax

The following ingredients will be needed:

1 Tbsp. carnauba wax	1/4 Cup white vinegar
1/2 Cup linseed oil (food grade)	5 Drops essential rose oil fragrance
1 Tbsp. clean beeswax	(if desired)

Place all the ingredients in the top of a double boiler, then heat and stir until all the ingredients are melted together. Pour into a heat-resistant container and allow the mixture to cool until the wax becomes a solid again. The vinegar will go to the bottom and will not be needed. Rub the wax on your furniture with a soft cloth, then dip another cloth into some white vinegar and rub the waxed area until polished. The vinegar will cut the oil in the wax and make the waxed surface very smooth.

Did Your Friends or Family Leave you a Ring

When a family member or friend places a glass that is damp or has condensation on a waxed, wood surface, it may leave a white ring or spots. If the surface is cleaned off within a short period of time, the spot may be easily removed. However, if it is allowed to remain, it will leave a stain that may be more difficult to remove. A mild abrasive made into a paste will usually remove almost any ring or watermark. The paste can be prepared from any natural oil, which includes olive oil, petroleum jelly, margarine and even butter combined with baking soda or salt. In many instances toothpaste, especially the powdered variety can be used with excellent results. After you remove the stain, be sure and apply a good coating of polish.

Ring Remover for Wood #1

The following ingredients will be needed:
  1/2 Cup virgin olive oil
  1 Tbsp. pure beeswax

Place the beeswax and olive oil in a small saucepan and heat on a low flame, stirring until the wax is melted. Transfer the mixture into a heat-resistant container and allow it to cool before placing the mixture into a jar for future use. Rub the remover on the stained area, then buff with a clean soft cloth that has been lightly dampened with white vinegar.

Ring Remover for Wood #2

The following ingredients will be needed:

    10 Drops lemon oil

    2 Cups denatured alcohol

Place the ingredients into a small bottle and mix well before each use. Dab a clean, dry cloth into the mixture and rub the area, then dry with a clean, dry cloth.

Water Stain Remover

The following ingredients will be needed:

    1 Oz. toothpaste (not gel)

    1/2 Tsp. baking powder

Place the ingredients into a small bowl and mix well. The mixture will be a little gritty, which is OK. Gently rub the area and allow the mixture to remain on until it is dry before buffing it off and placing a coat of furniture polish on the area.

Removing Wood Polish Buildup

The following ingredients will be needed:

    1/2 Cup white vinegar

    1/2 Cup cold tap water

Place the ingredients in a small bowl and mix well. Dampen a clean soft cloth and wipe the wood surface. Dry immediately; do not allow the solution to sit on wood after it has been cleaned. Polish as usual afterwards.

Basic Woodwork Cleaner #1

The following ingredients will be needed:

    1 Qt. vinegar (acetic acid)   2 Oz. alcohol (any)

    2 Oz. butter of antimony   1 Qt. vegetable oil

Place all the ingredients into a bottle with a lid and shake well before each use. Works good on varnished surfaces.

Basic Woodwork Cleaner #2

The following ingredients will be needed:

1 Part shellac   25 Parts alcohol (any)

1 Part linseed oil

Place all the ingredients into a container and mix well. This is best for polished woodwork surfaces. If the wood has any disfiguring areas, clean then first with boiled linseed oil.

Basic Oak Woodwork Cleaner

The following ingredients will be needed:

7 Parts linseed oil   1 Part powdered lead acetate

2 Parts powdered litharge   16 Parts turpentine oil

2 Parts powdered minimum

This formula may be purchased as "Brunoline" or prepared with these ingredients. Place the linseed oil in a very large pot (lots of foam will be made), then add the litharge, minimum and the lead acetate. Place the mixture on the heat and boil while continually stirring until the color is dark brown. Remove it from the heat and add the turpentine oil, then stir very well. The turpentine oil is very flammable so keep it away from any heat source. The oak woodwork should be cleaned with a weak ammonia solution and dried before applying a thin coating of Brunoline.

Removing Water Stains from Wood Furniture

The following ingredients will be needed:

White wax

Olive oil

Water stains can easily be removed from varnished wood surfaces by melting a small amount of white wax in olive oil over low heat, then rubbing the stain with the solution on a soft cloth.

Making Cleaner for Painted Wood Surfaces

The following ingredients will be needed:

    2 Oz. brown soap   *17 1/2 Oz. cool tap water*

    1/2 Tbsp. powdered borax

The soap needs to be cut up into small pieces and placed in a pot, then add the borax and dissolve the mixture into the water over low heat. Mix the solution well, remove from the heat and allow it to cool. A flannel cloth should be used to apply this cleaner and it should be rinsed off immediately afterwards and the area dried with a clean soft cloth.

Never store your furniture in an area that gets very hot or damp like an attic or basement. Never place a piece of wood furniture near a radiator.

CARPET CLEANING AND DEODORIZING

Protection, a Must

Carpet should be vacuumed regularly to protect the fibers from excessive wear due to the accumulation of dirt and grime that will damage the fibers. Do not attempt to use the following carpet formulas or any commercial formula on oriental, old carpets or wool rugs that are more than one color. These carpets should be cleaned by a professional company. Most carpeting sold is made of synthetic fibers, which may be cleaned with the following formulas. However, always try the formula in an inconspicuous location to be sure that the carpet is colorfast.

The legs of furniture should be protected with a small plastic bag so that the wood will not be damaged by the shampoo. Try to shampoo when the weather is warm and dry so that the carpet will dry as fast as possible. A small fan works really well. The carpet should not be saturated or it will take days to dry out. Any serious stains should be treated and removed before cleaning the carpet. Carpet shampoos will clean the surface satisfactorily, but special care and work will be needed if the stain is deep into the carpet or has entered the padding.

Pine Needles Clog Vacuums

To avoid the problem of pine needles clogging your vacuum hose, just place a piece of old pantyhose over the nozzle and affix it with a rubber band.

General Cleaning

The following ingredients will be needed:

1/2 Cup Castile soap (grated fine)	5 Drops wintergreen essential oil
2 Tsp. washing soda	4 Cups boiling water
8 Drops vanilla essential oil	

Place the soap flakes into boiling water with the pot removed from the heat. Stir until the soap flakes are fully dissolved, then allow the mixture to cool to room temperature. Add the washing soda and the essential oils and mix well in a large bowl. Check an area of the carpet for color-fastness before cleaning the carpet, just to be safe. Many older carpets are not colorfast.

Basic Carpet Cleaner

The following ingredients will be needed:

4 Parts Fuller's earth	8 Parts pearlash
1 Part spirits of turpentine	Soft soap

Place all the ingredients into a container and add enough soap to prepare a stiff paste. Make sure the carpet is colorfast in an out-of-the-way area before using this solution on the stained area.

Carpet Cleaner Without Soap

The following ingredients will be needed:

1 Cup white vinegar
1 Qt. denatured alcohol (cheap vodka would do)

Place the ingredients into a small bucket and mix, then sponge off the bad spots and rinse lightly with cool water. Allow the carpet to dry and then vacuum.

Inexpensive Carpet Deododorizer

The following ingredients will be needed:

8 Oz. baking soda (fresh)
16 Drops essential lemon oil

Place the ingredients into a container that has holes in the top, mix well, then sprinkle the mixture on your carpet. Allow the deodorizer to remain for 30 minutes, then vacuum it up.

WOOD FLOORS

Wood Floor Cleaner

The following ingredients will be needed:

    1 Cup Fuller's earth clay   1 1/4 Cup washing soda

    2 Cups Castile soap (grated fine)   5 Cups cold tap water

    1/2 Cup cornstarch (fresh)

Place all the ingredients in a large pot and bring to a slow boil, while stirring continually. Reduce the heat and allow it to simmer for 8-10 minutes, then cool to room temperature before using. Small amount should be applied with water, then mopped up immediately, using a clean mop that is dirt-free with all applications.

Polish for Wood Flooring

The following ingredients will be needed:

    1/3 Cup linseed oil (food grade)   2 Tbsp. wheat germ oil (fresh)

    1/2 Cup beeswax   3/4 Cup turpentine

Place the beeswax into a medium pan and heat on low until all the wax is dissolved, then add the oils. Remove from the heat and stir well, then allow the mixture to cool to room temperature. Add the turpentine and mix all ingredients well. It is best to use a sponge when applying the polish, then allow the polish to set for about 16 hours. Best to do this at night and allow the polish to dry overnight.

Pet Odor Remover

The following ingredients will be needed:

    3/4 Cup white vinegar
    3/4 Cup warm tap water

Place the ingredients into a small bowl and mix well. Place the solution on the area that has been soiled and allow the solution to stand for about 40 minutes before cleaning off with warm tap water. Care should be taken if the floor has a wax coating, since the vinegar is mild acid and may remove the wax coating. Re-waxing may be necessary, but at least the odor will be gone.

Wax Floor Polish

The following ingredients will be needed:

    12 Oz. beeswax   1/2 Pt. turpentine
    2 1/2 Oz. powdered resin

Place a large bowl into a container of very hot water, then add all the ingredients into the empty bowl and mix very thoroughly. This is a flammable mixture and the mixing should not be done on a range or near any source of high heat or fire. Use a soft cloth to apply the wax, then polish with a brush polisher.

Oil Floor Polish

The following ingredients will be needed:

    4 Oz. potassium carbonate   3 1/2 Pt. cool tap water
    8 Oz. beeswax (shredded or grated)

Place 1 pt. of the water in a container and dissolve the potassium carbonate in it. Place the beeswax in the balance of the water and place on the heat to melt and mix well. Combine the two solutions as soon as the beeswax is melted and boil the solution until it looks creamy.

CERAMIC TILE AND VINYL FLOORS

Super Cleaner

The following ingredients will be needed:

1/2 Cup Castile soap (grated fine)   1/4 Cup white vinegar

1/2 Cup household ammonia (sudsing)   7 Cups warm tap water

Place all the ingredients in a medium bucket and mix well. Place some of the solution into a spray bottle and spray on the floor (or mop with a sponge mop) and wipe off with a soft cloth.

GROUT CLEANER

Killing Mold and Eliminating Mildew

Mold loves to grow and multiply in warm, damp places and the grout around tile is just the location for them. It is usually damp and warm from the hot water giving them a nice home to thrive in. Cleaners that will kill the mold can easily be prepared and commercial preparations are not really necessary. The best tool to use on grout when cleaning is an old toothbrush that is not too stiff. If the brush is too stiff, it will remove a small amount of the grout every time you clean it and eventually you will have to re-grout. Mildew is really easy to remove with the following formula.

Inexpensive Grout Cleaner

The following ingredients will be needed:

2 Parts liquid laundry bleach   3 Parts rubbing alcohol

1/2 Part phosphate-based liquid   4 1/2 Parts of cool tap water
floor cleaner

Place all the ingredients into a large container and mix well. Place a small amount into a spray bottle and use as you would any other grout cleaner.

Keep out of the reach of children and pets.

WALLPAPER CLEANER

Wallpaper Requires a Gentle Touch

When cleaning wallpaper, you best not scrub hard or you will be replacing the paper. Older wallpapers, while they may have lasted for many years are somewhat delicate and easily damaged. One of the reasons paper may have lasted for long periods is that it was not cleaned too often. Be gentile with old paper and always try an inconspicuous location before cleaning the center of the wall. Newer papers have been coated to protect them when used in kitchens and bathrooms, making them easier to clean and allowing them to take more abuse from the cleaning methods.

Cleaning Dough #1

The following ingredients will be needed:

    4 Oz. powdered pumice   Sufficient cool tap water
    1 Qt. all-purpose flour

Place all the ingredients into a large bowl and mix. Reduce the formula if desired. Add enough water to prepare stiff dough, then form into rolls 2 in. wide and 6 in. long. Place each roll into a cotton cloth and sew each closed. Boil the bags for 40 minutes to make them firm, then remove from heat and lay the bags out on a cookie sheet and allow it to cool and set for 4-5 hours. Remove the crust that may have formed and use on wallpaper.

Cleaning Dough #2

The following ingredients will be needed:

2 Parts standard bread dough   1 Part of plaster of Paris

Place the bread dough and the plaster of Paris in a medium bowl and mix well, then bake in the oven, remove and use the next day. The paper should be dry and recently dusted before using this cleaner. Rub the cleaner on the wallpaper with single strokes in only one direction. Do not go back and forth or you will damage the wallpaper.

Strong Cleaner for Very Soiled Wallpaper

The following ingredients will be needed:

1 Gal. cool tap water   4 1/2 Oz. kerosene
5 Lb. table salt   9 3/4 Lb. all-purpose flour
4 Oz. aluminum sulfate

Place the water, salt and aluminum sulfate into a pot and heat to 180° F., while stirring occasionally. Remove from the heat and stir in the kerosene and allow the solution to cool to 170° F., then sift in the flour very slowly and stir continually to prevent lumps from forming. This is abrasive and should be used with care.

DISINFECTANTS

Basic Disinfectant Formula #1

The following ingredients will be needed:

6 Oz. aluminum sulfate   2 Oz. sodium chloride
1 1/2 Oz. zinc chloride   3 Oz. calcium chloride

Place all the ingredients into a container and add enough water to make 2 pt.

Basic Disinfectant Formula #2

The following ingredients will be needed:

5 Parts rosin

2 Parts very hot tap water

2 Parts caustic soda (380 Baume)

7 1/2 Parts creosote

Place the water in a pot and dissolve the caustic soda and rosin by boiling. Reduce the temperature below boiling and stir in the creosote, then continue to stir until the solution looks uniform.

Making Cesspool Disinfectant

The following ingredients will be needed:

10 Parts calcium oxide (quicklime)

1 1/4 Parts potassium carbonate

2 Parts chlorinated lime

Wear gloves. Place all the ingredients into a container and mix well, then sift thoroughly. Store in a tightly sealed glass or metal container. Do not get on your skin.

Making Pine Oil Disinfectant

The following ingredients will be needed:

5 Parts of pine oil

1 Part caustic soda (25% solution)

2 Parts of rosin

Place the pine oil and the rosin in a porcelain container and heat until the rosin has dissolved. Remove from the heat and allow it to cool to 140° F., then slowly stir in the caustic soda solution. Wait 30 minutes until saponification is completed. Mix 1 part of the solution in 40 parts of cool tap water. This solution should be strong enough to clean toilets, bathtubs and even garbage cans. Can also be used as a spray.

Making Toilet Disinfectant and Deodorant

The following ingredients will be needed:

2 Parts ferric chloride

2 1/2 Parts zinc chloride

2 1/2 Parts aluminum chloride

2 Parts calcium chloride

36 Parts cool tap water

5 Grains thymol

1/4 Oz. oil of rosemary

3 Qt. alcohol (any)

Place the water into a container and dissolve all the chlorides into water. In another container, place the alcohol and add the thymol and rosemary and mix well. When using the chloride solution, you need to mix the alcohol solution to every 1/2 gal. of the chloride mixture and mix well.

WALL CLEANERS

Don't Be a Paint Remover

While spots may be easily cleaned from most wall surfaces, remember that depending on the type of paint you used, you may be repainting the area you are going to clean. Depending on the type of stain and the type of paint, they may be incorporated into one another, if the stain has been on the wall for too long a period. Wall stains should be removed as soon as possible, once you notice them. It doesn't take very much rubbing to remove the paint with the stain.

Grease Spot Remover

The following ingredients will be needed:

    2 Oz. fresh white talcum powder

    New powder puff

Place the powder puff into the talcum and gently rub over the grease spot. Continue with additional applications until the spot is completely gone.

Removing Paste from Walls

The following ingredients will be needed:

    3 Oz. cornstarch

    Cool tap water

Add the water to the cornstarch to produce a paste that can then be applied with a brush to the paste stain. Allow it to remain for about 1 hour, then remove the paste with a brush and repeat if necessary.

Wall Cleaner with Ammonia

The following ingredients will be needed:

    1/4 Cup washing soda   1/2 Cup household ammonia

    1/4 Cup white vinegar   1 Gal. warm tap water

Place the water in a bucket and add the other ingredients, then mix well. Store in a well-sealed container in a cool dry location. This will work well on enamel and surfaces that are painted with a flat oil or water-based paint.

BASEBOARD CLEANER

Works Great

Dissolve 1 tbsp. cornstarch in a spray bottle in 2 cups of hot water, then add 1/4 cup of white vinegar. Mix and spray.

Caring
FOR FURNISHINGS & APPLIANCES

Milk Bath

Dishes that have developed micro-cracks and may be on the road to being discarded can be saved by placing the glass dish in fresh milk that is slightly boiling for 1 hour. The protein from the milk will enter the cracked area.

Be Careful, I'm Very Fragile

If you want to strengthen your glassware so that it won't be so fragile, just place the glassware in a pot filled with slightly salted water that you allow to slowly come to a boil. The slower the boil, the harder the glassware will become.

Whooosh

To prevent the colors from running and ruining your lampshade, just turn an electric fan or a blow dryer on them as soon as they have been rinsed.

Crackkkkkkk

If glasses become stuck, don't try and force them apart or you may break one. All you have to do is to place cold water in the top glass, then dip the bottom one in hot water until they separate.

My Left Side Is my Best Side

Delicate glassware may crack if placed into hot water bottom first. However, if you slip the glasses in sideways, they won't have the tendency to break.

Rub Me, Rub Me

If a good glass gets a slight nick, it can easily be repaired. Just wrap a piece of "00" emery paper around a spoon handle and rub it back and forth across the nick until it disappears.

Then Read the Leaves

If you have a deep vase that is stained, just place some tea leaves in the bottom and add warm water, then allow it to stand for 12 hours before washing in hot soapy water. Using hot vinegar and allowing the vase to stand for 1-2 days or until the residue is gone also works.

If you rub furniture polish on silver vases or picture frames, it will keep them free of any tarnish.

Where Are my Sunglasses?

To revive an old mirror, just clean the surface with white vinegar. The sun will cause a mirror to become cloudy.

Easy on the Salt

If your piano keys are getting yellow, just dip $\frac{1}{2}$ a lemon in salt and rub on the keys to whiten them up.

Begone Stains

Mix equal parts of salt and white vinegar and scrub the cup to remove the stains from tea and coffee.

Disappearing Act

To eliminate coffee stains, place the juice of one fresh lemon and enough ice to cover the bottom of the carafe; then add 2 tbsp. table salt, swirl the contents for a few seconds and the coffee stains should disappear.

Taking a Snooze

You can easily deodorize any container, thermos bottle or decanter by just filling the container with warm tap water and adding a teaspoon of salt. Allow it to stand overnight before washing in warm, soapy water.

It's Getting Slippery in Here

Because of the moisture in a refrigerator, the racks may rust. To prevent this, just coat the racks with floor wax.

Odor Eaters

A number of foods are capable of removing odors. Vanilla extract placed in a bottle top in the refrigerator will remove odors, while dry mustard is commonly used to eliminate onion odors from hands and cutting boards.

Plastic Container Odors

To remove odors from a plastic container, just place crumpled up newspapers in the container, seal it well then allow it to remain overnight.

WILL It Ruin the Dinnerware?

Dinnerware being imported from foreign countries may still contain traces of lead and other heavy metals. Salad dressings that contain a mild acid, such as vinegar and even tomatoes may be strong enough to release these metals.

Shake It

To remove an unsightly residue buildup from inside a flower vase or wine bottle, try using a solution of 2 tbsp. of salt, some raw rice, and 1 cup of white vinegar and shake vigorously.

Cover-Up

To cover a scratch on your refrigerator or freezer, try using the same color enamel paint. This really works great and will last a long time.

Just a Little Mayo if You Please

If you run out of wood oil, try using mayonnaise. A very light coating rubbed into the wood will help protect the finish. It should be rubbed in well and be sure not to leave a residue. Leftover tea is a beverage that can be used on wood furniture and also to clean varnished furniture.

How Smooth I Am

If you want your sheer curtains to come out of the washing machine "wrinkle-free," just dissolve a package of unflavored gelatin in a cup of boiling water and add it to the final rinse. The protein has a relaxing, or softening effect on the fabric.

Going to Have a Break-Up

If you place a small piece of chalk in a silver chest, it will absorb moisture and slow tarnishing. Calcium carbonate (chalk) absorbs moisture very slowly from the air. If you break the chalk up and expose the rough surface, it will be more efficient.

Personal Hygiene
TIPS

Don't Chug-a-Lug It
If you want your hair to be shiny, just add a small amount of vodka to the shampoo bottle.

Smells Pretty
For inexpensive bath oil, try using sunflower oil and either lavender or rose petal herb.

New Life
Hair, brushes and combs may be revived by soaking them in a pot of warm water and 1 tbsp. baking soda or ammonia.

Ouch!
One of the best methods of removing chewing gum from a child's hair is to use a small amount of non-

chunky peanut butter (not the natural kind). Other methods; such as placing the person's head in the freezer for 45 minutes, is not recommended.

Reflect on This

If you lose a contact lens, turn the lights off and use a flashlight. The lens will reflect the light.

Save on Polish

To save the shoe polish that clings to the sides of the container, just hold the tin over low heat and the wax will melt forming a new cake of polish.

Save Shoe Laces

If a child's shoelaces get raggedy on the tips, just dip the tips in glue and allow them to dry.

Works Great

If you want your hair to really sparkle, try adding a tsp. of vinegar to your final rinse.

A Little Chilly, But Works

If you are unable to remove a ring, try placing your hand in a bowl of very cold water for a few seconds.

Or Wear Gloves

If you would like to keep dirt from getting under your nails when you are working in the garden, just rub your nails over a bar of soap before starting work.

Even Gets Rid of Grease

Laundry detergent makes an excellent hand cleaner for very hard-to-clean hands.

No Cream or Sugar Please

If you have red hair or are a brunette, try rinsing your hair with black coffee, then clear water to add luster.

Smells Like Lemonade

If you want to freshen your feet, try using a few fresh lemon slices. Just rub them in.

Life Extension

The life of pantyhose can be extended if they are placed in the freezer for the first night only. It will strengthen the fibers, but make sure you thaw them out before wearing them, unless you are having trouble waking up in the morning.

Face It!

An inexpensive facial treatment is as follows: for normal to somewhat oily skin, use 1 cup of yogurt, 1 tsp. fresh lemon juice, 1 tsp. fresh orange juice, and 1 tsp. carrot juice. Blend all ingredients well and apply to your face for 10-15 minutes then rinse with warm water.

You Can Also Have it for Breakfast

For a great facial scrub, try using a paste of oatmeal and water. Apply the paste, then allow it to dry until your skin feels tight. Then remove it with your fingers with a back and forth motion to remove the dead skin.

Odor Retainer

Perfume should be stored in the refrigerator if you're not going to use it up over a reasonable period of time, approximately 30 days.

Scares the Children

A great facial can be had by mashing $\frac{1}{2}$ avocado and spreading it thickly on your face. Wait 20 minutes, then wash off with warm water. Don't let your husband see you.

Works Wonders

Place a small amount of vegetable oil on the threads of nail polish bottles and the lids won't stick.

Stop Sweat Goo

To make your own deodorant, mix 2 tsp. baking soda, 2 tsp. petroleum jelly, and 2 tsp. talcum powder.

For a Real Treat, Add Whipped Cream

To remove the yellow from your teeth, try using mashed fresh strawberries to brush with.

Make Your Own

Some toothpaste is now adding baking soda to their formula. However, you could just use a small amount of baking soda to brush your teeth. Just dampen your brush and sprinkle it on.

Why Not Just Use White Vinegar?

For bad sunburn, try making a paste of baking soda and water? It works almost as good as the white vinegar.

How Dry I Am

If you want to make a bar of soap last longer, try unwrapping it before you use it and allow it to dry out.

Getting a Shiner

To add shine to your hair and to remove shampoo buildup, try adding 2 tbsp. apple cider vinegar to the rinse water.

Acid to the Rescue

Before polishing your nails, try applying a small amount of white vinegar to your nails. They will stay shiny longer and it will clean them. Bleaching your fingernails is easy. All you have to do is soak them in lemon or lime juice. The mild citric acid will do the job.

Baby oil will do the same job as a fancy cleansing cream at about a third of the price.

Then Use It in a Salad

For puffy eyes, place slices of cucumber on your eyes. There is a chemical in cucumber that acts as an anti-inflammatory.

Old Trick Really Works Great

If you want your perfume to last longer, try applying a small amount of petroleum jelly first on the area.

Slow Process, But Works

Skin blemishes can be cleared up quickly by dabbing them with lemon juice 4-6 times per day.

Restoration

If you want to restore the natural acid balance to your skin, try using ½ cup of apple cider vinegar in a basin of water. Splash it on your face, then allow it to dry before removing with a towel.

Save Bucks

To make an inexpensive shampoo, mix ½ cup white vinegar, ½ cup dish detergent, ¼ cup water with 2 tsp. mayonnaise (not low-cal).

Gentle Cleaning

To remove garden stains from your hands, try placing about ½ tsp. sugar with the soap lather when you wash your hands. You will be amazed how easy the stains are removed.

Soap Formula

The formula for good liquid hand soap is one 4 oz. bar of soap, preferably one that has a moisturizing cream, and 3 cups of water. Grate the soap as fine as possible then add the water. Microwave on high till dissolved, stirring every few minutes; then allow it to cool before using.

SAVE MONEY MAKING YOUR OWN DENTURE PRODUCTS

Penny Pinchers

Denture Soak #1

The following ingredients will be needed:

1 Cup isopropyl alcohol   Drops of peppermint oil

1 Tsp. citric acid

Place all the ingredients in a small bowl and mix well, then place the dentures in for 20-30 minutes. Rinse the dentures off in cold water.

Denture Soak #2

The following ingredients will be needed:

1 Tbsp. baking soda (fresh)   1 Cup cool tap water

1 Tbsp. powdered laundry detergent (no bleach)

Place all the ingredients in a small bowl and mix well, then place the dentures in for about 30 minutes. This will clean and freshen the dentures up, then rinse them well with cool water.

Adhesive for Dentures

The following ingredients will be needed:

1/2 Cup powdered tragacanth (from pharmacy)   1 1/2 Tsp. boric acid

2 Tbsp. powdered acacia (from pharmacy)

Place all the ingredients in a small dish and mix well, then sprinkle a small amount on a wet dental plate.

A Little Spritz

If you want your makeup to last longer, try spraying your face first with mineral water and allowing it to dry.

Lipstick Repair

If you break your lipstick, try heating the broken ends over a matchstick until they are soft, then place them together and place in the freezer.

Rub-a-Dub-Dub

If hangnails are bothersome, try rubbing vitamin E oil around the cuticles.

Bubbles Galore

To make your own bubble bath liquid, try placing soap slivers in a porous drawstring bag. Attach the bag to the tap while the water is filling the tub and instant bubble bath. Place herbs in the bag for a pleasant fragrance!

LATHER-UP AND SHAVE 'EM OFF

Since many men still use the old-fashioned method of shaving, a number of the formulas relate to those special preparations. Shaving soaps are used to lather the face with a wet brush and were used with a straight razor. The brushless creams were applied with fingers. The type of cream and method was related to the type of beard and how difficult it was to remove. To use these preparations, you must first wash your face to remove any traces of oiliness for the best results. The shaving creams must come into full contact with the facial hair to soften it properly before removal.

Bergamot Cologne

The following ingredients will be needed:

1/2 Tsp. oil of lavender (fine)	1 Tsp. oil of sandalwood
1/2 Tsp. oil of cloves	1/2 Pt. ethyl alcohol
1 1/2 Oz. oil of bergamot	1/2 Pt. cool tap water
2 Tsp. oil of lemon	

Place all the ingredients except the water in a medium bowl and blend well, then add the water and mix thoroughly. Pour into a sealed glass bottle and shake before each use.

No Lather Shaving Cream

The following ingredients will be needed:

    1 Tsp. white mineral oil   5 Tsp. boiling water

    1 Tsp. glycosterin

Place the mineral oil and the glycosterin in a saucepan and heat to 150°F., while stirring well, then add the boiling water and stir again very well. Remove from the heat and continually stir until the mixture is cool. Pour into a sealed porcelain jar.

Old-Fashioned Lather Shaving Cream

The following ingredients will be needed:

2 Oz. acetyl alcohol	4 Oz. coconut oil
2 Oz. caustic potash pellets	2 Oz. virgin olive oil
1/2 Oz. boric acid	1 Oz. sodium lauryl sulfonate
2 Oz. glycerin	1 Oz. carbitol
10 Oz. stearic acid	1 Pt. cool tap water

Place the water in a medium saucepan and dissolve the pellets, boric acid and the glycerin. Place the saucepan on medium heat and boil the mixture for 15-20 minutes. Place the stearic acid in another saucepan with the coconut oil, olive oil and sodium lauryl sulfonate and heat the ingredients until they are well blended. Add the oil mixture to the pellet mixture along with the acetyl alcohol, mix well and remove from the heat. Continue to stir as the mixture is cooling and add the carbitol when the shaving cream is almost cold, stir well and pour into jars with lids.

Soap for Shaving

The following ingredients will be needed:

2 Oz. caustic potash pellets	1 1/2 Oz. stearic acid
4 Oz. very hot tap water	1/2 Oz. ethyl alcohol
7 Oz. lard	Perfume spray as desired or essential oil
5 Oz. tallow	

Place the pellets in a bowl of very hot tap water and allow them to dissolve Place the lard, tallow and stearic acid in a double boiler and allow it to melt, then add the pellet mixture to the lard mixture and continue stirring until the ingredients are all blended well. Remove from the heat and add the alcohol and any perfume or essential oil that you desire and continue mixing until the soap is cool. Pour the soap into a dish or shaving mug to harden.

Old Belt Razor Sharpener

The following ingredients will be needed:

1 Oz. prepared putty powder

20 Grains powdered gum Arabic

1/4 Oz. powdered oxalic acid

Place all the ingredients into a small container and mix well with adequate cool tap water to prepare a paste. Apply a thin coating of the paste to the razor strop and cover the other side with a layer of grease.

Brushless Shaving Cream for Dry Skin

The following ingredients will be needed:

2 1/2 Oz. stearic acid

1/2 Oz. carbitol

3 Oz. mineral oil

14 Oz. cool tap water

2 Tsp. triethanolamine

4 Drops of essential lavender or rose oil

2 Tsp. borax

3 Containers/saucepans

Place the mineral oil in the first small saucepan and place on low heat. Place the stearic acid in the second saucepan and melt it on low heat, then add it to the mineral oil. Place the water, borax and triehtanolamine in the third saucepan, stir well and heat on low heat, then pour it into the mixture of mineral oil and stearic acid mixtures and stir well until it becomes smooth and uniform in appearance. Remove from the heat and add the carbitol and any perfume or essential oil if so desired. Mix until the cream is almost totally cool and then pour it into a glass jar with a lid.

Brushless Shaving Cream for Oily Skin

The following ingredients will be needed:

5 Oz. stearic acid

2 Tsp. carbitol

1 Oz. anhydrous lanolin

14 Oz. cool tap water

1 Tsp. triethanolamine

4 Drops of essential lavender or rose oil

1 Tsp. borax

3 Container/saucepans

Use the same directions for the oily skin brushless cream as you used for the dry skin preparation. The oily formula change will be to substitute the anhydrous lanolin for the mineral oil.

Grandpa's Brush Shaving Soap

The following ingredients will be need:

2 1/4 Cups cold tap water

5 Cups Castile soap (grated)

2 Oz. dark rum

1 Tbsp. ground allspice

1 Tbsp. finely ground cinnamon

1 Oz. bay essential oil

1 Oz. sweet orange essential oil

1 Oz. vitamin E

Place the essential oils, rum, cinnamon and allspice in a sealed jar and mix well, then allow it to stand for 2 days. Strain the mixture through a piece of cheesecloth. Place the water and rum mixture into a double boiler and heat to 180°F., then add the grated soap and stir only until the soap melts. Add the vitamin E as soon as the mixture looks clean and all the ingredients have blended well. Stir and place the soap into molds. When the soap cools and has a thick skin, remove the soap from the molds and allow it to mellow for about 5 weeks.

Bay Rum Face Splash

The following ingredients will be needed:

1 1/2 Tsp. oil of bay leaves

1/4 Tsp. oil of orange peel (very fresh)

1/4 Oz. magnesium carbonate

1 Oz. tincture of orange peel

1/2 Pt. ethyl alcohol

1/2 Pt. cool tap water

Place the magnesium carbonate and the oils in a medium bowl and mix well. Place the tincture of orange peel, alcohol and water in another bowl and mix well, then slowly add this mixture to the oil mixture and stir well. Pour into a well-sealed glass bottle and shake before each use.

Pantyhose Life Prolonger

The following ingredients will be needed:
2 Cups table salt
1 Gal. cold water

Place the salt and water in a medium bucket or pot and mix well. Place the pantyhose in (brand new ones only) and allow them to soak for about 3 hours, then drip dry. This will make the pantyhose stronger and they will last linger.

FACIAL MASKS

When preparing a mask, be sure to clean your face thoroughly and be sure it is dry before applying the mask. The mask ingredients should never be placed close to your eyes, which are very sensitive. All ingredients should always be as fresh as possible, so don't use up the old leftovers in the cupboard or refrigerator. Masks are capable of removing dirt, grime and especially dead skin. They are capable of increasing circulation, reducing eruption of pimples, lowering the level of oiliness, providing moisture and smoothing the skin.

Commercial preparations are expensive compared to the following recipes for facial masks and they are just as effective when used properly. The more common ingredients used in facial masks include cooked oatmeal, egg whites, yogurt, brewer's yeast, honey, vegetable oils and mashed fruits. Brewer's yeast is excellent for improving circulation and honey is capable of balancing the acid/base balance of the skin. A mask should not be used more than three times per week.

Squeaky Clean Cleansing Mask Formula

Mix the following ingredients together in a small rounded bowl:

1 Tbsp. fresh plain yogurt

1 Tsp. fresh sesame oil (no more than 2 weeks old)

Allow the mixture to rest for 10 minutes before applying to your face and neck. The mixture should remain in place while you remain still for 12 minutes, then massage the mixture very gently into the skin and immediately wash off with a very warm washcloth. Repeat the rinsing 3 more times and your skin should be squeaky clean.

A Real Skin Tightener

Mix the following ingredients together in a blender until a smooth pasty mixture is obtained:

1 Tbsp. mashed very ripe avocado   2 Egg whites from medium eggs

1 1/2 Tbsp. pure honey   (less than 3 days old)

(no artificial ingredients)

Pour off any excess liquid and use the paste only. Gently massage the paste onto your face and neck and sit still until the mask dries, which should take about 15 minutes. After the 15 minutes, wash your face and neck with a warm washcloth. This mask will tighten the skin and increase your circulation.

Oily Skin Begone

Mix the following ingredients together in a small bowl:

2 1/2 Tsp. Fuller's Earth (from health food store)   1/2 Tsp. fresh plain yogurt

1 1/4 Tbsp. pure aloe vera juice

The ingredients, when mixed, should have the consistency of a smooth paste. If any small lumps appear, crush them with the back of a teaspoon until they disappear. Apply the paste to your face and allow it to remain on for 15 minutes. Wash the mixture off with a warm washcloth.

How Dry I Am

Mix the following ingredients together in a small bowl:

1 Medium banana (not too ripe)

1/4 Tsp. pure honey (no artificial ingredients)

Apply the banana/honey paste to your face and neck and allow it to remain in place for 15-20 minutes. This mixture will stimulate the skin to become more moist and should eliminate dry skin. Remove the mask with a warm washcloth. The neck is important since it does not contain any oil glands. Wrinkled necks are very common as you age.

Super Dry Skin Care Cream

The following two sets of ingredients are needed:

Step One Ingredients:

1/3 Cup avocado oil	3/4 Cup cocoa butter
1 Tsp. lanolin	2/3 Oz. finely, grated pure beeswax

Place all the ingredients in a small saucepan and heat over low heat until the beeswax melts and blends with the other ingredients. Stir and remove from heat and allow it to cool while you prepare the ingredients from step two.

Step Two Ingredients:

1/2 Cup pure aloe vera gel	2 Drops of rose oil fragrance
2/3 Cup rosewater	2 Vitamin E ampoules (contents only)

Place all the ingredients from step two to the cooling solution from step one and with a small metal whip, blend all the ingredients together until the mixture looks like, and has the texture of a light-colored hand cream. Place the hand cream in a well-sealed jar and use as needed.

Frown Line Remover

The following ingredients will be needed:

    1 Bottle of milk of magnesia   1 Bottle of witch hazel (refrigerated)

    1/4 Cup virgin olive oil

Clean your face thoroughly with a mild soap and warm water. Dry your face and wait 10 minutes. Spread milk of magnesia on your face with a piece of cotton and allow it to thoroughly dry. After it has full dried, spread another layer of milk of magnesia on your face, which will dissolve the first layer. Remove the milk of magnesia with a damp warm wash-cloth. Place a small amount of olive oil in a small saucepan and heat on low heat until it is just barely warm to the touch (do not overheat). Apply the olive oil to your face with a cotton ball and allow it to remain on for 5 minutes. Wipe off the olive oil with the witch hazel. The process should be used twice a week and after 2-3 weeks, you will be amazed at the difference.

Strawberry Facial

The following ingredients will be needed:

    5 Medium-sized ripe strawberries

    1/3 Cup white vinegar

Place the vinegar in a small bowl, then mash the strawberries into the vinegar and allow it to sit for 3 hours. Strain the solution through a piece of cheesecloth, then dab the solution on your face and neck just before bedtime. Wash thoroughly with warm water in the morning. This treatment can be done once per week.

Tighten Those Pores

The following ingredients will be needed:

    2 Tsp. Fuller's earth   1 Large egg (slightly beaten)

    2 Tsp. witch hazel   2 Drops of essential rose oil

Place the Fuller's earth and the witch hazel in a medium bowl and mix well until they are made into a paste. Add the egg and the essential oil and blend well. Place the mixture on your face and allow it to sit for 10 minutes, then remove it with cool tap water and pat dry with a soft cloth.

Facial Mask from Clay for Blackheads and Oily Skin

The following ingredients will be needed:

2 Tbsp. aloe vera   1 1/4 Tsp. grapefruit juice

1 Tsp. witch hazel   1/2 Tbsp. bentonite

1 Tbsp. kaolin (from pharmacy)   2 Drops of essential lemon oil

Place the aloe vera, grapefruit juice and witch hazel in a small bowl and mix well, then very slowly add the bentonite and kaolin to the mixture while continually stirring. Strain the mixture through a strainer, then add the essential oil and mix well. Apply the mask and allow it to remain on for 12 minutes before washing off with warm tap water.

New Radiance Mask

The following ingredients will be needed:

1 Tbsp. Fuller's earth   3/4 Tbsp. pure honey

1 1/2 Tbsp. papaya (mashed)

Place all the ingredients into a small bowl and mix well into a paste. Place the mask on your face and allow the mixture to remain for 15 minutes before washing it off with warm tap water.

Mask That Peels Off

The following ingredients will be needed:

1/2 Cup apple juice (unsweetened)   1 Drop of essential rose oil

1 Packet of unflavored gelatin (fresh)

Place the ingredients in a double boiler and slowly dissolve the gelatin into the apple juice. Remove from the heat and allow it to cool until almost set before adding the oil, then immediately mix and apply the mixture to your face and allow to fully dry. When the mask is fully dry, peel it off and rinse your face with warm tap water.

Mask for Sensitive Skin

The following ingredients will be needed:

1 Tbsp. instant oatmeal	2 Drops of essential rose oil
3/4 Tsp. pure honey	1 Drop of essential lavender oil
1 1/4 Tsp. avocado (mashed)	1 Drop of essential frankincense oil
1 Tbsp. rose clay (from health food store or beauty supply)	

Place all the ingredients except the essential oils into a medium bowl and blend well using warm tap water to prepare a paste. Just before the consistency becomes a paste, add the essential oils and blend well until a paste exists. Place the mask on your face and allow the mask to remain for 15 minutes before washing off with warm water.

Problem Skin Mask

The following ingredients will be needed:

1 Tbsp. fresh cucumber	1 Tbsp. fresh parsley (chopped)
1 Tbsp. plain yogurt	

Place all the ingredients into a blender and blend until it is somewhat pasty. Clean your face, then apply the mixture and allow it to remain for 10-15 minutes before removing and washing with warm water.

MOISTURIZERS

A Healing Moisturizer

The following ingredients will be needed:

1 Tsp. beeswax (grated)	1/2 Tsp. borax
3 Tbsp. grapeseed oil	1 Oz. lavender infusion
1 Tsp. cocoa butter	8 Drops of lemon essential oil

Place the wax, butter and grapeseed oil in a double boiler and slowly melt and mix well. Place the borax in the lavender infusion and heat over low heat in a small saucepan. Add the borax mixture to the wax mixture very slowly, stirring continually. Remove from heat and allow it to cool. Store in an opaque container in the refrigerator.

Delicate Skin Rejuvenator

The following ingredients will be needed:

    2 Tsp. evening primrose oil   5 Drops of patchouli essential oil

    4 Tsp. grapeseed oil   5 Drops of germanium essential oil

    4 Drops of rose absolute

Place all the ingredients in a small bowl and mix thoroughly. Store in a dark bottle in a cool, dry location and it will last about 5 months. Should be applied 5 nights a week as a gentle massage skin toner and moisturizer.

HAIR CARE

Need Body for Thinning Hair

Mix the following ingredients together in a small bowl:

    1 Medium raw egg

    1 Tsp. of your normal shampoo

Wash your hair with this mixture and allow it to remain on your hair for 5-7 minutes. The protein in the egg will bind with the protein in your hair and make the hair strands thicker. Rinse your hair well with warm water (not hot).

Pre-Shampoo Treatment for Men

The following ingredients will be needed:

1 Tsp. dark rum   1 Tsp. lecithin

1 Tsp. jojoba oil   3 Drops of Bay essential oil

Place all the ingredients into a small dish and blend well. Massage the solution into your scalp; wrap a towel around your head and allow it to remain for 1 hour. Wash your hair with shampoo and a small amount of lemon juice.

Oily Hair Shampoo

The following ingredients will be needed:

1 Cup cold tap water   1 Tbsp. dry sage

2 Tbsp. dry peppermint   2/3 Cup baby shampoo

2 Tbsp. dry spearmint

Place the peppermint, spearmint, sage and water in a medium saucepan and bring to a boil. Remove from the heat and allow the mixture to steep for 15 minutes. Strain the herbs out and mix the baby shampoo in with the water from the herbs. Store in a sealed plastic bottle.

Dry Hair Shampoo

The following ingredients will be needed:

1 Cup cold tap water	2/3 Cup of baby shampoo
1 Tbsp. dry rosemary	1 Large egg (beaten well)
1 Tbsp. dry comfrey root	1/3 Cup whole milk
1 Tbsp. dry chamomile	

Place the rosemary, comfrey root, chamomile and water in a medium saucepan and bring to a boil. Remove from the heat and allow the mixture to steep for 15 minutes. Strain the herbs out and mix the baby shampoo, egg and milk into the water from the herbs. Store in a sealed plastic bottle.

Conditioner for your Hair

The following ingredients will be needed:

1/2 Cup virgin olive oil	1/2 Cup pure honey
1/2 Cup corn oil	

Place all the ingredients into a small saucepan and heat until just before it begins to boil. Remove and allow it to cool. Conditioner should be used on your hair while the hair is still very damp. A warm towel should then be wrapped around your hair and allowed to remain for 1 hour. The solution should then be shampooed out of your hair, rinsed and dried. Store the mixture in a cool, dry location in a sealed bottle.

Scrub-a-Dub-Dub

Commercial shampoos will be considerably thicker than most formulas you prepare yourself. In most cases, this is done so that you will think that the product is more substantial and that the quality is high. Almost all of these products contain a sudsing agent and a non-sudsing agent so it will break down or you would never get the soap out of your hair. The following formulas will do the job, remove the dirt and freshen your hair just as well as most of the commercial products, even though they are for the most part thinner and more watery.

Shampoo to Make your Hair Lively and Shiny

The following ingredients will be needed:

1 Large egg

1 Tsp. lemon juice

3 Tbsp. of an unscented shampoo

Fragrance if desired

Place all the ingredients in a small bowl and blend well. Shampoo the solution into your hair and then rinse with warm water. The protein in the egg acts as a conditioner for the protein in the hair. The lemon juice tends to provide a pleasant sheen to the hair.

Hair Brush Cleaner

The following ingredients will be needed:

1 Pt. cold tap water

1/4 Cup household ammonia

1/2 Tsp. liquid dish detergent

Place the ingredients in a medium bowl and mix thoroughly. Place the brush or comb in the bowl and allow it to remain for 10 minutes, before removing and cleaning the residue off with an old toothbrush. Clean under warm running water and allow it to dry overnight before using.

Dandruff Remover

The following ingredients will be needed:

1 Cup apple cider vinegar

5 Aspirin tablets (powdered)

1/3 Cup witch hazel

Place all the ingredients in a sealed bottle and shake to mix well. Shampoo with your normal shampoo, then place the dandruff solution on your hair and allow it to remain for about 10 minutes before rinsing it out with warm tap water. The solution should be shaken well before each use.

Shampoo Paste

The following ingredients will be needed:

2 Tbsp. white Castile soap (grated)   1 Tbsp. glycerin

2 Tbsp. ammonia water   12 Tbsp. cool tap water

1 Tbsp. cologne water

Place the water in a saucepan on low heat and add the grated Castile soap. Allow the soap to dissolve fully. Remove from the heat and allow the mixture to cool before adding the balance of the ingredients. Mix the soap well and use the same as any soap shampoo. Store in a closed container.

Shampoo for Head Lice

The following ingredients will be needed:

20 Drops of essential lavender oil   20 Drops of essential tea tree oil

20 Drops of essential germanium oil   6 Tbsp. coconut oil

20 Drops of essential rosemary oil   1 Tbsp. jojoba oil

Place all the ingredients into a small bowl and mix well. Massage into the scalp and allow it to remain with the head covered with a towel for 3-4 hours. Massage the hair with the shampoo; then rinse well with warm water. The treatment should be repeated, after 2 days and then again in 7 days to be sure they are all gone.

Old Egg Shampoo Formula

The following ingredients will be needed:

2 Egg whites (large eggs)   1/3 Oz. cologne water

5 Oz. cool tap water   4 Oz. ethyl alcohol

3 Oz. water of ammonia

Place the egg whites in a rounded-bottom bowl and beat until they are frothy, then add the balance of the ingredients in the order they are given in the formula. Mix each ingredient thoroughly into the mixture after you add each one. Store in a sealed bottle in a cool dry location.

Shampoo Cream

The following ingredients will be needed:

    6 Tbsp. white soap   5 Tbsp. borax

    9 Tbsp. glycerin   10 Tbsp. cool tap water

Place the water in a small pot on low heat and add the soap allowing it to dissolve, then add the glycerin and borax. Stir well and add any perfume or essential oil if so desired.

Hair Bleach #1

The following ingredients will be needed:

    1 Oz. 3% hydrogen peroxide   Powdered white henna

    10 Drops of ammonia water

Place the peroxide and water in a small container and mix well, then add just enough powdered white henna to prepare a paste. Apply the paste to the hair and allow the paste to remain for 15 minutes or longer depending on the shade you desire. Excessive bleaching can damage hair.

Hair Bleach #2

The following ingredients will be needed:

    1 Pt. cool tap water

    4 Lemons (juice only) (commercial juice OK)

Place the ingredients in a small bowl and mix well, then rinse the hair with the solution. This will lighten up the hair.

1940's Hair Tonic for Dandruff

The following ingredients will be needed:

    1 Tbsp. resorcin   2 Tbsp. castor oil

    3 Tbsp. tincture of capsicum   20 Tbsp. ethyl alcohol

Place all the ingredients into a small bowl and mix thoroughly. Massage the scalp before bedtime for 6 nights.

1950's Wave Set Lotion

The following ingredients will be needed:

1/4 Oz. quince seed	1/2 Tsp. ethyl alcohol
9 3/4 Oz. distilled water	1/2 Tsp. glycerin
1/2 Tsp. borax	4 Drops of essential rose or lavender oil

Place the borax into the distilled water in a medium bowl and dissolve. Place the quince seed in the borax solution and allow it to remain soaking for 10-12 hours, which should produce a pasty substance, which should be strained through a piece of cheesecloth. To the resulting liquid, add the alcohol, glycerin and essential oil and mix well. Go for the waves.

Scaly Scalp Formula

The following ingredients will be needed:

2 Oz. hydrous lanolin	1/2 Tsp. boric acid
2 Tsp. virgin olive oil	1/2 Tsp. cholesterin
1/2 Tsp. salicylic acid	1/4 Tsp. bergamot oil

Place the hydrous lanolin in a small saucepan over low heat and melt, then add the olive oil, salicylic acid and cholesterin and mix well. Remove from the heat as soon as all ingredients are blended well. Add the bergamot oil as soon as the formula has cooled and mix well.

Hair Root Stimulator #1

The following ingredients will be needed:

4 Oz. bay rum	2 Tsp. resorcinol
4 Oz. ethyl alcohol	Perfume or essential oil as desired
2 Tsp. glycerin	

Place all the ingredients into a bowl and mix well. Massage into scalp with a vigorous motion to stimulate the hair follicles to grow. Store in sealed bottle and shake before each use. Should be used at least 4 timer per week.

Hair Root Stimulator #2

The following ingredients will be needed:

4 Oz. distilled water	1 Tbsp. glycerin
2 Oz. ethyl alcohol	10 Drops of oil of bay
3 1/2 Oz. bay rum	

The directions are the same as for hair root stimulator #1.

Brilliantine Hair Luster Restorer

The following ingredients will be needed:

4 Oz. virgin olive oil	2 Oz. glycerin
4 Oz. ethyl alcohol	Essential oil if desired

Place all the ingredients into a small glass bowl and mix thoroughly. Apply the brilliantine to the hair to obtain a bright luster that will not be sticky.

1950's Pomade

The following ingredients will be needed:

1/2 Oz. white beeswax	1 Tbsp. extra virgin olive oil
2 Oz. odorless castor oil	2 Tsp. oil of bergamot
2 Oz. purified lard	

Place the beeswax into a small saucepan and place on low heat until melted. Place the purified lard, olive oil and castor oil in another saucepan and heat over low heat. Mix well and add the beeswax to this mixture. Remove from the heat and allow the pomade to cool. Stir well, then add the oil of bergamot and mix thoroughly. Store in well-sealed container in a cool location.

Grandmother's Hair Straightener

The following ingredients will be needed:

1 Lb. beef suet	12 Grains of benzoic acid
2 Oz. yellow wax	30 Drops of lemon oil
2 Oz. castor oil	5 Drops of cinnamon oil

Place the wax and suet in a double boiler and melt, then add the castor oil and the benzoic acid. Mix and remove from heat and allow to cool a little before adding the oils. Blend all ingredients well and rub a small amount into the hair twice a day. Massage with the fingertips and this preparation should make kinky hair straight and allow it to lie flat.

FOR THE BATH

Bath Salts with Vinegar

The following ingredients will be needed:

4 Cups white vinegar	1/2 Cup Epsom salts
1 Cup baking soda (fresh)	1/4 Cup salt

Place all the ingredients in a medium bowl and mix well. Store the mixture in a sealed jar and use about 1/2 cup for each bath. Add the solution while the bath water is running for the best results.

Formula for Standard Bath Salts

Mix the following ingredients together in a medium jar:

1 Oz. vegetable glycerin (health food store)   5 lb. quality sea salt

1/2 Oz. rose oil   2 Drops any food coloring (optional)

Blend all the ingredients thoroughly and keep near bathtub. Use about 3/4 cup with each bath for a soothing, relaxing bath.

Make Cookies for your Bath

The following ingredients will be needed:

1/2 Cup baking soda (fresh)   2 Cups powdered sea salt (health food store)

2 Tbsp. light corn oil   3 Drops rose oil fragrance

2 Eggs (large)

Place all the ingredients in a medium bowl and knead by hand until workable dough is formed. Form the dough into small tablespoon-sized balls and place them on an ungreased cookie sheet. Place the cookies in a pre-heated 3500 °F. oven for 10-12 minutes, keeping an eye on them so that they do not burn. They should be just lightly browned, not black. A soothing bath can be achieved by adding 2 "cookies" to your bath water.

Making Bath Oil

The following ingredients will be needed:

1 Cup pure honey   1/4 Cup baking soda

1 Cup table salt   1/2 Cup baby oil

2 Cups whole milk   Essential oil fragrance if desired

Place the milk, honey, salt and baking soda in a medium bowl and blend well. Place the entire mixture in a tub of very warm water; then add the baby oil and 3-5 drops of the fragrance if desired. Add one rubber duck.

Making Bubble Bath

The following ingredients will be needed:

2 Cups grated Ivory soap · · · · · · · · · · · 1 Gal. cold tap water

1/2 Cup glycerin · · · · · · · · · · · Essential oil fragrance if desired

2 Cups liquid dishwasher detergent

Place the grated soap, water and 2 tbsp. glycerin in a large saucepan and cook over low heat, while stirring continuously until the soap has been dissolved. Place 2 cups of the solution and the balance of the glycerin and shampoo and mix well. Store in a container that is well sealed. Add 1 cup to a very warm tub as it is filling.

Fragrant Bath Soap

The following ingredients will be needed to make soap:

1 Lb. glycerin soap · · · · · · · · · · · 1/2 Cup standard oatmeal

1 Cup boiling water · · · · · · · · · · · 1/4 Oz. rose oil

Using a double boiler with one cup of boiling water, melt the glycerin soap and add the oatmeal and rose oil. After the ingredients are blended well, allow it to cool but maintain the solution in a state that it can still be poured. Pour the mixture into small molds or a box that has been lined with plastic wrap. When the soap hardens, remove and use. The soap will last longer if it is allowed to dry at room temperature for a few days before being used.

Milk Bath

The following ingredients will be needed:

2 Cups dry non-fat milk powder · · · · · · · · · · · 1/8 Tsp. rose oil fragrance

1 Cup cornstarch

Place all the ingredients into the blender and blend well. Add 1/2 cup to very warm bath water.

Milk Bath for Babies

The following ingredients will be needed:

1 Cup powdered whole milk   3 Tbsp. distilled water

1/2 Cup cornstarch   4 Drops essential rose oil

1/2 Cup pure honey

Place the honey, powdered milk and cornstarch into a blender and blend on low while adding the water very slowly. The mixture should become a paste. Add 1 cup of the mixture to bath water while the water is running and stir if necessary.

Fizzing Bath Beads

The following ingredients will be needed:

3 Tbsp. powdered vitamin C (ascorbic acid)   2 Tbsp. confectioners sugar (10X)

1/4 Cup baking soda   5 Ampoules of vitamin E (liquid only)

1 Tbsp. borax   1/2 Tsp. rose oil fragrance

2 Tbsp. almond oil

Place the vitamin C, baking soda, borax and sugar into a medium bowl and blend thoroughly. Slowly add the almond oil while stirring until the mixture is dampened. Place the vitamin E and the rose oil in and continue to stir until well blended. Form small balls of the mixture and place on a piece of waxed paper (in a location that they can be left alone for about 10 days) and allow to dry for 2 hours. Check the balls and re-shape back into as round a ball as you can. Place the balls back on the waxed paper and allow them to dry out for 10 days. The balls should be stored in an airtight container and in a location with low humidity.

A Bomb for the Bath

The following ingredients will be needed:

1 Cup cornstarch   1 Cup citric acid powder (vitamin C)

2 Cups baking soda (fresh)   2 Drops essential rose oil

Place all the ingredients into a medium bowl and mix well into dough. Roll the dough into small balls and place on a cookie sheet to dry. Store in a sealed container away from moisture and place a bomb into your bath water. It will look like fizzing bath. Very refreshing.

Bath for Lovers

The following ingredients will be needed:

3 Drops essential ginger oil   3 Drops essential Ylang Ylang oil

3 Drops essential rose oil   2 Drops essential sandalwood oil

3 Drops essential lavender oil

Place the oils into a very warm bath, 1 drop at a time, while the water is running, then get in with your spouse.

Effervescent Bath Powder

The following ingredients will be needed:

10 Parts tartaric acid (from drug store)   6 Parts rice flour

9 Parts sodium bicarbonate   Essential oil as desired (lavender or rose)

Place the ingredients into a container and mix well. Place two tbsp. in your bath water for an invigorating bath.

1920's Flabby-Flesh Bath Tonic

The following ingredients will be needed:

1 Pt. white vinegar   8 Grams of camphor

8 Grams of rosemary   8 Grams of lavender

8 Grams of rue

Place the vinegar in a container and allow the herbs to soak for 2-3 hours, then strain through a piece of cheesecloth. Store in a well-sealed bottle and add to your bath water.

POWDERS

The base of most cosmetic powders is the mineral talc. Making your own powders is easy and the formulas can easily be altered with the addition of any number of perfumes or essential oils. When talc is called for in the formula, always use USP (United States Pharmacopoeia) talc powder, which will be the best quality. The majority of chemicals that are recommended in the powder formulas can be obtained from a chemical supply house, pharmacy or health food store. If they do not carry the ingredient, they should be able to send you to another source.

When preparing a powder, it is best to use an enameled container and if perfume is added to provide a pleasant aroma, it should be sprayed on and not be in the form of a liquid, which will cause the powder to become lumpy. While it is not mentioned in the formulas, all powder should be forced through a fine sieve after it is produced to assure that there is no extraneous material in the powder and that it will not be abrasive.

Children's Body Powder

The following ingredients will be needed:

5 Oz. talc   1/2 Oz. orris root

2 Oz. boric acid   1/2 Oz. zinc oxide

1 Oz. precipitated chalk   Perfume spray as desired

1 Oz. magnesium carbonate

Place all the ingredients into a small bowl and mix well, then place the powder through a fine sieve before storing in a sealed container.

Body Powder

The following ingredients will be needed:

    4 Tbsp. kaolin   8 Drops essential lemon Oil

    10 Drops calendula tincture

Place the kaolin in a fine sifter and sift evenly on a small plate. Place the tincture and essential oil in a small dish and mix well, then place the mixture into a small fine spray bottle and spray on the kaolin. Mix together and store in a small shaker and use as a body powder.

Dry Skin Face Powder

The following ingredients will be needed:

6 Oz. talc	1 Oz. precipitated chalk
2 Oz. magnesium carbonate	1 Oz. magnesium stearate
2 Oz. zinc oxide	Perfume spray as desired

Place all the ingredients into a porcelain bowl and mix well, then place through a sieve before using as you would any other face powder. Store in a sealed container that will not allow any moisture in.

Oily Skin Face Powder

The following ingredients will be needed:

5 Oz. talc	1 Oz. precipitated chalk
3 Oz. magnesium carbonate	1/2 Oz. titanium dioxide
2 1/2 Zinc oxide	Perfume spray as desired

Place all the ingredients into a porcelain bowl and mix well, then place through a sieve before using as you would any other face powder. Store in a sealed container that will not allow any moisture in.

Basic Talcum Powder

The following ingredients will be needed:

5 Oz. talc	1 Oz. magnesium stearate
3 Oz. precipitated chalk	Perfume spray as desired
1 Oz. boric acid	

Place all the ingredients into a porcelain bowl and mix well, then place through a sieve before using. Store in a sealed container.

Rose Talcum Powder

The following ingredients will be needed:

    5 lb. powdered talc   4 Oz. extract of jasmine
    7 Drops essential rose oil

Place all the ingredients into a container and blend well.

Dry Rouge Powder #1

The following ingredients will be needed:

    1 Oz. talc   1/2 Oz. zinc oxide
    1 Oz. heavy precipitated chalk   1/2 Oz. powdered tragacanth
    1 Oz. rice powder   Perfume spray as desired

Place the ingredients into a small bowl and mix well, then dampen the mixture a little and force the rouge into a compact to replace old rouge.

Dry Rouge Powder #2

The following ingredients will be needed:

    7 1/2 Oz. talcum powder   3 Tsp. powdered carmine
    1 1/2 Tbsp. gum Arabic

Place all the ingredients into a small bowl and mix well, then add a small amount of cool tap water to form a paste. Force the mixture into an empty compact, instead of using a mold.

1940's Douche Powder

The following ingredients will be needed:

    12 Drops Lysol   12 Grains powdered potassium
    12 Grains menthol   permanganate
    1 Oz. boric acid   Sodium bicarbonate as needed

Place all the ingredients into a small bowl and add enough sodium bicarbonate to produce a total of 6 oz. of powder. Place 2 oz. of powder in 1 qt. of very warm tap water (105°F. to 115°F.) and use for 15 minutes.

Liquid Face Powder

The following ingredients will be needed:

3 Oz. rose water	1/4 Oz. glycerine
1 Oz. pink calamine (powder)	1/4 Oz. wheat starch
1/2 Oz. zinc oxide	Essential oil as desired for aroma

Place the calamine, zinc oxide and wheat starch into a sifter and sift into a bowl, then mix the powder into the rose water and glycerine to dissolve all the powder. The calamine may be added to provide a pink color to the powder if desired and the essential oil added last. Blend the mixture well and then pour the powder into a well-sealed jar. Shake well before each use.

EYE CARE

Eye Makeup Remover #1

The following ingredients will be needed:

1 Tbsp. light corn oil	2 Tsp. canola oil
1 Tbsp. castor oil	

Place all the ingredients into a small bowl and apply to remove the eye makeup. This will work as good as almost any commercial remover at a tenth of the cost. May be stored in a well-sealed jar if it has not been contaminated with makeup. Best to pour out a small amount into a cap and not dip into the main supply.

Eye Makeup Remover #2

The following ingredients will be needed:

1 Tsp. beeswax (grated)	1/2 Tsp. shea nut butter (from health food store)
2 Tsp. of almond oil	10 Drops of chamomile infusion (from health food store)
1/2 Tsp. aloe vera juice	2 Tsp. acetyl stearyl alcohol (from pharmacy)
1/4 Tsp. cocoa butter	

Place the beeswax, cocoa butter and the nut butter in a double boiler and heat until melted. Place the chamomile infusion in a small saucepan, add the aloe vera juice, then mix well and add the alcohol and heat on a low flame in a small saucepan. The wax and infusion mixtures need to be at 158 °F. (use thermometer) before mixing them together, stirring continually. Allow the solution to cool, then store in a sealed glass container in the refrigerator.

Hard Contact Lens Storage Fluid

The following ingredients will be needed:

1/4 Tsp. table salt	1 Cup sterile water
1/4 Tsp. baking soda (fresh)	

Place the ingredients into a sterile container and mix until the baking soda and salt are fully dissolved. Pour the mixture through a coffee filter to remove any particles and store in a sterile bottle with a dropper. Used as storage fluid for hard contacts only.

Professional Lens Cleaner

The following ingredients will be needed:

1 Tbsp. glycerin	1/4 Tsp. turpentine (flammable)
2 Tbsp. potassium oleate	

Place the glycerin and the potassium oleate in a double boiler and melt, then mix in the turpentine and stir well. Remove the mixture from the heat, allow to cool. Apply a very small amount to the lens with a soft cloth that will not scratch the lens. Polish the lens with another clean soft cloth. Many cloth fibers may be somewhat abrasive; so be careful what type of cloth you use.

Making Black Mascara #1

The following ingredients will be needed:
        2 Tbsp. tincture of benzoin
        5 Drops black dye (oil base)

Place the ingredients in a small glass bottle and shake well to mix, then apply with a small mascara brush. Store in a well-sealed container and shake well before each use. This should last for 2-3 months.

Making Black Mascara #2

The following ingredients will be needed:
        2 1/2 Tbsp. Castile soap (finely powdered)   2 Drops essential rose oil (if desired)
        1 Tsp. lampblack

Place the soap and lampblack into a small bowl and blend well, then add the essential oil if desired.

Making Blue Wax Mascara

The following ingredients will be needed:
        1 1/2 Tbsp. white beeswax   1 Tsp. Vaseline
        1 Tbsp. stearic acid   1 Tsp. oleic acid
        3 Tsp. triethanolamine   1 Tsp. cosmetic ultramarine blue

Place the beeswax, stearic acid, triethanolamine, Vaseline and oleic acid in a medium saucepan and place on low heat, melt and blend thoroughly, then remove from heat, add the ultramarine blue and blend well. Allow the mascara to cool before placing in a sealed jar.

Making Eye Shadow

The following ingredients will be needed:
        5 Tsp. spermaceti   2 Drops essential lavender oil
        1 Tbsp. virgin olive oil   Cosmetic color if desired
        1 Tsp. hydrous lanolin

Place the lanolin and spermaceti in a small saucepan on low heat and melt. Do not boil. As soon as they melt, add the olive oil, remove the mixture from the heat and add any cosmetic color you desire. Blend well and allow the mixture to cool before adding the essential oil. Blend well and stir until it is the consistency of a paste.

Makeup Remedy for a Black Eye

The following ingredients will be needed:

  1 Tsp. ammonium chloride 10 Tsp. distilled water
  1 Tsp. ethyl alcohol

Place all the ingredients into a small bowl and blend well, then dab on with a piece of cotton or a swab.

SKIN TONERS AND BALANCER

Lemon Skin Toner

The following ingredients will be needed:

  2/3 Cup witch hazel 1 Cup pure distilled water
  1/2 Cup lemon juice (from fresh lemon, not reconstituted)

Place all the ingredients into a small bowl and blend well. Transfer into a jar with a lid and use by dabbing on with a fresh cotton ball. Do not contaminate the batch by using it from the jar.

Facial Toner and Tightener

The following ingredients will be needed:

  2 Oz. 100 proof cheap vodka 1/2 Oz. essential tea tree oil
  2 Oz. witch hazel

Place all the ingredients in a small dish and mix well, then place into a small spray bottle. Spray a small amount on a cotton ball and dab on your face after washing.

After Cleansing Balancer

The following ingredients will be needed:

  1/3 Cup apple cider vinegar 7 Drops essential oil (any fragrance)
  3 Cups pure distilled water

Place the water, apple cider vinegar and oil into a medium bowl and mix thoroughly. Transfer the mixture into a jar, then only pour out what you need into another small container each day. A balancer is used to return your skins pH balance to normal after you have used a cleanser.

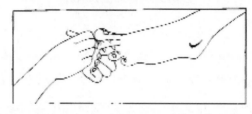

Reducing Pregnancy Stretch Marks

The following ingredients will be needed:

3 Oz. emu oil (from health food store)   5 Drops essential rose oil

8 Drops essential lavender oil   7 Drops essential bergamot oil

Place the emu oil in a bowl in a pot of very warm tap water and allow it to remain for 10 minutes before adding the essential oils and mixing well. Store in a well-sealed jar in the refrigerator and apply twice daily to areas that may develop stretch marks. Seal oil may be substituted if emu oil is difficult to locate.

NAIL CARE

When preparing nail preparations at home, it is safer to prepare powders, pastes and waxes. The flammable lacquer polishes are not as safe but more popular. Carmine or eosine in powdered form may be added to most formulas to produce the desired level of coloring.

Nail Strengthener

The following ingredients will be needed:

1 1/2 Tbsp. horsetail infusion   1 Tbsp. lanolin
(from health food store)   10 Drops of myrrh

Place the horsehair infusion in a small bowl and place your nails in for 4-5 minutes. Mix the lanolin and the myrrh in another small bowl and rub the mixture into the nails with a soft cloth and wash off any excess with warm water.

Making Nail Polish Remover

The following ingredients will be needed:

6 Parts acetone (from pharmacy)

4 Parts ethyl acetate (from pharmacy)

Place the ingredients into a small glass bowl and mix thoroughly. (Avoid fumes). Store in a well-sealed jar.

1950's Paste Nail Polish

The following ingredients will be needed:

     4 Tsp. tin oxide   1 Drop of essential rose oil

     2 Grains of powdered carmine

Place all the ingredients into a small bowl and add just enough water to prepare a paste. Store in a sealed jar in a cool location.

Conditioner for Cuticles

The following ingredients will be needed:

     1/2 Tsp. cocoa butter   9 Drops essential lemon oil

     1 1/2 Tsp. shea butter

Place the cocoa butter and shea butter in a double boiler and melt, then slowly stir in the essential oil. Remove the mixture from the heat and allow it to cool. Store in a jar, but allow it to set before placing a lid on it. This will take about 10 hours and the conditioner will stay fresh for about 3 months.

Softener for Cuticles

The following ingredients will be needed:

     1 Tsp. virgin olive oil   1 Drop of essential lemon oil

     5 Ampoules of 400IU vitamin E (liquid)

Place all the ingredients into a small bowl and blend well, then massage the solution into your cuticles.

Lacquer for Nails

The following ingredients will be needed:

     2 Drams of celluloid (photographic film)   7 1/2 Oz. acetone

     2 1/2 Oz. amyl acetate   1 1/4 Grams of phloxine

Place the amyl acetate and acetone in a small bowl and mix well, then dissolve the celluloid in it and mix well. Apply with a small camel's hairbrush once the nails have been well cleaned. Apply two coats, but be sure the first coat is completely dry before applying the second coat.

Bleach for Nails #1

The following ingredients will be needed:

2 1/4 Oz. rose water   1 Tsp. zinc oxide
1/4 Oz. citric acid

Place the rose water in a small bowl, add the citric acid and zinc oxide to the water and mix thoroughly.

Bleach for Nails #2

The following ingredients will be needed:

2 1/2 Oz. hydrogen peroxide   1/2 Oz. glycerin
2 Oz. rose water

Place the rose water in a small bowl, add the hydrogen peroxide and glycerin to it then stir very well. Store in a well-sealed container.

Nail Whitener

The following ingredients will be needed:

2 Oz. hydrous lanolin   1/2 Dram of zinc peroxide
1 Oz. talc   1/4 Tsp. glycerin
1 Oz. zinc oxide   2 Drops of essential rose oil
1/2 Oz. almond oil

Place the lanolin in a small saucepan and melt, but do not allow it to boil. Then add the other ingredients, except the essential oil and mix thoroughly. Remove from the heat and allow the mixture to cool before mixing in the essential oil. Use a small flat-sided nail stick to apply the whitener under the nails.

Softener for Nails

The following ingredients will be needed:

2 Oz. hydrous lanolin   1 Tsp. virgin olive oil
1/2 Oz. Castile soap (grated) 2 Drops of essential lavender oil
2 Tsp. glycerin

Place the lanolin in a small saucepan on low heat and melt, then mix in the soap, glycerin and olive oil. Remove from the heat and stir continuously until the mixture cools. Add the essential oil and mix well, then store in a sealed glass container in a cool location.

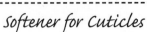

Softener for Cuticles

The following ingredients will be needed:

2 1/2 Oz. cocoa butter   1/2 Oz. glycerin

1 Oz. hydrous lanolin   1 Dram of trisodium phosphate (TSP)

1 Oz. almond oil

Place the cocoa butter and lanolin in a double boiler and melt while stirring. When they have melted, add the other ingredients and blend well. Remove from the heat and allow the mixture to cool while continually stirring. Store in a sealed container in a cool location.

BALMS

Conditioning Balm

The following ingredients will be needed:

2 Tsp. cocoa butter

10 Drops of essential grapefruit oil

Place the butter in a double boiler and allow it to melt before adding the essential oil. Remove from the heat and allow the mixture to cool and set for about 10 hours. The balm is an excellent natural moisturizer and antiseptic for dry lips.

Foot Balm

The following ingredients will be needed:

2 Tsp. beeswax (grated)   1 Tsp. mallow tincture

3 Tbsp. almond oil   7 Drops of essential tee tree oil

1 Tbsp. wheat germ oil

Place the beeswax and the almond oil in a double boiler and melt, then add the wheat germ oil, and the tinctures while stirring continually. Remove from the heat and allow it to cool slightly. Add the essential oil and mix thoroughly, then place the balm into a glass jar and allow it to set before placing the lid on.

Penny Pinchers

Itch-Reducing Balm for Pregnant Women

The following ingredients will be needed:

   1 Tbsp. wheat germ oil   *1/4 Cup cocoa butter*
   1 Tbsp. beeswax (grated)   *3 Tbsp. almond oil*

Place all the ingredients into a double boiler and blend well until the wax is melted. Remove from the heat and allow the balm to cool. Add a few drops of essential oil after it cools if desired.

HAND AND FACE CREAMS

Creams are used to lubricate the skin and should be applied with a gentle massage action. They cannot restore skin and remove wrinkles, but can keep the skin moist and slow the aging problem. There are a variety of creams, some of which will soften the skin, prevent roughness and some will serve as a foundation for powders. One of the more common ingredients in many creams is mineral oil, which does not have the ability to penetrate the skin, but is used mainly as a cleansing agent.

Lanolin and certain vegetable oils will be more effective and should replace mineral oil in some formulas. Cream formulas will have a better consistency and be well mixed if an eggbeater or electric mixer is used to thoroughly blend the ingredients. Be aware that metal spoons and utensils can discolor many cream formulas; wooden spatulas are recommended.

When preparing creams, small batches are usually best and should be used up within 3-5 months. Higher strengths of rose water and witch hazel may be purchased then is called for in a formula, and then diluted with distilled water to save money.

Rose Hand Cream

The following ingredients will be needed:

   1 1/2 Tsp. cocoa butter   *3 Tbsp. rosewater*
   1 Tsp. beeswax (grated)   *1/2 Tsp. borax*
   2 Tbsp. almond oil   *8 Drops of essential rose oil*

Place the beeswax, cocoa butter and almond oil in a double boiler and melt while mixing well. In a small saucepan, heat the rosewater and borax over low heat for a few minutes, then slowly stir the rosewater into the wax mixture. Remove from heat and continue stirring until it cools and forms a creamy texture. Add the essential oil and mix well, then store in a small bottle in the refrigerator. The cream should last for at least 2 months.

Quality Hand and Body Cream

The following ingredients will be needed:

2/3 Cup baby oil	4 Oz. anhydrous lanolin
2 1/2 Oz. beeswax (grated)	3/4 Cup cool tap water
1 Tsp. borax	4 Drops of essential rose oil
(cosmetic or chemical grade 1 sodium borate)	

Place the beeswax, lanolin and oil in a double boiler and melt them to 160°F. In another saucepan, heat the water and borax to 160°F., then remove from heat, making sure that the borax has melted. Add the water mixture to the oil and stir rapidly until the mixture looks like smooth cream, then continue stirring until the mixture cools to 100°F. Then pour into small jars and store in a cool, dry location.

Basic Cold Cream

The following ingredients will be needed:

1/2 Cup virgin olive oil	1/8 Tsp. borax (powder)
1/4 Cup distilled water	5 Drops of essential rose oil
2 Tbsp. beeswax (grated)	

Place the beeswax and oil into a double boiler and heat until melted and blended well. After the wax has melted, dissolve the borax in the distilled water in a small saucepan and mix well, then bring to a very, light boil and slowly pour the water mixture into the oil while stirring continuously. This process can also be done in a blender if you prefer. When the mixture cools, add the essential oil, blend well and store in a glass jar with a well-sealed lid. The cream will become thick as it cools.

Liquid Cold Cream

The following ingredients will be needed:

1 Tbsp. essential oil of sweet almond	1 Oz. borax
1 Oz. spermaceti	1/2 Oz. quince jelly
1 Oz. beeswax	1 Tbsp. ethyl alcohol
1 1/2 Oz. Castile soap (powdered or liquid)	2 Oz. very hot tap water

Place the hot water into a container and dissolve the soap and borax into the water. Place the beeswax and the spermaceti into a double boiler and melt together, then add the soap mixture to the beeswax and mix thoroughly. Remove from the heat and add the other ingredients. Allow it to cool somewhat, mix well, then strain the cold cream through a piece of cheesecloth.

Almond Facial Cold Cream

The following ingredients will be needed:

1 Tsp. white wax	6 Tsp. rose water
10 Tsp. oil of sweet almonds	2 Drops of essential rose oil
10 Tsp. spermaceti	

Place the wax, oil and spermaceti in a double boiler and melt together. Remove from the heat and add the rose water. Beat the mixture with an eggbeater or electric beater until it starts to thicken before adding the rose oil and mixing well. The almond oil should be the best grade obtainable.

Massage Cream

The following ingredients will be needed:

1 Oz. white wax (from hobby shop)	4 Oz. oil of sweet almonds
1 Oz. spermaceti (from pharmacy)	2 Oz. orange flower oil
2 Oz. coconut oil	5 Drops of tincture of benzoin
2 Oz. lanolin	

Place the wax, spermaceti, coconut oil, lanolin and oil of sweet almonds in a porcelain pot and heat until the ingredients are melted and mixed. Add the flower water and tincture of benzoin and beat or place in a blender to mix until it is the consistency of a thick cream.

Greaseless Cold Cream

The following ingredients will be needed:

5 1/4 Oz. glycosterin	3 1/2 Oz. mineral oil
2 Oz. petrolatum	1 Pt. cool tap water
1 1/2 Oz. paraffin wax	

Place the wax, glycosterin and petrolatum in a double boiler and heat to 170°F., then stir in the water after it has been heated to the same temperature in another pan. Allow the mixture to heat until all the air bubbles have disappeared. Remove from the heat and add any essential oil to create a pleasant aroma. Allow the cream to cool to about 120°F. before pouring into a jar. This cream has the ability to cool the skin and evaporates very fast.

Mineral Oil Cold Cream

The following ingredients will be needed:

1/2 Pt. mineral oil	1 1/2 Tsp. borax (powder)
1 Oz. paraffin	1/2 Pt. warm tap water
3 Oz. white wax	2 Drops of essential rose oil

Place the paraffin, mineral oil and white wax in a double boiler and melt. In another container, place the borax into the warm water and allow it to dissolve, then combine the ingredients, remove from the heat and allow the cold cream to cool for a few minutes. Add the essential rose oil and blend well until it is a creamy consistency.

Vanishing Cream

The following ingredients will be needed:

3 Oz. stearic acid	1 Pt. cool tap water
1 Tsp. triethanolamine	1/2 Tsp. perfume oil (health food store)
2 Oz. glycerine	

Place the triethanolamine, glycerine and water into a double boiler and heat to 170 °F. In another double boiler, heat the stearic acid to the same temperature, then add the stearic acid to the glycerine mixture and stir rapidly for 3-4 minutes. Remove from the heat and add the perfume oil as soon as the temperature lowers to 135 °F., then continue to stir slowly until the vanishing cream is cold. Store in a well-sealed container in a cool, dry location.

YOU DON'T HAVE TO GET STRETCH MARKS

Stretch marks may be the result of a number of factors; these include heredity (which there is little you can do to prevent) people with naturally dry skin that has less elasticity, weight gain and loss, and of course, pregnancy. The marks occur when the skin is abnormally stretched for a long period of time, then returned to its original position. If a good quality cream is used at least 3-4 times per day on areas that may be affected, most stretch marks can be avoided, even during pregnancy. Another common cause of stretch marks in children is caused by rapid growth or weight gain.

Massage Cream for Stretch Marks

The following ingredients will be needed:

2 Tsp. beeswax (grated)	1 1/4 Tsp. apricot kernel oil
1/3 Cup cocoa butter	4 Ampoules of 400IU vitamin E (liquid only)
1 Tsp. light sesame oil	1 Tbsp. wheat germ oil

Place all the ingredients into a double boiler and heat until the wax and cocoa butter have melted and the oil has blended well. Remove from the heat and allow it to cool, then store in a well-sealed jar. Massage the cream into the stretch mark area twice each day.

Tissue Lubricating and Toning Cream

The following ingredients will be needed:

5 Oz. almond oil	1/2 Oz. spermaceti
2 Oz. anhydrous lanolin	1/2 Oz. witch hazel
1 Oz. rose water	Small dash of borax
1 Oz. white beeswax	Essential oil as desired for pleasant aroma

Place the beeswax and spermaceti in a double boiler and melt. In a saucepan, place the almond oil and heat for a minute or so before stirring in the melted beeswax solution. In another container, heat the rose water, lanolin and witch hazel together for a short time, then add the borax and be sure it dissolves totally. When the borax is fully dissolved, add this mixture to the other mixture, remove from the heat and beat well for 35 minutes before adding the perfume or essential oils. Mix well and store in a well-sealed jar.

Tissue lubricating cream is designed to tone the texture of dry skin and prevent roughness. The lanolin is very effective in penetrating the skin and is used as a carrier. However, lanolin does not have a very good aroma and needs to be made more pleasant-smelling with the addition of a perfume oil or essential oil.

FOOT CARE

Soothing Foot Bath #1

The following ingredients will be needed:

Gal. very warm water

3 Tbsp. sodium bicarbonate

1 Tbsp. citric acid

2 Drops essential rose oil

Place all the ingredients in a large foot bowl and mix well, then place your feet in. Make sure the water is very warm or even hot.

Soothing Foot Bath #2

The following ingredients will be needed:

1/8 Tsp. menthol crystals

9 Tbsp. Epsom salts

4 Tbsp. alum (powder)

8 Tbsp. boric acid

Place all the ingredients into a container and blend well, then place 1 tsp. of the mixture into 1 gal. hot tap water and mix well.

Deodorant for Smelly Feet

The following ingredients will be needed:

2 1/4 Tbsp. witch hazel

4 Drops essential lavender oil

4 Drops lemon essential oil

2 Drops orange essential oil

Place all the ingredients into a small spray bottle with a fine mist setting and spray feet. Be sure and shake the mixture before each use.

Shoe Foot Powder

The following ingredients will be needed:

1 Tbsp. dried sage	3 Drops essential lemon oil
2 Tbsp. black current leaves	1 Drops essential lavender oil
1 Tbsp. kaolin	

Place the sage and black current leaves into a mortar and use a pestle to crush into a fine powder, then add the kaolin and mix well. Blend in the essential oils and mix well. Works well when placed in a cheese shaker with small openings.

Foot Scrub

The following ingredients will be needed:

3 Tbsp. clean filtered beach sand (sandbox sand)	3 Drops essential rose oil
3 Tbsp. virgin olive oil	

Place the ingredients into a small bowl and mix into a paste consistency. Massage gently on feet, then wash off with warm water.

Deodorant Powder for your Feet

The following ingredients will be needed:

3/4 Cup baking soda (fresh)	3 Drops essential rosemary oil
3/4 Cup cornstarch	3 Drops essential lemon oil
3 Drops essential rose oil	

Place all the ingredients into a medium bowl and mix thoroughly, then store in a well-sealed glass jar. Sprinkle a thin layer of the powder in the shoes and shake to be sure it reaches all areas.

Dusting Foot Powder

The following ingredients will be needed:

2 Oz. boric acid	3 Oz. talcum
1 Oz. zinc oxide	

Place all the ingredients in a container and blend well.

Athlete's Foot Powder

The following ingredients will be needed:

1 Cup boric acid

1/3 Cup sodium thiosulfate (powder)

2/3 Cup talc

Place all the ingredients into a container and mix thoroughly, then place a small amount of the powder between the toes twice each day.

MOUTH CARE PRODUCTS

The majority of most homemade toothpaste consists of a base of glycerine or honey that is mixed with water to form the base. The mixture is heated to the boiling point and then the other ingredients are added and blended thoroughly before the flavorings are added. Flavorings are easily destroyed and therefore are always added last. Your favorite flavoring can always be substituted for the flavoring in any formula. All homemade toothpaste needs to be tightly covered or the flavoring will be lost in a short period of time.

Homemade Toothpaste #1

The following ingredients will be needed:

2 Tbsp. bicarbonate of soda

1/4 Cup cold tap water

1 Tbsp. table salt

3 Tsp. glycerin
(vegetable source from pharmacy)

Place the bicarbonate of soda, salt, water and glycerin in a small bowl and mix until it is a thick paste. Add additional water if needed A few drops of peppermint oil can be added to improve the flavor. Store in a sealed container.

Homemade Toothpaste #2

The following ingredients will be needed:

1/4 Cup glycerin
(vegetable source from pharmacy)

1/2 Cup powdered pumice

2 Drops cinnamon oil

Place all the ingredients into a small wide-mouth container with a lid and mix well. To brush your teeth, just place the dry bristles of your toothbrush into the mixture and brush away.

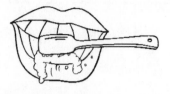

Homemade Toothpaste #3

The following ingredients will be needed:

1 Tsp. sodium bicarbonate	3 Drops peppermint oil
1 Tsp. glycerin (vegetable source)	

Place the bicarbonate and the glycerin in a small dish and mix well, then add the peppermint oil.

Homemade Toothpaste #4

The following ingredients will be needed:

5 Oz. glycerin	2/3 Oz. Castile soap (powdered)
2 Oz. cool tap water	2/3 Oz. borax
6 Oz. precipitated chalk	2 Tsp. starch
3 Oz. magnesium carbonate	1 Tsp. virgin olive oil
1 Oz. confectioners sugar (10X)	2 Drops peppermint oil

Place the water and glycerin in a medium saucepan and heat to the boiling point, then add all the other ingredients except the essential oil. Mix the solution well and remove from heat. Allow the mixture to cool before adding the peppermint oil. The mixture should be stirred for 45 minutes to be sure it is well blended. Store in a well-sealed jar or bottle in a cool dry location.

Toothpaste #5

The following ingredients will be needed:

5 Oz. honey	2 Oz. magnesium carbonate
4 Oz. cool tap water	2 Tsp. virgin olive oil
4 Oz. precipitated chalk	1 Powdered tragacanth
3 1/2 Oz. milk of magnesia	Pinch of soluble saccharine or Equal

Place the honey and water in a medium saucepan and heat to boiling, then remove from the heat, add all the other ingredients and blend well. Continue stirring for 1 hour to be sure it is well blended. After the mixture cools completely, place the toothpaste into a sealed container.

Tooth Powder #1

The following ingredients will be needed:

- 4 Oz. precipitated chalk
- 3 1/2 Oz. magnesium carbonate
- 1 Oz. confectioners sugar (10X)
- 1/2 Oz. sodium bicarbonate
- 1/2 Oz. borax
- 1/2 Oz. powdered white toilet soap
- 2 Drops peppermint oil

Place all the ingredients into a medium-sized bowl and blend very thoroughly. Store the tooth powder in a well-sealed bottle and shake before each use.

Tooth Powder #2

The following ingredients will be needed:

- 5 Oz. precipitated chalk
- 3 Oz. magnesium carbonate
- 1 Oz. powdered white toilet soap
- 1 Oz. boric acid
- 2 Oz. salol
- 1/2 Tsp. thymol
- 2 Drops peppermint oil

Place all the ingredients into a medium-sized bowl and blend thoroughly. Store the powder in a well-sealed container and shake well before each use.

Tooth Powder #3

The following ingredients will be needed:

- 1 Parts menthol
- 8 Parts salol
- 10 Parts pumice
- 20 Parts Castile soap (finely grated)
- 20 Parts calcium carbonate
- 60 Parts magnesia carbonate
- 2 Parts essential mint oil

Place all the ingredients in a bowl and mix well. All ingredients should be finely powdered. The pumice is added to remove tartar.

Tooth Powder for Children

The following ingredients will be needed:

10 Parts magnesia carbonate

10 Parts Castile soap (finely grated)

80 Parts sepia powder

3 Drops essential peppermint oil

Place all the ingredients into a bowl and mix into a fine powder.

Super Mouthwash

The following ingredients will be needed:

3 Cups cold tap water

3 Tsp. fresh parsley

2 Tsp. whole cloves

2 Tsp. peppermint extract

Place the 2 cups of water in a small saucepan and bring to a boil, then remove from the heat. Add the dry ingredients and allow them to steep for 15 minutes. Add the peppermint extract, mix thoroughly and store in a sealed bottle. Any flavoring can be used in place of the peppermint.

Lemon Mouthwash

The following ingredients will be needed:

10 Tsp. glycerin (vegetable source)

3 Tsp. lavender tincture

3 Tsp. calendula tincture

4 Drops lemon oil

4 Drops peppermint oil

Place all the ingredients into a small bottle and shake well to blend. To use, dilute 1 tsp. in 2 oz. water, shake the solution and use.

Old-Fashioned Mouthwash

The following ingredients will be needed:

1 Tsp. table salt 1 Qt. cool tap water

1 Tsp. baking soda (fresh)

Place all the ingredients into a bottle and mix well. Always shake well before using.

Foaming Wintergreen Mouthwash

The following ingredients will be needed:

7 Oz. ethyl alcohol 1/4 Tsp. saponin

2 1/2 Oz. rose water 5 Drops cinnamon oil

1/4 Oz. peppermint oil 3 Drops wintergreen oil

1/4 Oz. glycerin Pinch thymol

Place all the ingredients into a medium-sized bowl and blend thoroughly. To use, place 3 oz. in 8 oz. of cool tap water and use as any other mouthwash. This is a foaming action mouthwash. Store in a cool location in a sealed bottle.

PRE-SHAVE AND AFTERSHAVE

Pre-Shave for Electric Shavers

The following ingredients will be needed:

1 Tbsp. glycerin 4 Oz. cheap 80-proof vodka

1/2 Tsp. spirit of camphor 15 Drops essential lime oil

(from pharmacy)

Place the vodka and camphor in a small bowl and mix well, then add the glycerin and the essential oil and blend thoroughly.

Homemade Aftershave

The following ingredients will be needed:

2 Cups rubbing alcohol

1 Tbsp. glycerin

1 Dried lavender (health food store)

1 Tsp. dried rosemary
(from health food store)

1 Tsp. ground cloves

Place all the ingredients into a medium-sized bowl and blend well, then place the mixture into a sealed jar in the refrigerator for 4 days. Shake the mixture twice each day, then strain through a piece of cheesecloth and retain the liquid in a sealed jar. Should keep under refrigeration and keep its potency for 2 months.

Wake Up Fast Aftershave

The following ingredients will be needed:

2 Tsp. witch hazel

2 Tsp. 100-proof cheap vodka

1 Tbsp. cool tap water

1/2 Cup aloe vera gel

5 Drops essential bay oil (optional)

Place all the ingredients into a small bowl and mix well. Do not drink the aftershave. This aftershave can be used on legs as well as the face.

TANNING OIL AND SUNTAN LOTION

Tanning Formula

The following ingredients will be needed:

5 Lipton tea bags

1 Cup wheat germ oil

2/3 Cup cold tap water

1/4 Cup sesame oil

1/4 Cup apple cider vinegar

2 Tbsp. aloe vera gel

1 Tsp. iodine

1/2 Tsp. almond extract

Place the teabags in 2/3 cup of water and bring to a boil, then allow the tea to steep for 5 minutes. Squeeze the teabags into the water and throw the bags away. Place the oil and vinegar in a small bowl and mix well, then gently beat in the aloe vera gel. Add the extract and iodine, mix well and store in a well-sealed jar until needed.

Note: Not to be used by people who are fair-skinned, have sensitive skin or children. This is an excellent natural method of tanning without the risks related to exposure to ultraviolet rays from the sun.

Suntan Lotion #1

The following ingredients will be needed:

4 Oz. witch hazel	2 1/2 Oz. zinc oxide
4 1/2 Oz. pink calamine powder	1 Oz. glycerin
4 Oz. rose water	2 Tsp. boric acid

Place all the ingredients in a medium-sized bowl and blend well, then pour into well-sealed bottles. Shake well before each use.

Suntan Lotion #2

The following ingredients will be needed:

7 1/2 Oz. peanut oil	3 Tsp. laurel-berry oil
4 1/4 Oz. virgin olive oil	1 Tsp. chlorophyll
1 Tsp. bergamot oil	

Place the olive oil and the peanut oil in a medium-sized bowl and blend well, then add the other ingredients and blend well. Store in a bottle and shake well before each use.

Suntan Lotion #3

The following ingredients will be needed:

2 Oz. salt-free mayonnaise	2 Tbsp. lemon juice
2 Oz. black tea	5 400 IU vitamin E ampoules (liquid only)

Place the mayonnaise, lemon juice and tea in a blender, then blend on low for a few seconds. Place into a container and add the contents of the 5 ampoules and stir well. This formula needs to be refrigerated or it will turn rancid.

BODY SOAPS

Caution: Whenever you use lye, you need to wear protective gear, just to be safe. This includes plastic goggles, rubber gloves and a facemask. Never breathe the fumes and make your soap outside. Also, please read information in the glossary regarding lye.

Get Out the Old Soap Kettle

The main ingredients in most soap formulas utilize three ingredients: lye, water and fat. The lye is used as an emulsifying agent that keeps the ingredients in suspension and has the ability to remove the dirt from the clothing or hands. The fat retains the lye in a state that produces lather and holds the dirt in a state, which then allows the water to wash the dirt away. The water also has the ability to dissolve the lye eliminating any residue. Beef tallow is preferred over pork lard since it will produce a longer-lasting harder soap.

Jojoba Clay Soap

The following ingredients will be needed:

1 1/2 Tbsp. clay	2/3 Cup pure distilled water
1 1/4 Lb. glycerin soap (vegetable base)	3 Drops essential rose oil
2 Tbsp. jojoba oil	Soap molds

Place the soap into a double boiler and slowly melt, then remove about 1/2 pound and place it in a small dish. Add the clay to the 1/2 pound of soft soap and mix well before adding this mixture back into the soap in the double boiler and mixing well for a few seconds. Remove the mixture and allow it to cool somewhat, then pour into your molds to set.

Grandma's Old-Fashioned Soap

The following ingredients will be needed:

2 Qt. distilled water   3 1/2 Lb. grease

1 Can lye   1/3 Cup borax

Place the grease in a small bucket and add the lye while continually stirring. Use precautions mentioned above when working with lye. Mix in the borax, then add the water slowly, while continually stirring the soap solution. Place into molds or cardboard tubes to set. This recipe will produce about 8 1/2 pounds of soap.

Basic Hand Soap

The following ingredients will be needed:

5 Parts oleic acid   1 Part of sal soda

2 Parts caustic soda solution (400 Baume)   4 Parts cool tap water

Place the oleic acid and the caustic soda in a pot with the water and place on low heat just enough to prepare a clear paste. Then boil the mixture and remove it from the heat. After it has been removed, add the sal soda and continue to stir until the soap becomes lukewarm. Pour into molds and allow the soap to cool.

Clear Hand Soap

The following ingredients will be needed:

7 Parts of cochin coconut oil   5 1/2 Parts granulated sugar

4 Parts compressed tallow   6 Parts cool tap water

3 Parts castor oil   4 Parts ethyl alcohol

8 Parts caustic soda lye (380 Baume)

Place the coconut oil, tallow and castor oil in a double boiler and heat to a temperature of 111 °F., then stir in the lye and cover the pot for 1 hour. Dissolve the sugar in the water in another container; then add the sugar water and the alcohol to the mixture. Mix thoroughly until the mixture is very well blended. Pour into molds to cool.

Combination Body and Shampoo Bar

The following ingredients will be needed:

12 Oz. coconut oil	1 Oz. rose essential oil
5.6 Oz. lye	1/2 Oz. lavender essential oil
6 Oz. palm oil	15 Oz. lukewarm tap water
10 Oz. castor oil	2 Set of plastic goggles, face
3 Oz. jojoba oil	mask and rubber gloves
1 Oz. aloe vera oil	1 Cooking thermometer
8 Oz. virgin olive oil	Soap molds as desired

Place the water into a large pot and slowly pour in the lye. A chemical reaction will take place and the solution will become very hot. Place the pot in a cold water bath and using your thermometer, reduce the temperature to 100°F., which should only take 2-3 minutes. The solution will look cloudy.

In another pot, place the solid oils to be melted and place the pot on the stove on medium heat, then add the other oils as soon as they have melted. Cool the oils to 100°F in a cold water bath. The lye solution will take longer to cool so it will be necessary to gauge the two batches and be sure that they are both the same temperatures before mixing them together.

The lye solution can be placed into a warm water bath to set the temperature again if it has become too cool. Very slowly add the lye mixture into the oil mixture while stirring continually. Keep stirring until the mixture starts to thicken (about 15 minutes), rest for a few minutes, then stir for another 8-10 minutes until it thickens more.

This stirring and waiting while the soap thickens can take 1-2 hours. When the soap is thick, but still workable, add the essential oils and mix them in well. Pour the soap into your molds and cover with a piece of cardboard to stop the soap from cooling too fast.

Wear your gloves when you remove the soap from the mold, then allow the soap to air dry (curing reduces the alkalinity), thus lowering the pH (making it more acidic) of the soap into a safe range.

Homemade Liquid Pump Hand Soap

The following ingredients will be needed:

    3 Cups Castile soap (grated)   2 Tbsp. baby oil

    10 Oz. very hot tap water   2 Drops essential rose oil

Place the water in a bowl and mix in the soap, stirring well. Add the oil slowly while continually mixing since the soap has the tendency to separate out of suspension. Add the essential oil and store in a well-sealed container until needed. Shake well before each time you fill a bottle.

Making Soap Powder for Hard Water #1

The following ingredients will be needed:

    4 Parts powdered soap   2 Parts silicate soda

    3 Parts sal soda

Place all the ingredients into a container and mix well. Be sure that all the ingredients are very dry before mixing.

Making Soap Powder for Hard Water #2

The following ingredients will be needed:

    10 Parts powdered soap   1 Part sodium carbonate (soda ash)

    1 Part borax   1/2 Part powdered pumice stone

Place all the ingredients into a container and mix well. If all the ingredients are not finely powdered, they will have to be placed in a mortar and pestle and powdered before blending together.

GENERAL SKIN CARE

Dead Skin Remover

Mix the following ingredients together in a medium-sized saucepan that contains 1 cup of warm tap water:

> 4 Tbsp. raw barley (fresh)
>
> 2 Tbsp. pure oats

Heat the mixture at slow simmer for 8 minutes then allow it to cool to lukewarm. Thoroughly mix in the contents of 3 ampoules of liquid lecithin and add 1 cup of hot tap water to the mixture. Place the mixture into a blender and blend for a few seconds. Strain the mixture through a piece of gauze to remove all particles of the barley and oats that did not blend into suspension. Place the mixture into a bathtub with very warm (not hot) water and bathe for 10-15 minutes.

Natural Oily Skin Cleanser

The following ingredients will be needed:

> 6 Oz. plain oatmeal
>
> 1 Oz. lavender buds
>
> 6 Oz. cornmeal
>
> 1 1/2 Oz. rose petals

> 1 Oz. Irish moss powder
>
> 1/2 Oz. kelp granules (very fine)
>
> 1/2 Oz. comfrey root powder

Place the oatmeal and rose petals in the blender and make a powder. Place the balance of the ingredients into a medium-sized bowl, add the oatmeal and petals and mix well. Rinse your face with warm water, then place a small amount of the mixture in your hands with a small amount of water, just enough to make a paste and rub your skin gently. Rinse with warm water, then splash your face with cold water to close the pores.

Caution: Pregnant women should leave out the comfrey root powder.

Skin Massage and Stimulator

The following ingredients will be needed:

> 1 Cup table salt
>
> 1 Cup light corn oil

> 1 Cup liquid hand soap

Place the ingredients into a medium-sized bowl and mix well. Massage into the skin lightly before your shower.

Cleanser for Dry Skin

The following ingredients will be needed:

    6 Oz. plain oatmeal   1/2 Oz. Elder flowers

    6 Oz. cornmeal   1 Oz. Irish moss powder

    1 Oz. chamomile flowers   1 Oz. slippery elm powder

Place the oatmeal, elder and chamomile flowers in a blender and powder. Place the balance of the ingredients in a paper bag and mix well, then add the blended powder and mix thoroughly. Rinse your face with warm water, then prepare a small amount of paste using the powdered herbs and apply to your face in a circular motion (only light touches). Rinse the paste off with warm water, then use a cold water splash to close the pores.

Facial Rinse

The following ingredients will be needed:

    4 Cup bottled water   2 Tbsp. dried chamomile

    1 Tbsp. dried rosemary   3 Cup dried rose petals (fresh is OK)

Place all ingredients is a small glass or enameled pot and boil over medium heat for 10 minutes. Remove from heat and allow the mixture to cool to room temperature before straining out the herbs. Store in sealed bottle in the refrigerator and dab on your face to remove all traces of soap.

What is an Astringent?

Very simply, an astringent is a substance that has the ability to tighten, draw together or cause contracting of tissue. It is also used to control bleeding by the use of a styptic.

Making an Astringent #1

The following ingredients will be needed:

    3/4 Cup ethanol (from pharmacy)   1/2 Orange (thinly sliced)

    1/2 Lemon (thinly sliced)

Place all the ingredients in a blender and blend until the fruit is totally pulverized. Remove the liquid by straining through a doubled piece of cheesecloth and store in a sealed jar. This is an excellent solution to tighten skin and remove oil.

Making an Astringent #2

The following ingredients will be needed:

> 1/2 Paper-thin sliced orange   3/4 Cup alcohol (ethanol)
> 1/2 Paper-thin sliced lemon

Place all the ingredients into a blender and blend until well pulverized. The liquid is then strained through a piece of cheesecloth and stored in a well-sealed jar. Store in the refrigerator and the solution should last about 6 months.

Making an Astringent #3

The following ingredients will be needed:

> 3 Tsp. pure lemon extract   1/2 Cup rubbing alcohol
> 2 Tsp. lime juice

Place all the ingredients into a capped jar and shake well. Store in the refrigerator.

Skin Oil to Prevent Parasites

The following ingredients will be needed:

> 1/3 Cup almond oil   10 Drops essential wild thyme oil
> 8 Drops essential lavender oil   10 Drops essential rosemary oil
> 10 Drops essential palmarosa oil   10 Drops essential lemon oil

Place the almond oil into a small bowl and slowly add each essential oil while continually stirring. Store the oil in a well-sealed glass bottle in a dry, dark location. The oil should remain good for about 10 months.

Basic Skin Scrub

The following ingredients will be needed:

> 1 Cup instant oatmeal   1 Cup mild liquid hand soap
> (for face, use extra fine cornmeal)   3 Drops essential rose oil
> 1 Cup virgin olive oil

Place all the ingredients in a medium-sized bowl and mix well. Apply the mixture to your skin just before you start the shower and rub in gently, then shower or bathe as usual.

No-Soap Facial Cleanser

The following ingredients will be needed:

    1 1/2 Cup instant oatmeal   1/2 Cup raw sugar (turbinado OK)

    1 1/2 Cup powdered whole milk

Place all the ingredients into a small covered container and mix well. When ready to use, just place about 2 tbsp. in your hand and add a small amount of water to prepare a paste. Dab on your face and allow it to remain for about 8-10 minutes before washing it off with warm water and then a cold rinse.

Oatmeal Scrub

The following ingredients will be needed:

    2 Tbsp. instant oatmeal   2 Tbsp. powdered milk (whole)

    2 Tbsp. pure powdered honey   2 Vitamin E ampoules (liquid only)

Place the oatmeal and the vitamin E into a blender and blend for a few seconds until well blended. Add the milk powder and powdered honey and blend for another few seconds to allow all the ingredients to mix well. Place 2 tbsp. of the mixture into a small bowl and add just enough water to prepare a paste. A few drops of your favorite essential oil may be added.

Floral Water

The following ingredients will be needed:

    1 Cup pure distilled water   4 Drops essential rose oil

    1/8 Cup cheap vodka

Place all ingredients into a well-sealed bottle and mix well, then allow it to stand for 1 week in a cool, dark location before disturbing.

LOTIONS

Back to Basics

Most lotions are prepared utilizing a larger amount of water than oil and are used to remove excess oil from the skin on all areas of the body. Grandpa used to make the lotion from glycerin and rose water (from rose petals). Lotions do not have a long shelf life and should be used up in a short period of time or they may grow bacteria. Most of the over-the-counter brands, however, do contain some preservatives, which give them a longer reasonable shelf life.

Creamy Baby Lotion

The following ingredients will be needed:

1 Cup pure distilled water	20 Drops essential lavender oil
2 Tbsp. beeswax (grated)	5 Drops essential rose oil
3/4 Cup virgin olive oil	

Place the water in the top of a double boiler and add the wax. Heat until all the wax has melted then transfer the mixture to a blender. Blend on low and add the oil very slowly while continually blending. As soon as all the oil has been blended, add the essential oils and mix for a few seconds only. Allow the mixture to cool in a heat-safe dish until it is creamy. Store in a well-sealed container and use just like any other lotion.

Honey and Almond Hand Cream

The following ingredients will be needed:

1 1/2 Oz. sweet almonds	2 Tbsp. ethyl alcohol
5 1/2 Oz. almond oil	1/2 Tsp. oil of bergamot
2 Tbsp. honey	1/2 Tsp. essential clove oil
2 Tbsp. virgin olive oil	1/2 Tsp. essential rose oil

Place the sweet almonds in boiling water to scald them for 6 minutes, then skin them and place them into a medium bowl. Add the almond oil, olive oil and the honey and mix. Pound the almonds with a mallet until they are very soft. Place all the ingredients into a saucepan and heat until a lotion consistency is obtained. Remove from heat and allow the mixture to cool, then strain the mixture through a piece of cheesecloth or muslin. Place the mixture in a bowl and add the oil of bergamot and the essential oils; blend and pour into a sealed glass bottle. Shake before each use.

Luxurious Lotion Bar

The following ingredients will be needed:

6 Oz. beeswax

2 Oz. almond oil

2 Oz. Virgin olive oil

3 Drops essential lavender oil

Place all ingredients except the essential oil into a double boiler and melt until the wax is melted and well mixed with the oils. Place the essential oil in and stir well, then pour into a mold to set. Best to refrigerate the bar, then allow the mixture to return to room temperature before using in place of body or hand lotion. Just rub it on for the best results.

Aloe Lotion

The following ingredients will be needed:

1 1/4 Cup aloe vera

1 Tsp. lanolin

1/3 Cup virgin olive oil

3 Ampoules of vitamin C (liquid)

3/4 Cup beeswax

2 Drops essential rose oil

Place the aloe vera, vitamin E and lanolin in a small bowl and mix well. Place the beeswax in a double boiler and melt slowly, then add the aloe mix and remove from heat. Allow it to cool, but while it is still warm, place the mixture into a blender and blend on slow, while adding the oil in a slow stream. Blend for an additional 2-4 seconds after depleting the oil. When finished, you should have a smooth cream.

Moisturizing Lotion

The following ingredients will be needed:

2 Tsp. castor oil

1 Tsp. lanolin

2 400 IU ampoules of vitamin E (liquid)

1 1/2 Tsp. cocoa butter

4 Drops essential rose oil

3 Drops essential tea tree oil

Place the castor oil, cocoa butter and lanolin into a double boiler and melt together well. Remove from heat and whisk the liquid from the vitamin E ampoules into the mixture. Allow it to cool, then add the essential oils and mix. Store the lotion in a well-sealed glass bottle in a cool dry location.

Suntan Lotion

The following ingredients will be needed:

3 Tea bags (standard, not instant)	1/4 Cup sesame oil
1/4 Cup lanolin	3/4 Cup cool tap water

Place the water in a small saucepan and bring to a boil, then add the teabags and brew for 15 minutes pushing them against the wall of the pan with the back of a spoon to release the maximum amount of tea. Remove from heat and allow the tea to cool a little before placing 25% of the tea into a blender with the lanolin and oil. Blend on low for a few seconds then add the balance of the tea in a slow stream. If you would like to add 3-4 drops of your favorite essential oil, add it just before you finish blending. The cream will repel water and will screen out about 50% of the sun's harmful rays. People who burn easily should not use this cream!

Glycerin Hand Lotion

The following ingredients will be needed:

4 Tbsp. glycerin	2 Tbsp. ammonia water
2 Tbsp. bay rum	2 Tbsp. rose water

Place the glycerin and the bay rum in a medium-sized bowl and mix well, then add the ammonia and rose water. Blend well and store in a sealed glass container.

LIP GLOSS AND LIPSTICK

Keeping Your Lips Kissable

Lipstick was originally formulated to protect your lips. Today it still provides a degree of protection; however, lip glosses seem to do a better job. Lip glosses will protect the lips from the heat of the sun or any other type of excessive dry condition that reduces the moisture of the lips. Skiers are especially at risk since the lips are exposed to cold and wind.

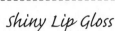

Shiny Lip Gloss

The following ingredients will be needed:

1 Tsp. pure honey

2 1/2 Tsp. beeswax (grated)

7 Tsp. jojoba oil

4 Drops essential rose oil

Place the beeswax and oil in a double boiler, remove from the heat and add the honey. Blend all the ingredients well and allow it to cool before adding the essential oil. Mix well and place into a small glass jar with a good lid. Store the lip gloss in a cool, dry location and it should last about 3-4 months.

Basic Lip Gloss

The following ingredients will be needed:

1/4 Cup sesame oil

2 Tsp. beeswax

1/2 Oz. Camphor

1/2 Oz. menthol

Place the beeswax in a double boiler and melt, then add the oil and menthol and mix well. Remove from the heat and beat until the mixture is cool. Transfer into a clean container and continue beating until it is cold and set up.

LIP SALVES

Lip Pomade

The following ingredients will be needed:

80 Parts paraffin

80 Parts Vaseline

1/2 Part anchusine

1 Part bergamot oil

1 Part lemon peel

Place all the ingredients in a container and blend well.

Natural Lipstick Formula #1

The following ingredients will be needed:

2 1/2 Oz. almond oil

1 Oz. white beeswax

1 Oz. spermaceti

Essential oil as desired for aroma

Natural Lipstick Formula #2

The following ingredients will be needed:

4 Oz. coconut butter

1 Tbsp. almond oil

1/2 Oz. spermaceti

Essential oil as desired for aroma

Place the first three ingredients in each lipstick formula in a double boiler and heat until they are thoroughly blended together with gentle stirring. Remove from the heat and allow it to cool almost completely before adding any essential oil. The reddish coloring for lipstick is dependent on the amount of powdered carmine that is added. This coloring agent should only be added at the same time as the essential oil. After the lipstick has cooled completely, it can be poured into molds or any container you wish. Other coloring pigments are available through a chemical supply house for different colors.

GLITTER GELS

Sparkler Gel

The following ingredients will be needed:

1 Tsp. glycerin

1/4 Cup aloe vera gel

1/4 Cup fine polyester glitter

4 Drops essential rose oil

1 Drop food coloring

Place the aloe vera and the glycerin in a small bowl and mix well, then add the glitter, color and essential oil and blend.

LEG WAX

Making Leg Wax

The following ingredients will be needed:

    2 Cup granulated sugar   1/4 Cup lemon juice

    1/4 Cup cold tap water   2 Drops essential lavender oil

Place the sugar, water and lemon in a small saucepan, mix and bring to a boil. Cook until the mixture is at the softball stage or about 250 °F. Remove from heat and allow it to cool, then pour into a jar and store in a cool, dry location.

NO-SOAP HAND WASH

Soapless Hand Freshener

The following ingredients will be needed:

    1 Tsp. rubbing alcohol   1 Cup aloe vera gel

    2 Tsp. glycerin (vegetable source)   7 Drops essential tea tree oil

Place all the ingredients into a small bowl and mix well, then store in a well-sealed glass jar. This is not recommended to remove heavy soil from hands, but as a freshener and germ killer.

MASSAGE OILS

Touch of Magic Oil

The following ingredients will be needed:

1/4 Cup sweet almond oil	2 Drops essential lavender oil
4 Drops essential jasmine oil	2 Drops essential bergamot oil

Place all ingredients in a small bowl and mix thoroughly. Store in a well-sealed jar in the refrigerator and allow it to return to room temperature before using.

BODY WRAPS

Olden Times Spa Wrap

The following ingredients will be needed:

1/2 Cup chamomile	5 Drops essential lavender oil
1/2 Cup dried rosemary	6 Cup very hot tap water
1/4 Cup peppermint leaves	

Place the water in a medium-sized pot and bring to a boil, then remove from heat. Place the herbs in a piece of cheesecloth and tie the cheesecloth to retain the herbs. Crush the herbs just slightly and place the cheesecloth into the water, push it down under the water and place a lid on the pot and allow it to stand for 20 minutes, creating an herbal infusion. Remove the cover and stir, then add strips of linen fabric, saturate them well, wring them out and place them around your lower arms and feet. Make sure the wrap is not too hot or it will burn you.

This process is normally done twice with plastic wrap placed on top of the wrap the second time. Do not allow wrap to remain on more than 15 minutes. Allow your body to cool for 20 minutes before taking a bath or shower. Do not use if you have any type of cardiovascular problem without consulting your physician.

DEODORANTS

Le Pew

Deodorants are formulated to do two different things: eliminate perspiration from forming and reduce or eliminate the odor that it causes. There are many herbal preparations that can be used to mask the unpleasant odor but do not have the ability to stop the wetness. Many of the commercially prepared products contain chemicals that may be harmful and the more natural products are recommended in all cases. Diet has a lot to do with body odors and the healthier the diet, the less body odor a person will have, even if they perspire.

Powder Deodorant #1

The following ingredients will be needed:

2 Oz. bicarbonate of soda

2 Oz. boric acid

1/2 Oz. zinc peroxide

2 Drops essential rose oil

Place all the ingredients into a small bowl and blend well. Store in a sealed jar or bottle and store in a cool dry location. Shake well before each use.

Powder Deodorant #2

The following ingredients will be needed:

5 Oz. boric acid

1 Oz. zinc oxide

1 Oz. talc

2 Drops essential rose oil

The directions for preparation are the same as for the powder deodorant #1.

Paste Deodorant

The following ingredients will be needed:

1 Oz. zinc oxide

1 Oz. prepared chalk

4 Oz. cold cream

2 Drops essential lavender oil

Place the zinc oxide and the chalk in a small bowl and mix well, then add the cold cream and essential oil. Blend well and store in a sealed glass jar.

AFTERSHAVE

Basic Aftershave

The following ingredients will be needed:

  1 Tbsp. witch hazel

  1 Tbsp. rosewater

Place the ingredients into a small container and blend well. Store in a well-sealed bottle.

Apple Cider Aftershave

The following ingredients will be needed:

  1 Tbsp. apple cider vinegar

  1 Tbsp. vegetable glycerin

Place the ingredients into a small container and blend well. Store in a well-sealed bottle.

Grandpa's Aftershave Lotion

The following ingredients will be needed:

  5 Oz. rose water   1 Oz. ethyl alcohol

  2 1/2 Oz. witch hazel   1 Oz. glycerin

  1/2 Oz. boric acid   1 Tsp. tincture of benzoin

Place all the ingredients into a medium-sized bowl and mix well. Pour into a glass-sealed container and use as needed. Shake well before each use. This will really wake you up and make you bright-eyed.

FRECKLES

Can I Count Your Freckles?

I'm sure anyone who has freckles has heard that one before. Freckles are the result of exposure to the sun's rays on the face, back of the hands and upper torso. They are small brownish pigmentation spots and are more noticeable in the spring and summer when you start getting out in the sun more and exposing your skin. Fair-skinned individuals are more likely to have freckles. Freckles can be faded somewhat, but are impossible to remove. Many preparations have been tried from lemon juice to all kinds of herbal remedies.

Old-Fashioned Freckle Remedy

The following ingredients will be needed:

1 Part poppy oil	5 Parts tincture of quillaia
2 Parts lead acetate	1 Part spirit nitrous ether
1 Parts tincture of benzoin	95 Parts rose water

Place the oil and the lead acetate into a double boiler and saponify (turn into soap), then add the rose water, mix well and add the rest of the ingredients and blend well.

COMPLEXION CLAY

Special Cream

The following ingredients will be needed:

4 Oz. modeling clay (powdered and sifted)	7 Grains of benzoate of soda (finely powdered)
1 Oz. calamine powder	2 Oz. witch hazel
1/2 Oz. oxide of zinc	1 Oz. glycerine
1/4 Oz. infusorial earth	

Place all the dry ingredients into a mortar and pestle and make sure they are finely powdered. Place the powder in a container and add the witch hazel and glycerine and prepare a paste. Water may be added to produce the consistency you desire. Store in a well-sealed container. The less contact the cream has with the air, the better.

MUSTACHE FIXER

Grandpa's Fixing Fluid for Mustaches

The following ingredients will be needed:

    1 Part balsam of tolu   1 Part jockey club

    3 Parts rectified spirits

Place the liquids in a container and dissolve the balsam into them. Apply just a few drops to your mustache with a brush, then twist into the desired shape. The mustache will keep its shape for a long period of time.

BABY PRODUCTS

Baby Wipes

The following ingredients will be needed:

    6 Large plastic container with high sides 7 Tbsp. baby oil

    1 Roll of Bounty paper towels   2 Tbsp. baby bath liquid

    2 Cups cold tap water

Slice the roll of paper towels in half and remove the center cardboard. Place the ingredients into a medium bowl and mix but do not mix too much or the solution will foam and you will have to start over. Place the paper towels in the container and pour the solution over the top. It will take about 1 hour for all the liquid to be absorbed into the paper towels. Place the baby wipes in a well-sealed plastic container and use as needed.

Anti-Fungal Baby Wipes

The following ingredients will be needed:

1/2 Cup distilled water	1 Tbsp. calendula oil
1/4 Cup white vinegar	1 Drop essential rose oil
1/4 Cup aloe vera gel	1 Drop essential tea tree oil

Place all the ingredients into a container and mix well. Store in a well-sealed glass jar in the refrigerator and use a piece of paper towel as needed for an anti-fungal wipe.

Bath and Baby Powder

The following ingredients will be needed:

1/4 Cup cornstarch	1 Tbsp. orrisroot (powdered)
2 Tbsp. powdered dried chamomile	1/2 Tsp. alum

Place all the ingredients in a small bowl and mix well, then sift the powder through a fine sieve and place in a powder-type shaker.

Mild Baby Massage Oil

The following ingredients will be needed:

4 Oz. virgin olive oil
4 Drops essential rose oil

Place the ingredients into a well-sealed bottle and shake to blend.

Baby Teething Gel

The following ingredients will be needed:

1 Oz. pure vegetable glycerin
2 Drops essential oil of cloves

Place the glycerin into a small glass container and add 1 or 2 drops of oil of cloves depending on the strength desired. Virgin olive oil may be substituted for the glycerin. Rub on the gums as needed to bring relief.

PERFUME, COLOGNE AND TOILET WATER

Smell Pretty and Save Money

Next time you visit the health food store, smell the essential oils and choose your favorite ones to mix with either pure ethyl alcohol or distilled water. It's as easy as that to prepare a cologne or toilet water that will smell just as good as the high-priced brands. Commercial brands are expensive because of the packaging not the ingredients. They are sold as eye-appealing containers that you will keep after you use up the fragrance.

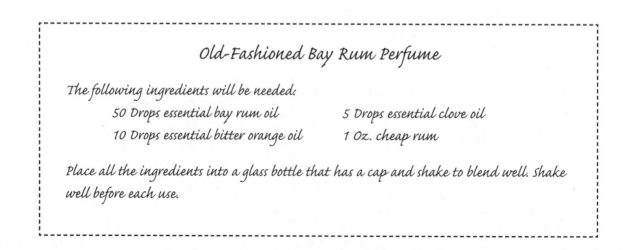

Old-Fashioned Bay Rum Perfume

The following ingredients will be needed:

- 50 Drops essential bay rum oil
- 10 Drops essential bitter orange oil
- 5 Drops essential clove oil
- 1 Oz. cheap rum

Place all the ingredients into a glass bottle that has a cap and shake to blend well. Shake well before each use.

Autumn Leaves Perfume

The following ingredients will be needed:

2 Drops essential lavender oil

2 Drops essential rose oil

2 Drops essential grapefruit oil

4 Drops essential germanium oil

2 Drops essential sandalwood oil

2 Drops nutmeg oil

2 Drops essential vanilla oil

3 Drops essential rosewood oil

1/8 Oz. jojoba oil

Place all the oils into a glass bottle with a good lid and shake to mix. Shake before each use.

Making Solid Perfume

The following ingredients will be needed:

1/2 Oz. beeswax

1 1/2 Oz. infused myrrh oil

1/2 Oz. infused clary sage oil

25 Drops essential clary sage oil

9 Drops essential patchouli oil

7 Drops essential rose oil

5 Drops essential chamomile oil

Place the beeswax into a double boiler and melt, then remove from the heat and allow the wax to cool to lukewarm. Place the wax into a glass jar that has been held under very warm running water for a few seconds, then NOTE: SOMETHING'S MISSING HERE all the oils and blend well and pour into small metal tins or molds to harden.

Lilac Toilet Water

The following ingredients will be needed:

    1 Tsp. of terpineol   6 Drops neroli oil

    4 Grains heliotropin   6 Oz. ethyl alcohol

    1/2 Tsp. bergamot oil   2 Oz. cool tap water

Place all the ingredients into a container and blend well, then strain through a piece of fine cheesecloth.

Lavender Cologne

The following ingredients will be needed:

    1 1/2 Tsp. essential oil of lavender   1/2 Tsp. tincture of benzoin

    1/2 Tsp. essential oil of bergamot   6 Oz. ethyl alcohol

Place all the ingredients into a container and blend well, then allow the cologne to stand for 30 days. Strain the mixture after it has stood through a funnel with gray filter paper before using.

Food and Household
FREEBIES

The following information is provided for the consumer to acquire a number of free food samples to try before they purchase them. Some of the "free" samples, however, do require you to pay for the shipping and handling charges, which are minimal. All offers were good as of the date of the printing in September 2003. The author takes no responsibility if any of the offers have expired and are no longer available.

CATALOGS RELATED TO FOOD

The following food catalogs are free. The companies prefer that you call them to receive their catalog. These are some of the finest companies in their product line.

Baked Goods

H & H Bagels
(800) 692-2435

New Bakery
(312) 925-0064

Suzanne's Muffins
(800) 742-2403

Baking Supplies

Northwest Specialty Bakers
(800) 666-1727

Brumwell Flour Mill
(319) 622-3455

Crabtree & Crabtree, LTD.
(800) 944-0153

Butters and Cheeses

House of Wisconsin Cheese
(800) 955-0238

Mousehouse Cheesehaus
(800) 526-6873

Rogue River Creamery
(503) 664-2233

Candy and More

Grand Finale
(800) 748-6271

My Sister's Carmels
(800) 735-2915

Chocoholics
(707) 677-3405

Cereals

The Natural Gourmet
(800) 542-2898

Michaelene's Granola
(810) 625-0156

Christine & Rob's
(503) 769-2993

Ethnic Foods

Col. Sanchez Foods
(310) 313-6769

Mrs. Maltz's Knishes
(800) 87-KNISH

El Galindo
(800) 447-8905

Fruits, Nuts and Vegetables

Giant Artichoke
(408) 633-2778

The Garlic Survival Co.
(800) 342-7542

Bland Farms
(800) 843-2542

Red Cooper Grapefruits
(800) 876-4733

Pinnacle Orchards
(800) 955-6569

Just Tomatoes
(800) 537-1985

Hazy Grove Nuts
(800) 574-NUTS

Mac Farms of Hawaii
(808) 737-0645

Callaway Gardens
(800) 280-7524

Jams and Preserves

Sarabeth's Kitchen
(800) 552-5267

Green Briar Jam Kitchen
(508) 888-6870

Wood's Cider Mill
(802) 263-5547

Texas Traditions
(800) 547-7062

Oregon Wild Berries
(503) 728-3742

The Cherry Hut
(616) 882-4431

Honey and Syrups

Butternut Mountain Farm
(800) 828-2376

Everett & Kathryn Palmer
(802) 496-3696

C.S. Steen Syrup
(318) 893-1654

Pasta, Rice and Beans

Raviolismo
(800) 80-PASTA

Mrs. Britt's Oregon Kitchen
(800) 323-0566

Ray's Brand Chili
(217) 523-2777

Pastries and More

Moon Pies
(800) 251-3404

Mrs. Wick's Pies
(317) 584-8401

Chef's Shadow
(800) 833-6583

FOOD SAMPLES AND BOOKLETS

Pumpkin Seeds

Send $3.00 and you will receive a packet of pumpkin seeds. However, there are many varieties and you may want to go their website and choose one.

Free Seeds: Big Pumpkin.com

P.O. Box 325

Broad Brook, CT 06016-0325

www.bigpumpkin.com/seeds.asp

Importing Foods and Agricultural Products

If you have ever wondered about how to import foods and agricultural products, there is a great booklet that can be sent for called "AgExport Action Kit" that will put you in touch with foreign importers.

Free Booklet: AgExport Connections Staff, U.S. Department of Agriculture

14th and Independence Ave., SW, Room 4939 South Bldg.

Washington, DC 20250

(202) 720-7103

www.fas.usda.gov/exporter.html

How About Some Mulled Cider?

If you have ever wanted to try mulled cider, you can get a free sample by sending a stamped (1 stamp), self addressed, business size envelope to J. Crow Co. for 1 sample pack. If you want a larger free sample, send $2.00 and an envelope with 2 stamps.

Free Sample: J. Crow Co.

P.O. Box 172

New Ipswich, NH 03071

www.jcrows.com/Free.html

Turkey Stuffin' Sack

This is by far the best turkey stuffing sack I have ever seen. It is a no-waste method of stuffing a turkey with out having to dig out the remains of the stuffing from between the ribs. For a free Mrs. Cubbison's Stuffin' Sack, just send a SASE with 44 cents postage.

Free Sack: Stuffin' Sack Offer

P.O. Box 48051

Los Angeles, CA 90048

www.mrscubbisons.com/freeoffer/index.htm

Seasoning Sample

If you would like to try an excellent seasoning, just send a SASE and you will receive a sample packet of the seasoning.

Free Sample: Everglades Foods, Inc.

P.O. Box 595

LaBelle, FL 33975

Food Information to Lower Cholesterol and BP

Articles and booklets are available free to help you lower your cholesterol and blood pressure by changing eating patterns and foods. Also, information regarding exercise.

Free Articles: Information Center, National Heart, Lung and Blood Institute

P.O. Box 30105

Bethesda, MD 20824

(301) 251-1222

www.nhlbi.nih.gov/nhlbi/nhlbi.htm

Food Labeling Information

This information will include labeling standards, pesticide residues, fad diets, food preparation, diet books, fast foods and general nutrition.

Free Booklets: Information Office of Consumer Affairs, FDA

5600 Fishers Lane

Rockville, MD 20857

(800) 532-4440

www.fda.gov

Tea Sample

If you would like to try a new tea called Scripture Tea, just send a SASE and a sample of the tea will be sent.

Free Sample: Free Sample Offer

Scripture Tea

P.O. Box 195524

Winter Springs, FL 32719

Toll-Free Phone Numbers for Free Food Samples

Chinese Herbals.	(800) 1704 X2020
EdenSoy Products.	(888) 424-EDEN
Saco Buttermilk Blend	(800) 373-7226
Soy Sauce	(800) FREE-SOY
Herbal Tea	(800) 373-3832
Valerian Herb	(800) 992-1672

Hot, Hot Sauce

To receive a sample of a hot Texas habanero sauce, just send a SASE and you will get a real kick out of this one.

Free Sample: Toby's of Texas Sample
3113 Timber Lane
Dickinson, TX 77539

A Real Southern Seasoning

This seasoning will make you feel like you are in the deep south. For a free sample, just send a SASE.

Free Sample: Cahaba Products, Inc.
P.O. Box 691
Selma, Alabama   36702-0691
www.southernflavor.com/sample.htm

Chef Paul is Giving it Away

If you would like samples of three Magic Seasoning Blends and a copy of Chef Paul's catalog, just send one dollar or a SASE with 3 first class stamps.

Free Samples: Magic Seasonings Blends
P.O. Box 23342
New Orleans, LA 70183-0342
www.chefpaul.com/exclu.html

Fowl Facts

Send for information regarding meat and poultry facts, safe handling and ground meats. Provides cooking times and safe cooking information.

Free Booklets: Food Safety and Inspection Service/USDA
Washington, DC 20250
(800) 535-4555
www.usda.gov/fsis

World's Greatest Cocktail Onions

To receive a 2-ounce jar of McSweet Pickled Cocktail Onions, just send the shipping charge. These onions have no onion smell and will never give you onion breath.

Free Sample: JMC Sales

McSweet Cocktail Onions

P.O. Box 607

Maple Valley, WA 98038

(877) Mcsweet

www.mcsweet.com

Great Beef Seasoning

If you would like to receive a $1^1/_2$-ounce packet of great beef seasoning, just send a SASE with 2 37¢ stamps.

Free Sample: Spade L Ranch Seasonings

P.O. Box 128

Selma, CA 93662

www.spadelranch.com/freesamples.htm

Need Information on Food-born Illnesses?

If you would like the latest up-to-date information regarding food-born illness problems in the United States, the USDA and the FDA have the answers.

Free Booklets: USDA/FDA Foodborne Illness Education Information Center

National Agricultural Library/USDA

Beltsville, MD 20805

www.nal.usda.gov/fnic/foodborne/foodborn.htm

Are Eating Disorders a Problem?

In the United States 3% of all young women have either a problem with anorexia or bulimia. There is an excellent publication that can be obtained.

Free Booklet: National Institute of Mental Health, Room 7C-02

5600 Fishers Lane

Rockville, MD 20857

(301) 443-4513

www.nimh.nih.gov

Candy, Candy, Candy

If you would like some free candy samples of candy made the old-fashioned way, just send $3.95 to cover shipping charges.

Free Sample: The Fawn Confectionaries

4271 Harrison Ave.

Cincinnati, OH 45211

(513) 574-9612

Hot Stuff Seasoned Salt

To receive a free sample of Cory's Hot Stuff Seasoned Salt, just send a business-size SASE. This is a seasoning you will fall in love with.

Free Sample: Cory's Hot Stuff Free Sample

413 W. 9th Ave.

Escondido, CA 92025

e-mail - Cory1356@yahoo.com

Guide to Cheese Pairing

This free offer will provide you with a free printed copy of the new poster "Cheese Guide." It has a complete guide to cheese pairings.

Free Poster: Cheese Guide/Customer Service

Organic Valley

507 West Main Street

La Farge, WI 54639

www.organicvalley.com/new/cheesechart.html

GARDENING

How Green it is!

Information regarding lawn care provides a list of do's and don'ts to help you have a healthy and attractive lawn.

Free Booklet: National Center for Environmental Publications & Information
P.O. Box 42419
Cincinnati, OH 45242
(800) 490-9198
www.epa.gov

Grow Your Own Herbs

Information available will cover such topics as poisonous plants, soil erosion, pesticides in foods, medicinal plants and edible wild plants.

Free Booklets: Science and Technology Division, Reference Section
Library of Congress
Washington, DC 20540
(202) 707-5580

INFORMATION FOR MOTHERS-TO-BE

Pregnant? Having to Eat for Two

The government has an excellent booklet called "All About Eating for Two" that will provide information regarding the type of foods and nutrients needed to maintain a healthy pregnancy.

Free Copy: FDA, Division of Consumer Affairs, HFE-88

               5600 Fishers Lane

               Rockville, MD 20857

               (800) 532-4440 or www.fda.gov

Alcohol and Pregnancy

There are a number of very good booklets regarding the use and abuse of alcohol, smoking and drugs during pregnancy. They are called: "How to Take Care of Your Baby Before Birth," "Healthy Women, Healthy Lifestyles" and "Pregnant? Drugs and Alcohol Can Hurt Your Unborn Baby."

Free Copies: National Clearinghouse for Alcohol and Drug Information

               P.O. Box 2345

               Rockville, MD 20847

               (800) 729-6686 or www.health.org

Are You Going to Breastfeed?

If you are unsure whether to breastfeed or bottle-feed, there is an excellent publication you should read. The booklet is called "Breastfeeding: Consumer Education Materials or Surgeon General's Workshop on Breastfeeding and Human Lactation."

Free Copies: National Maternal and Child Health Clearinghouse

2070 Chain Bridge Rd., Ste. 450

Vienna, VA 22182

www.circsol.com/mch

PET PRODUCTS

Commercial Foods for Exotic Pets

The Brisky Pet Products Company will send you a sample of their pet products that are specifically designed for exotic pets. They do not have dog or cat food, just for the exotics. The free offer only applies to U.S. residents only.

Free Samples: Call for samples

(800) 462-2464

WEIGHT CONTROL

Use it or Lose it!

Great facts regarding losing weight and keeping it off. Talks about phony diet plans, gadgets, harmful pills and poor programs.

Free Booklet: Center for Food Safety and Applied Nutrition

200 "C" Street

Washington, DC 20204

(800) 532-4440

www.vm.cfsan.fda.gov/list.html

Repairing
FOODS

QUICK REFERENCE

Anchovies

Too Salty

Soak them in cold tap water for 10-12 minutes. If you are not going to use them immediately, store them for 1 day in fresh extra virgin olive oil in the refrigerator.

Apples

Poor Flavor

Quarter the apples and dip them in powdered anise or sprinkle them with cinnamon.

Artichokes

Falling Apart

Cannot be fixed. Best to wrap the artichoke in cheesecloth before you cook it and then remove the cheesecloth just before serving.

Too Bland

Sprinkle a small amount of fennel in the cooking water, about $\frac{1}{3}$ tsp. should do the trick.

Asparagus Spears

Not Sweet Enough

Asparagus tends to lose sweetness, the older it gets. Add a small amount of sugar to the cooking water and if they are too old, add 1/4 tsp. salt to the water to help them retain their color.

Overcooked

Cannot be revived, best to cut up and use in soup.

Avocados

Not Ripe Enough

Place the avocado in a wool sock and place in a dark location for 24-30 hours.

Beets

Discoloring

If you see the color fading, just add 1 tbsp. lemon juice or white vinegar to the cooking water.

Too Bland

Usually only occurs when beets get too old. Just add a pinch of allspice to the cooking water. You can also add a small amount of sugar to the cooking water to sweeten them up.

Berries

Bland

Berries may get a little bland if they are too many days old. Just sprinkle them with brown sugar to perk them up.

Overripe

Not much you can do except to make an ice cream topping.

Bread

Dried Out

Try wrapping the bread in a very damp kitchen towel and refrigerate overnight, remove the towel and bake in a 350°F. oven for no more than 5 minutes.

Breading

Won't Stay Put

Make sure the food is dry before placing it in the breading mixture. Place the food in the refrigerator for 45 minutes before cooking.

Broccoli

Cooked Too Much

Broccoli will only store in the refrigerator for 3-4 days.

Too Bland

To perk up broccoli, just add a small amount of mustard seed to the cooking water.

Too Salty

Rinse the broccoli gently under hot water; then continue cooking for a short period of time.

Butter

Burned

Discard it; there is no way to save it. Next time add a little canola oil to raise the smoke point.

Cabbage

Overcooked

Cannot be revived, use in soup.

Purple Color

If this occurs when cooking red cabbage, just add 1 tbsp. white vinegar to the cooking water and in a minute or so it will turn red again. If it turns blue, this will work as well.

Cake

Burned Area

Allow the cake to cool before you scrape off the burned area, then replace the area indentation with thick icing.

Stuck to Pan

Reheat briefly or place a damp kitchen towel under the pan.

Candy

Sugaring

If chocolate candy starts to sugar during cooking, just add a small amount of whole milk and continue cooking until the candy returns to the proper temperature.

Carrots

Limp

Soak the carrots in ice water overnight in the refrigerator with 1 tbsp. concentrated lemon juice.

Cauliflower

Discolors

If you notice the cauliflower getting darker when you are cooking it, just add a very small amount of white vinegar to the boiling water.

Too Salty

Place the cauliflower in fresh boiling water for 1-2 minutes.

Cheese

Dried Out/Hard

Grate it and use it for a topping.

Moldy

Remove at least $^1/_2$ inch or more from the mold area before using.

Rubbery

Place the cheese into a food processor and chop into small bits, then place it in the top of a double boiler and cook slowly. This usually occurs when too high a heat is used or cheese is cooked too fast.

Coconut

Got Stale

Place the shredded coconut in a bowl and add $^1/_3$ tsp. sugar and enough whole milk to cover. Allow it to stand for 3-4 minutes; then drain well.

Cookies

Burned

Stop using brown cookie sheets; use shiny ones. Make sure that the cookie sheet is full and does not have just a few cookies on it.

Dough Crumbly

Allow the dough to remain at room temperature for 30 minutes and cover the dough with a lightly dampened kitchen towel.

Dough Sticks to Hands

Place your hands in a bowl of ice water (with ice cubes) for 20 seconds.

Dough Sticks to Rolling Pin

Store the rolling pin in the freezer.

Corn
Overcooked
Cream the corn.

Crackers
Soggy
Place the crackers on a shiny cookie sheet in a 350°F. oven for 3 minutes.

Cream
Getting Sour
Place a pinch of baking soda in the cream and it will sweeten for a day or two.

Cucumbers
Too Soft
Place the cucumbers in a large bowl of ice water in the refrigerator for 1-2 hours.

Custard
Slightly curdled
Place the custard in a jar and shake it up hard.

Dates
Stuck Together
Place the dates on a lined cookie sheet and place in a warm oven for 2-3 minutes.

Eggs
Undercooked
If you crack open an undercooked egg, just place it in aluminum foil and twirl the ends, then place it back in the water to finish cooking.

Eggplant
Discoloring
If eggplant starts to discolor while it is cooking, just add a small amount of salt to the water.
Hard to Skin
Slice the eggplant into quarters and then peel the skin off.

Fish

Too Salty

Soak raw fish in cold water for 10-12 minutes, then change the water and store it in water if you are going to cook it soon.

Garlic

If you have used too much garlic in your soup or stew, just simmer a sprig or small quantity of parsley in it for about 10 minutes. To remove the garlic odor from your hands, try rubbing your hands with salt on a slice of lemon. Read the label before you buy a garlic product. Garlic products should contain an anti-bacterial or acidifying agent, such as phosphoric acid or citric acid. If this is not on the label, the product must be sold and stored under refrigeration at all times. Garlic butter does not have a long shelf life and should be stored in the refrigerator for no more than 14 days. Most butter is not made with a preservative. Garlic, once processed, is more perishable than most other herbs.

Gelatin

Won't Set-Up

Place the gelatin in an ice-cold bath: a bowl with ice cubes set under the gelatin until it sets up.

Gravy

Burned

Place 1 tsp. non-chunky peanut butter to the gravy.

Lumpy

Place the gravy in a blender for a few seconds.

Not Brown Enough

Add 1 tsp. instant decaf coffee to the gravy and cook for a few minutes more.

Not Thick Enough

Use instant potato powder, arrowroot or cornstarch.

Greens

Badly Wilted

Submerge the greens in hot water, then immediately in ice water that contains $1/3$ tsp. white vinegar. Shake off the excess liquid and place into the refrigerator for about an hour before serving.

Ham

Too Salty

Place the ham in the oven and cook for $1/2$ the time, remove and pour a can of gingerale over the ham, then rub salt on the outside and finish cooking. The gingerale and salt will draw salt water out of the ham.

Ice Cream

Melted

Best not to re-freeze ice cream!

Mayonnaise

Separated

Place 1 tsp. prepared mustard in a warm bowl, then add 1 tsp. mayonnaise and beat until creamy. Continue adding 1 tsp. at a time of the mayonnaise and beating until it is all back in suspension.

Curd led

Place 1 large egg yolk in a cold bowl and VERY slowly add the mayonnaise while continually stirring. Add a small amount of boiling water to the mixture and continue to mix. Mayonnaise should not be made on humid days.

Too Thick

To retain the creaminess, thin it out with cream or evaporated milk.

Meringue

Condensation Droplets

This tends to occur when the meringue is cooled too fast. Try turning the oven off just before it is done and allow it to cool somewhat in the oven.

Milk

Soured

Place 2 tsp. baking soda in each qt. of milk and that will extend the life for 1-2 days.

Burned

To remove the burned taste from scorched milk, just place the milk pan in cold water and add $\frac{1}{8}$ tsp. salt to the milk.

Muffins

Moist Bottoms

Muffins were allowed to remain in the pan too long and moisture from condensation occurred. Muffins should be removed from the pan and cooled on a wire rack.

Stuck to Pan

Place the pan on a wet towel for 2-3 minutes to cool the pan and release the muffins.

Too Tough

Caused by beating the dough, instead of folding it. They can't be fixed, just slice them up and toast them.

Mushrooms

Shriveled

All you have to do is peel the outer covering off.

Too Light

Cook them in an iron pan and use real unsalted butter.

Too Dark

Add 4-5 drops of concentrated lemon juice to the butter and cook for a few minutes longer.

Onions

Difficult To Peel

Place the onion in boiling water for 8-10 minutes.

Punch

Too Bland

Give it a boost with $^1/_2$ cup powdered cardamom dissolved in $^1/_2$ cup of very warm fruit juice or use 1 tsp. rosemary dissolved in the same fruit juice before adding to the punch.

Pancakes

Sticking to Griddle

Add more shortening to the next batch.

Pasta

Sticks Together

Place the pasta back into boiling water for a few seconds. A small amount of olive oil in the water helps and remember so does a warm colander.

Popcorn

Will Not Pop

Soak the kernels in warm water for 4-5 minutes before trying again.

Potato Chips

Too Soggy

Place on cookie sheet in a 350°F. oven for 5 minutes.

Prunes

Too Hard

Place them into a pot and cover with boiling water; then place them in the refrigerator overnight.

Puddings

Curdling

As soon as curdling begins, stop the cooking and place the pan into a cold water bath. Beat the pudding with a whisk or eggbeater until smooth.

Skin Has Formed

Remove skin and place a piece of plastic wrap on top, if it's not too hot, to eliminate another skin forming.

Quiche

Crust is Soggy

Usually caused by using vegetables that have not been properly drained and dried off before being added. Many vegetables are naturally high in moisture and ruin the crust.

Raisins

Sinking to the Bottom

Because of their weight, they need to be coated with flour so that they will adhere to the dough or batter better.

Sticking Together

Place the mess of raisins on a cookie sheet in a 300°F. oven for 2 minutes.

Rice

Burned

If you accidentally burn rice, just remove the good rice and place it into a clean pot. Place a fresh piece of white bread or a thin layer of onionskins on top of the rice. Continue cooking for about 10-15 minutes before removing the bread or onionskins and discarding them.

Souffles

Browning Too Soon

Make a tent with aluminum foil and cover, but do not remove from oven (going to be tricky).

Soups

Cloudy Bouillon

Place a number of eggshells in and continue cooking. Strain through fine sieve or cheesecloth before you serve it.

Too Salty

There are a number of solutions: you can add tomatoes, some brown sugar, or a piece of raw potato to sop up the excess salt.

Squash

Very Stringy

Place the squash in a food processor or electric mixer for a few seconds.

Stew

Burned

Carefully remove the portion that was not burned and put it into another pot, using a wooden spoon. Adding onions will overcome any burnt flavor or odor that remains.

Tomatoes

Can't Get The Skin Off

The easiest method is to pour boiling water over the tomatoes and allow them to stand for 3-4 minutes.

Veal

Too Dark a Color

If you want the veal to be nice and white, just soak it overnight in whole milk in the refrigerator.

Whipped Cream

Beat It Too Long

Enjoy the homemade butter.

Difficult To Whip

Make sure all utensils and bowls are ice cold.

29

Shelf Life
OF COMMON FOODS

Baking Related

All-purpose flour.	unopened 12 months, opened 6-8 months
Whole Wheat flour	unopened 1-2 months, opened 6 months if refrigerated
Granulated sugar	unopened 2 years, opened 6 months
Brown sugar	unopened 4 months, opened 4 months if stored in freezer
Confectioners sugar	unopened 18 months
Solid shortening	unopened 8 months, opened 3 months
Cocoa	unopened 2 years, opened 1 year
Baking soda	unopened 18 months, opened 6 months
Baking powder	unopened 6 months, opened 3 months
Cornstarch	18 months opened or unopened

Spices

Whole spices	2-4 years, opened or unopened, away from heat
Ground spices	2-3 years, opened or unopened, away from heat
Paprika	2-3 years if refrigerated
Cayenne pepper	2-3 years if refrigerated chili powder

Canned Goods (High Acid)

Tomato products	1-2 years unopened
Fruit juices	1-2 years unopened

Canned Goods (Low Acid)

Soups	3-5 years unopened
Meats	2-4 years unopened
Gravy	3-5 years unopened
Vegetables	3-4 Years unopened

Miscellaneous

Pasta (no eggs)	unopened 2 years, opened 1 year
Dry egg noodles	unopened 2 years, opened 1-2 months
Salad dressing	unopened 1 year, opened 3 months if refrigerated
Honey	1 year opened or unopened
Ground coffee	2 years unopened, 2 weeks in refrigerated if opened
Coffee (instant)	1 year unopened, 3 months opened
Bottled water	2 years unopened, 3 monhs opened
Jams, jellies, preserves	1 year unopened, 6 months opened if refrigerated
Peanut butter	6-9 months unopened, 2-3 months opened

30

Formulas for Pest
CONTROL

Pest control services can run from $20.00 to $35.00 per month depending on the size of your home. You can save hundreds of dollars every year by using the following formulas and information.

GETTING RID OF ANTS

Giving the Queen Heartburn

Mix the following ingredients together in a small bowl:

    3 1/2 Oz. Strawberry jam   1 Tbsp. boric acid

    1 1/2 Tbsp. wet, canned cat food

This concoction is a treat for ants and the workers will bring the treat to their queen. The queen gets excited quickly gobbles up the goody and within a few hours, they will die of heartburn. This works well on carpenter ants and termites. Make sure this treat is out of reach of children and animals that you wish to have around for a while. It will make them very sick. It doesn't take very much to do the job.

The Ant Trapper

The following ingredients will be needed:

    6 Tbsp. granulated sugar   1/2 Cup standard grade molasses or honey

    6 Tbsp. active dry yeast (fresh)   10 Small plastic lids or bottle caps

Place all the ingredients in a small bowl and mix thoroughly until it is smooth. Place the mixture into the lids or caps and place near an ant trail or near their mound. The mixture can also be spread on a piece of cardboard or small stick and placed in their pathway or in a crevice.

Ant Dust

The following ingredients will be needed:

    1/4 Lb. dried peppermint   1/4 Lb. alfalfa meal

    (from health food store)   (organic, from health food store)

    1/4 Lb. rock dust (from nursery)   1/4 Lb. cayenne pepper

    1/4 Lb. seaweed powder

Place all ingredients in a well-sealed jar or plastic container and shake well to mix. Avoid getting any of the powder on your hands and then into your eyes. Use a small amount of the powder where the ants frequent. This will keep them away but not kill them. **Keep away from children and pets.**

Ant Spray for the Garden

The following ingredients will be needed:

2 Tbsp. flaked Ivory soap   5 Drops Jungle Rain

1 Tbsp. Tabasco sauce   1 Gal. spray bottle

5 Drops sesame seed oil

(from health food store)

Place all ingredients in the gallon bottle and shake to mix well. This can be sprayed directly on the ants or on their pathways. **Keep away from children and pets.**

Fire Ant Remedy

The following ingredients will be needed:

1 Qt. cold tap water   2 Oz. powdered Ivory soap

1/4 Oz. peppermint powder   1 Oz. Citra Solve (from health food store)

5 Tbsp. Jungle Rain (from a nursery)   1 Spray bottle

Place all ingredients in a plastic bottle with a lid and shake to mix. Spray the solution anywhere ants have been seen and in their nest, if you can find it.

Getting Rid of Ant Hills

The following ingredients will be needed:

1/4 Cup liquid hand soap

1 Gal. cool tap water

Place the ingredients into a bucket and mix well, then pour 1-2 cups on the anthill and repeat after 1 hour to be sure that the mixture penetrates well into the chambers.

GETTING RID OF MOSQUITOES

Kill Those Little Blood Suckers

In the United States alone there are over 150 species of mosquito and most can mature from an egg in one to two weeks. Mosquitoes need water to reproduce and they can usually find some standing water in pets' dishes, drainage ditches, fishponds, old tires, damp mulch, rain gutter lines, sewers, planters, leaks around spickets, etc. Mosquitoes like to live near your home and are smart enough to know that there are plenty of free meals there; you and your family. During the day they will seek shelter from the sun and are more active when it cools down or in a shady spot. They will never go too far from water. Getting rid of any location that has even the slightest amount of standing water should help to eliminate the problem.

For Arms and Legs

The following ingredients will be needed:
    4 Parts glycerin (from pharmacy)
    1 Part eucalyptus oil

Place the ingredients into a small bowl and mix thoroughly. Place in a well-sealed container. Rub a small amount on arms or legs to keep mosquitoes from biting.

Mosquito Repellant #1

The following ingredients will be needed:

3 Cups rubbing alcohol   1/2 Cup eucalyptus leaves

1 1/2 Cup red cedar wood shavings   1 Spray bottle

Place all the ingredients in a large bowl and mix well. Cover the bowl and allow it to stand for 6 days before straining the solution through a piece of cheesecloth. Place the liquid in a small spray bottle and spray on skin as needed.

Mosquito Repellant #2

The following ingredients will be needed:

1 Oz. oil of citronella (from health food store)

4 Drops of corn oil

Place the ingredients in a small bowl and mix well. Rub the mixture on your skin before going into mosquito-land.

Mosquito Repellant #3

The following ingredients will be needed:

1 Cup peanut oil   1/4 Cup sweet basil

1/2 Cup dried chamomile   1/2 Cup sweet orange oil

1/2 Cup dried nettle   1 Tsp. boric acid

1/2 Cup dried pennyroyal

Place all the ingredients in a double boiler and crush the herbs into the oil, then heat, stirring occasionally for about 45 minutes. Cover the mixture and remove from the heat and allow it to cool. Strain the mixture through a fine sieve, mashing the herbs to acquire the most fluid possible. Store in a well-sealed container in the refrigerator until needed. It will not take very much to do the job. Rub on exposed areas.

GETTING RID OF ROACHES

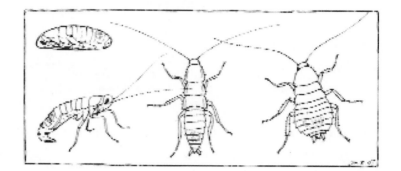

A Roach by any Other Name is still a Roach

Roaches do not mind living outside, but if you give them a chance, they will move in with their whole family. Roaches are known by a number of different names; such as water bugs, palmetto bugs and of course, cockroaches. They are bugs of the night and will go looking for any drop of water or food that may be within their grasp. They are not fussy at all. Outside, they will take up residence almost anywhere, such as a tree, woodpile, planter, under rocks, etc. In many instances, roaches will find a warm, damp location, which is where they prefer to breed. Cleanliness will reduce or eliminate most roach problems, but frequent professional spraying if a problem exists by an expert or placing out bait also works well. Roaches will not come back to an area where they are frequently poisoned.

The Roach Exterminator #1

The following ingredients will be needed:

1/2 Lb. borax	1/2 Oz. cocoa powder
30 Oz. powdered sugar	1 Oz. sodium chloride

Place all the ingredients into a medium plastic container and mix thoroughly. The bug poison should be sprinkled around wherever the problem exists. This is harmful to pets and children and should be used with caution.

The Roach Exterminator #2

The following ingredients will be needed:

1/2 Lb. borax	1/2 Oz. cocoa powder
2 Lb. powdered sugar (10X)	1 Oz. sodium fluoride (from pharmacy)

Place all the ingredients in a small bucket and mix thoroughly. Sprinkle in areas where the roaches frequent. Keep out of reach of children and pets.

Penny Pinchers

The Roach Exterminator #3

The following ingredients will be needed:

> 1/2 Cup all-purpose flour   8 Oz. boric acid
>
> 1/8 Cup granulated sugar (any will do)   Cool tap water
>
> 1/4 Cup lard

Place all the ingredients into a small bowl and blend thoroughly into small balls of dough. Place 1-3 dough balls into a small plastic bag and place where the roach problem exists. This is toxic and needs to be kept out of reach of children and animals.

Roach and Ant Repeller

The following ingredients will be needed:

> 1 Cup borax   1/4 Cup crushed bay leaves
>
> 1/4 Cup crushed fresh black pepper

Place the ingredients in jar with a well-sealed lid and shake well. Sprinkle a small amount of the mixture in the corners of the cupboards and drawers. You should never see another cockroach or ant ever again.

GETTING RID OF FLIES AND FLEAS

Fly Eliminator

The following ingredients will be needed:

1 1/2 Oz. of formalin	1 Gal. cold tap water
6 Oz. granulated sugar	1 Spray bottle

Place all the ingredients in a 1-gal. container and mix thoroughly. Fill a small spray bottle and spray the solution in the windowsills. Dead flies will start appearing very shortly. Keep out of reach of children.

Making Flypaper #1

The following ingredients will be needed:

1 Tbsp. brown sugar	1 Brown paper bag
1 Tbsp. granulated sugar	1 Cookie sheet
1/4 Cup inexpensive maple syrup	

Place all the ingredients in a small bowl and mix thoroughly. Cut 8-inch strips, about 2 inches wide from a brown paper bag and place them on the cookie sheet. Pour the mixture over the strips and allow the strips to soak overnight. Hang up the strips where needed.

Making Flypaper #2

The following ingredients will be needed:

9 Parts rosin	1 Part honey
3 Parts canola oil	

Place all the ingredients into a saucepan and melt together, stir well and apply to the paper while still warm. The paper should be prepared cutting strips of paper, folding them over and stapling them so that they will be strong. Size the paper with shellac or varnish to prevent the mixture from spreading too far.

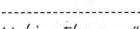

Making Flypaper #3

The following ingredients will be needed:

    1 Oz. Venice turpentine   1 Oz. castor oil

    4 Oz. rosin   1 Oz. granulated sugar

Place all the ingredients into a double boiler and mix well, then apply to the paper prepared in the same manner as in flypaper #2. A brush may be used and the solution should always be applied while still warm.

Flea Control

The following ingredients will be needed:

    1 Lb. diatomaceous earth (from nursery)   2 Oz. peppermint powder

    8 Oz. table salt

Place the ingredients into a container that you will be able to sprinkle it out of. The container should have a sealed cap for shaking and mixing it and another cap with holes for sprinkling it out. Shake the powder (try not to breathe in the mixture) on carpets where there may be a flea problem, then allow the powder to stand for 1 hour before thoroughly vacuuming it up. Keep kids and pets off the carpet until it has been well vacuumed.

Flea-Eliminator Floor Cleaner

The following ingredients will be needed:

    1 Tbsp. liquid dish soap   5 Drops of pennyroyal (from health food store)

    4 Lemons (sliced thin)   1 Gal. very warm water

Place the sliced lemons in a medium-sized saucepan, cover with cold tap water and allow them to simmer on low heat for 1 hour. Remove the juice from the lemons and strain well. Place the juice into a bucket and add the soap, pennyroyal and water. Mix the solution very well before applying with a damp sponge mop. Allow the floor to dry before rinsing with a clean damp sponge mop.

Flying Insect Potpourri

The following ingredients will be needed:

1/2 Cup of pennyroyal	1/2 Cup santolina
1 Cup of southernwood	1/4 Cup tansy
1 1/2 Cups of lavender flowers	8 Yellow tulips (dried well)
1 1/2 Cups rosemary	1/4 Cup of mugwort
1/2 Cup of spearmint	1/4 Cup of cedarwood chips
3 Tbsp. orris root	(fresh as possible)

Place all the ingredients into a container and blend well and place into a few potpourri baskets around the house. The aroma is pleasant except to flying insects.

RODENTS, GOPHERS AND MOLE CONTROL

A Tunneling Nuisance

Moles are great at tunneling with their powerful claws on their front feet. They normally prefer to live on insects, but when the insects are intermingled with the root system of a plant, they will eat both the insect and the plant's roots. Their favorite bug is the grub and if you can control the grub population, you will probably be able to control the mole population in your yard. Spraying your yard in early spring for fleas will eliminate the majority of the grub population and reduce the overall number of insects for moles to feed on. Many different types of methods have been tried to remove moles including; smoke bombs, high-pressure water, poisons, rat bait, hand grenades and dynamite. The following works better than all of these put together.

Mice, Gophers and Moles

The following ingredients will be needed:

    1 Tsp. oil of peppermint   1 Pt. cold tap water

    1 Tsp. chili powder   Cotton balls

    1/2 Oz. Tabasco sauce

Place all the ingredients into a medium-sized bowl and mix well. Place about 10 drops of the solution on a cotton ball and place the cotton ball anywhere a rodent problem exists or drop the cotton ball down a gopher or mole hole. Rodents are allergic to peppermint spicy peppers.

Watch 'em Run

The following ingredients will be needed:

    1 Oz. peppermint oil

    1/4 Oz. cayenne pepper

Place the ingredients in a small bowl and mix. Dip a cotton ball in the mixture and drop the cotton ball down the gopher or mole hole. You will never see those critters again.

Gopher and Mole Killer

The following ingredients will be needed:

    4 Oz. powdered seaweed   2 Oz. of any vegetable powder

    2 Oz. powdered vitamin D3

Place all the ingredients in a small plastic container and mix well. Rodents have difficulty regulating their calcium absorption and the vitamin will eventually kill them off. Just place a small amount of the mixture inside a small piece of any vegetable (potato, etc.) by cutting a small plug out and inserting the mixture, then replace the plug and drop the vegetable down the gopher or mole hole.

Plugging up the Mouse Hole

The following ingredients will be needed:

1 1/2 Cups asphalt	1 3/4 Cups powdered asbestos
1 1/3 Cups kerosene (flammable)	(do not inhale)

Place the asphalt and kerosene in a safe container and mix well, then add the powdered asbestos just until the mixture becomes a smooth paste. Seal up the hole with the mixture and the rodents will not use that hole ever again. If you prefer not to use asbestos or have it around the house, just mix up some cement and add a small amount of red pepper to it and that will work just as well.

Rodent Poison that is Harmless to Humans

The following ingredients will be needed:

2 Oz. barium carbonate	1/2 Lb. bread crumbs
1/2 Oz. granulated sugar	

Place all the ingredients into a bowl and mix well, then add a small amount of water to dampen and allow the mixture to be made into small balls that can be placed out for the rodents.

GETTING RID OF MOTHS

Making Moth-Paper

The following ingredients will be needed:

4 Parts naphthalene

8 Parts paraffin wax

Place the ingredients into a medium-sized saucepan on low heat and melt the wax. Mix the solution thoroughly and brush on a piece of thick paper while the solution is still warm. The chemical will attract and kill the moths. Place out of reach of children and pets.

Moth Repeller

The following ingredients will be needed:

All herbs may be purchased at a health food store

4 Tsp. orris root powder	1 Cup cedar chips
1 Cup wormwood	10 Bay leaves
1/2 Cup lavender	1 Tablespoon whole cloves
1 1/2 Cups yarrow	3 Clothespins or bag clip
1 Cup mint	1 Stainless steel fork
10 Drops of oil of cloves	

Place the orris root powder in a small bowl and add the oil of cloves, then mix well (crush any lumps) with the stainless steel fork. Place all the other herbs in a brown paper bag and shake to mix. Add the oil and orris root to the bag and shake well to mix. Seal the bag with the clothespins or a bag clip and place the bag in a dry, cool location for 2 weeks. After the herb mixture has mellowed place a portion in a number of old socks and hang them up in the closets. You will never see another moth, they will be fighting to get in next door.

GETTING RID OF SNAILS

Slugging it out with Snails

The preferred meal for a slug is a succulent plant, especially their favorite, pansies. They feed differently from any other insect in that they eat the leaf from the middle to the end, leaving you half a leaf. They feed at night and they are easy to track since they leave a trail of slime. Snails are hermaphrodites, which means that they contain both the male and female sex organs and do not need another snail to mate. Their breeding seasons are spring and fall. They love moisture and the dark, which is where they will nest. Plain beer seems to attract them and when they consume it, it has the ability to dry them out, killing them.

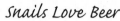

Snails Love Beer

The following ingredients will be needed:

1 1/4 Tbsp. brewers yeast	1 Cup warm tap water
1 Qt. of very cheap beer	2 Tbsp. granulated sugar
1 Qt. apple cider vinegar	1 1-gal. bottle
1 Tbsp. Jungle Rain	

Place the cheap beer and vinegar in the gallon bottle and shake. Add the brewers yeast and the water with the sugar dissolved in the beer and vinegar solution and mix. Add the Jungle Rain, mix well and pour into small lids or holders that can easily be placed where the snails frequent. This will attract every snail in the neighborhood and do them all in.

Slippery Gunk for Snails

The following ingredients will be needed:

10 Oz. Vaseline	1 Oz. cayenne pepper
8 Oz. castor oil	1 Oz. Tabasco sauce

Place the Vaseline and the castor oil in a medium-sized plastic container and mix. Add the pepper and Tabasco to give it a real boost. This mixture works great if placed on the trunk of a plant.

WORMS

Cabbage Worm Cure

The following ingredients will be needed:

- 1/2 Cup table salt
- 1 Cup all-purpose flour

Place the ingredients in a small dish and mix well. Sprinkle the powder on the plants early in the morning when the plants still have some dew on them.

Mealybug Killer Spray

The following ingredients will be needed:

    2 Tbsp. light corn oil   *1 Gal. cold tap water*

    2 Tbsp. liquid dish soap

Place all the ingredients in a medium-sized bucket and mix well. Place a small amount in a sprayer and spray the plants that have the mealybugs on them. Give the bugs a good squirt or two.

JAPANESE BEETLES

An Unwelcome Visitor

The Japanese beetle migrated to the United States around the turn of the century, probably in the root system of a plant. They are not fussy eaters and will consume almost any type of plant they come upon. Their favorites, however, are rose bushes, purple plum trees, cherry trees and myrtle. Most beetles will lay their eggs in the grass and one excellent method of reducing or eliminating the problem is to treat the grass with a killer in early spring before they hatch.

Beetle Eliminator

The following ingredients will be needed:

    2 Lbs. hydrated lime (use with caution)   *10 Gal. cool tap water*

    5 Oz. alum

Place the water in a large bucket; then add the other ingredients slowly while stirring well. Place the solution in a sprayer and spray the tops and bottoms of the leaves.

ANIMAL REPELLENTS

Deer Deterrent #1

The following ingredients will be needed:

    1 Tbsp. cayenne pepper   *1/2 Tsp. oil of peppermint*

    3 Tbsp. kelp   *1 Pt. warm water*

    3 Tbsp. liquid hand soap

Place all the ingredients into a medium-sized bowl and mix well. Be careful not to get the cayenne pepper in your eyes. Place the mixture into a spray bottle and spray the areas where the deer frequent. Do not use on plants that you will be consuming.

Deer Deterrent #2

The following ingredients will be needed:

1 Tbsp. dried blood (garden supply house)   *2 Gal. cool tap water*
4 Cloves of powdered garlic

Place the water into a bucket and add the dried blood, then mix well. Place a portion into a sprayer and spray the area that the deer frequent. Use sparingly since this formula is high in nitrogen and may burn plants. Works great to keep rabbits away as well.

TERMITES

Down with the Queen

Termites; are really not a bad insect. They are the best wood recycler around and will turn a dead log into food for many other insects. Unfortunately, they are not fussy where they find wood and your home is a handy source of food. The queen is the key to the termite "swarm." One method of killing the queen is to mix up a batch of queen delicacy food. This is a small amount of grape jelly, some canned cat food and a teaspoon of boric acid. The workers will not eat a treat of this magnitude, but bring it back to the queen as a treat.

Termite Protection

The following ingredients will be needed:

1 Cup paradichlorobenzene (moth crystals, very toxic)
8 Cups denatured alcohol (any type)

Place the ingredients into a container and mix well. This formula is for outside use only and should be mixed outside wearing a mask. Brush at least two coats on exposed wood surfaces. There will also be an odor, which cannot be helped. However, this treatment is very effective.

31

Children's
MAKE AND PLAY FORMULAS

This chapter will not only save you money, but will entertain the children for hours on end. All of the ingredients are safe and easy to obtain as well as being very inexpensive.

Caution:
Adults should supervise ALL formulas. Even though the following formulas are harmless, the formulas may result in discomfort if they get into eyes or are consumed. Most formulas are non-edible and need parental or teacher supervision. These formulas are used at your own risk and safety precautions should be taken.

GLUE FORMULAS FOR USE BY CHILDREN

Long-Lasting, All-Purpose Paste

The following ingredients will be needed:

1 Cup granulated sugar	1 Cup cold tap water
1 Cup all-purpose flour	1 Tbsp. powdered alum
4 Cups boiling water	(from pharmacy)

Place the all-purpose flour and the granulated sugar in a medium-sized pot and slowly add the cold water, making a paste solution. Then slowly add the boiling water and stir continually, making sure there are no lumps forming. Bring the mixture to a boil while stirring until the mixture is thick and clear. Remove the mixture from the heat, continue stirring and add the powdered alum. Blend well before using. If the mixture will be stored it would be best to also add 1/2 teaspoon of cinnamon oil to the glue. After storage, to re-harden, just thin with hot water.

Play Glue

The following ingredients will be needed:

2 Tbsp. Karo™ syrup	1/2 Cup cornstarch (fresh)
3/4 Cup cool tap water	1 Tsp. white vinegar (5%)
3/4 Cup ice water (from refrigerator)	

Place the Karo™ syrup, white vinegar and cool water in a saucepan and mix well, then heat on medium until the mixture begins to become somewhat solid (rolling ball state). In a medium-sized bowl, blend the cornstarch and ice water together, then slowly add this mixture to the syrup mixture while stirring well at all times. Remove from the heat and allow the glue to cool for at least 8-10 hours before you use it. Store the glue in a well-sealed container. If the glue becomes too hard, just heat for a short period of time.

Standard Paper Paste

The following ingredients will be needed:

2/3 Cup all-purpose flour

2 Cups tap water

4 Tbsp. granulated sugar

1/2 Tsp. cinnamon oil

Place the all-purpose flour and the granulated sugar in a medium-sized saucepan then gradually add the water, while continually stirring to avoid lumps. Continue cooking over low heat until the mixture is clear. Remove the mixture from the heat and slowly add the cinnamon oil while continuing to stir. Does not need to be refrigerated and will keep for 2-3 weeks.

Collage and Papier Mache Paste

The following ingredients will be needed:

1/2 Cup of granulated sugar

1/2 Cup of all-purpose flour

3 1/2 Cups of tap water

1 Tsp. powdered alum

1/2 Tsp. cinnamon oil

Place the flour, sugar and alum in a medium-sized saucepan and gradually add 1 3/4 cups of water while continually stirring to eliminate lumps. The mixture should be boiled until it is clear and lump-free. Add the balance of the water and the cinnamon oil and continue to stir until smooth and blended well. Will store for 3-4 months at room temperature.

Glue for Paper Labels

The following ingredients will be needed:

1 Oz. unflavored gelatin

1 Tbsp. cold tap water

3 Tbsp. boiling water

1/2 Tsp. white peppermint extract (or other flavor)

2 Drops boric acid in solution

Place a small pot on the stove and boil the 3 tbsp. water. In a small bowl, place in the cold water then sprinkle the gelatin on top. Pour the gelatin mixture into the boiling water and stir continually until completely dissolved. Add the flavoring and the boric acid solution and blend all the ingredients together. Apply the glue with a small brush to the back of any paper item or stamp, allow it to dry and just moisten when you wish to use it. The glue should be stored in a jar with a good sealing lid. If the glue becomes somewhat hard, just warm slightly until it has become soft.

PAINTS

Simple Finger Paints

The following ingredients will be needed:

    1 Cup quality liquid starch   Cold tap water

    2 Cups powdered tempura

Place the starch and tempura in a medium-sized bowl and mix thoroughly until the mixture is smooth and creamy. Add the water slowly while mixing until the solution is somewhat thick. Place the mixture into dishes and add additional color if desired.

Finger Paint From Salt and Flour

The following ingredients will be needed:

    2 Cups all-purpose flour   2 Cups very hot tap water

    2 Tsp. table salt   Food coloring

    3 Cups cold tap water

Place the salt and flour in a medium-size saucepan and gradually add the cold water. Use an eggbeater to blend the mixture until it is very smooth, then add the hot water and place on a medium flame until the mixture is boiling and is smooth. Remove the mixture from the heat and stir in the food coloring.

Painting on Cement

The following ingredients will be needed:

    1/2 Cup cold tap water   5-7 Drops food coloring

    1/2 Cup cornstarch (fresh)

Place the ingredients into a container and blend well. This paint can be used on any type of smooth solid surface and can easily be removed with cold tap water or a garden hose.

Finger Painting Goo

The following ingredients will be needed:

1/2 Cup all-purpose flour

2 Cups cold tap water

1 Tbsp. glycerin

5 Small jars

Food coloring

Place the flour and 1/2 cup of water in a medium-sized saucepan and mix until it becomes a paste. Add the balance of the water and heat slowly, while mixing continually until the mixture becomes thick and clear. Allow it to cool, then add the glycerin. If the mixture is too thick, add additional water as needed. Pour the mixture into the individual jars, then add a few drops of food coloring to each and stir. Poster paint may be used instead of food coloring if you so desire.

Finger Paints from Kool-Aid®

The following ingredients will be needed:

2 Cups all-purpose flour

2 Packages of unsweetened Kool-Aid® (any colors)

1/2 Cup table salt

3 Cups boiling water

3 Tbsp. corn oil (any vegetable oil)

Place the salt, flour and Kool-Aid® into a bowl, then add the oil and boiling water slowly while mixing well.

Finger Paints From Jell-O®

The following ingredients will be needed:

1 Package of Jell-O®

Boiling water

Prepare the Jell-O as per directions and make the consistency loose goo so that it can be used for finger painting.

Radiant Poster Paint

The following ingredients will be needed:

1 Tsp. household liquid starch	5 Tbsp. tempura paint (powder)
2 Cups cool tap water	4 Tbsp. cool tap water
1/2 Cup all-purpose flour	

Place the 2 cups of water and the flour into a saucepan and heat on low while stirring until the solution has been blended smooth. Continue to heat and as soon as the solution thickens, remove it from the heat and allow it to cool. After it has cooled, place the solution into a medium-sized bowl. In another bowl, place the tempura paint, 4 tbsp. water and the liquid starch and blend well, then add the mixture to the flour solution and blend well. Store the paint in a well-sealed container in a cool, dry location.

Vanilla Pudding Finger Paint

The following ingredients will be needed:

1 Package of vanilla pudding
Food coloring as desired

Prepare pudding as per package directions, then add food coloring as desired. Finger painting may be done on a plate and then consumed.

Detergent Paint

The following ingredients will be needed:

1 Cup powdered tempura paint	2 Tsp. liquid dishwashing detergent
4 Tbsp. quality liquid starch	Cold tap water

Place the powdered tempura, liquid starch and liquid dish detergent in a medium-sized bowl and mix well. Add water slowly and continue mixing until the mixture appears creamy and has a smooth texture.

Standard Fingerpaint

The following ingredients are needed:

1/2 Cup cornstarch (fresh)	2 Cups of very hot water
1 Cup cold tap water	1/2 Cup liquid detergent
1 Envelope of unflavored gelatin	Food coloring

Place 1/4 cup of cold water and the gelatin in a small bowl and mix well, then allow it to stand. Place the cornstarch and 3/4 cup of cold water in a small saucepan and cook on low heat until fully dissolved. Add the very hot water and cook on medium heat until, stirring continually until the mixture is clear and starts to boil. Remove the mixture from the heat and add the gelatin mixture and the liquid detergent. Continue stirring until all the lumps have been removed then allow it to cool completely. Place the finger paints in 4-5 small jars or containers and then add food coloring to each.

Water Color Paint

The following ingredients will be needed:

1 Tbsp. white vinegar	1/4 Tsp. glycerin
1 Tbsp. cornstarch (fresh)	mall metal or plastic pans or trays
2 Tbsp. baking soda (fresh)	Food coloring

In a medium-sized bowl, mix the white vinegar with the baking soda. The mixture should bubble. When the bubbling stops, add the cornstarch and the glycerin, mix well then pour the mixture into the small containers. Food coloring can be added to each and colors mixed to make different colors as desired.

Water Color Paint with Kool Aroma

The following ingredients will be needed:

1 1/2 Tbsp. unsweetened Kool-Aid®	5 Small baby food jars or
(5 different colors)	small plastic containers
1 1/2 Tbsp. warm tap water	

Place the water into the 5 jars or small plastic containers, then add the Kool-Aid® and mix well. Use the solution to paint pictures, then allow the pictures to dry at least 6-8 hours. When the Kool-Aid® painted areas are scratched, the aroma of that flavor will be released.

All-Purpose Flour Paint

The following ingredients will be needed:

2 Cups all-purpose flour   2 Tbsp. liquid dish washing soap

3/4 Cup cold tap water   Food coloring or powdered tempura
paint

Place the all-purpose flour, liquid dish soap and water in a medium-sized bowl and blend until the mixture is the consistency of thick paste. Add the food coloring or powdered tempura as desired.

Starch Paint

The following ingredients will be needed:

1 Cup dry laundry starch   1 Cup cold tap water

1 Cup mild hand soap powder   2 Tbsp. powdered tempura

Place the starch, soap powder and powdered tempura in a medium-sized bowl and add the water until the mixture has medium consistency. More water may be added if needed. If the consistency is too thick, it will not be useable.

High-Gloss Milk Paint

The following ingredients will be needed:

3/4 Cup canned, condensed milk

1 1/4 Tbsp. tempura paint (liquid)

Place the ingredients into a container and blend well. This produces a very shiny and reflective color when dry. Food coloring may also be used if desired; however, the paint will not be quite as glossy.

Soap Chip Fingerpaint

The following ingredients will be needed:

1 Cup liquid laundry starch   6 Cups warm tap water

1/2 Cup Castile™ soap (grated)   Food coloring

Place just enough warm water in a bowl to dissolve the soap, making sure there are no lumps. Add this mixture to the starch and remaining water and mix well, then store the mixture in a covered plastic container. Food coloring may be added as desired.

Anywhere on the Body Paint #1

The following ingredients will be needed:

    1/4 Cup non-irritating baby lotion   1-2 Tbsp. tempura paint

    2 Tbsp. liquid detergent

Place the lotion, detergent and the tempura paint in a small bowl and mix thoroughly. Additional tempura may be needed to achieve the level of color desired. The paint washes off very easily.

Anywhere on the Body Paint #2

The following ingredients will be needed:

    4 Tbsp. cornstarch (fresh)   2 Tbsp. warm tap water

    2 Tbsp. cold cream   4 Drops red food coloring

Place the cornstarch and cold cream into a small container and blend well, then add the water slowly while continually mixing until the solution is blended smooth. Add the food coloring and mix. If desired, place a smaller portion into different containers then add different food colors.

Indian Face Paint

The following ingredients will be needed:

    3 Tsp. solid shortening   4 Drops glycerin

    2 1/2 Tsp. cornstarch   5 Cold cream cotton swabs

    1 Tsp. all-purpose flour   Food coloring

Place the shortening, cornstarch and all-purpose flour into a medium-sized bowl and blend thoroughly until they are blended well into a paste. Add the glycerin, stirring continually until the solution is easy to spread and has no lumps. The food coloring can then be added slowly until the desired color is achieved. The cold cream swabs should be used to trace a design on the child's face before placing the paint on. The paint will be easy to remove with a mild soap and water solution.

Fun Face Paint

The following ingredients will be needed:

1 1/2 Tsp. cold cream	Glitter as desired
1 Tsp. cornstarch	Food coloring as desired
1/2 Tsp. warm tap water	

Place all the ingredients into a small container and blend well, then add enough water to prepare a thin paint that can be applied with a small paintbrush. Glitter may be applied while the paint is still damp.

Soap Paint

The following ingredients will be needed:

1 Cup laundry soap (flakes)	1/3 Cup laundry starch (liquid)
1/4 Cup cool tap water	

Place all the ingredients into a container and blend thoroughly for at least 3-4 minutes. Food coloring may be added if desired.

Puffer-Upper Paint

The following ingredients will be needed:

1 Cup all-purpose flour	1 Cup cool tap water
1 Cup table salt	Tempura paint as desired

Place all the ingredients into a bowl and mix well, then add enough tempura paint to color as desired. Place the mixture into a plastic squeeze bottle and squeeze a design, then paint and allow it to dry. The paint will puff up when it dries.

Paint from Powdered Milk

The following ingredients will be needed:

      1/2 Cup powdered non-fat milk   Tempura paint (powder)
      1/2 Cup cool tap water

Place the milk and the water into a container and mix until all the milk is dissolved, then only add as much tempura as will be needed. This paint does not keep well and should be stored in a well-sealed jar in the refrigerator. It will dry fast and produce a glossy, somewhat opaque finish. After you mix the powdered milk and water, it would be best to allow the mixture to stand in the refrigerator for 3-4 hours or it may be somewhat grainy.

DOUGHS, CLAYS AND PUTTY

Workable Putty

The following ingredients will be needed:

      2 Tbsp. white school glue   Food coloring
      1 Tbsp. liquid starch

Place the liquid starch in a small bowl, then add the white glue and allow this to stand for about 5 minutes before adding the food coloring. Blend all the ingredients thoroughly, making sure all the starch has been absorbed and the color is evenly dispersed. Allow the mixture to set overnight and you have made putty that will pick up pictures and even bounce.

Gelatin Putty

The following ingredients will be needed:

      0.3 Oz. package of unsweetened gelatin   4 Tbsp. cream of tartar
      2 Cups all-purpose flour   2 Cups boiling water
      1 Cup table salt   2 Tbsp. corn oil

Place the flour, gelatin, salt and cream of tartar in a saucepan and mix well, then add the boiling water and the corn oil and mix thoroughly. Place the pan over medium heat and stir until the mixture forms a ball, then allow to cool slightly and remove the ball placing it on a piece of waxed paper. Allow to fully cool before making objects. Store the remainder in a well-sealed container.

Children's Dough Recipe

The following ingredients will be needed:

    3 Cups cornstarch (fresh)   *2 1/2 Cups cold tap water*

    4 Cups baking soda (fresh)

Place the cornstarch and baking soda into a medium-sized saucepan and blend well. Add the cold water and place on medium heat for 5-7 minutes or until the mixture starts to thicken. Remove the pan from the heat, cover the pan with a piece of damp paper towel and allow the mixture to cool before using.

Oil Fundough #1

The following ingredients will be needed:

    4 Cups all-purpose flour   *3 Tbsp. corn oil*

    1 Cup table salt   *1 Cup cold water*

Place the flour and salt in a medium-sized bowl and mix well. Blend in the corn oil and water to make dough with a pliable consistency. More water may be added a small amount at a time if needed. The dough will store well in a sealed plastic container in the refrigerator.

Oil Fundough #2

The following ingredients will be needed:

    2 Cups all-purpose flour   *Tablespoons of corn oil*

    1 Cup table salt   *Package of Kool-Aid® powder*

    2 Cups cold tap water

Put all the ingredients into a medium-sized saucepan and place on low heat, stirring continually until the mixture forms a semi-solid mass. Remove from heat and allow it to cool. Store in a well-sealed container in the refrigerator.

Cornmeal Fundough

The following ingredients will be needed:

     1 1/2 Cups cornmeal (fresh)   *1 1/2 Cups all-purpose flour*

     1 Cup table salt   *1 Cup cold tap water*

Place all the ingredients in a medium-sized bowl and blend together into dough. Additional water may be added if the mixture is not pliable enough. The dough will keep for 4-6 weeks if stored in an airtight plastic container.

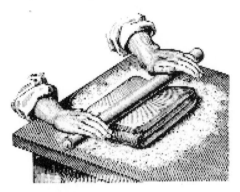

Real Simple Dough

The following ingredients will be needed:

     4 Cups all-purpose flour   *1 1/2 Cups warm tap water*

     1 Cup table salt

Place the all-purpose flour and the salt in a large bowl and add the warm water slowly while mixing the solution with your hands. Place a piece of waxed paper on the counter and lightly flour it, then knead the dough for about 10 minutes or until the dough is pliable and smooth. Wrap the dough in the waxed paper and place it in a well-sealed plastic container. Use as needed.

Frosting Fundough

The following ingredients will be needed:

     1 Can white frosting mix   *1 Cup smooth peanut butter*

     1 1/2 Cup powdered sugar (10X)

Place all the ingredients into a medium-sized bowl and blend well into dough that can be used for modeling.

Super Fun Dough

The following ingredients will be needed:

1/4 Cup corn oil	1 Cup table salt
3 Cups all-purpose flour	3 Tbsp. white vinegar
1 Cup cold tap water	

Place all the ingredients into a large bowl and blend well. More water may be added if needed to provide a workable consistency. Fun dough stores well in a plastic bag for 2-3 months. Best to dampen occasionally and work the water in to keep the dough workable.

Cooked Fun Dough

The following ingredients will be needed:

1 Cup all-purpose flour	1 Cup cold water
1 Cup granulated sugar	5 Cups boiling water

Place the sugar, flour and water into a medium-sized saucepan and mix. Add the boiling water slowly and cook for 6 minutes while stirring constantly. Allow the mixture to cool before using. This is very pliable dough, but will not keep well.

Experimental Gunk

The following ingredients will be needed:

1 1/2 Cups cornstarch	2 Drops red food coloring
2/3 Cup cool tap water	

Place the water and the food coloring in a container, then very slowly sprinkle in the cornstarch without mixing. Allow the solution to remain still for about 3 minutes before reaching in, grabbing a handful and forming it into a ball. The heat from your hands and the friction will cause the solution to become a solid until you release it from your hands and allow it to return to a liquid.

Used Coffee Grounds Dough

The following ingredients will be needed:

    2 Cups dry coffee grounds   1/2 Cup table salt

    1 1/2 Cups cornmeal (fresh)   Warm tap water

Place the coffee grounds, cornmeal and salt in a medium-sized bowl and add just enough warm water to moisten well. Work the mixture with your hands until it becomes workable dough. Store in a well-sealed plastic container.

Edible Fun Dough

The following ingredients will be needed:

    1 Cup peanut butter (not chunky or natural)   1 1/2 Cups powdered sugar (10X)

    1 Small can of ready-to-use frosting

Place all the ingredients into a medium-sized bowl and mix thoroughly. If the mixture becomes too thick and not workable dough, add a small amount of cold water to loosen it up. Store in the refrigerator in a plastic container. All items made will be edible. Molds may be used to make different shapes and figures.

Milk and Honey Fun Dough

The following ingredients will be needed:

    1 Cup pure honey   1 Cup smooth peanut butter

    2 Cups powdered low-fat milk   (not natural)

Place all the ingredients in a medium-sized bowl and mix thoroughly by hand until a workable dough is made. If needed, additional powdered milk can be added and a small amount of cold water if the consistency is too thick. Corn syrup can be used to replace the honey.

Oatmeal Fun Dough

The following ingredients will be needed:

    1 Cup all-purpose flour   1/4 Cup cold tap water

    2 Cups cooked instant oatmeal

Place all the ingredients in a medium-sized bowl and mix with the water until the dough can be easily molded. While this is edible, the taste leaves a lot to be desired and may not appeal to all children.

Granola Fun Dough

The following ingredients will be needed:

    1 Cup plain granola   1/4 Cup brown sugar

    1/4 Cup smooth peanut butter (not natural)

Place the peanut butter and brown sugar into a small bowl and mix with your hands. If you feel that the mixture is very sticky, add more brown sugar to reduce the stickiness. If the mixture becomes too dry, add a little more peanut butter. Add as much of the granola as desired, if desired.

Honey of a Fun Dough

The following ingredients will be needed:

    1 Tbsp. pure honey   1/2 Cup creamy peanut butter (no chunks)

    1 Cup non-fat skim milk   1 Qt. sized plastic zip-lock bag

Place the honey, dry milk and peanut butter into the plastic bag, seal the bag well and knead the ingredients until it becomes workable dough. After playing with the dough it would be best to discard it since the peanut butter will not store well when mixed with the dry milk.

Glue Fun Dough

The following ingredients will be needed:

    1 Cup cornstarch (fresh)   Cold tap water

    1 Cup all-purpose flour   Food coloring as desired

    1/2 Cup white liquid school glue

Place all the ingredients into a medium-sized bowl and mix thoroughly, adding the water as needed to produce workable dough. This dough can be worked and molded, then will dry into a hard solid.

Microwave Fun Dough

The following ingredients will be needed:

    2 Cups all-purpose flour   2 Cups cool tap water

    1 Cup table salt   1 Tbsp. corn oil

    1/2 Cup cornstarch   3 Drops food coloring (any color)

    1 Tbsp. baking soda (fresh)

Place the dry ingredients in one bowl and the wet ingredients into another bowl and mix each separately. Place the contents of both bowls into one large bowl and mix well, then place the bowl in the microwave on high for 3-4 minutes. Stop and stir the mixture every minute. Place the mixture on a board and knead into workable dough.

Jewelry-Making Clay

The following ingredients will be needed:

    1/2 Cup table salt   1/2 Cup of cornstarch (fresh)

    3/4 Cup of all-purpose flour   Warm tap water

Place the salt, flour and cornstarch in a medium-sized bowl and blend well, then slowly add the warm water while continually mixing until the solution turns into a dough and is easy to mold. If small balls are shaped, they can be pierced with a toothpick before they completely dry and strung like beads. The beads can then be painted different colors.

Greatest Modeling Clay

The following ingredients will be needed:

    1/2 Cup table salt   1/2 Tbsp. corn oil

    1 Cup all-purpose flour   1 Cup cold tap water

    2 Tbsp. cream of tartar (fresh) Food coloring

Place all the ingredients into a medium-sized saucepan, then stir and heat over medium heat for 3 minutes. Be careful not to overcook and allow it to burn on the bottom of the saucepan. Remove the mixture and allow it to cool until the mixture can be kneaded. Knead the clay until it is smooth, then store in a plastic bag.

Kids' Clay from Dryer Lint

The following ingredients will be needed:

1/2 Cup all-purpose flour	1 Day-old newspaper
1 Cup cold tap water	2 Drops wintergreen oil flavoring
1 1/2 Cups dryer filter lint	Non-toxic paint
(fine, no large pieces)	

Place the dryer lint and water into a medium-sized saucepan (be sure all the lint is covered with water) and allow the lint to become fully saturated. Add the flour and stir the mixture continually, until it is very smooth before adding the wintergreen oil flavoring. Continue to stir until the solution can be lifted with a spoon and will form peaks. When the peaks are formed, it means that the consistency will be great for modeling. Place the mixture on a piece of newspaper to cool. When the clay is cool, model the clay into any shape you wish, then allow the sculpture to dry for 3-4 days before painting it.

Sand Clay for Modeling

The following ingredients will be needed:

2 Cups clean sandbox sand	1 1/2 Cups household liquid starch
1 Cup cornstarch (fresh)	

Place the cornstarch and the sand in a container and mix well, then add the starch and blend all ingredients well. Place the mixture in a saucepan and place on medium heat while stirring continually until the mixture becomes a thick mass. Remove the saucepan from the heat and allow the modeling clay to cool before using. Knead the dough to make it more pliable before starting to work with it.

Flubber Dubber #1

The following ingredients will be needed:

1/2 Cup laundry starch (liquid)	Food coloring as desired
1/2 Cup Elmer's™ Glue (no substitutions)	

Place the glue in a small container and slowly add the starch while kneading with your fingers. The mixture will gel up better the more you mix. Then add any coloring you desire.

Flubber Dubber #2

The following ingredients will be needed:

    2 3/4 Cups warm tap water   2 Cups Elmer's™ glue (no substitutes)

    4 Tsp. borax   Food coloring (as desired)

Place the glue and 1 1/2 cups of warm water into a medium-sized bowl and add food coloring as desired. In another bowl, place the borax and 1 1/3 cups of warm water and mix well. Pour the glue water into the borax water and DO NOT mix. Just remove the flubber dubber and store in plastic bags. A little like silly putty.

Cotton Ball Fun Dough

The following ingredients will be needed:

    1 Cup all-purpose flour   3 Cups cotton balls or puffs

    2 1/3 Cups cool tap water   4 Drops food coloring

Place very small pieces of the cotton into a small saucepan and add the water while mixing. Place the saucepan over low heat and slowly add the flour while stirring continually. Allow the mixture to become semi-solid before removing from the heat and placing the cotton fun dough on a double-thickness dishtowel with one layer of paper towel underneath. As soon as the fun dough has cooled, make your objects, then allow the object to dry and harden for about a day. This is common kindergarten fun dough for making snowmen in the wintertime.

MISCELLANEOUS FUN STUFF

Giant Bubble Mix #1

The following ingredients will be needed:

    1 Cup quality dishwashing liquid   3 Tbsp. glycerin (from pharmacy)

    (a real grease-cutter)   10 Cups cold tap water

Place all the ingredients in a small plastic bucket and blend well with a wooden spoon. If you have any old bubble wands with large openings, these would be ideal. A hanger can be bent in a circle and use with good results. The bubbles will be the largest you have ever seen and will retain their shape longer than most of the products you purchase commercially. Best not to use this mixture if the bubbles will go into traffic.

Giant Bubble Mix #2

The following ingredients will be needed:

    2 Cups Karo® syrup   *4 Tbsp. liquid dishwashing soap*

    1 Cup warm tap water

Place all the ingredients into a container and mix well. If the solution is too thick, add a small amount of water to thin out.

Standard Bubble Mix

The following ingredients will be needed:

    1/2 Cup liquid dish soap   *1 Tbsp. corn oil*

    1/2 Cup warm tap water

Place all the ingredients into a container and blend very slowly, otherwise it will bubble up too much and be hard to use.

Long, Fat Bubbles

The following ingredients will be needed:

    1 Cup warm tap water   *1 Tsp. table salt*

    1/4 Cup liquid dishwashing soap

Place all the ingredients into a container and blend well. Make sure that all the salt is dissolved before using.

Disappearing Ink

The following ingredients will be needed:

1 Laxative tablet	2 Cotton balls
(X-Lax™ or any other will do)	1 Tbsp. household ammonia
1 Tbsp. rubbing alcohol	1 -1 1/2 -2 Tbsp. measuring spoon

Place the laxative tablet into a very small bowl and mash it into powder using the back of a teaspoon. Place the alcohol into the measuring spoon and add the powdered laxative. Mix until all the laxative tablet is fully dissolved, then use the solution to write a message with a small, thin paintbrush. When the solution dries, the message will disappear. To read the message, just slightly dampen the cotton ball in the household ammonia and dab it on the area that was written on.

Floating Apple Seeds

The following ingredients will be needed:

2/3 Tsp. baking soda	1/2 Cup cold tap water
1 Tbsp. white vinegar	5+ Apple seeds

Place the water into a thin, tall glass, then add the baking soda and stir until it is dissolved. Add the apple seeds, then the white vinegar and mix the solution gently. The apple seeds will rise to the top of the glass propelled by carbon dioxide bubbles. When the bubbles hit the top, they will break and the apple seeds will keep falling down.

Chalk for Drawing on Concrete

The following ingredients will be needed:

3/4 Cup warm tap water	1 1/2 Cup Plaster of Paris
3 Tbsp. powdered tempera paint	Toilet, gift-wrap or paper towel cardboard tubes

Place the warm water in a medium-sized plastic container or bowl and slowly sprinkle 1 1/2 cups of the plaster on the water until it will no longer dissolve. Blend well until the mixture is very thick. Add the tempera to the mixture and stir until it is blended well. Pour the mixture into the cardboard tubes (cut the longer ones into small tubes) and gently tap the sides all the way down to get rid of any air pockets. Allow it to dry for about 2 days. Remove the cardboard and you have pieces of sidewalk chalk.

New Crayons for the Millennium

Researchers have developed a new crayon that is made from soybeans instead of paraffin, which is a petroleum waste product. There has always been the possibility of toxic compounds in paraffin and soybean oil is an excellent substitute. Over a period of 8 years, the average child uses up over 700 crayons. There are over 2 billion crayons produced every year and up till now, none were really biodegradable. Within 5 years, most paraffin-based crayons will be the crayons of the past.

Crayons from Soap #1

The following ingredients will be needed:

1 3/4 Cups Ivory Snow Powder® (works the best)	Small candle molds
1/4 Cup cold tap water	Food coloring

Place the Ivory Soap Powder® and water into a medium-sized bowl and mix thoroughly. To make a number of different colors, use more bowls and add the food coloring you desire to each bowl. The soap powder and coloring should be added to the water until a pasty consistency is achieved. The mixture can then be poured into the candle molds to harden, which should take about 5-7 days. Remove the soap crayons from the molds and allow it to dry an additional 3 days before using.

Crayons from Soap #2

The following ingredients will be needed:

1 Cup Castile™ soap (grated)	4 Drops food coloring
1/4 Cup warm tap water	

Place all the ingredients into a container and blend well until it begins to become somewhat stiff, then place the mixture into a bowl with a rounded bottom and knead until it is the consistency of dough. Place the dough into cookie cutters or other molds and freeze for 8-10 minutes, then remove the crayons and allow them to dry until they are hard, usually 8-10 hours.

Balloon Filler-Upper

The following ingredients will be needed:

4 Tbsp. white vinegar	2 Tbsp. cold tap water
1 Tsp. baking soda (fresh)	1 Clean plastic soda bottle

Place the baking soda and the water in the bottle, then add the vinegar and very quickly fit the balloon over the top of the bottle. The carbon dioxide that is made from the baking soda and the vinegar will easily inflate the balloon.

Note: Stretch a good-sized balloon a few times to make it more pliable before you start to add the ingredients.

Horror Movie Slime

The following ingredients will be needed:

1 1/2 Tsp. borax powder	1 Cup cold water
8 Oz. white school craft glue	Tempura paint in green color
1 Cup warm water	

Place the glue into a large bowl and add the cold water, then mix until the water and glue until blended well. Add the paint gradually, just a few drops should do. Add more and different colors if desired to make a number of weird colors. Mix all ingredients well, then allow it to stand. Place the warm water in a small bowl and add the borax powder gradually, then mix until it is totally dissolved. Add the borax solution to the glue mixture and stir continually for 2 minutes. The "slime dough" now needs to be kneaded by hand until it stretches easily and is very smooth to the touch. It is best to store the slime in an airtight container, since it does dry out easily.

No-Bake Crawlees

The following ingredients will be needed:

2 Tbsp. white glue   1 Envelope of unflavored gelatin

2 Tbsp. hot tap water   1/2 Tbsp. tempura paint

Place the gelatin and hot water into a small bowl and mix well, then allow the gelatin to sit until the gelatin is dissolved. In another bowl, place the paint and glue and mix well. Mix the gelatin into the paint mixture and blend well until the mixture is good and thick. When the mixture is thick, pour it into a cookie mold that resembles insects or worms and then place the mold into the freezer for about 4-6 minutes or until it firms up. After removing the crawlees, allow them to fully dry before storing them in a plastic baggie. The crawlees should have a rubbery texture.

The Dancing Worms

The following ingredients will be needed:

5 Strands of cooked spaghetti   2 Tbsp. baking soda

(cut into 10-15 worms)   2 Drops red food coloring

1 Cup white vinegar   2 Drops blue food coloring

1 Cup cool tap water   1 Medium clear glass bowl

Place the vinegar and water in the bowl and mix well, then place the food coloring in and mix well. While mixing, slowly add the baking soda. Place the spaghetti worms into the solution and watch them come to life and wiggle around in the water as if they were "real" worms. The "bubbles" released from the reaction of the vinegar and baking soda moves the "worms." When the "worms" reach the top and the gas is released, they fall back to the bottom and may pick up more gas and head for the top again.

Chalk from eggshells

The following ingredients will be needed:

       7 Large eggshells (cleaned well and dry)   1 Tsp. very hot tap water
       1 Tsp. all-purpose flour

Place the eggshells in a small plastic bowl and crush them into a fine powder with the back of a tablespoon (a mortar and pestle would be great). It requires 1 tablespoon of powder to produce 1 stick of chalk. Remove any pieces that would not grind up leaving only the finest powder. Place the water and flour into a small bowl and blend well into a paste, then add the tablespoon of eggshell to the paste and mix thoroughly. Use the back of a tablespoon to crush the mixture into a thick paste. Shape the paste into a cylinder and wrap it up in a piece of paper towel. Allow the chalk to dry out at room temperature for 2-3 days or until very hard. This eggshell chalk is best used on cement surfaces not chalkboards unless you like the screeching.

Making a Volcano Eruption

The following ingredients will be needed:

       1 Small juice glass   1 Tbsp. baking soda
       1/4 Tsp. liquid dish soap   2 Drops red food coloring
       4 Oz. white vinegar

Place the white vinegar and food coloring into the juice glass and place outside on a thick piece of newspaper or other safe surface. The best location would be a volcano-shaped mound of sand. Add the baking soda and dish soap to the vinegar and the reaction will take place. This needs adult supervision.

Ocean Waves in a Bottle

The following ingredients will be needed:

       1 2-liter plastic soda bottle (empty)   1/2 Tbsp. powder tempura paint (any color)
       1 Cup corn oil   1 Funnel

Place the corn oil in a medium-sized bowl, then add the tempura powder. Mix them together, stirring continually. Allow the mixture to sit for 5-7 minutes and set up. Slowly pour the mixture into the bottle, using the funnel to avoid spillage. Add cool tap water until the bottle is full, then seal the bottle and place on its side to watch the ocean waves.

Kids' Lip Gloss

The following ingredients will be needed:

    2 Tbsp. Crisco® solid shortening   1 Small plastic tube (film type is fine)

    1 Tbsp. flavored Kool-Aid® (powder)

Place the Crisco® and powdered Kool-Aid® in a small microwave container and blend until they are smooth. Place the container in the microwave and cook on high for 30 seconds or until the mixture becomes a liquid, then pour the liquid gloss into the small container and refrigerate for 30 minutes or until solid. Use sparingly as a lipstick.

Squirt and Color

The following ingredients will be needed:

    4 Tbsp. cornstarch   4 Drops food coloring

    1 Cup warm tap water   1 Spray bottle

Place all the ingredients into the spray bottle and shake well before each use. This makes a great paint spray when the snow is clean. If used on cement, it will easily wash off with a garden hose.

Have a Taffy Pull

The following ingredients will be needed:

    1 Cup granulated sugar   2 1/4 Tbsp. butter (unsalted)

    2/3 Cup cool tap water   1 Tsp. table salt

    3/4 Cup light Karo® syrup   2 Tbsp. vanilla extract (pure)

    1 Tbsp. cornstarch   1 Candy thermometer

Place all the ingredients except the vanilla in a medium-sized saucepan and heat until boiling on medium heat, while stirring continuously. Stop stirring and cook until the thermometer reads 256°F. or until a hard ball stage is formed when dropped in cold water. Remove the mixture from the heat, stir in the vanilla and pour into a square 8-in. pan with 2-in. sides that have been buttered. Allow the mixture to cool until the taffy is workable and not too hot to the touch. Pull the taffy into long strips about 1/2 inch wide and cut into pieces with a scissors. Wrap the taffy in individual pieces in plastic wrap and keep in a cool, dry location.

Halloween Blood

The following ingredients will be needed:

5 1/2 Tbsp. clear corn syrup

2 1/2 Tbsp. cool tap water

60 Drops red food coloring

10 Drops yellow food coloring

2 Drops blue food coloring

Place the food coloring and the water in a medium-sized bowl and mix well, then slowly add the corn syrup stirring continually until the mixture thickens up, but is not too solid. The fake blood can be smeared on any part of your body, but the solution may stain some garments, so wear old clothes.

Crystal Flower Garden

The following ingredients will be needed:

1/2 Cup cool tap water

4 Tbsp. liquid bluing

4 Tbsp. table salt

4 Tsp. household ammonia

Food coloring

The following supplies will be needed:

Cotton swabs (cut in half)

Pip cleaners (cut in 2-in. pieces)

Few pieces of oil-based clay

Plastic margarine tubs or similar container

The day before, you will need to soak the ends of the cotton swabs in food coloring and make sure they are dry before you start the garden. Also, place a few drops of the food coloring on the pipe cleaners the day before. Place a piece of clay on the bottom of the plastic tub and insert 3 cotton swabs or pipe cleaners about 1/2 inch into the clay. Mix the solution of bluing, salt, ammonia and water in a bottle and blend well, then pour a small amount into the plastic cup, making sure that the solution covers up to about 1/2 inch up the cotton swabs or pipe cleaners.

Color Copier for Comics

The following ingredients will be needed:

    1 Tsp. real vanilla extract (do not use imitation)

    1 Tsp. liquid dishwasher soap

Place the ingredients into a small bowl and mix well. Place the cartoon on a solid surface or board and brush a thin layer of the solution on the picture, then cover it with a sheet of white bond or copy paper. Gently rub the back of the paper until the picture has been transferred, then remove the paper with the transferred picture now on the white paper.

The Eggsperiment

The following ingredients will be needed:

1 Fresh large egg	1 Deep medium bowl
2 Drops yellow food coloring	2 Cups very hot tap water

Place the hot water in the bowl, then place the egg gently on the bottom with a spoon (don't burn your hand). To prove that eggs contain air, watch closely as tiny air bubbles are forced to escape from the egg because of the heat from the water. The heat makes the air expand and literally forces the air out. An egg is very porous and not an airtight compartment for the chick. It has about 6,758 small openings in the shell or pores to allow the air to escape. The food coloring allows you to see the bubbles more easily.

Making Butter

The following ingredients will be needed:

1 Cup heavy whipping cream (cold)	1 Measuring cup
1 Metal mixing bowl (chilled)	1 Hand mixer (electric)

Place the heavy cream into the chilled bowl and mix until you see small clumps of yellow (about 8-10 minutes). The yellow clumps should be in a liquid, which must be poured off at regular intervals. Keep pouring the liquid off, allowing the yellow clumps to remain. Cream consists of butterfat and water and all you are doing is separating the two. The butter molecules are released and clump together, forming the recognizable butter. This butter will not have a long shelf life and must be refrigerated and used within 3-5 hours, then the remainder discarded.

Sand Art

The following ingredients will be needed:

      1/2 Cup tempura paint (dry)

      1 Cup clean sandbox sand

Place the ingredients into a container and mix well. The amount of tempura paint can vary. Spread a small layer of glue on a picture and sprinkle the colored sand. Smaller amounts can be made to produce different colors as needed.

Kids' Glittering Gel

The following ingredients will be needed:

      1 1/4 Tsp. glycerin   3 Drops essential rose oil

      1/2 Cup aloe vera gel   Food coloring as desired

      1/4 Tsp. quality polyester glitter (hobby shop)

Place the aloe and glycerin in a small bowl and mix well, then add the glitter, essential oil and food coloring, if desired. The gel can be placed on arms or legs as a fun glittering gel.

Salt Art

The following ingredients will be needed:

      1/2 Cup table salt   1 Baggie (good closure)

      1 Stick colored chalk   1 Baby food jar

Place the salt in the baggie and add the piece of chalk, then seal the baggie well. Rub the bag between your hands until all the salt is colored. This may be done with any number of colors. Place the colored salt in the jar in layers or make a design. Make sure the jar is filled to the top before gluing the top on.

Pet Celery Feeding Time

The following ingredients will be needed:

      1 Stalk celery (with leaves)

      1 Tsp. red food coloring

Place the celery stalk in 3/4 of a glass of water and add the food coloring, then mix well. The leaves of the celery stalk will turn red, showing how plants feed by absorbing food from the soil and water.

Salvaging Less than Perfect Fruit

Making fruit leather can be a fun way to preserve fruit that has over-ripened or is not that appealing. Most of the nutrients are retained and the fruit is now in a fun form to eat. There are many methods of preparing fruit leather, including using a dehydrator, but the following are a few of the easiest methods. Fruits that turn brown easily, such as bananas and pears are not recommended.

Leather You Can Eat #1

The following ingredients will be needed:

> 8 Oz. flavored applesauce
>
> Plastic wrap

Place the applesauce on a flat plate and place the plate into the microwave for about 5 minutes, depending on the wattage. Keep an eye on it and do not allow it to burn. The applesauce will dehydrate and become a solid mass that can then be placed between two pieces of plastic wrap and consumed the same as fruit roll.

Leather You Can Eat #2

The following ingredients will be needed:

> 4 Cups fresh fruit (no bananas)   2 Tsp. apples or berries for additional flavor
>
> cleaned well, no stems, etc.   1 Cookie sheet with sides
>
> 1 Envelope unflavored Knox™ gelatin

Place a piece of plastic wrap on the cookie sheet and lightly spray it with oil. If you are using a citrus fruit, it will need to be peeled. Place the fruit into a blender and puree it until it is good and smooth. Pulp is OK and will give the leather a little texture. Place the puree into a small saucepan and place over low heat until it just begins to bubble, then add the gelatin and a small amount of sugar if desired.

Remove from the heat and pour on the cookie sheet, then place into the refrigerator and let it cool and set overnight. It will take 3-4 days before you see drying around the edges telling you that it is done. Make sure that it is spread evenly and always watch for mold. If any appears, discard the batch. Roll the leather and use kitchen shears to cut the strips then roll up.

Plain Old Gunk

The following ingredients will be needed:

     1 Cup cornstarch

     1 Cup cool tap water

Place the ingredients into a small bowl and mix well, then play with the gunk.

Colored Gunk

The following ingredients will be needed:

     1/3 Cup granulated sugar   *4 Cups cold water*

     1 Cup cornstarch

Place all the ingredients into a small saucepan and cook on low heat until thick, then remove from heat and allow the mixture to cool. Place the mixture into a well-sealed plastic baggie, add some food coloring and allow the child to experience the weird mixture.

Making Colored Pasta for Crafts

The following ingredients will be needed:

     8 Oz. bag of pasta   *1 Tsp. rubbing alcohol*

     8 Drops food coloring

Place all the ingredients into a plastic bag and shake well, then place the pasta on a cookie sheet and allow it to dry for about 15 minutes. Do not eat the pasta.

Making Ice Cream in a Baggie

The following ingredients will be needed:

1 Tbsp. granulated sugar	1 Gal.-size plastic bag with good closure
1/2 Cup whole milk (reduced-fat is OK)	1 Pt.-size plastic bag with good closure
1/4 Tsp. real vanilla (no imitation)	Ice cubes as needed
6 Tbsp. rock salt	

Fill the large plastic bag half full of ice cubes, then add the rock salt and seal the bag tight. Place the milk, sugar and vanilla into the smaller plastic bag and seal it tight. Open the gallon bag and place the smaller bag inside, leaving the smaller bag sealed tight. Shake for 5-7 minutes or until you observe the ice cream forming, then remove the ice cream bag and wipe the closure well before opening to be sure there is no rock salt residue that might get into the ice cream. A small amount of chocolate syrup, food coloring or small candies may be added.

Telling the Identity of Salt and Sugar

The following ingredients will be needed:

1 Tbsp. table salt	2 Cups
1 Tbsp. granulated sugar	1 Ice-cube tray (with metal or plastic divider)
2 Drops red food coloring	Cool tap water
2 Drops blue food coloring	

Fill the cups half full with water, then add the different food colors to each glass, one red and the other blue. Place the salt into one cup and the sugar in the other cup and allow them to dissolve fully. Pour the solutions in opposite ends of the divided ice-cube trays and place into the freezer. The water with the sugar will freeze and the water with the salt will not freeze.

The Secret Hiding Place

The following ingredients will be needed:

1 Cup all-purpose flour	1/4 Cup sanitized sandbox sand
1 Cup used coffee grounds	3/4 Cup cool tap water
1/2 Cup table salt	

Place the flour, coffee grounds, salt and sand into a container, blend well then very slowly add the water while continually mixing until the consistency is that of a workable dough. Roll the dough out in a cylinder about 1-2 inches thick, then cut into even pieces about 3 inches long. Roll each piece between your hands as if preparing meatballs, which is what they will look like. Make a hole in each one and insert a small prize or toy, then seal the hole with leftover dough. Allow the balls to harden for about 3 days at room temperature or bake in the oven if you are in a hurry at 140°F. for about 20 minutes.

Magical Glitter

The following ingredients will be needed:

Karo™ syrup	Drop of food coloring (if desired)
Cold tap water	Metallic glitter strands (confetti-style)
Small plastic bottle with screw cap	

Place the Karo™ syrup into the plastic bottle to about 3/4 full, then add about 1 1/2 tablespoons of the metallic confetti and fill the bottle with cold tap water and seal well. Turn the bottle upside down 2-3 times slowly and watch it sparkle.

The Magical Moving Coin

The following ingredients will be needed:

1 Cup cold tap water	1 Quarter
1 2-liter soda bottle	

Place the quarter in the cup of water at room temperature; then place the empty 2-liter plastic bottle in the freezer for 5-6 minutes. Remove the bottle from the freezer and place the quarter over the mouth of the bottle to cover the opening completely. While the bottle was in the freezer, the air in the bottle cooled down, moved close together and thus took us less room. When this occurred, more air entered and occupied the empty space. When you removed the bottle from the freezer, the air started to warm up and expand, thus causing the quarter to jump up and down as the warm air has to escape. The quarter will also make a weird chattering noise as this occurs.

Making a Frozen Dessert with Natural Heat Energy

The following ingredients will be needed:

1/2 Cup of apple juice (pasteurized)	6 Cups crushed ice
1 Tbsp. pure lemon juice	1 Medium mixing bowl
1/2 Cup rock salt	1 Small jar with screw top lid

Place the apple juice and lemon juice into the small jar, then seal and shake well. Remove the lid and place the jar in the center of the mixing bowl and pour the ice around the jar almost up to the top. Sprinkle the rock salt on top of the ice (not in the juice) then wrap a few dishtowels around the bowl to insulate it and place it in a location or next to an object that will hold the dishtowels firmly against the bowl. In about 2 hours, the juice will turn into a slushy treat. The salt and ice has the ability to draw the heat from the juice and bring the juices to a near freezing point.

Scary Make-Up

The following ingredients will be needed:

1 Tsp. plain yogurt	1 Tsp. cool tap water
1 Tsp. Fuller's earth (from pharmacy)	3 Drops of vegetable food coloring

Mix all the ingredients together in a small bowl and be sure and blend well. The solution can then be applied to your face (not in your eyes, up your nose or in your mouth). If you use different colors of food coloring and make small batches, you can really create a scary and weird look.

EASTER EGG DYE

The Old-Fashioned Way

The directions are the same for all dyes. Place all the ingredients in a medium-sized bowl and mix well. Dip the eggs in the dye and allow the eggs to dry in an egg container. Polish the eggs with a small amount of olive oil to make them shine.

The following ingredients will be needed:

Green

$^1/_4$	Oz. brilliant green dye
2^3_4	Tsp. citric acid
1	Oz. dextrin
1	Pt. warm tap water

Yellow

$^1/_4$	Oz. napthol yellow or yellow onion skins
5	Tsp. citric acid
$1^1/_4$	Oz. dextrin
1	Pt. warm tap water

Blue

½ Tsp. marine blue
5 Tsp. citric acid
1¼ Oz. dextrin
1 Pt. warm tap water

Brown

½ Oz. vesuvin
5¼ Tsp. citric acid
½ Oz. dextrin
1 Pt. warm tap water

Red

½ Tsp. diamond fuchsin
2½ Tsp. citric acid
1¼ Oz. dextrin
1 Pt. warm tap water

Orange

1 Tsp. azo orange
2½ Tsp. citric acid
1¼ Oz. dextrin
1 Pt. warm tap water

Violet

½ Tsp. methyl violet
2½ Tsp. citric acid
1¼ Oz. dextrin
1 Pt. warm tap water

32

Jewelry
CLEANING

GENERAL INFORMATION

All diamonds and gold jewelry can easily be cleaned by mixing a solution of 50/50 white vinegar and warm water. Dip a soft toothbrush into the solution and brush gently. Opals, emeralds, and pearls are too delicate for this type of treatment. Costume jewelry should only be cleaned with a weak solution of baking soda and water to avoid damaging the glue bonds.

Diamonds
- Diamonds can be chipped and should never be worn when doing rough jobs.
- Chlorine bleach will discolor the setting.
- Have the prongs holding the stone checked annually.
- When storing your jewelry, make sure they don't touch each other.

- Diamonds will scratch other pieces of jewelry very easily.
- Clean your diamonds regularly with a milk detergent and warm water.

Colored Gemstones

- Never expose the gemstones to salt water or harsh chemical solutions.
- Check with your jeweler for cleaning methods for colored stones.
- Emeralds need special care, check with your jeweler.
- Hairspray will dull gemstones.
- Wipe gemstones with a soft cloth after each wearing.

10-24 Karat Gold Jewelry

- Gold scratches easily, keep pieces away from other jewelry.
- Do not bathe or shower using soaps and shampoos.
- Use a soft bristle brush.
- Grease is easily removed with rubbing alcohol.
- Try not to get makeup and powders on the gold.

Silver

- Store silver in a cool, dry location.
- Only rub silver with a soft cloth. Paper towel and tissues will scratch it.
- Never wear silver into a swimming pool that is chlorinated.

Pearls

- Put on pearls after applying cosmetics, perfume and hair spray.
- Quality pearls should be re-strung annually with knots between each pearl if worn regularly.
- Store pearls in a chamois bag or wrap in tissue to store.
- Never use harsh chemical to clean pearls.
- Special pearl formulas or mild soap and warm water can be used to clean them.

Making Jewelry Cleaner

The following ingredients will be needed:

1 Tbsp. household ammonia

1 Tbsp. washing soda
(from supermarket)

1 Tbsp. liquid dishwashing detergent

3 Cups very warm tap water

Place all the ingredients in a medium-sized bowl and mix thoroughly. The solution should be stored in a sealed glass jar. When you want to clean your jewelry, just soak the pieces in the solution for 5-7 minutes and brush with a soft-bristled toothbrush. Rinse the jewelry in warm water and dry well.

Caution: Do not place pearls or emeralds in this solution and never add chlorine bleach to these chemicals. Keep out of the reach of children.

Silver Jewelry Cleaner

The following ingredients will be needed:

1/2 Cup white vinegar

2 Tbsp. baking soda

Place the ingredients in a small bowl and mix well. Place the jewelry in the bowl and allow it to stand for 2 hours before rinsing with cold water and drying with a soft dry cloth.

Gold Cleaner

The following ingredients will be needed:

1 Cup Fuller's earth

1 Cup calcium carbonate

2 Tbsp. ammonium sulfate

1 Tbsp. aluminum powder

Place all the ingredients in a container and mix well. Apply the cleaner to oxidized gold jewelry with a damp sponge, then rinse with cool water. Store the mixture in a well-sealed container in a cool, dry location.

Making Tarnished Gold Cleaner

The following ingredients will be needed:

20 Oz. sodium bicarbonate	1 Oz. table salt
1 Oz. chlorinated lime	16 Oz. cold or lukewarm tap water

Place all the ingredients into a container and mix well, then apply with a soft brush. It only requires a small amount of the solution to do the job.

Restoring Tarnished Gold

The following ingredients will be needed:

20 Oz. sodium bicarbonate	1 Oz. table salt
1 Oz. chlorinated lime	16 Oz. cool tap water

Place all the ingredients into a container and mix well, then apply with a soft bristle brush. The solution may be applied either cold or lukewarm.

Jewelry Polish

The following ingredients will be needed:

1 Tbsp. ferric oxide	Cool tap water
2 Tbsp. calcium carbonate	

Place the ingredients into a small bowl and mix well using just enough water to produce a paste. Rub on the jewelry with a soft cloth and the buff with another clean soft cloth.

33

Cleaning
AROUND THE KITCHEN

POTS AND PANS

Metal pie and cookie pans need to cool down before you wash them or they will tend to warp when you cook with them.

Brass and Copper Pots for Everyday Use
Most brass and copper pots and utensils may have a lacquer coating that should be removed before using the item to hold or cook food in. If the item is just for decorative purposes, then the lacquer coating should not be removed and the item just cleaned with lukewarm water with mild detergent. If the item is to be used with food, then the lacquer must be removed by placing them into a bath of 1 cup of washing soda mixed into 2 gal. of boiling water. After a short time, the lacquer will just easily peel off.

If you are having problems removing crusted food from a casserole dish, just fill the dish with warm water and add a tsp. of baking soda to the water. Allow to stand for 1 hour and the crusted material will easily be removed.

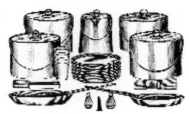

Brass and Copper Cleaner

The following ingredients are needed:

1/2 Fresh lemon or	1 Tbsp. salt
2 Tbsp. lemon juice	

Place the salt in a shallow dish and dip the exposed end of the lemon in the salt and use to scrub the stained area. Another method is to make a paste of lemon juice and salt and use a cloth dipped in the solution to clean the brass or copper surfaces. If the pot has a green spot, use a solution of ammonia and salt to remove the area that has turned green. Gloves should be worn when using ammonia and always try not to breathe the fumes and work in a well-ventilated area.

If you are tired of cleaning brass objects, just apply a thin coat of fresh white shellac on the item. A second coat really helps as well.

Cast Iron Pots

Mix the following ingredients together in a small bowl:

1 Tsp. ascorbic acid (vitamin C)

2 Cups tap water

To remove rust from cast iron pots, just briskly rub the area with a paste made from the ascorbic acid and water. If the rust spot still persists, try allowing the mixture to remain overnight.

Iron pots and kettles will not rust if they are wiped very dry after washing. Then rub a small amount of lard or vegetable oil on them.

Aluminum Pot Cleaner

The following ingredients will be needed:

1/2 Cup white vinegar   *1/2 Cup baking soda (fresh)*

1/4 Cup soap flakes   *1/2 Cup cream of tartar*
(OK to shave Ivory soap bar)

Place the baking soda and the cream of tartar in a medium-sized bowl and mix well, then add the vinegar and blend until a soft paste is formed. Add the soap flakes and mix thoroughly before placing in a well-sealed jar. This mixture should be applied with a steel wool pad, then rinsed with hot water.

Enamelware should be seasoned by placing the pot in water and slowly bringing it up to a boil. This will lengthen the life of the pot.

WHAT IS IT AND IS IT SAFE TO USE?

Basically, teflon is a plastic material that has a high chemical and heat stability. Teflon is extremely difficult to destroy once it is produced. The coating has the ability to protect surfaces from friction and corrosion. Teflon is not really dangerous to humans unless it is heated above 400^{0}C. When this high a heat is maintained in a pan that is empty, fumes are released causing teflon particles to become airborne and cause a poisoning known as "polymer fume fever." The fumes will easily kill birds and is very hard to diagnose. Teflon is very safe under normal cooking conditions. If a piece of teflon chips off and is swallowed, it will not break down in the body but will pass through and be excreted.

Teflon Surface Cleaner

The following ingredients will be needed:

3 Tbsp, baking soda   *1 Cup hot tap water*

3 Lemon slices

Place the baking soda and the lemon slices on the stained area, then add the water to cover. Simmer the pot on low heat until the area appears clean.

Silverstone Pot Cleaner

The following ingredients will be needed:

1/2 Cup white vinegar   1 Cup cool tap water
2 Tbsp. baking soda (fresh)

Place all the ingredients into a container and mix well. Pour into the Silverstone pot and boil for 10-15 minutes; then rinse the pot in soapy water and rinse. Best to rub oil on the surface to re-season.

Porcelain Cleaner

The following ingredients will be needed:

3 Tbsp. cream of tartar
Tbsp. alum

Place the ingredients into a container and shake well to mix. Sprinkle the powder onto a well-dampened surface and allow the powder to remain for 2-3 hours before cleaning with a sponge. Rinse the area well.

Enameled Pot or Surface Cleaner

The following ingredients will be needed:

3 Tbsp. sodium carbonate (from drug store)
1 Tbsp. sodium metaphosphate (from drug store)
2 Tbsp. Castile soap (powdered, from health food store)
1 Cup pumice powder (very fine grain, from hardware store)

Place all the ingredients into a container and blend well, then apply to the stained enameled surface with a damp sponge. Rinse with cool water.

Teapot Lime Deposit Cleaner

The following ingredients will be needed:

1 1/2 Cups apple cider vinegar   3 Tbsp. table salt
1 1/4 Cups of cool tap water

Place all the ingredients into the teapot and mix well, then boil the mixture for 15-20 minutes, then allow the mixture to remain for 10 hours before rinsing well with clear, cool tap water.

Stainless Steel Pot Cleaner

The following ingredients will be needed:

　　1 Tbsp. household ammonia

　　1 Pt. cool tap water

Place the ingredients into a container and mix well, then apply to the stainless steel pot.

CLEANING SILVERWARE

Dirty Cutlery Cure

The following items are needed:

　　6 Wide strips of aluminum foil　　　　4 Tbsp. baking soda

　　1 Qt. boiling water

This should be done if you have a large amount of silverware to clean after a dinner party. Just use a medium-sized plastic container and place the aluminum foil strips on the bottom of the container, then add all the silverware and cover with boiling water. Add the baking soda by sprinkling it over the top of the mixture and allow the cutlery to soak for 10-15 minutes. If this is done after each use, the silverware should not tarnish as easily.

Silver Cleaning Cloth

following items are needed:

　　Cotton cloth　　　　　　　　Liquid silver polish

　　Ammonia　　　　　　　　　　Cold water

In a small plastic bowl, mix 2 parts ammonia (use gloves) with 1 part of silver liquid polish and 10 parts cold water. Saturate the cloth and allow to air dry overnight. More than one cloth may be made if so desired.

Silver Polish #1

The following ingredients will be needed:

1 1/2 Cups warm tap water	1/2 Tsp. washing soda
2 Tbsp. stearic acid (caution: flammable)	1 Cup diatomaceous earth
1/2 Tsp. trisodim phosphate	

Place a double boiler with water on the stove and boil the water. Wear rubber gloves and a dust mask. The top insert will remain empty. Remove from heat and place the acid and water in the insert and stir until the stearic acid has melted. Mix in the balance of the ingredients while continually stirring to produce a creamy paste, silver polish.

Silver Polish #2

The following ingredients will be needed:

1 Lb. oleic acid	8 Oz. Tripoli powder
1 Pt. kerosene	

Place all the ingredients into a container and add just enough water to prepare a paste.

Silver Polish #3

The following ingredients will be needed:

8 Parts whiting	6 Parts paraffin oil
2 Parts paraffin	1 Part oleic acid

Place the paraffin and the paraffin oil in a double boiler and melt together, then add the whiting and the oleic acid and blend well. Remove from the heat and allow it to cool before placing in a well-sealed jar.

Silver Polish #4

The following ingredients will be needed:

2 Cups cool tap water	1/4 Cup soap flakes
1/2 Cup whiting	1 1/2 Tsp. household ammonia

Place the water in a medium-sized saucepan (not aluminum) and remove from the heat and dissolve the soap flakes. Then, while stirring continually, add the whiting and beat vigorously until all the lumps are gone. Allow the mixture to cool before adding the ammonia and mix well. Shake well before each use.

GENERAL CLEANING

Formula for Air Freshener

The following ingredients will be needed:

2 Cups pure distiller water

4 Packages of Knox™ gelatin

10 Drops rose essence fragrance

2 Tbsp. table salt

Food coloring

Place one cup of distilled water in a medium-sized saucepan and bring to a boil. Add the gelatin and blend until dissolved, then remove from the range and add one more cup of distilled water, salt and the rose fragrance. If you would like a colored freshener, add a few drops of food coloring. Place the mixture into small jars and allow it to remain at room temperature for about 12 hours. The result will be a very effective gel air freshener. The addition of the salt should eliminate the possibility of mold forming.

Making Scouring Powder #1

The following ingredients will be needed:

1 Cup baking soda

1/4 Cup borax

1/4 Cup washing soda

Place the ingredients in a sealed container and shake to mix well. Rinse well after using the powder.

Making Scouring Powder #2

The following ingredients will be needed:

1 Cup baking soda (fresh)

1 Cup borax

1 Cup table salt

Place all the ingredients into a glass jar and cover with a tight lid and shake to mix thoroughly. Use the same as any other cleanser.

Soft-Scrubber Cleanser

The following ingredients will be needed:

1/4 Cup baking soda

Liquid hand soap to make a paste

Place the baking soda into a small bowl and slowly add the liquid soap while stirring. You should end up with a creamy-textured soft cleanser.

Non-Abrasive Cleanser

The following ingredients will be needed:

1/4 Cup chalk

Liquid hand soap to make a paste

Place the chalk into a small bowl and slowly add the liquid soap while stirring. You should end up with a creamy non-abrasive cleanser that will not scratch surfaces.

Refrigerator Freshener

The following ingredients will be needed:

1 Tsp. baking soda   2 Cups very hot tap water

1 Tsp. lemon juice   1 Spray bottle

Place the hot water into a spray bottle, then add the ingredients and mix well. A light mist sprayed inside the refrigerator next time you clean it out can remain on the walls and shelves. Allow the mixture to dry for a few minutes. This spray freshener can be used anywhere you need a freshener.

Making Liquid Dishwashing Soap

The following ingredients will be needed:

3 Bars of soap   1 Container
(good use for those motel bars you have been saving)
1 Grater

Grate the bars of soap very fine and place them in a small saucepan. Completely cover the fine gratings with water and simmer over low heat until they are all melted. Pour into the container and use the same as any liquid soap.

Dishwasher Spot Remover

The following ingredients will be needed:
- 1 Cup liquid chlorine bleach
- 1 Cup white vinegar

After loading the dishwasher with only glass dishes or glasses (no silver, aluminum or other metal) place the bleach into a small glass bowl and sit it on the bottom shelf so that it will not spill. Run the washer cycle only, then turn off the dishwasher. Then pour the vinegar into the bowl and run through the entire cycle.

Dishwasher Cleaner

The following ingredients will be needed:
- 2 Tsp. baking soda (fresh)
- 1 Tsp. cream of tartar
- 1 Tsp. borax

Place all the ingredients into a small cup and mix well, then add the mixture to the soap holder when the dishwasher is empty and run it on a cycle with hot water or a pot cleaner cycle.

Making Oven Cleaner #1

The following ingredients will be needed:
- 2 Tbsp. Castile soap (grated or liquid)
- 2 Tbsp. borax

Place the soap and the borax into a spray bottle and fill with hot water, then shake well until all the soap and borax are in solution. Spray on the oven stains and allow it to remain for about 20 minutes before rinsing with clear warm water. Some scrubbing may be needed for stubborn stains.

Making Oven Cleaner

The following ingredients will be needed:

    4 Oz. baking soda   1 Tsp. table salt

    1/4 Cup washing soda

Place all the ingredients into a small bowl and mix thoroughly, adding enough water to make a paste. Use a damp sponge to clean the area. For difficult spots, prepare some of the paste with more water to make it runny and allow it to sit for 1 hour before cleaning it off.

Cleaning the Oven Overnight

The following ingredients will be needed:

    3/4 Cup household ammonia   1 Qt. hot tap water

    1 Tbsp. liquid hand soap

Place the ammonia in a cup, close the oven door and leave the cup in the oven overnight. The following morning remove the ammonia and clean the oven with the liquid soap and hot water. The ammonia fumes should turn the black stuck-on residues to dust.

Formica® Counter Cleanser

following ingredients will be needed:

    3 Tbsp. white vinegar   1/2 Cup very warm tap water

    1/2 Tsp. liquid dish soap   1 Spray bottle

    1/2 Tsp. virgin olive oil

Place all the ingredients in a spray bottle and mix thoroughly. Spray the counter, allow to remain for a few seconds before wiping off with a damp sponge. Rinse the area well to remove all residues.

Cleaner for Food Processors

The following ingredients will be needed:

    1/2 Cup white vinegar   1/2 Cup warm tap water

    1/2 Tsp. liquid dish detergent

Place the ingredients in a small bowl and mix, before placing in the food processor or blender. Cover the machine and run for 30 seconds. Remove the solution and rinse thoroughly.

Household Appliance: Antiseptic Cleaner (Harmful if ingested)

The following ingredients will be needed:

2 Cups trisodium phosphate (TSP)   1 Cup sodium pyrophosphate

1 Cup sodium bicarbonate   2 Drops essential rose oil

Place all the ingredients into a bucket and mix well (wear gloves and mask), then store the mixture in a glass container that can be well sealed. Dilute before using at about 1/2 cup to each gal. of cool tap water.

Porcelain Sink Stain Remover

The following ingredients will be needed:

1 Tsp. liquid detergent   1/2 Cup white vinegar

1/2 Cup liquid chlorine bleach

Place a closure over the drain, then place 2-3 inches of warm water in the sink. Place all the ingredients into the sink, mix well and allow the mixture to remain for about 8-10 hours. Rinse with hot water.

Kitchen Odor Remover

The following ingredients will be needed:

1/4 Cup chalk   1/4 Cup silica gel

1 Cup Portland cement   Cool tap water

1 Cup vermiculite

Place all the ingredients except the water into a container and mix well, then slowly add the water and stir until the mixture turns into a creamy paste. Pour the mixture into molds and allow to air dry for 2-3 days, then place the molds into the oven at 350°F. for 2 hours. The cakes will last from 2-3 weeks and can be re-activated 3-4 times by placing them back in the oven at the 350°F. for 2 hours each time.

FLOOR CLEANING

Grease Cutter for Serious Cleaning

The following ingredients will be needed:

    1/4 Cup white vinegar   *1/4 Cup washing soda*

    1 Tbsp. liquid dish soap   *2 Gal. very warm tap water*

Place all the ingredients into a bucket and mix well until sudsy. Mop the area with the solution. Not recommended for waxed floors, it may make the wax gunky.

34

Home Remedies
CAN SAVE BIG

The following remedies are for your general information only and do not take the place of qualified medical advice or treatment by a licensed physician. They are formulas that have been used by our grandparents when a drugstore or physician was not very handy. Many may still work great and have been used by many members of my family since the turn of the last century. We do not guarantee that they will work!

Grandpa's Arthritis Relief

The following ingredients will be needed:
- *4 Tbsp. pure orange juice*
- *1 Tbsp. cod liver oil*

Place the cod liver oil in a small glass and mix with the orange juice. Complete your evening meal no later than 6 PM. Do not eat anything for 3-4 hours, then consume the juices mixture just before going to bed. The stomach must be empty with the digestive system is quiet and no bile flowing. The oil will then be absorbed by the joints and possibly alleviate the problem. This is an old historical remedy that was used in the 1800s. Many people claimed that it achieved excellent results. This is not a treatment for a disease recommended by the author; it was included for informational purposes only.

PHYTO (NOT FIDO) TO THE RESCUE

While modern science just recently identified hundreds of phytonutrients in fruits and vegetables, it seems that grandpa must have known something a long time ago. The following combination of fruit juices provides a person with an excellent blend of phytonutrients that are presently being studied in relation to reducing the risk of heart disease and lowering cholesterol levels.

Grandpa's Cholesterol Lowering Secret Formula

The following ingredients will be needed:
- *1 Cups purple grape juice*
- *2 Cups pure cranberry juice (from concentrate)*
- *2 Cups pasteurized apple juice*
- *1/3 Cup apple cider vinegar*

Place all the ingredients in a sealed pitcher and mix thoroughly. Drink one eight-oz. glass twice a day to lower cholesterol.

Some States are Poison-Plant Free

Three states: Alaska, Hawaii and parts of Nevada do not have any poison oak, ivy or sumack; all the rest have at least one variety. The poison ivy plant gives off an oil called "urushiol," which can remain active for some time on clothing or even your pet and transfer the oil to your skin to cause the allergic reaction. Approximately 2 out of every 3 people are allergic to the poison plants. Reactions can occur in as little as

10 minutes and the rash will occur, possibly blister and almost always itch. It takes about 10 days for the rash and itching to subside. If you are very susceptible, then you should see your pharmacist for the latest preparation that will block the oil from penetrating your skin.

Poison Ivy and Poison Oak Relief

The following ingredients will be needed:

  2 Oz. potassium permanganate

  5 Cups cold tap water

Place the ingredients in a medium-sized bowl and mix thoroughly. Apply the solution to the affected area twice daily, more if needed for relief of the symptoms. If a brown stain appears, it can be removed with a weak solution of oxalic acid and water.

Prickly Heat/Mosquito Bite Formula

The following ingredients will be needed:

  2 Tsp. calamine   6 1/2 Tbsp. lime water

  1 Tbsp. zinc oxide   3 1/4 Oz. rose water

  5 Tsp. glycerin

Place all the ingredients into a medium-sized bowl and blend thoroughly, then apply to the affected area. Store in a well-sealed bottle and mix well before each use.

Remedy for Boils

The following ingredients will be needed:

  1 Cup white vinegar   1 Fresh medium egg white only

  1/4 Cup turpentine

Place all the ingredients in a medium-sized bottle and shake until well mixed. The solution should look milky. Apply a small amount to the boil and allow to air dry. This should be done twice a day for the best results.

Corn Formula for People Who Wear too Small a Shoe

The following ingredients will be needed:

      1/2 Tsp. resorcin   5 Tsp. collodion elasticum

      1/2 Tsp. salicylic acid

Place all the ingredients in a small bowl and mix well. The mixture is then applied to the corn for 6 days and the foot should be bathed in very hot water. The corn should be easy to remove. Pressure from poor-fitting shoes is usually the cause of the problem.

Digestive Aid

The following ingredients will be needed:

      2 Tbsp. apple cider vinegar

      2 Cups tepid tap water

Place the ingredients in a tall glass and drink it before each meal if you are having digestive problems. A small amount of pure honey can be added to improve the taste.

Brown Age Spots

The following ingredients will be needed:

      2 Tsp. white onion juice

      2 Tsp. white vinegar

Place the ingredients in a small bottle and shake well to mix. Apply by rubbing the solution into the spots twice a day until the spots are gone. May have to be repeated if they decide to return.

Gramps Anti-Dizziness Formula

The following ingredients will be needed:

      2 Tsp. apple cider vinegar   1/2 Cup warm tap water

      2 Tsp. pure honey

Place the ingredients in a cup and mix well, then drink twice per day to relieve the symptoms.

Sunburn Relief #1

The following ingredients will be needed:

2 Tbsp. white vinegar

2 Tbsp. virgin olive oil

Place the ingredients in a small bowl and mix well. Use a cotton ball and dab on affected areas. Relief is almost instantaneous, but will need to be repeated when the discomfort returns.

Sunburn Relief #2

The following ingredients will be needed:

1 Cup white vinegar

5 Tbsp. table salt

5 Tbsp. plain yogurt

2 1/4 Tbsp. aloe vera gel

Place all the ingredients in a small bowl and mix thoroughly until it is creamy. Store in a well-sealed jar in the refrigerator. Always shake before using and apply to affected areas every hour until relief has occurred. A cloth can be soaked in the solution and placed on the burned area as an alternative method of relief.

Sunburn Relief #3

The following ingredients will be needed:

2 Tsp. aloe vera (liquid)

15 Drops calendula tincture

4 Drops essential rose oil

Place all the ingredients in a small spray bottle and shake well, then use as needed to relieve the heat of sunburn. Store in a cool, dry location and shake well before each use.

Sunburn Relief #4

The following ingredients will be needed:

4 Parts borax

2 Parts potassium chlorate

10 Parts glycerine

4 Parts ethyl alcohol

90 Parts rose water

Place all the ingredients into a container and mix well. Store in a well-sealed bottle and shake before each use.

Cough Suppressant

The following ingredients will be needed:

    1 Cup pure honey   1/4 Cup warm tap water

    3 Tbsp. lemon juice

Place the honey and lemon juice in a small bowl and slowly add the water while mixing. Should be stored in the refrigerator in a sealed jar and used as needed. One to two tbsp. are the normal dosage.

Cold Relief

The following ingredients will be needed:

    1 Cup fresh cranberries   1 Tbsp. potato starch

    1/2 Tbsp. pure honey   2 Cups cold tap water

Place the cranberries and the water in a small saucepan and heat on medium until the cranberries pop open. Strain the mixture and add the honey to the liquid and bring to a boil. Remove from the heat and allow it to cool. Place the potato starch in a small bowl with 2 tbsp. cold tap water and mix. Very slowly add the starch mixture to the cranberry mixture while stirring continually. Return the pan to the heat and bring to a boil. Keep stirring until it thickens and becomes almost transparent. Store in the refrigerator.

Old-Fashioned Mustard Plaster

The following ingredients will be needed:

    1 Tbsp. dry mustard   Lukewarm tap water

    1/4 Cup all-purpose flour

The mustard and the flour should be sifted together in a small bowl. Add water to the mixture slowly until a paste is formed, which is then spread on a piece of muslin the size of a person's chest. Place the mustard plaster on the chest and place another piece of muslin on top of it. The skin must be dry before placing the plaster on. If any allergic reaction is observed, such as a rash, discontinue using the plaster and wash the area with warm soapy water. Only leave the plaster on for about 20 minutes or until the skin turns red. This was used twice per day until the congestion subsided.

Sore Muscle Relief

The following ingredients will be needed:

    1 1/4 Tsp. peppermint oil   1 Pt. white vinegar
    (from health food store)   1 Pt. warm tap water

Place all the ingredients in a small container and mix well. Massage the solution into the area of the sore muscle for relief.

Remedy for Sore Throat

The following ingredients will be needed:

    1/2 Cup apple cider vinegar   4 Tbsp. honey
    1 Tsp. cayenne pepper   1/2 Cup cool tap water
    (from health food store)

Place all the ingredients in a small bowl and blend thoroughly. Store in a small, capped bottle. Take 2-3 tbsp. every 4 hours to relieve the discomfort of a sore throat. The cayenne will help increase the circulation and speed up the healing process.

Quick, Fill the Tub with Tomato Juice

There is an "old wives' tale" that says that tomato juice will solve the problem of skunk smells. However, a number of studies have been done and the tomato juice only masked the smell for a short period of time. The following formula will do a great job of removing the smell. An alternative would be to use hydrogen peroxide and bicarbonate of soda.

Removing Skunk Smell From Pets

The following ingredients will be needed:

    1 Cup apple cider vinegar   5 Drops vanilla essential oil (from health food store)
    6 Oz. baking soda (fresh)   1/4 Cup baby shampoo
    2 Tbsp. lemon juice   Enough warm water to bath your animal

Place all the ingredients into a medium-sized bowl and mix very easily. If you mix too violently, the shampoo will foam up. Pour the mixture into the bath water, place a clothespin on your nose, then wash the poor pet.

GET ME A CRACKER, QUICK!

Morning sickness affects about 50% of all pregnant women in their first trimester. It may not be bothersome just early in the morning, but may cause nausea any time of the day or night. The sickness usually lasts through the first three months only and is rarely a problem after that. The cause is related to the change in hormones and the associated problems that cause poor metabolism of carbohydrates. Usually, if you consume a few smaller meals during the day while in the first trimester, the problem will be minimal or will not be a problem at all. Moving about very slowly when you first arise also tends to help reduce the frequency of morning sickness. When it does occur, a cracker seems to help.

Grandpa Cures Morning Sickness
(Most of the Time)

The following ingredients will be needed:

1 1/4 Tbsp. ginger root (fresh)	1 Tsp. dried lemon balm
1 Tsp. dried peppermint	3 1/2 Cups cold tap water
2 Tsp. dried chamomile	

Place the ginger root in a small saucepan with enough water to cover and simmer for 15-20 minutes, then add the balance of the ingredients and allow the mixture to steep for 10 minutes. Strain the mixture through a piece of cheesecloth or fine strainer and place into a covered glass for use the next morning. Best to double or triple this recipe if you have problems every morning and store the remainder in the refrigerator, then place a cup next to the bed every night. It wouldn't hurt to have a saltine cracker next to the cup, just in case.

There's a Fungus Among Us - Athlete's Foot

The following ingredients will be needed:

25 Cloves fresh garlic (grated very fine)	3 Tsp. powdered cloves
3 1/4 Tsp. ground cinnamon	6 Oz. 100-proof cheap vodka

Place the vodka in a jar (do not drink), add the garlic and cinnamon, then shake to mix and store in a cool, dark location for 12 days. The mixture should be shaken (and not stirred) every 2 days. Strain the mixture through a piece of cheesecloth and place in a well-sealed bottle until needed. The solution can be applied to the affected area with a cotton ball, morning and night.

Sore Muscle Relief

The following ingredients will be needed:

    2 Tsp. cayenne pepper   2 Drops essential bay oil

    2 Tbsp. virgin olive oil

Place the ingredients into a small bowl and mix well, then place the bowl into the micro-wave until warm, not hot. Rub into sore area with a clean cloth. Do not use on open sores or wounds and discontinue use if a rash occurs.

FACE IT, IT'S NO FUN

The majority of acne cases are related to heredity and the development of the sebaceous (oil secreting) gland in the skin. The problem has been related to a mild excessive hormone secretion that seems to trigger the problem around puberty. However, the problem can occur at almost any age, even infancy. Treatment varies from individual to individual and is somewhat dependent on the person's overall body hormonal functioning mechanisms. One treatment regimen is to prescribe the drug tetracycline, which is able to reduce the fat enzyme (lipase) in the secretions from the gland.

Acne Salve

The following ingredients will be needed:

    1/2 Tsp. helichrysum absolute (from drug store)

    2 Oz. rose hip seed oil (from health food store)

Place the ingredients in an opaque glass bottle and place in a water bath to blend well for 1 minute. Shake and apply a few drops to the pre-cleaned skin area.

Hot, Hot, Hot

Capsicum is the compound that makes a hot pepper hot. About 80% of the compound can be found in the seeds and membrane and almost nothing will reduce the potency, including cooking and freezing. The hotness can be neutralized with either a dairy product or beer. When capsicum is used in preparations, it has the ability to improve circulation and is a common ingredient in many herbal remedies.

Capsicum Salve

The following ingredients will be needed:

6 Tsp. tincture of capsicum
2 Tsp. tincture of camphor
3 Tsp. ammonia water

3 Tsp. ethyl alcohol
2 Tsp. soap liniment

Place all the ingredients into a small bowl and mix very well, then store in a sealed glass container. This formulation has been used historically for localized relief of pain.

1930's Chest Salve

The following ingredients will be needed:

4 Oz. brown Vaseline
4 Oz. paraffin wax
1 Tbsp. eucalyptus oil

1 Tsp. menthol crystals
1/4 Tsp. cassia oil
1 Tsp. turpentine

Place the paraffin and Vaseline in a double boiler and melt together, then add the menthol crystals and dissolve them by mixing well. Remove from the heat and allow the mixture to cool. While the mixture is cooling, add the turpentine and the oils and blend thoroughly. As soon as the salve thickens, pour it into a sealed container for storage. Apply the salve to the chest and cover with a warm towel.

Capsicum Liniment

The following ingredients will be needed:

1 Oz. tincture of capsicum
1/2 Oz. tincture of myrrh
1 Dram menthol
1/2 Oz. oil of sassafras

1 Oz. oil of origanum
1 Oz. camphor
1 1/2 Pt. rubbing alcohol

Place all the ingredients into a medium-sized container and blend thoroughly. Use as you would any other liniment. The capsicum has been used historically to increase circulation and speed healing.

Aunt Em's Nasal Inhaler

The following ingredients will be needed:

1 Very small amber or dark blue bottle   25 Drops essential rosemary oil
1/2 Oz. sea salt

Place the salt and oil in the very small bottle, close with a lid and shake. One sniff of this and your nose will clear right up.

Grandpa's Antacid Relief

The following ingredients will be needed:

1 Tbsp. bicarbonate of soda   4 Drops peppermint oil (or other flavoring)
1 Tsp. granulated sugar   1 Cup water

Place all the ingredients in a small container and mix well. Take 1 or 2 tbsp. to relieve indigestion or over-acidity.

Grandpa's Shaving Nick Reliever

The following ingredients will be needed:

1/2 Tbsp. glycerin   1 Tbsp. alum
1 1/2 Cups cool tap water

Place all the ingredients into a small bottle and shake well to mix. Apply with a cotton swab to the nick to relieve the discomfort and slight bleeding. Store in a well-sealed bottle and shake well before each use.

Old Indian Styptic

The American Indians used the two herbs: calendula and yarrow made into a paste, formed into stick shapes and rubbed on a bleeding wound. Sometimes the paste was just placed into the wound with excellent results.

Styptic Pencil Formula

The following ingredients will be needed:

    5 Oz. potassium alum crystals   *2 Tsp. glycerin*

    2 1/2 Tsp. finely powdered French chalk

Place the crystals in a small saucepan and heat on low heat until they liquefy, then remove any top scum leaving a clear liquid. In a small bowl, mix the chalk and glycerin into a paste and then add the paste into the liquid crystals and blend well. Remove from the heat and then pour the mixture into a small greased pan and allow it to cool down enough to cut into pencil-sized pieces. These pencils were used to stop bleeding from miner cuts made from shaving with a straight razor.

THE ORIGINAL SMELLING SALTS

The earliest record of the use of smelling salts goes back to the 1400s in China, when a person would carry a small bottle of rock salt ammonium carbonate. The pungent odor was said to be able to revive a person who was not feeling well. If a woman felt faint, she would sniff the rock salts. Physicians and medical personnel presently use a small ampoule that says "aromatic ammonia" to revive a fainting victim.

Old-Fashioned Smelling Salts Formula

The following ingredients will be needed:

    5 Minims tincture of orris   *30 Minims extract of violet*

    10 Minims oil of lavender   *2 Oz. ammonia water*

Place all the ingredients into a small bottle with a good seal and shake to mix. Shake before each use and only use when grandma faints.

1930´s Antiseptic Vaginal Jelly

The following ingredients will be needed:

1 1/2 Tsp. gum tragacanth	25 Tsp. distilled water
2 1/2 Tsp. glycerin	1 1/4 Tsp. boric acid

Place the gum tragacanth and the glycerin in a medium-sized bowl and mix well, then very slowly add the water and boric acid while continually stirring. Allow the solution to remain at room temperature for 10 hours before using. Mix well before using.

Touched a Toad Lately?

Warts are really not caused by touching a toad, but are tumors or small growths that occur on the skin caused by infection with the human "pappiloma virus." There are over 70 different type of warts and are more common in youngsters than adults. Almost all warts will disappear over time, but seem to take longer in adults than in children. Warts are not serious; however, there are treatments that will remove them. Surgically removing the wart usually leaves a scar. Other methods include freezing it off with liquid nitrogen, chemical treatment and the use of electricity.

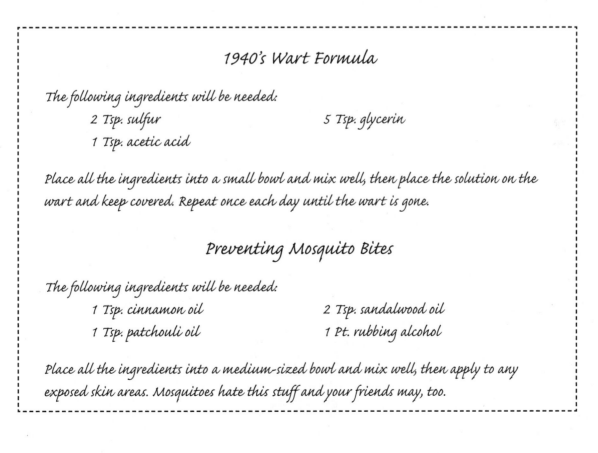

1940's Wart Formula

The following ingredients will be needed:

2 Tsp. sulfur	5 Tsp. glycerin
1 Tsp. acetic acid	

Place all the ingredients into a small bowl and mix well, then place the solution on the wart and keep covered. Repeat once each day until the wart is gone.

Preventing Mosquito Bites

The following ingredients will be needed:

1 Tsp. cinnamon oil	2 Tsp. sandalwood oil
1 Tsp. patchouli oil	1 Pt. rubbing alcohol

Place all the ingredients into a medium-sized bowl and mix well, then apply to any exposed skin areas. Mosquitoes hate this stuff and your friends may, too.

1950's Sore Throat Spray

The following ingredients will be needed:

4 Oz. white mineral oil	10 Grains camphor
5 Grains menthol	5 Grains eucalyptus

Place all the ingredients into a small bowl and mix thoroughly, then place into a small throat sprayer and spray while holding the tongue down.

Diaper Rash Powder

The following ingredients will be needed:

2 Oz. goldenseal powder	2 Oz. dry clay

Place the ingredients into a small container and mix well, then store in a sealed bottle in a cool dry location.

Natural Laxative

The following ingredients will be needed:

1/2 Cup virgin olive oil	1/2 Cup fresh orange juice

Place the ingredients into a glass and mix well. Take just before bedtime.

Sleepytime Tea

The following ingredients will be needed:

1 Tbsp. lemon verbena	1 Tbsp. powdered valerian root
1 Tbsp. lemon peel	

Place all the ingredients into a small container and blend well. Place 1 tbsp. into an infuser and place into a cup of hot water, then allow it to steep for 4 minutes. Strain the mixture and drink.

Grandpa's Ointment for Barber's Itch

The following ingredients will be needed:

30 Grains ichthyol	45 Drops mercury oleate (10%)
12 Grains salicylic acid	1 Oz. lanolin

Place all the ingredients into a container and mix well, then keep applying to the affected area.

Grandma's Nipple Ointment

The following ingredients will be needed:

24 Grams white wax	40 Grams clarified honey
80 Grams sweet almond oil	25 Grams balsam Peru

Place all the ingredients into a container and blend well, then apply a small amount.

Old-Fashioned Smelling Salts

The following ingredients will be needed:

2 1/2 Oz. strong tincture of orris root	30 Drops spirit of ammonia
45 Drops violet extract	

Place a small amount of coarsely powdered ammonium carbonate into a container. Mix all the ingredients in another container, then add the mixture to the ammonium carbonate. This will really bring you around in short order.

Homemade Tallow for Soap-Making

The following ingredients will be needed:

    5 Lb. beef fat

    Tap water as required

Place the beef fat in an old large pot and melt on low heat, while stirring occasionally to make sure that the fat does not burn. After the fat has melted, cook the fat for 45 minutes, then allow the fat to cool for a few minutes before pouring through a sieve into another pot and discard any solid residues. Make sure that the fat has cooled enough to accept water without splattering. Add half the volume of cool tap water and bring to a boil, then reduce the heat to a low point, cover and allow the mixture to simmer for 3-4 hours.

Remove from heat and allow the fat to cool somewhat before pouring through a sieve again into a plastic container to cool. Place the container in the refrigerator or in a very cool location for about 24 hours until a layered mixture is formed. There will be three distinct layers, the top layer will be the pure tallow, the middle layer will be a mixture of fat and water with residues and the bottom layer will be the heavier protein jelly.

Place the mixture in a large pan and carefully separate the tallow from the other layers, wrap it in plastic wrap and store the tallow in a cool, dry location or in the refrigerator. The tallow should remain usable for about 4-6 weeks depending on storage conditions.

35

Vinegar
ALL-AROUND MONEY-SAVER

HOUSEHOLD CLEANING USES FOR VINEGAR

Remove Water Rings

Mix vinegar and olive oil in a one-to-one ratio and apply with a soft cloth, using slight pressure in a circular motion.

Polish Leather Furniture

Boil 2 cups of linseed oil for 1-minute, then allow it to cool before stirring in 1 cup of white vinegar. Apply with a soft cloth then allow it to stand for 1-2 minutes and then rub off gently.

Remove Carpet Stains

Only works well if the stain is fresh. Combine 1 part of white vinegar to 3 parts of water and allowed to remain on the stain for 3-4 minutes. Using a sponge, rub the area gently from the center out then dry with a clean soft cloth. Try an area that is out-of-the-way to be sure that the carpet is colorfast.

Chewing Gum Remover
White vinegar is capable of dissolving and softening chewing gum from a number of fabrics and carpeting.

Decal Remover
Apply warm vinegar on a sponge and allow it to stand for a few minutes, then wipe with a soft dry cloth.

Mildew Remover
For severe buildup of mildew, use white vinegar full strength. For all other mildew buildup, use a solution of vinegar and water.

Plastic Upholstery Cleaner
Combine vinegar and water one-to-one and wipe the furniture with a dampened soft cloth. Follow with a dry cloth to buff.

Metal Cleaner
Use a small amount of vinegar, baking soda or salt to prepare a paste and use the paste to clean bronze, copper or brass pots or utensils.

Clean Aluminum Pot Stains
Black stains on aluminum pots can be removed by boiling white vinegar in the pot up to the area of the stain. For large pots, boil the vinegar in a small pot and pour it on the stain.

Wash Windows
Mix one tablespoon of white vinegar to one quart of water.

Grease Cutter
Place a capful of vinegar in the dishwasher to cut grease.

Crystal Clear Glassware
If you want your crystal to sparkle, just rinse them in a solution of: one part white vinegar to three parts warm water.

Remove Lime Residue
Coffee pots, tea kettles and irons are notorious for hard water residue buildup. When they get really bad,

fill them with white vinegar and run them through a cycle.

Drain Cleaner I
Boil 2 cups of vinegar and pour it down the drain a small amount at a time. Allow the vinegar to remain in the drain for about 5-10 minutes before pouring a pot of very hot water down the drain. The alternative is to use 1/2 cup of baking soda poured into the drain followed by 1/2 cup of warm vinegar, cover the drain and allow it to stand for 5-10 minutes before running cold water down the drain.

Drain Cleaner II
Drop 3-4 Alka-Seltzer® tablets down the drain, then pour a bottle of white vinegar down. After 3-5 minutes, run hot water down.

Clean Shower Head
Remove the head and place it in a container that will allow you to cover the head with vinegar. Allow soaking overnight, rinse and replace.

Weed Killer
Pour white vinegar on weeds in sidewalk or driveway cracks and they will be killed.

Pet Flea Killer
Add 1 tsp. of cider vinegar to every qt. of water. Fleas will not go near your pet.

Cement Remover
When you are working with concrete or cement, try cleaning your hands with vinegar, works great.

Ant Remover
If you are having a problem with ants, just wipe your counters off with a solution prepared from equal parts of vinegar and water. Crawling insects hate vinegar.

Remove Scorch Marks
If you rub a scorched mark with a clean soft cloth that has been lightly dampened with vinegar, it may remove a scorch mark if it not too badly imbedded.

Brighten Clothes
If you add 1¹/₂ cups of white vinegar to your rinse water, it will brighten up the colors.
If you are dying a fabric, add 1 cup of vinegar to the final rinse to set the color.

Remove Crayon Stains

Moisten a toothbrush with white vinegar and rub the area lightly until the crayon is removed.

Eliminate Deodorant Stains

Perspiration stains can be removed by rubbing the area with vinegar before laundering.

Ink Stain Remover

Vinegar will remove most ink stains if they are fresh.

Rust Remover

To remove rust, just moisten the fabric with white vinegar, then rub the area lightly with salt. Place the garment in the sun to dry, then launder.

MEDICINAL USES FOR VINEGAR

Dandruff

Massage white vinegar into the scalp 3-4 times per week, then shampoo.

Nail Polish Saver

To make nail polish last longer, just soak the fingernails in a solution of 2 tsp. of white vinegar and 1/2 cup of warm water for 1-2 minutes before applying the polish.

Sunburn Reliever

Place a piece of cloth that has been lightly dampened with apple cider vinegar on the burn. Replace every 20-30 minutes.

Athlete's Foot

Rinse your feet 3-4 times per day in apple cider vinegar.

Morning Sickness

When morning sickness occurs, just combine 1 tsp. of apple cider vinegar in a glass of water and drink it.

Indigestion

To relieve indigestion, just place 2 tsp. of apple cider vinegar into a glass of water and drink during a meal.

A Bunion Sandwich

In a small bowl, soak 2 slices of white bread, 2 slices of red onion in 1 cup of vinegar for 24 hours. Place the bread on the corn (bunion) and place a slice of onion on top. Wrap with a bandage and allow it to remain overnight.

AROUND THE KITCHEN WITH VINEGAR

Storing Pimientos

If you want to store pimiento peppers after opening a can or jar, just place then into a very small bowl, cover them with vinegar and refrigerate. They will last for 2-3 weeks.

Keeping Ginger Fresh

Prepare a clean jar filled with balsamic vinegar and add the grated ginger, seal tight and refrigerate.

Flavor Enhancer

When preparing soup or tomato sauce, add one or two tbsp. of vinegar to the soup or sauce during the last 5 minutes of cooking time. This will really enhance their flavor.

Over-Salted Foods

Add 1 tsp. of vinegar and 1 tsp. of sugar then reheat the dish or sauce.

Mold Eliminator

Always remember to wipe down the outside of canning jars with vinegar to eliminate the possibility of mold growing.

Vegetable and Fruit Wash

Mix $2^{1}/_{2}$ tbsp. of vinegar in 1 gal. of water and use the mixture to wash the outsides of fruits and vegetables before peeling or slicing into them.

Stops Food Discoloring

If you add 1-2 teaspoons of vinegar to the water you are boiling potatoes in, they will not discolor for a longer period.

Great Mashed Potato Trick

Once you have mashed the potatoes and added the hot milk, try adding a tsp. of vinegar and beat a little bit more. It will fluff them up and they will hold their shape.

Firm Gelatin

In warmer weather, gelatin tends to lose its shape. Just add 1 tsp. of vinegar to the gelatin to keep it firm.

Saving Money
USING SALT

IN THE BATHROOM

Hair, Hair

To dissolve hair in a drain, just prepare a mixture of 1 cup of salt, 1 cup of baking soda mixed in $1/2$ cup of white vinegar. Pour the mixture down the sluggish drain and allow it to remain for 15-20 minutes before flushing with 2-3 quarts of boiling water. Wash out with warm water.

Cleans Porcelain

Get rid of old watermarks by preparing a gentle scouring powder. Mix together 1 cup of table salt and 1 cup of baking soda. Use as a paste to remove the stains.

Tub Turning Brown?

Mix up an equal solution of salt and turpentine and that should remove the yellow or brown stains.

GROOMING

Make a Mouthwash

You can easily make a mouthwash by mixing 1 tsp. table salt, 1 tsp. baking soda and 1/2 cup of cool tap water. If you prefer the mint flavor, just add a few drops of peppermint extract.

Get Rid of Rough Skin

To soften rough skin, just prepare a mixture of 1/4 cup table salt, 1/4 cup of Epsom salts and 1/4 cup Canola oil. Massage the mixture onto the dry skin and allow it to remain for 5-10 minutes.

Remove Dry Skin

As soon as you get out of the shower and while you are still wet, give yourself a rubdown with dry table salt placed on a damp sponge.

Revitalize Your Face

Prepare a mixture of 1 tbsp. olive oil mixed with 1 tbsp. salt. Wash your face, then apply a warm towel for 5 minutes before very gently massaging your face with the preparation. Use long upward and inward strokes for the best results. Allow the mixture to remain on your face for 5 minutes before rinsing and applying a pleasant facial lotion.

Save Money on Toothpaste

Prepare a mixture of 1 tsp. salt to 2 tsp. baking soda. Crush the salt mixture as fine as possible before using it as a teeth cleanser.

Salt Solves Itchy Skin

Take a bath and add 1 cup of salt to the water, then apply a coating of aloe gel.

AROUND THE HOUSE

Grease Spots
If you have a stubborn grease spot on your carpet, try using a solution of 1 part salt to 4 parts of rubbing alcohol. Always rub in the direction of the nap to be safe and not damage the nap.

Wine Stains
Pour salt immediately on a red wine stain and the salt will absorb the wine.

Works on Wicker
Use a stiff brush moistened with warm salt water, then allow the furniture to sun dry.

Refrigerator Cleaning
A solution of salt mixed with club soda should do an excellent job on your refrigerator shelves.

Broom Life Extender
When you bring home a new broom or brush, try soaking it in hot saltwater before you use them for the first time. Add 1 cup of salt to a bucket of very hot, steaming water and soak away for about 10 minutes.

Fish Tank Cleaner
You can clean all the glass on a fish tank by using a sponge that has been moistened with warm water, then add salt and clean away. It should remove the cloudy areas easily.

Settle Down Oversudsing
If you have a problem with the washer bubbling over from too many suds, just sprinkle salt on top of the bubbles to reduce them. This also works on beer foam when it gets too high.

FOOD USES

Cheese Protector
If you wrap cheese in a piece of paper towel that has been lightly dampened with saltwater before you refrigerate it, it will stop the mild spores from setting up housekeeping.

Whipping Secret
If you add just a pinch of salt to cream before you start whipping it, it will whip us easier. Works well with the egg whites as well.

Dairy Life Extender

If you add a pinch of salt to a 1/2 gal. of milk, it will retain its freshness for a longer period of time.

Coffeetime

If you place a pinch of salt in the coffee filter before starting to brew it, it will improve the flavor.

Stop Browning

If you keep apples, pears or potatoes in a bowl of lightly salted water after you peel them, they will not turn brown. Wash them off and they won't retain the salt taste.

The Shell Game

To make it easier to remove the shells from pecans and other thin-shelled nuts, just soak then in saltwater for 3-5 hours before removing their shells.

Deodorize Garbage Disposal

Just pour 1/2 cup of salt in the garbage disposal and run water while it is activated to deodorize it.

Fire Extinguisher

Pouring salt on a fire in a pan should put it out instantly by eliminating the oxygen.

AROUND THE CAR

Ice on Windshields

To eliminate the problem of ice forming on your windshield in the winter, just use a small muslin bag filled with salt, then rub it on the windshield every morning. Beats using a scraper!

AT THE RIVER OR BEACH

Kills Leeches

Pour salt on the leech and it will shrivel up, fall off and die.

Jellyfish Remover

Prepare a mixture of 1 tbsp. of salt mixed with 1 tbsp. of white vinegar and pour the solution on the area where you got stung. This will deactivate the tentacle and allow you to scrape it off with a towel or sand. The tentacles will keep releasing their poisons until they are removed.

Saving Money
USING BAKING SODA

WHAT IS BAKING SODA?

Baking soda is actually bicarbonate of soda, which is derived from the manufacture of common washing soda also, known as "sal soda." Baking soda is composed carbon and oxygen molecules, which combine to form carbon dioxide gas. If batter has a sufficient acidic nature then only baking soda is needed to produce carbon dioxide. If the batter does not have sufficient acid, then baking powder, which carries both acid and alkali, is needed. All baking soda in North America is mined from the mineral, Trona, which is found in Green River, Wyoming. The large deposit was discovered in the 1930s. Trona is actually composed of sodium bicarbonate and sodium carbonate, a very close relative. The ore is mined from deep mines, crushed, rinsed, and heated to produce sodium carbonate. The sodium carbonate is then dissolved in water and carbon dioxide is forced through the solution, releasing the sodium bicarbonate crystals, which is washed, then dried and packaged as baking soda.

When baking soda is added to a recipe, it has an immediate rising action with the release of the gas, which means that your oven must be preheated and your pans greased before you even combine the ingredients. Baking soda should be added to dry ingredients first and the wet ingredients just before placing the food into the oven. Baking soda will last for approximately 6 months if stored in an airtight container and in a cool, dry location. If you are not sure of the activity level of baking soda, try placing $1/4$ teaspoon in about 2 tsp. of white vinegar. If carbon dioxide bubbles appear, it still has good activity. Sodium bicarbonate is produced in the human body to assist in maintaining the acidity (pH) level of the blood as well as being found in saliva. It will neutralize plaque acids, which might otherwise dissolve our teeth. Another action in the body is to neutralize stomach acid so that we don't get ulcers, as well as assisting in the breathing process by transporting carbon dioxide from the tissues to the lungs for disposal.

Don't Have a Crackup
To keep icing on a cake moist and prevent cracking, just add a pinch of baking soda into the icing before icing the cake.

How Sweet it is
Wild blackberries can save a lot of money since they are very expensive in the markets. To sweeten them up when making pies or cobblers, just add $1/2$ tsp. of baking soda before adding any sugar to the recipe.

No Crystals Here
A common problem when boiling syrup is the formation of unwanted crystals. To avoid the problem, just add a pinch of baking soda to the syrup.

Good Idea When Boiling Milk
To avoid milk from curdling when it is being boiled, just add a pinch of baking soda to the milk.

Never a Separation
Gravy will always stay in suspension if you just add 2 pinches of baking soda to the gravy.

Tough Meat
Try rubbing baking soda on the surface of a piece of tough meat and allow it to stand for 2-3 hours in the refrigerator before rinsing it off and cooking it.

Wild Game
To eliminate the wild game taste from venison, just soak the meat in baking soda and water for 8 hours in the refrigerator. Rinse off well before cooking.

No Bitterness

When you cook turnips or mustard greens, try adding $1/2$ tsp. of baking soda to the cooking water to remove the bitterness.

Use Less Sugar in Rhubarb

If you add a pinch of baking soda to the cooking water, you will need less sugar in your recipe to achieve a somewhat sweet taste. Rhubarb should be a little tart and the baking soda will help.

Help! My Tomato Soup is Curdling

Homemade tomato soup has the tendency to curdle easily, unless you add a pinch of baking soda to the soup before you add the tomatoes.

Too Much Vinegar

If you add too much vinegar to a recipe, just add baking soda to neutralize it.

More Tea from a Bag

To get more tea out of a teabag, just add a pinch of baking soda to the teapot. Your tea won't cloud either, which is great for iced tea.

Stop Scouring Pad Rust

If you store the used pads in a solution of baking soda and water, they will not rust.

Stoneware Repair

To remove scratches from stoneware or at least make them less visible, try applying a thick paste of baking soda and water and allow the dish to remain for 5-10 minutes before washing.

Unclog Burners

To unclog burners on a gas range, try boiling them in a solution of $1/4$ of a box of baking soda in 2 qt. of water.

Avoid Grease Fires

Keep a little baking soda in the shallow drip pans that are under gas burners to lower the risk of fires from grease drippings.

Tub Appliqués

To get rid of stains on tub appliqués or the built-in strips, just sprinkle the stained area with baking soda and allow it to remain for 1 hour before rinsing off.

Shower Curtains

Place plastic shower curtains in the washing machine with 2 bath towels on the gentle cycle and add ½ cup of baking soda plus your normal detergent in the wash cycle. Then add 1 cup of white vinegar to the rinse cycle and allow the curtains to drip dry.

Christmas Tree Sap

If sap gets into the carpet, try removing it with a paste of baking soda and water and a mild, bristled brush. Test an area for colorfastness before attempting this.

Upholstery Cleaner

Sprinkle a generous amount of baking soda on your upholstery and allow it to sit for 10-15 minutes before vacuuming it off.

Dirty Clothes

Make a sachet filled with baking soda and place it in the dirty clothes hamper to keep it smelling fresh.

Pool Chlorine

Add 1 tbsp. of baking soda to a sink full of water and rinse out your bathing suit from the pool chlorine.

Green Hair

Fix a solution of ½ cup of baking soda dissolved in 1 cup of lemon juice. Wet your hair and pour the solution over it immediately as it bubbles up.

Clean Eye Glasses

Baking soda is excellent as a mild abrasive for cleaning eyeglasses. Rub gently over the lenses then rinse in cool tap water.

Dental Floss

If you dip dental floss in baking soda before flossing, it will remove more plaque.

Bug Remover

If you use a mild baking soda solution on a damp rag, it will remove bugs from your car paint safely. Allow the paste to remain for about 5 minutes before washing off.

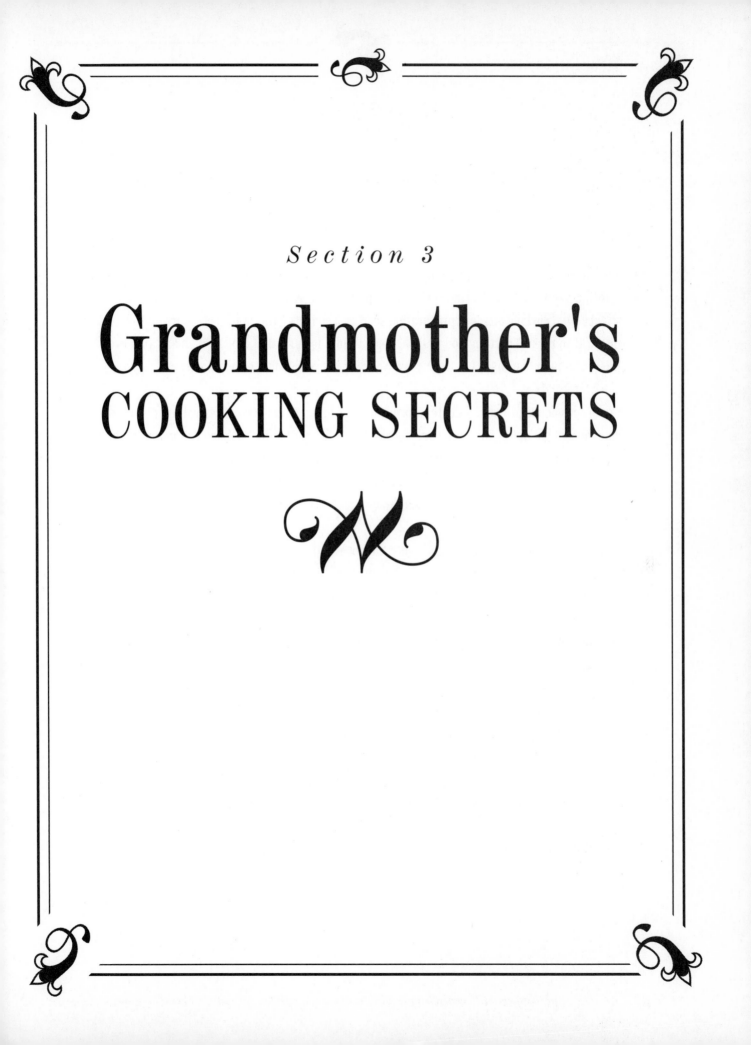

Section 3

Grandmother's
COOKING SECRETS

FORWARD

Not everyone can have the opportunity of going to cooking school and learning the methods, preparation tips, and secrets of cooking food. So I thought that it would be nice to write a book that just presented all the little secrets for the preparation of a particular dish, especially the more popular ones.

Since I have been writing kitchen reference books for many years and have learned thousands of individual facts regarding foods, the idea for this book was to provide you with a totally different book that contained thousands of actual cooking and food preparation secrets. The tricks, tips, and secrets are all "food specific." When you want to make a certain food or dish, you can just look up that food or dish and find every tip or secret that pertains to that dish that twenty-five years of research could come up with.

Kitchen reference books provide in-depth information not found in cookbooks regarding almost every food imaginable, household hints, stain removal information, etc., while The Cookbook's Companion is related only to food preparation of specific dishes and foods. For example, reference books may only have four or five facts regarding cooking with cheese, cookbooks may only have one or two tips when giving you a recipe, while The Cookbook's Companion has thirty-five cooking tips regarding cheese.

Another example is if you are preparing a roast: the book will provide you with thirty-four tips and chef's secrets to preparing the perfect roast but not the actual recipe. It is amazing how many secrets there are when cooking different dishes that cookbooks never reveal.

Every cookbook in the world needs The Cookbook's Companion
to make it a real cookbook.

This book just goes into the basics of each food or dish and presents the tips (just the facts) that will assist you in general preparation, allowing you to prepare the perfect food.

Many of the facts came from chefs worldwide, and many from grandmothers and great grandmothers, collected and tried over a period of twenty-five years of research into food and how to prepare a perfect dish.

This is one book that will never leave your home unless you have a very long string on it

38

General Cooking
SECRETS

COOKING METHODS

BARBECUING

- Best not to use "real" charcoal to barbecue with. Fat dripping on the coals produces a chemical that gets on the meat.
- If you do get a flare-up, place lettuce leaves on top of the coals to cool them without extinguishing them.
- Never cook foods next to each other. Leave about 1 inch between foods.
- If you are in a hurry, partially precook foods that take a long time to cook, such as chicken breasts.
- Make sure you spray the grill before you start the fire so that the food will not stick.

Barbecue Sauces

- The base for most barbecue sauces include dark brown sugar, lemon juice, pepper, Worcestershire sauce or soy sauce, salt, and garlic.
- When barbecuing, the sauce should not be placed on the food during the first $^3/_4$ of the cooking time or it may burn and produce a bitter taste.

BOILING

- Always: place vegetables into the water after the water begins to boil.

Allow the water to boil for 2 minutes to release a percentage of the oxygen. This will help retain some of the nutrients longer. Excess oxygen will reduce the potency of a number of nutrients and vitamins.

BRAISING

- Braising may be done either on the stove or in the oven. This method is preferred for certain foods since the heat surrounds the pot.
- A heavy pot with a lid that closes tightly is recommended.
- The liquid used for braising is always used as either all or part of the sauce.
- Braising (browning) is almost always the initial step in the cooking process of any meat on which a brown crust is desired.
- Pan-frying is the typical method for braising.
- If braising is called for in a vegetable recipe it usually refers to cooking the vegetables in a small amount of liquid at a low temperature without browning the vegetables first.
- When braising, food is never completely covered by the liquid.
- Braising can be used for many cuts of meat. The meat is first browned in a very small amount of oil or butter. The pan is then covered as tight as possible while the meat continues to cook.
- If you oven-braise, set the temperature to 325°F for a more even braise.

Sprinkling a small amount of flour on the meat during cooking will help it to brown.

- Make sure that there is only a very small amount of liquid, or the steam generated will poach the meat.
- The liquid in the pot should only be simmering, not boiling.
- Occasionally blot the top of the meat with a paper towel to eliminate excess moisture for the best results.

BROILING

Broiling is done under the heating element in an oven. Grilling is done on a grill, usually outside. High-heat cooking methods are used for tender cuts of meat.

- Lower heat is used for large, thick meats.
- Meats are sometimes dipped in oil to reduce sticking and to keep them moist.

Always place meats under the broiler as dry as possible.

- Meat and fish will brown more evenly at room temperature instead of directly from the refrigerator.
- Always heat the broiler or the pan before placing any meat on it.
- Use higher heat for thinner cuts and for meat that is to be cooked rare.
- Fat around meat may catch fire if it gets too hot or if it is too close to the flame or element.
- The distance from the top of the meat and the flame given in the recipe needs to be adhered to.
- If the meat you are cooking is thin, it should be cooked close to the flame or element so that it will cook faster and retain its moisture.
- If you are going to baste the meat, be sure and use a warm solution. If the solution is cool or cold it will slow down the cooking time.
- A thin basting solution can be placed in a spray bottle.
- To reduce the risk of flare-ups place a few slices of bread on the bottom of the pan to soak up the excess fat drippings.
- If you want your steaks to be rare or medium-rare then they need to be cooked close to the heat source.
- Chicken breasts or thick cuts of meat are cooked away from the heat source.
- Only turn meats once when broiling.

Broiler Times

Cut of Meat	Thickness	Rare	Medium	Well Done
			minutes per side	
Beef	1 in.	5 min.	6 min.	7 min.
(all steaks)	1½ in.	9 min.	10 min	12 min.
	2 in.	16 min.	18 min.	20 min.
Lamb	1 in.	N/A	6 min.	7 min.
(loin, rib, or chops)	1½ in.	N/A	9 min.	11 min.
	2 in.	N/A	15 min.	17 min.
Pork				
(ham shoulder slice)				
Raw	1 in.			10 min.
Precooked				5 min.

CLAY POTS

- Place the whole pot in warm water for 15-20 minutes before using. A cold pot may crack.
- Never preheat the oven when using a clay pot. The temperature must rise gradually to protect the pot.
- When you remove the pot from the oven, never set it on a cold (or even cool) surface. Place the pot on a rack or on folded kitchen towels.
- Never attempt to use a clay pot on the stovetop or any direct heat source or it will crack.

CONVECTION OVEN

A convection oven is similar to a standard oven. The main difference is that in a convection oven there is a fan that increases the distribution of the heated air molecules, providing heat to all areas more evenly and faster. The fan makes the heat circulation more efficient, so the oven can be run at a lower temperature.

- If you are going to use a convection oven reduce the recommended temperature for a recipe by 25°-75°F.
- It is not necessary to preheat a convection oven. They heat up very quickly and evenly surround the food with heat.

CROCK-POTS

- Never use a crock-pot to reheat leftovers. The food needs to be reheated at higher temperature to kill bacteria that may have grown since it was first cooked.
- Vegetables should be placed in crock-pots just before serving in the order of their thickness.
- All foods should be at refrigerator or room temperature before placing them into a crock-pot.
- Never put partially or totally frozen foods in a crock-pot.
- Make sure that the cooker is $^1/_2$ to $^2/_3$ full or the food will not absorb enough heat.
- The food must be covered with a liquid to generate sufficient steam.

- The original lid should be used and be tight-fitting.
- If possible allow the cooker to remain at a high setting for the first hour.
- Make sure to follow the manufacturer's recommended temperatures for foods.

FRYING

- Never use "all-purpose oil" for frying.
- Peanut oil is good for frying but not for baked goods.
- Frying oil should never be reused. Oil breaks down as it is heated. Once that breakdown occurs it is not healthy to use.
- One of the best oils for frying is canola, which has a smoke point of 525°F.
- Dry foods thoroughly before placing them into a fryer.
- If you are going to use shortening to fry with, heat the shortening slowly. Shortening will scorch easily.
- Never crowd a deep-fat fryer for the best results.
- Always start shortening at 225°F and keep it there until all melted before raising the temperature.
- Never allow even a hint of soap scum to remain in the fryer or it will affect the results.
- If you coat the inside of the fryer with a very thin coating of white vinegar before you place the oil in the foods will be less greasy.
- To test the fat to see if it too old, just drop a small piece of bread into it. If the bread develops dark specs the oil is bad.
- Frying oil should never exceed 380°F.
- To slow the deterioration of the oil between batches it would be best to reduce the temperature of the fat to 250°F until you are ready to use the oil again.

A low frying temperature results in a high fat product.

- Always allow the temperature to return to the normal frying temperature when frying a number of batches.
- Frying oil will darken prematurely if your frying pan is the slightest bit dirty.
- Too many food particles accumulating in the fryer can cause problems with discoloring the food.
- Never use brass or copper utensils in the fryer or they will react with the oil creating foam.
- If the fryer starts smoking while you are cooking it is probably because excess food has built up or the fat is too old.
- Never salt foods to be fried until you are ready to serve them or the salt will draw liquid out of the food.

GRILLING

- Normally done on an open grill over charcoal, or gas, or an electric element. Cooking is regulated by moving the food to a hotter or cooler location on the grill.

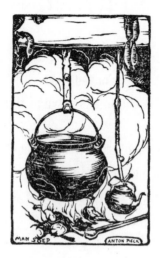

HIGH-ALTITUDE COOKING

- When cooking above 3,500 feet the atmospheric pressure gets lower and this will affect cooking and baking temperatures.
- When baking cakes or cookies at temperatures over 3,500 feet you will need to increase the temperature 25°F and add 1 tablespoon of flour to your recipe, then continue adding 1 tablespoon of flour for every 1,500 feet.
- If you are using leavening and 1 teaspoon is needed at sea level, then use $^2/_3$ teaspoon at 3,500 feet, $^1/_2$ teaspoon at 5,000 feet and $^1/_4$ teaspoon at 6,500 feet.
- Boiled foods will take longer to cook the higher the altitude.
- Additional liquid may be needed for certain recipes the higher the altitude.
- All meats will take longer to cook at high altitudes.
- Legumes will take longer to cook and may require extra liquid.

Yeast breads will not need an adjustment at higher altitudes. Allow the dough to rise twice for the best results.

- Egg whites should only be beaten to soft-peak stage and not beaten until stiff over 3,500 feet.
- When deep fat frying it will be necessary to decrease the temperature 3°F for every 1,000 feet above sea level.
- Water will boil at 198°F instead of 212°F at 7,500 feet above sea level.

Boiling Point vs. Altitude

- As the altitude increases, the atmospheric pressure decreases placing less pressure on water that is trying to boil. When this occurs it makes it easier for the water to boil and the water molecules are released more easily. Water will boil at a lower temperature at a 5,000 foot elevation. For every 1,000 feet of elevation water will boil at approximately 2° F. less than at sea level.

ALTITUDE (feet)	FAHRENHEIT	CELSIUS
0	212°	100°
1,000	210°	99°
2,000	208°	98°
3,000	207°	97°
4,000	205°	96°
5,000	203°	95°
10,000	194°	90°

MICROWAVE COOKING

- Shorter cooking times will retain nutrients.
- Foods need to be turned unless the microwave has a moveable turntable or the food will have "cold spots."
- Use a special dish that is specifically designed for browning if you wish to brown food. The dish should be preheated for the best results.

When cooking meats with bones, remember that the bones will absorb more energy than the meat and the meat may not cook evenly.

- If you are baking a dish it will rise higher in a microwave.
- If a food is frozen it will take longer to cook in a microwave, since it does not work well on frozen water.
- Meats with a high fat content will cook more rapidly than lean meats.
- Meats should be slightly undercooked since they will continue cooking after they are removed from the oven.

PAN-FRYING

- It is best to use fat with a high smoke point, such as canola.
- Never use fat that has been heated before. It may have deteriorated too much.

- Always place the presentation side in first since it will probably look the best after cooking.
- Small bubbles will appear on the side of the pan when the food is finished cooking.
- Make sure that you use a heavy pan, which normally conducts heat better than a thin one. Thin pans may develop hot spots.

Pan-frying is similar to sautéing with the exception that more oil is used and the cooking time is usually longer.

- Used for larger cuts of meats.
- Pan-fried foods should only be turned once.
- The level of fat used should come halfway up the sides of the meat or fish.
- Don't use a thick batter on a thin food or it will hide the flavor.
- Season all food before you place it in the pan.
- The pieces are not tossed up like when you sauté.
- Pan-frying is usually done over low heat.
- Pan-fried foods are often completed in the oven for the best results.
- If you desire a very crisp coating, complete the cooking in the oven after cooking the first side.

POACHING (GENERAL)

- The best temperature for poaching is 160°-180°F.
- The cooking is done in a small amount of liquid. The liquid should be very hot but not boiling.
- Mostly used to cook more delicate foods such as eggs (out of the shell) and fish.
- Partially poaching certain meats will eliminate the harsh flavors before they are cooked using some other method.
- Poaching will also firm-up meats.

PRESSURE COOKING (GENERAL)

- Make sure that your pressure cooker has a 6 quart capacity or more for greater efficiency.
- Never fill the pressure cooker more than 65% full if you are cooking a food that has a high liquid content.
- Recommended highly for soups, stews, and chili. Beans will not have to be soaked, which saves a great deal of time.

ROASTING

- The cut of meat to be roasted should be large enough so that it will retain enough moisture through this dry-cooking method.
- For the best flavor, purchase a roast with the bone in to increase the flavor and to act as a heat conductor shortening the cooking time.
- Allow a roast to remain out of the refrigerator for about 1-2 hours before cooking.

Always start a roast in a preheated oven to help retain the juices.

- Give the roast a massage with olive oil to help retain moisture.
- Place the roast on fresh celery stalks to allow fat to drip to the bottom and to allow the heat to circulate around the roast more efficiently.
- Never use any seasoning that contains salt on a roast or it may draw moisture from the meat.
- If you marinated the roast, the olive oil massage is even more important to help retain the moisture.
- Placing vegetable juice in the bottom of the pan will provide more flavor than using water.
- Use a roasting pan that has a very heavy lid, the heavier the better, to keep the steam in so that it will recirculate into the cooking liquid.
- Searing a roast contributes to drying out the roast and is not recommended by most chefs.

If the roast has high fat content and thick fat covering, just sprinkle the surface with a small amount of dry mustard to neutralize the fattiness.

- If the roast has a fat layer or if you are barding it, cook the roast fat-side up to naturally baste it.
- If you would like a nice brown coating on the roast, brush the outside lightly with white vermouth about 15 minutes before the roast has completed cooking. If you have covered the roast remove the covering.
- If you slow-cook a roast it will retain more moisture and will not shrink as much, however, it will not be browned very well.
- A fast method of cooking a pot roast is to tightly wrap the roast in heavy-weight aluminum foil after sprinkling 2 packages of dry onion mix over it. Cook in a preheated 300°F oven for 3 hours. Vegetables can be added to the pot after 2 hours of cooking time has elapsed.
- If you want a nicely browned roast that retains its moisture and does not have too much shrinkage, place the roast in a very hot oven for the first 20-25 minutes, then reduce the heat back to the recommended setting.
- If the roast does not have a fat layer on top then it should be turned once or twice and basted with the juices for the best results.

- To deep brown the roast, just raise the oven temperature toward the end of the cooking time. The juices that have been released will be available to brown.
- Try not to baste with too much liquid. The addition of additional liquid may have the tendency to create too much steam and the roast will not brown properly.

Allow the roast to rest for about 15 minutes after you remove it from the oven. The juices tend to go toward the center during cooking and will return closed to the surface after the roast is allowed to rest.

- While the roast is resting cover it with tin foil.

SAUTÉING

The meaning of sauté is "to jump" in French referring to the fact that the food is tossed in the sauté pan while it has been cooking.

- Heat the pan and the fat before adding any food.
- The food should be at room temperature. If the food is cold it may stick to the pan.
- Any dense foods such as carrots should be parboiled before being sautéed.
- Use a straight-sided sauté pan for large items. Sloping sided pans are best for smaller items.

Before sautéing meats, always dredge the meat in a light coating of flour to hold the meat together and provide a protective coating.

- Before browning meat, sprinkle a small amount of sugar on the meat to help it brown.
- Salting food that is being sautéed will affect the browning.
- Never use salted butter when sautéing. The salt may separate and impart a bad taste to the food.
- Only use a small amount of oil, and heat it to a high temperature.

Never overcrowd the pan when sautéing. Always choose a pan that will accommodate the full amount of food in a single layer. If the pan is too large, the juices will burn.

- Remove any excess fat with a bulb baster.
- Never cover a pan when sautéing or the food will become mushy from the steam. Steam may also prevent caramelizing.

SMOKING MEATS

- Make sure that the wood you are using is clean and has no glue or nails in it.
- If you are using a gas grill, be sure to use presoaked wood chips in the smoker box or at least wrap them in aluminum foil with holes so that your grill does not fill up with ash.
- If you are using a smoker the wood may be placed directly in the box.
- If you would like a different smoked flavor, try using an old wine or whiskey barrel.
- Depending on the thickness of the meat, smoking can take up to 20 hours.
- The best temperature for smoking is between 200°-220°F and the internal temperature of most meat should be 165°-170°F.
- Higher temperatures will not allow the smoke time to infiltrate the meat adequately.
- The smoke imparts the flavor you are looking for.
- Slow cooking also has the ability to tenderize the meat.
- Using a good quality thermometer is a must.
- Make sure that the meat is totally surrounded by the smoke.

Types of Wood

ALDER- This wood has a soft flavor that is used primarily to smoke fish and poultry.

ALMOND- Has a nutty, somewhat sweet flavor, and is used on all types of meat.

BLACK WALNUT- Has a heavier flavor than most wood and works best when added to other types of wood. Sometimes it may give foods a bitter flavor.

FRUIT WOOD- The most popular are cherry or apple-tree wood.

GRAPEVINE- Never use with poultry or lamb unless you desire a real hearty flavor.

HICKORY- Best with beef or lamb, but tends to impart a somewhat strong flavor and may overpower the flavor of the meat.

MAPLE- Best used for ham and poultry and is similar to fruit wood.

MESQUITE- Provides a strong flavor but burns very quickly. Works great on meats that only have to be cooked for a short period of time.

OAK- Best used on beef or lamb, providing flavor but not overpowering the meat.

PECAN- Imparts a delicate flavor and burns cooler than most other wood.

STANDARD OVEN

- Best to use an oven thermometer and check your oven temperature at least every 6 months.
- Ovens can be as much as 25°-75°F off depending on the age of the oven and how often it is used.
- Debris and oven cleaning solution may leave a residue that causes temperature changes.
- If you find that the oven temperature is off, you can either make the adjustment in the recipe baking time or have the oven serviced.
- If food spills in the oven, cleanup will be easy if you pour salt on the spill as soon as possible.
- Place foods on the rack recommended at all times.

STEAMING

- Steaming cooks vegetables in a short period of time and retains a high percentage of the nutrients. Start with the more solid vegetables such as carrots, then add the softer ones to the steamer after.

The following are approximate steaming times for the more common vegetables

VEGETABLE	STEAM TIME
Artichokes	6-10 minutes
Green beans	45 minutes
Beets	45 minutes
Broccoli with stalk	25 minutes
Brussels Sprouts	20 minutes
Cabbage	15 minutes
Carrots	25 minutes
Cauliflower	12 minutes
Celery	20 minutes
Corn on cob	15 minutes
Green peas	20-40 minutes
Green peppers	5 minutes
Onions	20-30 minutes
Potatoes (all)	35 minutes
Tomatoes	15 minutes

WOK COOKING

- Only 1 tablespoon of oil is needed for four servings.

- All ingredients should be prepared before you start cooking, since the wok will cook very fast.
- The oil should be drizzled around the upper surface and allowed to fall down the sides for the best results.
- The food should be moved around continually during the cooking.

The wok should be preheated before placing food in to reduce sticking.

- Never wok more than $\frac{1}{2}$ pound at a time for the best results.
- Before cooking beef, pork, or chicken, partially freeze the meat for 1 hour so that it will be easier to thinly slice uniform pieces.
- Placing the meat in marinade for a few minutes will make the meat more flavorful and help to tenderize it.
- Make sure that all vegetables and meats have been cut into small uniform pieces.
- When thicker vegetables are used they should be added first to soften.

GENERAL COOKING TEMPERATURES

Food	Temperature
Ground Beef, Pork, Lamb	160°F
Beef, Lamb, Veal	
Rare	140°F
Medium Rare	145°F
Medium	160°F
Medium-Well	165°F
Well-Done	170°F
Pork	
Medium	160°F
Well-Done	170°F
Precooked	140°F
Poultry	
Ground Meat	165°F
Whole Birds	185°F
Parts	175°F
Stuffing (alone or in bird)	170°F
Egg Dishes	165°F
Leftovers	170°F

THERMOMETERS

Deep-fat/Candy

- The bulb should be fully immersed in the candy or food and should never be allowed to touch the bottom of the cooking container.
- To check the accuracy of the thermometer, place it in boiling water for 3-4 minutes. The temperature should read 212°F or 100° C.

Freezer/Refrigerator

- These thermometers read from -20° to 80°F.
- Frozen foods should always be stored at 0°F, or below, to slow nutrient loss and maintain the quality of the food.

Meat

- Insert the thermometer into the center (or thickest part of the meat), making sure that it is not resting on a bone.

Oven

- It is wise to check your oven temperature accuracy at least once a month.
- If the oven temperature is not accurate it can affect the results of the food being prepared, especially baked goods.
- When checking the temperature the thermometer should be placed in the middle of the center rack of the oven.

39

Cooking
LAMB & PORK

COOKING LAMB

Lamb is one of the leaner meats with an excellent taste and texture. Most lamb sold in the U. S. comes from animals that are about 1 year old. New Zealand supplies 12% of all lamb sold in the United States. New Zealand does not allow their lamb to be fed hormones. Most cuts of lamb are smaller than beef cuts, which make them more tender. Overcooking will, however, cause some cuts of lamb to become tough. Mutton is produced from lamb that is only 3-12 months old. Lamb is produced from lambs that are at least 2 years old. Prime lamb is only sold to restaurants. Lamb should never be aged.

Chops

- The blade-end chops have a higher fat content than loin-end chops. However, the loin-end chops are more tender.
- A thin layer of fat is desirable on lamb chops.
- The darker the meat, the stronger the taste and the older the animal.
- Cuts of lamb that have the bone in will be more flavorful.
- Serve hot or cold, never just warm, for the best flavor.
- The rack will cook in about 30 minutes at 450°F.
- If the stock is to be used add a clove or two of garlic then caramelize and use on rack.
- The normal serving size is two chops.
- Rack of lamb is usually roasted medium or medium-rare.

Leg of Lamb

- The best way to grill leg of lamb is butterflied.
- Leg of lamb is cooked for 24 minutes per pound for medium at 325°F, to an internal temperature of 153°F.
- If you are going to grill leg of lamb, it should be covered and cooked over indirect heat in a covered grill.
- The leg of lamb should be allowed to stand in a warm location for 20-30 minutes before serving.

Rack of Lamb

- Each rack should have 8 ribs.
- Score the membrane and remove it, as well as the fat, from the ribs. This leaves the ribs "naked" and without any fat. This process is called "Frenching."
- Only a thin layer of fat should be left on the eye of the chop.
- Rack should be placed fat side up in roasting pan that is just large enough to hold it.
- Bones that are left over from racking should be placed on the bottom of the pan under the roast.

A rack of lamb needs to stand before being carved more than any other type of meat.

- Allow the rack to remain in a warm location for 15 minutes before carving.
- The rack should only be served medium and never any more done than that.
- Rack of lamb should be cooked for 12 minutes per pound at 400°F until the internal temperature is 145°F.
- Make sure that the butcher removes the central backbone (chine bone) for you.

Shish Kebob

- The lamb should be prepared the day before by cutting it up into cubes and placing it in a marinade overnight.
- Portions should be 6 ounces per person.
- Place the lamb cubes on the skewers and grill, or broil, separately from the vegetables.
- The most common vegetables are mushrooms, onions, tomato, and green pepper.
- Broil or barbecue the vegetables separately and place them between the lamb cubes just before serving.
- When the vegetables are placed on the skewers and cooked at the same time, the steam from the released liquid makes the lamb too moist.

COOKING PORK

Wild pigs originally crossed the Bering Straight, although they may have originated in Africa. Explorers reported having seen wild pigs in Mexico in 1522, but the first actual domesticated pigs were brought from Spain to Tampa, Florida in 1539 by Hernando deSoto. Salting and smoking were the early methods of preserving pork. The old adage "living high on the hog" referred to someone who was eating the best cut of meat on the pig.

Bacon

In most countries of the world, bacon is not considered to be a breakfast food and will rarely ever appear on a breakfast menu. A "rasher" or portion of bacon is a term that originated in England in the 16th century and is still used to day to denote a "side of bacon." The pagans regarded bacon as a sacred food and a symbol of prosperity and used bacon as an offering to the gods.

- Bacon is derived from the fatty pork belly meat, which has been cured and smoked.
- Canadian bacon is prepared from the boneless loin, which only has a thin layer of fat.
- If you need to separate bacon slices in a hurry, just microwave them for 20-30 seconds on high.
- Always select bacon with the lowest amount of visible fat.
- Once a package of bacon is opened it will only stay fresh for one week.
- To separate bacon more easily, just allow it to remain at room temperature for 20 minutes.

- Unopened bacon can be stored for only 1 week past the expiration date on the package.
- Bacon does not freeze well.
- Never purchase bacon if it looks slimy.
- Salt pork bacon is from the belly and is only cured in a coarse salt. It is usually cooked in beans, added for flavor.

To reduce splattering, try soaking the bacon in ice water for 2-4 minutes, then dry very well before frying.

- Sprinkling the bacon with a small amount of flour also helps reduce splattering.
- To reduce shrinkage, try starting the bacon in a cold pan.
- Use a skewer to make small holes in the bacon before separating the slices and the bacon will not curl up when cooked.
- Raw bacon can be easily cut with a scissors if you need small pieces.
- Bacon is processed in brine, which causes more grease to be released resulting in excess splattering.
- Lower heat settings when cooking bacon will reduce splattering.
- Bacon should be placed in a room temperature skillet (no oil) and heated slowly for the best results.
- Turn bacon as it is cooking and never overcrowd the pan.
- Bacon can be baked in a 400°F oven on a rack for 10 minutes.
- When frying bacon it is best to drain off the fat once or twice.
- Removing some of the fat as the bacon cooks makes a crispier bacon strip.
- Cooked bacon strip will last 3-5 days in the refrigerator if wrapped tightly.
- Placed cooked bacon strips in a cookie sheet on a piece of paper towel in a preheated 200°F oven. Turn the oven off.

Ham (Leg of Pork)
- The ham bone is excellent for soups.
- The flavor of a ham can be improved by heating even if it doesn't require it on the label.

If you purchase a "country ham" it will have been smoked and aged through a special curing process. Unfortunately this process tends to make these hams relatively salty. These hams may need to be skinned, soaked for a period of time, and simmered.

- If you need to store the ham, check the wrapper for specific instructions.
- Many canned hams go through a special sterilization process and can be stored at room temperature for a prolonged period.

- Honey-baked hams will have the best flavor if allowed to warm to room temperature before being served.
- When you purchase a cured ham, be sure that it has the U.S. inspection seal on it. This a ssures you that the meat was cooked properly.
- A butcher will remove the bone from the ham for you if asked.
- To remove a canned ham, just immerse it in hot tap water for 2 minutes to loosen the gel.
- The rind can easily be removed if you slice it lengthwise straight down the center before baking. Cook the ham slit-side down, and remove the rind as soon as the ham is removed from the oven (while the rind is still hot).
- When using ham for soups, use a number of small pieces instead of large chunks to intensify the flavor.

If you are going to glaze a ham, it is best to remove about $\frac{1}{4}$ inch of the fat before glazing.

- To caramelize the exterior of a ham use light brown sugar.
- A glaze can be made by combining 1 cup of brown sugar, $\frac{3}{4}$ cup of unsweetened pineapple juice, and 1 teaspoon of dried mustard.
- If you would like to glaze a ham use 2 tablespoons of Dijon mustard with $\frac{1}{2}$ cup of honey.
- If ham slices are too salty place them in a container of low-fat milk for 20 minutes, rinse, and dry before cooking.
- If you think that you have a ham that is too salty, just cook it for half the cooking time, then remove it from the oven and pour a small bottle or can of ginger ale over it. This will desalt it about 30%.
- If you want to desalt a ham further, rub salt on the outside of the ham after pouring the ginger ale on and it will draw more salt water out of the ham and desalt it about 60%.
- Precooked ham slices dry out very easily and only need to be browned on each side.
- If you cook ham slices too fast they may become tough.

Pork Chops

Pork is no longer the high-fat meat that it was before the 1980s. New feeding methods have resulted in lower fat content in many of the more popular cuts. Preparation methods can also help reduce the fat content. In most cuts sold, pork will have a lower overall fat and cholesterol content than beef. Pork should never be aged at home unless you have special a refrigeration unit.

- Cook loin pork chops in a greased skillet adding a small amount of water to the pan, then cover and cook for about 30-40 minutes or until tender. The water will create just enough steam to keep the chops moist.

- When purchasing raw pork be sure that the meat is a nice, pale pink color. The darker the meat the older the animal.

- Check the color of the fat. It should be white on pork and beef, which indicates more tender meat. If the fat is yellow, the meat may be somewhat tough.

- Just to be safe, even though there is rarely a health problem with rare pork, cook it to an internal temperature of 155°-165°F.

- Pork chops should be purchased that are about 1 inch thick to maintain the juices when they are cooked.

- If you prefer thin pork chops, cook then with the lid on the pan for a short period of time since they dry out very quickly.
- Pork chops that are to be stuffed should be at least 1½ inches thick, and should be rib or loin chops.
- Always cut the pork chops to be stuffed from the fat side and make the slit almost to the bone. After you stuff the chop use small metal skewers to close the opening while they are cooking.
- Pork should never be left at room temperature for more than 1 hour before being refrigerated.

The juices should be clear when the pork chop is done.

- When cooking pork chops the excess fat should be removed.
- Pork chops do well on the grill, but be sure they are at least 1 inch thick for the best results.
- For a juicier pork chop allow them to stand for 10 minutes after they are cooked. Keep them warm and covered and they will be juicy all the way through.

Pork Loin
- When boiling a pork loin, allow it to remain in the water until it cools. This will result is a juicier, more tender loin.

If possible, try and find a pork loin that is graded "US No. 1." This is prime pork and the best for a loin.

- Cook at about 20 minutes per pound at 350°F to an internal temperature of 160°F to be safe.

Prosciutto
- Italian ham that been specially seasoned and salt-cured making it safe to eat without cooking.
- Make sure that the fat is very white and not yellow.
- If the ham is labeled "prosciutto cotto" it means that it has been cooked. If it is labeled "prosciutto crudo" it means that is has been cured.
- When you use prosciutto in dishes add it during the final 5 minutes of cooking time or it will become tough.
- Should be sliced paper-thin.

Ribs
- Bake on a rack in a shallow baking pan with your favorite seasonings at 325°F for about 1½ hours or until tender. Do not use high heat or they will dry out.
- Ribs do very well on the grill. Be sure and cover the grill for the best results.
- When grilling, be sure and remove any visible fat to avoid flare-ups.

- Cooks at 30 minutes per pound at 350°F until well done.
- Ribs can be cooked in the oven for about 30 minutes to cook off some of the fat before placing them on the grill.
- If you are going to smoke pork ribs, be sure and use a covering of yellow mustard, which will hold the spices in place and compliment them.
- Using mustard on smoked ribs will produce a crust that will not have a mustard flavor.

Pulled Pork

Pulled pork originated in North Carolina in the early 1800s when settlers brought pigs and allowed them to run wild. Since cattle were in short supply and there was an abundance of pigs, the pigs became the "meat of the south." The term "pulled pork" was a term used during that period to denote ham that was smoked over a low fire to the point when it could easily be "pulled" apart by hand.

- A pork shoulder is placed in a smoker and cooked until the internal temperature is 170°F. However, never cook the ham more than 190°F for the best results.
- The collagen in pork breaks down when smoked and turns into a simple sugar making the meat taste sweet.
- A good pork shoulder should weigh 12-15 pounds.
- Pork shoulders are sold either as a Boston butt or picnic variety. If you prefer less bone choose the Boston butt. However, they will both weigh about 7 pounds.

Cooking
FOWL

COOKING & PREPARING CHICKEN

The chicken as we know it today was originally bred from the wild red jungle fowl and was first domesticated about 2000 BC in India. The chicken appeared in English recipes about 2500 BC. Columbus brought the first chickens to the Americas in 1493.

Baked

- Always bake chicken on medium heat, since a high heat setting will result in a drier, stringier piece of chicken or turkey.
- Only bake chicken to 180°F. Any higher or lower and the fowl will be either underdone or dried out.

Chefs submerge chicken parts in buttermilk in the refrigerator for 2-3 hours to improve the taste.

- To keep the breast moist, try placing some bacon strips on top of the breast, alternating directions to hold them in place.
- Use low-salt soy sauce to brown the chicken parts. Just brush it on 30 minutes before the chicken is finished cooking.
- If you remove the white, hard tendon running lengthwise in the chicken breast it will reduce shrinkage when the breast is cooked.

Since the majority of the fat content in both chicken and turkey is found in the skin, removing the skin is recommended in almost all instances when preparing the fowl. The quality of the fowl you are purchasing is important and freshness is one of the most important factors, which will make the dish more flavorful and appealing. If you can purchase a bird that is fresh and has never been frozen you will probably notice the difference in taste. Because of the cleaning methods used, a kosher chicken will taste even better and will be a cleaner bird.

Barbequeued (Grilled)

- Only purchase Grade A chicken for barbecuing.
- If you plan on grilling a turkey the temperature needs to be kept at 325°F or slightly higher until the internal temperature reaches 165°F.
- A 14 pound turkey will take 2-3 hours rotating on a grill at 325°F.
- It is best to partially cook the chicken or turkey in the oven or microwave before barbecuing to save time.

When barbecuing a whole chicken, be sure and wrap the wings in aluminum foil to protect them from burning.

- Be sure that chicken is at room temperature when you start to grill it.
- Chicken will not stick on the grill if you rub mayonnaise on the chicken before barbecuing. The heat will burn it off and it will not flavor the meat.
- Make sure that you grease the barbecue rack before placing the chicken on it. The collagen in the chicken skin turns into a sticky gelatin and the chicken will stick to the rack. If you prebake

the chicken this will not occur.

- When spit-barbecuing a chicken, it is best to remove the breast bone so that the chicken will cook more evenly.
- After searing, use a cooler fire to complete the cooking for moist chicken.
- For excellent results, sear the chicken skin-side down, then turn the chicken over and grill it on a covered grill until the meat looks opaque.
- White meat pieces will cook faster than dark meat pieces and should be placed on the grill 15 minutes after the dark meat pieces have started cooking.
- When you cut into the chicken, the juices should run yellow, with just a slight hint of pink.

Boiled

- If you are going to use chicken or turkey in a casserole or pot pie, just boil the chicken until it is about $^3/_4$ cooked and allow it to remain in its own liquid, refrigerated, about one hour before using in the dish.
- Partial boiling for dishes produces a juicier piece of chicken.
- Can be basted with wine. Use a quality red or white wine. Sherry is highly recommended. Baste every 10-12 minutes for the best results.

Breaded Chicken

- Most breading recipes for chicken call for an egg-milk-water mixture (egg wash).
- Be sure to strain the mixture before using it to avoid large parts of the eggwhite in the wash.
- Straining the egg wash will also make the coating even.
- To avoid having lumps of flour and breadcrumbs on your fingers, which make breading more difficult, just designate one hand as "wet" and the other hand as "dry."
- The "wet" hand will handle the chicken pieces that are not coated, dip the pieces in the milk, and then place the pieces in the flour.
- The "dry" hand will sprinkle flour over the top of the piece, coating it, will remove it from the flour and place it in the egg wash, and then the "wet" hand will remove it.
- The above method is how chefs prepare large quantities of chicken pieces without getting lumps on their fingers or leaving clumps on the chicken pieces.

Broiled

- To reduce flare-ups, just wipe the surface of the chicken with paper towel and remove all visible excess fat.
- Chicken breasts should be placed on the pan as far from the burners as possible to avoid burning the tops.
- The breast meat should be white with no hint of pink.

- If you would like the skin to be crisp, just be sure and wipe the skin with a dry kitchen towel and do not place any salt on the skin.
- To obtain a nice brown glaze, just sprinkle some sugar through a sieve over the surface of the chicken during the last 1-2 minutes of cooking time.
- Glazing the skin will not produce a sweet skin, just a beautiful brown sheen.

Fried

- To bread fried chicken, dip the pieces in evaporated milk with a small amount of well-beaten egg before placing the pieces in the breading with the spices.
- If you soak the chicken pieces in milk for 1 hour before you bread the chicken it will be more tender.
- Use a paper bag to place your breading ingredients in after they have been mixed.

If you want real crispy fried chicken make the breading from equal parts of all-purpose flour and cornstarch instead of just flour.

- Before starting, soak the chicken pieces in cold, salted water for about 1 hour, one pint of water to 1 tablespoon of table salt. This will remove any blood residue and some bacteria.
- After breading the chicken, place the pieces in the refrigerator for 45 minutes to set the breading and it won't fall off.
- Chicken parts can be parboiled for 3-5 minutes before you fry them to speed up the process.
- Light meat fries faster than dark meat and should be fried in separate baskets.
- Fry chicken at 365°F for the best results, which should take about 15-20 minutes for the pieces to become brown.
- Fried chicken can be placed into the oven at 350°F after it has browned in the fryer to dry the coating and make the chicken even crispier.

Liver

- The center should be barely pink when cooked.
- Chicken liver is overcooked if it all brown inside and too dry to use.
- When making pate, push a skewer into the center and if it comes out hot the pate is done cooking.

Poached

- The chicken should be started in a cold broth or water.
- If you place the chicken into a pot of hot water the broth will be cloudy.
- Bring the poaching water to a simmer. A 3-4 pound chicken will cook in 40 minutes.
- Poaching should be done in an uncovered pot.

Roasted

A roaster chicken is between is between 2-6 months old when slaughtered and a fryer or broiler is only 6-8 weeks old.

- A free range chicken will be tastier if roasted.
- Roasting chickens have more fat than broilers.
- Roasters should weigh at least 3 pounds.
- After cleaning the chicken inside and out, rub "chef's salt" on the inside and allow the chicken to remain at room temperature for 20 minutes.
- Place all the vegetables plus one garlic clove in the bottom of the roasting pan and then place the chicken, breast-side up on top of the vegetables.
- Place very thin lemon slices under the skin to tenderize the chicken if you use an old bird.
- Heat about 5 tablespoons of corn oil almost to the smoke point and pour it over the top of the chicken before roasting.
- The roasting should be done in a 350°F oven for 1-1^1/$_2$ hours. Baste only once after 1 hour of cooking time.

When basting, try adding a small amount of ground turmeric to the basting solution (providing it has an oil base) and the chicken will have a great deep, rich-brown skin.

- For a great self-basting treat, just saturate a piece of cheesecloth with olive oil and place it over the breast of the bird. When the cheesecloth is removed after the bird is cooked the breast meat will be moist and the bird will have a brown skin.
- For deep brown chicken, just make a basting solution of some of the drippings and add a small amount of butter and corn syrup. Baste during the last 10 minutes of cooking time and raise the heat somewhat.
- The thermometer should read 185°F when finished cooking.

Sautéing

- It is best to sauté chicken in unsalted butter, extra virgin olive oil, or bacon fat.
- The choice of fat should relate to the dish.
- It requires 2-3 tablespoons of fat to sauté a whole chicken.
- Always sauté over medium to high heat.

Sauté skin-side down and serve the chicken skin-side up.

- Chicken browns well over medium heat because of the time it takes to cook it.
- If the skin sticks to the pan, allow a little more time and it should release by itself as soon as more of the fat renders down.

Sautéing Breaded Chicken

- If you are going to sauté breaded chicken, be sure and have $\frac{1}{8}$ inch of oil in the pan.
- Breaded chicken should be sautéed over medium heat, never high heat.
- If the breading is browning too fast reduce the heat.

If you use clarified butter, there will never be brown specks of milk solids clinging to the breading. Extra virgin olive oil works great as well.

- Try breading with half fresh bread crumbs and half grated Parmesan cheese.

Smoked Chicken

- Make sure you start with a plump bird weighing about 4-5 pounds.
- One chicken will feed 2-3 people.
- The smoker should be set at 180°F and the internal temperature of the chicken should be 165°F when cooked.
- If the internal temperature goes over 165°F the bird will be too well done.
- Placing beer inside the bird adds a great flavor.
- If you use a rub it should include sage, thyme, and bay leaves.
- Make sure the juices run clear when the bird is done cooking.

Smoked Turkey

- A 12-14 pound turkey will take 6-8 hours to smoke. However, the flavor is worth the wait.
- A smoked turkey will be more juicy than an oven-roasted turkey.

SPECIAL DISHES

Buffalo Wings

This dish was first served in Buffalo, New York at the Anchor Bar in 1964. The dish was fried chicken wings with a hot barbecue sauce. In 1977 Buffalo, New York declared "Chicken Wing Day" on July 29th to commemorate the occasion.

- When preparing buffalo wings, be sure to separate the wing from the joint.
- The tip is then cut off the wings and the wings fried in peanut oil.
- In many bars the complete wings are fried to reduce the work of removing the wing.

Chicken a la King

The first mention in print of chicken a la king was in 1912. The dish was originally served at the Brighton Beach Hotel in New York in 1898 and was prepared for the owners Mr. and Mrs. E. Clark King III. His chef was named George Greenwald. One year later the dish was being served at the famous Delmonico's Restaurant in New York City.

- The original recipe called for sherry and blanched, toasted almonds to be added just before serving.
- After you prepare the sauce, be sure and temper the eggs with a small amount of the sauce before adding the eggs.
- Onions, mushrooms, and green peppers were the vegetables of choice.
- The original recipe called for 4 pounds of butter, which may be replaced with olive oil if you are using a high butter recipe.

Chicken Breast Parmesan
- Use clarified butter in the recipe
- Make sure you coat the breast on each side, flour and seasoning first, then the egg mixture.
- Grate fresh Parmesan cheese.
- Do not use the leftover flour or egg mixture.

Chicken Cordon Bleu
- Always remove the skin from the chicken breast.
- The breasts must be pounded out to increase their surface.
- The pounding helps to make the thickness of the breast uniform so that the cooking time will be accurate for both halves.
- The temperature of the shortening is very important. To test the oil, just drop one or two breadcrumbs into it. If the breadcrumbs immediately rise to the surface in the center of a small amount of white foam, the oil is ready.
- After placing the cheese and slice of ham and folding the breast together, be sure and shape the pieces into a nice oval and freeze them for 2 hours so that they will retain their shape when cooked.

Chicken Fricassee
- One of the oldest chicken dishes ever recorded in a cookbook.
- Use a heavy-bottomed pan.
- The chicken pieces should be lightly browned in a combination of hot fat and butter.
- Remove the chicken from the pan before browning the onions.
- Onions are very important and the oil should be heated in the pan before adding the onions to lightly brown. The caramelized onions give the fricassee its characteristic flavor.

- After browning the onions return the chicken to the pan.
- When you are separating the whites from the yolks, it is critical not to leave any hint of white on the yolk or it will harden and the sauce will have lumps.

Chicken Kiev

This dish was invented by the Frenchman, Nicolas Appert, in 1801. The name Chicken Kiev was used in New York City by a restaurant that served the dish to Russian immigrants. In Europe the name was Chicken Supreme, but was eventually changed to Chicken Kiev.

- Make sure that when inserting the butter it is frozen as solid as possible.
- The chicken breast must be flattened evenly to allow for even cooking.
- The chicken needs to be fried until crisp.

The chicken should be very cold when the butter is inserted.

- If you leave the wing bone on it provides a little handle and makes a nice touch.
- Some chefs will flavor the butter with garlic and herbs. Soften the butter at room temperature, blend the herbs, and then freeze the butter before using.

Chicken Tetrazzini

- This dish was named after an Italian opera singer, Luisa Tetrazzini, who died in 1940. She was so popular in the United States around the turn of the century that the dish was named after her by the owner of a San Francisco restaurant and was first mentioned in print in 1951.
- The roux for the dish is prepared with 4 tablespoons of all-purpose flour and 4 tablespoons of butter.
- After the roux is prepared add 2 cups of heavy cream and 1 cup of defatted chicken broth.
- It is best to remove from the heat and add 3 cups of cooked chicken that has been cut into cubes.
- Butter a glass casserole dish and place $^3/_4$ pounds of cooked spaghetti in and pour in the chicken mixture.
- Most chefs sprinkle breadcrumbs or Parmesan cheese on top.

Sweet & Sour Chicken

- Many butchers will sell you chicken already cut in cubes. This will save a lot of time.
- The first step is to sprinkle the pieces with a small amount of soy sauce mixed with 1 tablespoon of white vinegar to give the chicken an oriental flavor.

Prepare the flour and seasoning mixture that your recipe calls for and dip the chicken pieces in one at a time (not all at once).

- After you fry the pieces, discard the oil (do not reuse it).
- If your sweet and sour sauce is not thick enough, use cornstarch to thicken it. Be sure and mix the cornstarch with cold water before adding it to the sauce. Only add the cornstarch drop by drop until the desired thickness is achieved.
- If you prepare the ingredients before you are ready to prepare the dish, never mix them until you are ready to make the dish.
- When preparing this dish, prepare the vegetables, sauce, and chicken separately and combine them in a casserole before placing them into a 350°-375°F oven for 45-60 minutes.

Stewing
- Never allow stewing chicken to come to a full boil. You will lose the flavor of the base in the chicken.
- Stewing should always be done on top of the stove or in the oven.
- Somewhat fatty chickens are best for stewing. Fat hens are the best and usually weigh about 4-5 pounds.
- If you are preparing a cream sauce, be sure and cook the chicken in unsalted butter.

Whole Chicken
- If you are going to stuff a chicken, figure $^3/_4$ cups of stuffing per pound.
- The chicken will be cooked through when the leg feels loose.
- A 3-4 pound stewing chicken will take 1-2 hours to cook.

Cooking Secrets

ROCK CORNISH GAME HENS

- These mini-chickens are about enough food for one person if they are not too hungry.
- It will take about 1 cup of stuffing to stuff the little bird.
- Serve adequate side dishes.

If you stuff the bird, the aluminum foil should be opened up 10 minutes before the bird has finished cooking to release the moisture built up from the stuffing.

- To obtain a delicate flavor, pour a mixture of 1 tablespoon of fruit-flavored brandy (not a sweet cordial) over the bird.
- Small game birds do not brown well in the oven due to the short cooking time.

Game hens should be browned on each side in a pan on top of the stove over a very high heat.

- Oven roasting only takes about 30 minutes.
- Before you grill, cut off the last two sections of the wings or fold them under the bird.

COOKING TURKEY (IN COOKING BAG)

- Turkey should be cooked breast-side down for the first hour on a "V" rack so that the breast will baste naturally. Turn the bird and continue cooking for the balance of the time.
- Allow turkey to rest for 20 minutes after cooking so that the steam dissipates out of the white meat and it won't fall apart when sliced.
- Turkey should be cooked at 325°F for the best results.
- The internal temperature of a cooked turkey should be 180°F.
- Turkeys should only be stuffed just before being placed into the oven, never before.

Stuffing Tips

- All ingredients that will be used for stuffing must be cooked before using them in the stuffing.
- Cool all the ingredients before combining.
- Never leave stuffing at room temperature for more than 1 hour.
- Stuffing causes the bird to cook longer and may dry out the meat.
- Over-mixing bread stuffing causes the stuffing to become too pasty.
- All ingredients should be lightly tossed for the best results.
- If you do stuff the bird do not overstuff it or force stuffing in. Never pack it in.

COOKING TURKEY(NO COOKING BAG)

- The outside of the turkey should be brushed with vegetable oil before placing it into the oven.
- Make sure that the oven is preheated.
- If the turkey starts to brown too early, just cover it with an aluminum foil tent.
- Brush the breast skin with white vermouth 20 minutes before the bird has completed cooking for a rich, brown, crispy skin.

CAPON

In ancient Rome it was against the law to eat any type of fowl except a hen that was not intentionally fattened. A Roman surgeon found a way around the problem (since roosters were more flavorful and in demand) by castrating the roosters and calling them "capon." A capon can weigh in from 6-8 pounds and has a better texture and flavor than a hen. The capon was declared to be within the Roman law.

41

Preparing
EGGS & EGG DISHES

BOILING

- If an egg cracks when it is being boiled, just remove it, leave it wet, then pour a generous amount of salt on the crack. Wrap the egg in aluminum foil, twirl the ends and continue cooking it.
- A soft-boiled egg must be cooked for $3^{1}/_{2}$ minutes to kill bacteria if it is present.
- Boiled eggs will slice easily if you use wax-free dental floss.
- Soft-boiled eggs should take about 2-4 minutes.
- Never freeze hard-boiled eggs, they become tough.
- The yolks and the white can be frozen separately for a short period of time. The white, however, may get rubbery.

Rub fresh lemon on the shell before placing the egg into the boiling water and it should not crack.

- Add salt to the cooking water to toughen the shell and make it easier to remove.
- Add a small amount of vinegar to the water to prevent the shell from cracking and soften the shell.
- Cool the egg before trying to slice it or it will fall apart too easily.
- Never place hard-boiled eggs in a bowl of cool water after you peel them or they will absorb water.
- To tell if an egg is hard boiled, just spin it. If it wobbles it is not hard boiled.
- Add a drop or two of vegetable coloring to the water and you can easily tell the hard-boiled eggs from the fresh ones.
- Roll hard-boiled eggs in your hands while crushing the shell, then place a tablespoon between the shell and the white and circle it around.

DEVILED EGGS

- To keep the yolk centered so that you will have a centered hollow to place the filling in, just stir the eggs while they are boiling.
- Using older eggs will make them easier to peel since the acidity level in the shell gets lower with age.
- Allow the eggs to remain in the hot water for 10-15 minutes instead of completely cooking them will provide you with a more tender white.
- Cool the eggs immediately when they have finished cooking or the yolk may get a greenish tint from the chemicals that have been released.

If you place the carton of eggs to be used for deviled eggs on its side the night before, the yolks will remain centered while they are cooking.

- If you cut a slice from the wide end of the egg, the egg will stand upright. Then you slice $1/4$ down from the top just enough to be able to remove the yolk and stuff into the opening.
- If you salt the water it will solidify any leaking white and help to seal the shell.

EGGNOG

Eggnog originated in England with the upper class who could afford eggs, milk, and brandy. The drink was originally called "egg flip." The drink was popularized in the southern United States and bourbon replaced the brandy. Mexican eggnog includes the addition of cinnamon and rum, which became popular in the United States.

- If you want to lighten the texture and sweeten supermarket eggnog, just fold in 2-3 stiffly beaten egg whites.
- Nonfat evaporated milk and egg whites can be used when preparing homemade eggnog. For every whole egg called for in the recipe you can substitute 2 egg whites. The nonfat evaporated milk is substituted equally for whole milk.
- If you would like a lighter homemade eggnog that is not as thick, just separate the egg whites and beat them until they are stiff and add them to the mixture right before you are going to serve it. Homemade eggnog will not last more than 1-2 days even under refrigeration.
- Try substituting eggnog for whole milk in other baked goods recipes.
- In Spain, red Spanish wine is used to flavor eggnog. In America we normally use bourbon and in other countries it is made with rum.

EGG SUBSTITUTES

- Check the recipe before using egg substitutes to replace whole eggs. If the recipe doesn't say its okay don't use them.
- Some egg-substitute products contain MSG.
- Egg substitutes without MSG can be used for Caesar salad.

FRIED

- Fried eggs can be shaped if fried into a cookie cutter. Make sure your spray the cookie cutter with oil to make the egg easy to remove.
- If you like a white film over the eggs when cooking them sunny-side up, just add a few drops of water to the pan before they are done and cover the pan for a few seconds.
- It is best to use a heavy pan since it conducts heat better.
- Add a small amount of flour to the pan and the fat won't splatter.

Fry egg at a low temperature and they will be more tender and have a smooth yolk.

Cooking Secrets

- When you microwave eggs, the yolk will cook first because the microwave tends to cook the fat first.
- Make sure that butter is very hot before adding the eggs, then reduce the heat.
- A small powdering of cornstarch added to the pan before adding the eggs will prevent splattering.
- Salted butter may cause eggs to stick to the pan. It is best to use unsalted butter.

OMELET

- Eggs should be at room temperature for the greatest volume.
- If you warm the eggs under hot tap water for 4 minutes, the omelet will be more tender. Cold eggs tend to produce a tougher omelet.
- Add a small amount of water instead of milk to create steam and fluff up the omelet.
- Never mix the omelet in an aluminum bowl or they may blacken.
- Do not mix the eggs until they are frothy.
- Use $\frac{1}{2}$ teaspoon of baking soda to every 3 eggs to increase the volume.

Make sure that the butter is very hot before adding the omelet to the pan.

- Ingredients should be warm before adding them to an omelet either inside or on top.
- An omelet pan with sloping sides is a must for shaping the omelet.
- Use a well-seasoned pan or one with a quality nonstick surface.
- When preparing an omelet you can replace the egg yolks with an equal amount of egg substitute.
- Eggs should be 3-5 days old for omelets.
- Never make an omelet with more than 3 eggs.
- If you have a stainless steel omelet pan, never wash it, just scrub it with kosher salt and wipe it out.
- If you would like a nice brown coating on top of the omelet, just brush the top with melted butter before you turn it.
- Slide the omelet out of the pan onto the plate to keep it in one piece.

POACHED

- Never salt the water you are placing poached eggs in or they will break up.
- The fresher the eggs the better. The whites will remain firmer and keep the yolk in shape.
- Eggs are less likely to stick in a heavy nonstick pan and the results are better.
- Make sure that you bring the water to a boil and then to a simmer before adding the eggs.

Add 1¹/₂ teaspoons of vinegar to 1 quart of water before adding the egg. That will cause the egg to remain firm and keep their white color.

- Always drain poached eggs well before serving. They should not be served with any water in the dish.
- Poaching should take 3 minutes for a soft yolk, and 5 minutes for the yolk to still be soft and the white hard. After 5 minutes they will be almost hard-boiled.
- Trim off ragged edges before serving for a better presentation.

QUAIL EGGS

- Opening quail eggs can be easy if you notice that the egg has a pointed end and a flat end. At the flat end, take a paring knife and very easily press the tip of the blade into the shell and crack the shell while you turn it. Continue to make a circle around the egg and lift off the top, and then pour out the contents.

RAW EGGS IN RECIPES

- Never pour raw eggs into any hot mixture. That may cause curdling.
- When beating raw eggs always use a copper bowl. Copper absorbs the heat built by friction from the beating and stops the formation of air pockets. It also releases ions that help the protein to become stiffer. Cream of tartar will not be needed if you use a copper bowl.
- If you use a stainless steel bowl to mix raw eggs, add a pinch of cream of tartar to help the protein stiffen up and increase the volume.

Allow raw eggs to go to room temperature for 1 hour before beating them.

- Never over-beat or the whites will look dry and curdled.
- If you do over-beat egg white, just add one more egg white and beat.
- Add a small amount of sugar and the whites will remain stiffer for a longer period.
- Over-beating will cause the peaks to be fragile.
- White strands should be strained out before using the egg. They will form lumps and affect the quality of the dish.
- Never break raw eggs into a mixing dish. Always break eggs separately into individual bowls in case one of them is bad.
- When adding eggs or egg yolks to a hot mixture it is best to add some of the hot mixture into the eggs, or yolks, slowly and stir well before adding to the balance of the mixture. This will make it easier to blend the egg yolks into the mixture.
- Eggs will separate easier when cold. It is best to separate them as soon as they are taken from the refrigerator.
- Sauces or Caesar salad that call for raw eggs may be a problem since salmonella may be present in the egg. It is best to use pasteurized liquid eggs.

SCRAMBLED

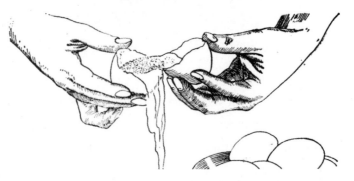

- If you want to increase the volume, use a bowl with a small rounded bottom.
- Preheating the pan will reduce the possibility of sticking.
- A small heavy pan with a nonstick coating and a plastic spatula is the choice of most chefs.
- If you want creamy, fine egg curds prepare the scrambled eggs in the top of a double boiler.

If you are going to use a standard pan and a nonstick spray, the pan should be warmed before spraying. Be sure and remove the pan from the heat before spraying. Warming the frying pan first expands the metal and makes the nonstick spray more efficient.

- Allow 3 eggs per person unless other ingredients are added, then 2 eggs will be fine.
- When making more than one batch of eggs, wipe the pan with paper towel dipped in salt to

clean the pan so that the eggs won't stick.

- Cook the eggs over medium-heat and start in a cool pan for the best results.
- Add 1 teaspoon of water per egg if you would like lighter eggs.
- Scrambled eggs hold the heat and will continue cooking after they are removed from the heat. It is best to remove them just before they are done cooking.
- Do not allow the eggs to brown. Stir continually.
- Overcooked scrambled eggs may turn greenish due to the chemicals being released from the yolk and uniting with other chemicals.
- If you use butter, it would be best to add a small amount of canola oil to raise the smoke point.

To make a fluffier dish, add $\frac{1}{4}$ teaspoon of cornstarch per egg before you beat them.

- To prepare light and fluffy scrambled eggs, just add a small amount of club soda to the eggs.
- The longer it takes to scramble an egg the better it will turn out.

SHIRRED EGGS (BAKED)

- Made in small individual glass dishes called "ramekins."
- The oven should be preheated to 350°F.
- Always butter the ramekin and place in 1 large egg, 1 teaspoon of salted butter and 1 tablespoon of half-and-half.
- The ramekin is placed into a pan with 2 inch sides and boiling water is added to about halfway up the sides. Bake the egg for 14 minutes or until it is fully set.

YOLKS

- If you are using egg whites and want to save the yolks, just place them into a bowl of water in the refrigerator. They will last for 2 days only.
- Egg yolks will coagulate at 144° to 158°F.

42

Baking
LIKE A BAKER

BASIC INGREDIENTS - TYPES OF FLOUR

All-Purpose Flour
- This flour is a blend of hard and soft wheat flour. It has a balanced protein/starch content which makes it an excellent choice for breads, rolls, and pastries.
- All-purpose flour may be used for cakes when cake flour is unavailable but is not highly recommended.
- Presifted, all-purpose flour has been milled to a fine texture, is aerated, and is best for biscuits, waffles, and pancakes. Contains 12% protein.

Bleached Flour
- White flour with a higher gluten-producing potential than other flours.

- Used mainly to make most bread.
- National brands such as Pillsbury and Gold Medal are not recommended for yeast bread due to high protein content.

Bran Flour

- Whole-wheat flour that is mixed with all-purpose white flour and tends to produce a dry effect on baked products.

Bread Flour

- Hard-wheat white flour with high gluten content used to make breads.
- Best for making yeast breads, pizza, and pasta.
- Has a high protein content.

Bromated Flour

- White flour in which bromate is added to the flour to increase the usefulness of the gluten.
- Bromated flour makes the dough knead more easily and may be used in commercial bread making plants.

Browned Flour

- This is really just heated white flour that turns brown adding color to your recipe.

Brown Rice Flour

- Contains rice bran as well as the germ and has a nutty flavor. Commonly substituted for wheat flour.

Cake Flour

- Very fine white flour, made entirely of soft wheat flour. It is best for baking cakes.
- Tends to produce a soft-textured, moist cake. It is also excellent for soft cookies.
- Has a lower protein content than most other flours.

Corn Flour

- Usually very starchy flour used in sauces as a thickener with a slightly sweet flavor.

Cottonseed Flour

- High protein flour used in baked goods to increase the protein content.

Durham Flour (semolina)

- White flour that has the highest protein content of any flour and has the ability to produce the most gluten.
- Used mostly in pastas.

Farina Flour

- Made from hard wheat flour with no Durham wheat added.

Gluten Flour

- Very strong white flour that has twice the strength of standard bread flour.
- Used as an additive flour with other flours.

Instant Flour

- White flour that pours and blends easily with liquids and is used mainly in sauces, gravies, and stews.
- Rarely used for baking due to its fine, powdery texture.
- Has lower protein content.
- Wondra is one of the better brands.

Oat Flour

- Milled from oats and primarily used to prepare porridge, some breads, and cookies.

Pastry Flour

- The gluten content is between cake flour and all-purpose white flour.
- Best for light pastries and biscuits.

Potato Flour

- Provides a thickening texture and used mainly for stews, soups, and sauces.

Rice Flour

- Excellent for making delicately textured cakes.
- If you add a small amount of Parmesan cheese to your recipe it will provide a great taste and will not affect the growth of the yeast.

Self-Rising Flour

- Soft-wheat white flour that should not be used in yeast-leavened baked goods. Contains a leavening agent that tends to cause deterioration.
- The flour should be used within 1-2 months of purchase.
- Best for quick breads, biscuits, and muffins.

Semolina

- White flour with a yellow tint made from Durham wheat.
- Used mainly in commercial pasta and bread.
- Has a high protein content.
- When using semolina flour, try adding a small amount of olive oil to your recipe to improve the flavor and increase the volume.

Soy Flour

- Produced from raw soybeans, which are lightly toasted.
- Soy flour has a somewhat sweet flavor and tends to produce baked goods that retain their freshness longer.

Tapioca Flour

- Made from cassava root and used as a thickener in gravy and sauces.

White Rice Flour

- This type of flour will absorb more liquid and may need additional liquid added as well as increased mixing time.

Whole-wheat flour

- Reconstituted flour made from white flour with the addition of the bran and endosperm.
- Wheat flour is sometimes sold as graham flour and has small specks of brown.
- 100% whole-wheat flour is more difficult to digest than white flour. It tends to cause flatulence and intestinal upsets in susceptible individuals.

BISCUITS/ROLLS

Biscuits

- Baking powder must be very fresh for good results.
- Buttermilk will make the biscuits slightly tart.
- When greasing a biscuit pan, try not to use too much oil or butter or it will cause the biscuits to over-brown.

Cream will make a light, buttery biscuit.

- If you dip your biscuit cutter in flour the dough won't stick to it.
- For soft biscuits, brush them with milk or melted unsalted butter, then place the biscuits into the pan touching each other.
- Sift all dry ingredients together. This is the key to a light, fluffy biscuit.
- Shortening is preferred over other fats or butter if you want the biscuits to be light and not heavy. Shortening is a more refined product.
- To make biscuits that will easily be broken in half, just roll the dough out to about a $1/4$ inch thickness and then fold it over before cutting the biscuits.

If you are going to use frozen biscuits, heat them frozen at 350°F for 15-20 minutes. Frozen biscuits should not be kept for more than 2-3 months.

- Replace the yeast with 1 teaspoon of baking soda and 1 teaspoon of powdered vitamin C and you won't have to wait for the dough to rise.

Never overwork dough. If you are gentle you will have lighter biscuits.

- One baker told us that when he mixes biscuit dough he only uses 20 turns and just the tips of his fingers and the heels of his hand.
- To remove muffins or biscuits from a sectioned pan, place the pan on a damp towel for about 30 seconds.
- To make biscuits that split open easily, just roll out the dough to $1/4$ inch, then fold it over before you cut it.
- To glaze the tops of rolls, just beat 1 egg white lightly with 1 tablespoon of milk and brush on the tops before baking.
- For flaky biscuits be sure that the fat used is cold.
- The more you handle biscuit dough the tougher the biscuits. Cut out as many as possible from the first rolling.

- For flaky biscuits, cut chilled butter into the flour before adding any other ingredients.
- To prepare soft, fluffy biscuits, place them very close together on the baking sheet.
- If you prefer crustier biscuits, place them about 1 inch apart.
- The term "turn" in biscuit making means to push the dough away from yourself, lightly touching the dough that is closest to you with the heels of your palms and then pushing away until the heels of your palms are at the other end of the dough. Then you need to gather the dough with your fingertips from either side, place it in front of you, and start pushing it away again, twenty times.
- Bake at 425°-450°F for the best results.
- Baking time is usually 20-30 minutes, but they need to be checked regularly after 20 minutes.
- For a nice brown top add a small amount of sugar to the recipe.

SWEET ROLLS

- Make sure that you do not mix the yeast and egg into the milk before it cools to lukewarm.
- The yeast must not be subjected to liquid that is too hot or it will impair the its ability to rise and may also partially cook the egg.
- Warm honey can be brushed on the top of rolls to provide a nice glaze.
- Try brushing the rolls with melted butter while they are still hot. This will enable the butter to seep into the rolls and make it unnecessary to serve butter with the rolls.
- Another trick is to remove the rolls and brush the bottom with butter then return them to the pan before buttering the top.
- Make sure that you only fill the muffin tin $^1/_2$ full to allow for expansion.

Method for Proofing (still active) Yeast
Dissolve 1 tablespoon of sugar into 1 cup of warm water (95°F) and add the yeast. The yeast should start bubbling after 5-7 minutes; if it doesn't bubble it is no good.

BLINTZES

Blintzes originated with the Jews of Russia and were first mentioned in an English cookbook in the late 1800s. Blintzes are a very thin pancake that is stuffed with a variety of ingredients depending on the occasion or holiday.

- The normal blintz batter is made from 3 beaten large eggs, $^3/_4$ cup of matzo meal, $^1/_2$ teaspoon of table salt, and $1^1/_2$ cups of tap water.

- Frying pans used for blitzes should be heavy and the size of the blintz. The pans should only be used for blintzes and kept seasoned and never washed.

- Blintzes are only browned on one side in a very slight layer of oil. Most chefs use a brush to just brush oil on the pan before adding the batter.

- The blintzes are folded over three sides, then rolled into shape.

- The most common filling is a mixture of cottage cheese, sugar, and sour cream.

- After the blintz has been filled it is placed back into the pan and lightly browned so that the filling is warmed before serving.

- Some chefs bake blintzes. However, frying seems to be the more desired method of cooking.

BREAD

The science of bread making, and how proteins in flour interact with water and leavening agents to produce a loaf of bread is interesting and educational for the professional baker. I have chosen to leave out this information and just provide the pertinent facts regarding the tricks and secrets used by bakers to produce the finest loaf of bread.

Baking Pans
- If you substitute a baking pan that is shallower than the pan the recipe calls for, it would be best to reduce the baking time by 25%.

- If you substitute a baking pan that is deeper than the pan recommended in the recipe, then increase the baking time by 25%.

- If you use a glass baking dish, reduce the temperature in the oven by 25°F.

Batter Breads
- Batter breads are always beaten and never kneaded.

Cornbread

- To make a crispy crust, preheat the pan before you place the cornbread batter in. The pan should be oiled and allowed to be in a 400°F oven for about 8 minutes before adding the batter.
- Use a cast iron skillet (the best choice) or glass baking dish for the best results.
- The fat that you use needs to be heated on the range until it just starts to smoke. Remove the skillet and spread the batter in evenly then place the skillet in the oven and bake for 30 minutes or until well browned.
- If you would like to sweeten up cornbread, just add 2 tablespoons of brown sugar and 2 pinches of ground nutmeg to the dry ingredients.
- Cornmeal batter should be mixed until it is smooth for the best results.

If you would like to avoid a lumpy batter, just add the liquid in two stages. Cornmeal does not absorb water very well so take it slow and easy.

- White cornmeal is best for biscuits.
- If you use coarse stone-ground cornmeal, the bread will have a gritty texture, which some people like.
- The fine yellow cornmeal will give the bread a softer texture.

Raisin Bread

- Adding raisins to bread slows down the staling, which is why raisin bread will last twice as long as regular bread at room temperature.

Rye Breads

- When baking rye bread do not place any containers with water in the oven to create steam. The steam will ruin the bread.
- Rye flour is low-gluten flour that will rise better if you use twice the amount of yeast called for in the recipe.

Quick Breads

- Combine the wet and dry ingredients until they are barely moistened.
- Too much mixing and the bread will be tough.
- When adding raisins or dried fruit, be sure and toss them in the same flour you are making the bread with.
- If frozen, they should be thawed at room temperature. If they were frozen in aluminum foil, then heat the bread in a 400°F oven.
- Quick bread should not be kept frozen for more than 2-4 months.
- The baking powder or baking soda must be very fresh.

- Allow the bread to cool for 5 minutes before removing it from the baking pan, then set it on a wire rack to cool.

Sourdough Breads

The Egyptians, not a baker on the wharf in San Francisco, invented sourdough bread around 2000 BC. However, the best flavored sourdough bread is produced in San Francisco.

- Make sure that no metal comes into contact with the sourdough starter. This can cause a chemical reaction that will kill the starter. If this happens, a black, blue, or pink liquid will come to the surface.
- Always use the least-processed flour. King Arthur or quality organic, unbleached flour is best.
- Clay or crock containers may also have metal in them and should not be used.
- Pressure in starters may build up and they need to be covered with loose-fitting lids.
- Starter should always be separated into two batches: one to use now and the other to store as a "back-up."
- If you use a sourdough starter instead of a mix the bread will have a more open texture.
- Starter that is being used should be refrigerated overnight.

Sourdough starter is really "wild yeast" that lives in a batter of flour and water. Starters were as valuable as gold in the early days, guarded and treasured. Prospectors actually slept with the starter on cold nights so it would not die from freezing. A 240 year old sourdough starter can be obtained by calling 1 (800) 827-6836.

- The "back-up" starter should be fed about every 2 months.
- Your main starter should be stored in a 3-4 quart container to allow you to build up enough "starter" to use for baking.
- Never use chlorinated water when making sourdough bread. The chlorine can injure the starter.
- Always use a clear container for starter (not glass) so that you can easily see the bubbles when the starter needs to be fed.
- Transfer the starter to a clean container every 2 months.
- If you would like to prepare bread with a sourdough flavor, just replace the milk or water with yogurt.

Yeast Breads

The basic formula for "enriched," white bread was invented by Dr. Clive M. McCay at Cornell University in 1934. The formula was one tablespoon of soy flour, one tablespoon of dry whole milk and one teaspoon of wheat germ to one cup of white flour. The formula added additional protein, calcium, and B vitamins. It was called the "Triple-Rich Formula."

- Always add yeast to water never water to yeast or you will kill a lot of the yeast.

Active dry yeast is a domesticated relative of the old "wild yeast." This type of yeast has been grown to produce predictable results when it comes to flavor and speed of growth.

- A wet measuring spoon is never placed into a baking powder box.
- If you store dry yeast in the refrigerator it will slow down the yeast's metabolic process and it will stay fresh longer. Be sure and warm it up to room temperature before using.
- On humid or very hot days most yeast dough rises faster and may be hard to knead due to a loss of elasticity.

If you want to increase the shelf life of your bread, try adding some raisin juice concentrate to the recipe as part of the liquid. Professional bakers use this trick instead of adding preservatives.

- If you want to slow the rising, just place the dough ball in a cool location.

Whole-wheat breads
- Whole-wheat bread will not rise as high as white bread due to its higher volume from lack of refining.
- When mixing whole-wheat bread dough, add 1 tablespoon of lemon juice as you are mixing it and the dough will rise faster.
- When making whole-wheat bread it will be moister if you slowly add the flour to the water and mix gently.
- Whole-wheat absorbs water more slowly than other flours.

Use of Eggs
- Whole eggs have the ability to provide a degree of leavening and hold the bread together.
- Egg whites also have leavening ability as well as lightening and strengthening the bread.
- Yolks have very little leavening ability.
- Egg yolk is the more efficient emulsifier by keeping ingredients such as fat and water in suspension.
- Egg yolks provide a creamier, smooth texture.
- Egg yolks will help bread stay fresher for a longer period of time.
- Egg whites are a drying agent and can be used if needed.

When working the dough you need to punch down and manipulate the dough a few times to break up any pockets of yeast that have gotten friendly and are sticking together. Yeast will tend to congregate in the center and does not get

enough oxygen to multiply to the degree required. **Make sure that you lightly oil your hands when you do this.**

- When starting to work all ingredients for baking should be at room temperature.

Use of Liquids

- Water from boiled potatoes can be used to replace water in a bread recipe. The bread will remain fresher for a longer period of time.
- Hard water should not be used for baking since it may cause the gluten to become tough.
- Using water that is too soft results in sticky dough. Low mineral water is best to tighten the gluten.
- Low-rising bread is usually cause by old yeast. If it is a high-riser you have added too much yeast or water.
- If you use milk in your recipe the bread will have a finer texture than if you use water.
- If you use buttermilk in place of milk, reduce the amount of baking powder by 2 teaspoons and replace it with $1/2$ teaspoon of baking soda for every cup of buttermilk used to replace the milk with.
- Always combine the wet and dry ingredients separately.
- When beer is added to the dough it will give the bread a smooth crust.
- A vegetable or meat broth added to the dough will provide you with a lighter, crispier crust.
- Nonfat dry milk has the ability to provide more moisture and flavor and can increase efficiency of the yeast growth.
- If you run out of yeast you can substitute 1 teaspoon of baking soda mixed with 1 teaspoon of powdered vitamin C.
- Adding a small amount of powdered vitamin C to your recipe will make the gluten development more efficient.
- To speed up dough rising, just place the pan on top of a heating pad on medium.
- Using honey in the dough will slow down the coagulation of protein, allowing the dough to increase in volume and making the loaf fluffier.
- To help your bread rise and provide better texture, add 1 tablespoon of cider vinegar for every $2^1/2$ cups of flour.

As a rule of thumb, count the number of cups of flour in your recipe. It takes 1 teaspoon of baking powder per cup of flour. If the recipe contains a cup or more of decorative ingredients, it would be best to add an additional $1/2$ teaspoon per cup of flour.

- If you make the loaves tight it will result in even loaves of the same shape.
- Instant flour will dissolve more readily than regular flour. Instant flour will not form lumps.

- Kneading very well is important to distribute the yeast and other ingredients throughout the dough.

Sifting flour is important to return the flour to its original fluffiness. Flour tends to settle and compact during shipping. If you don't want to sift the flour, just shake the bag and fluff it with a spoon really well to aerate the flour back to its original fluffiness before you measure it out.

Use of Salt
- The best salt to use is sea salt, which contains a variety of different salts and chemicals and may impart a somewhat sweeter taste to your bread.
- Adding salt to yeast dough makes the gluten in the dough stronger; however, it also increases the mixing time.
- If bread has a crumbly texture try adding a small amount of salt.
- Professional bakers prefer to knead the dough first, then work in the salt resulting in a shorter kneading time.
- Salt is added to strengthen the dough just before the rising and shaping.
- Be careful not to use too much salt or it will affect the growth of the yeast.
- Sea salt in the dough makes the crust crispier and slows down the growth of the yeast.
- Celery salt or garlic salt can replace salt in most bread recipes, and provide a different flavor.
- Only use noniodized salt (sea salt). The iodine will slow down the yeast activity during the first fermentation.

GENERAL BAKING INFORMATION

If you use a dough hook in a heavy-duty mixer, add 4-5 ice cubes to the dough to keep it cool so that the gluten will absorb more water and produce higher quality gluten and a lighter loaf of bread.

- Too much cinnamon or citrus fruit will actually stop the yeast activity completely.
- When adding yeast to water the water must be below 140°F.
- When the recipe calls for you to grease and flour the pan, the best method is to grease the pan with oil and then sprinkle the flour in and move the pan around to allow the flour to distribute evenly. However, chefs recommend that you use $\frac{1}{2}$ cup of room temperature shortening mixed with $\frac{1}{2}$ cup of vegetable oil and $\frac{1}{2}$ cup of flour. Blend all the ingredients well then grease the pan.
- When you are allowing the dough to rise be sure that there are no drafts or the yeast will not rise evenly or to slowly.
- To make sugar-free bread, just replace the sugar with 1 teaspoon of malt for each package of yeast used.

- Yeast breads are leavened with yeast and are always kneaded to stretch the gluten in the flour. Use room temperature ingredients for the best results.
- If the recipe stays to grease a pan, grease the whole pan including the sides.
- To slow down the rising time just add one extra cube of yeast to the batter. This won't change the taste just slow thing down 45 minutes to 1 hour.
- When working with sticky dough, just spray a small amount of oil on your hands.
- If you knead too much flour into the dough, just sprinkle the dough with warm tap water.

Brewer's yeast cannot be substituted for baker's yeast. Brewer's yeast has been heat-treated and kills the live organisms.

- A small gully is cut into the tops of some yeast breads before baking. This allows gasses to escape while the loaf is baking and prevents the top from becoming ragged.
- High wheat flour is recommended for pizza, rolls, and buns since they are best when they have a chewy texture.
- Other flours need to be added to rye flour when baking rye bread. Rye flour is not capable of developing adequate gluten bonds to hold the bread together.
- Never place bread pans next to each other for the best results.
- Bread crust will not become too hard if you place a safe container of water in the oven while the bread is baking. This will provide just enough moisture from the steam to keep the crust soft.
- If you want the loaf to have an arch, then fill the bread pan $^3/_4$ full.
- If you want the loaf to have a flat top, just fill the bread pan $^1/_2$ full.
- Never use the microwave to cause the dough to rise faster. It will rise faster but it will affect the flavor. But, if you do use the microwave, then use only a 10% power setting.
- If dough does not rise well it may be too cool for the yeast to be active enough. The temperature must be between 76°F and 85°F.
- Unbleached flour is the bakers choice for most baking projects.
- Breads should be baked at 400°F to allow the expanding gasses to sufficiently increase the dough volume before the protein has a chance to coagulate.
- If the bread you are baking has a high sugar content it should be baked at 325°-375°F or the

sugar will burn instead of caramelizing and turn black instead of brown.

- When baking bread, always preheat the oven since dough rises best in the first 15 minutes.
- If bread has started browning too fast, cover the bread with a loose tent of aluminum foil.

If your recipe calls for you to create steam in the oven, place a large roasting pan on the base of the oven and throw an ice-cube tray full of ice cubes in. This will cause enough steam to last for 8-10 minutes providing you with the original "hearth loaves" our grandmothers made.

- Always check the oven 10-15 minutes before the cooking time is up in case your oven temperature is not accurate.

  If you are getting coarse, crumbly loaves, the amount of liquid in your recipe may be too low. If using dry, whole grain, then be sure and soak the grains first.

- Excess yeast will cause the bread to go stale quicker.
- When freezing bread, be sure and use freezer paper or freezer bags, not plastic wrap or aluminum foil.

BREAD-MAKING (SOLVING PROBLEMS)

The Crust is Too Thick
- Used too much flour in the dough
- Did not allow sufficient time to rise
- The oven temperature was too low

The Dough Does Not Rise
- You may have used old yeast
- The dough was too stiff
- The water may have been too cold or too hot and killed the yeast
- You poured the water on top of the yeast
- The location you placed the yeast to rise was too cold

The Bread Is Too Chewy
- Too high-protein flour was used
- Too little fat added
- Fat added at wrong time

There's a Crack on the Side of the Loaf
- The oven may have been too hot
- Not enough time was allowed for rising
- The loaf was not shaped correctly

The Bread Falls in the Oven
- Usually happens when the dough rises too much and gets too light

The Bread Doesn't Brown on Both Sides
- Did not use dull pans, the pans were too shiny and reflected the heat
- Overcrowding in the oven

The Tops of the Loaves Are Cracked
- The bread cooled too rapidly and was in a poor location
- The dough may have been too stiff
- The dough was not mixed enough

The Bread Crumbled Easily
- The dough was not mixed well
- Too much flour was used
- The location that was used for rising was too warm
- The dough was allowed to rise for too long a period
- The oven temperature was too low

The Bread Has a Doughy Bottom
- The loaves were not removed from the pan and placed on racks after they were baked

The Bread Is Too Heavy and Dense
- Too much flour was used
- Not enough time was allowed for rising
- A heavier flour was used other than all-purpose unbleached flour

The Bread Is Soggy Inside with a Coarse Grain
- Not enough time was allowed for rising

The Bread Is Too Dry with a Coarse Grain
- Too much flour was used
- The dough was not kneaded long enough

- The rising period was too long
- The oven temperature was too low

The Bread Contains Dark Streaks
- The kneading or mixing was uneven
- Your bowl was greased too heavily
- The dough was not covered properly while it was rising

The Crust is Too Dark
- Too much protein in the dough
- The sugar content was too high

The Bread Has Holes in It
- The air was not completely squeezed out of the dough when shaped
- The dough rose for too long a period before being baked

The Bread Smells and Has a Yeast Taste
- The dough was allowed to rise for too long a period
- The rising location was too warm

The Bread Has a Sour Taste
- The dough rose too quickly
- The dough was allowed to rise for too long a period before baking
- Too much yeast was used

There Is an Air Space Under the Crust

- Was not slashed or vented
- The oven temperature was too high
- Bread needed to be on a lower shelf

The Bread Has a Cake-Like Texture
- Did not rise for the correct period
- Too much sugar was added
- Too much salt added
- The fat was added at the wrong time
- The oven temperature was too high

The Bread Got Stale Too Quickly

- Inadequate sugar or honey in recipe
- The dough rose too fast
- Too much yeast used

BREADING

- To produce a lighter coating when breading a food for frying, try adding $\frac{1}{2}$ teaspoon of baking powder per $\frac{1}{2}$ cup of flour in your batter.
- When using eggs in breading, be sure that they are at room temperature for the best results.
- Always place all food in the refrigerator for 45 minutes after it is breaded and the breading will stay on. Always allow the food to return to room temperature before cooking.
- Never over-beat the eggs or there will be too much air and the breading will not stay on.
- The smaller the breadcrumbs the better. Large breadcrumbs do not adhere well.
- Homemade breadcrumbs are coarser and will adhere better.
- Make sure that the food is dried well with paper towel before placing it in the flour.
- Sometimes milk is used in place of egg; however, it does not have the adhering power of egg.
- Many cereals can be used to bread foods. Be sure that they are unsweetened such as rice or corn flakes.
- To make breadcrumbs, just place toasted bread in to the blender; add any seasonings and blend to the texture you desire.
- Crackers can be placed into the blender for a few seconds and used as a breading.

BREAD MACHINES

- Most bread machines are timed for the use of dry yeast. Compressed fresh yeast should never be used.

- Dry yeast needs to be stored in an airtight container since it absorbs water easily.
- If you replace whole-wheat flour with $1/4$ cup of gluten flour it will give the bread better texture.

The flour to liquid ratio should be $2^1/_2$-3 cups of flour to $1^1/4$ cups of liquid. In the summer (due to higher humidity), however, you will need a little more flour and in the winter use a little less.

- The machine can be opened to check the dough as it is being kneaded, but don't touch the dough.

When using a machine with a delayed cycle, never use fresh ingredients in such as eggs, milk, or cheese. Bacteria may have a field day and give everyone food poisoning.

- Always soften butter at room temperature before adding it to the recipe.
- If you use too little yeast, the bread will not rise properly.
- If you use too much yeast, the bread will rise and then collapse.
- Time the completion of the bread to about 1 hour before you will be eating it.
- If the bread is undercooked and somewhat gummy on the inside, the bread did not rise sufficiently.

The ratio of salt to flour in bread is $1/2$ teaspoon of table salt for each cup of flour used. Some recipes call for less salt, but it would be best to use the $1/2$ to 1 ratio.

- The dough should be pliable around the blades. If it's chunky then it is too dry and additional liquid is necessary.
- For a great sweet loaf, just double the amount of yeast; cut back on the salt; use $1/8$ teaspoon of vitamin C powder; use the longest cycle on your machine; or remove the dough and form it by hand before baking it in the oven.
- If your bread machine does not have a cooling off cycle, be sure and remove the loaf as soon as it finishes baking.
- High-protein flour will produce high-rising bread.
- Whole grain flours will produce denser, heavier breads.
- If the bread rises, then collapses in the middle, you have used too much liquid.

Salt is used in bread for flavor and bread can be made without salt if you are on a salt-free diet. Remember, however, that salt inhibits yeast and the dough will rise more quickly if you don't use any salt.

- In most cases, bread machine dough is better than hand-kneaded dough.

- Use special instant yeast for sourdough or for sweet breads.
- Most bakers who use bread machines prefer instant yeast, either regular instant, or instant gold, for most all-purpose baking needs.
- If you add raisins or nuts to the machine, it would be wise to add 1-2 teaspoons of additional flour. This helps the dough "open up" more easily.
- Never use rapid-rise yeast in a bread machine.
- Normally 1-2 teaspoons of sugar is added to a 1 pound bread.
- Any kind of sugar can be used in bread machines. That includes corn syrup, molasses, honey, and all other syrups.

The best unbleached, all-purpose, high-protein flour for bread machines is King Arthur's.

- A one pound bread machine can handle 2-3 cups of flour.
- A 1$\frac{1}{2}$ pound bread machine can handle 3-4 cups of flour.
- Almost all bread recipes can be made in a bread machine.
- Whole-wheat flour may not be the greatest flour nutritionally as once thought. The additional fiber tends to cause a percentage of the nutrients obtained from the whole wheat to be flushed out of the body.
- Whole wheat is fine for additional fiber and texture.

BRIOCHE

- Quality bread flour should be used or King Arthur's all-purpose flour. By using this flour you will have a more tender brioche.
- The fresher the yeast the better. Fresh yeast will cause the dough to rise faster. Never use rapid-rise yeast.
- Test the yeast to be sure that it is active.
- Never allow dough used for brioche to rise in an area where the temperature is over 80°F.
- Only allow the dough to rise to the level desired or it will weaken the dough structure and the brioche may fall apart.
- Be careful not to deflate the dough before it is chilled or the butter will leak out.
- If the butter does leak out, chill the dough for 1 hour in the refrigerator, then knead the butter back in.
- If you plan on freezing the unbaked dough, add 25% more yeast to assure that the yeast will be active when it is thawed out.

BROWNIES

Brownies first appeared in print in the 1897 Sears, Roebuck and Company catalog.

- Brownie mixes are high in moisture and do well in the microwave.
- The old-fashioned formula for brownies calls for 2 cups of granulated sugar, $\frac{1}{2}$ cup of all-purpose flour, and $\frac{1}{2}$ cup of cocoa.
- To the above was added 4 beaten large eggs, $\frac{1}{2}$ pound of melted butter at room temperature, 2 teaspoons of pure vanilla, and 1 cup of nuts.
- Everything was mixed together and placed in a preheated 300°F oven for 45 minutes.

BUNS (CINNAMON)

- If you use raisins be sure and soak them before adding them to your recipe. They will add moisture and reduce the formation of mold..
- It is best to add an egg yolk to act as an emulsifier.
- Use evaporated milk. It will improve the overall flavor and increase the sweetness.
- Cinnamon has the ability to improve yeast activity.

CAKES

Until about 1870 cakes were all baked in bread pans and looked likes loaves of bread. When more modern ovens and leavening agents became available cake baking changed, and cakes were baked more like the cakes we know today.

Angel Food

Angel food cake: was first made by the Pennsylvania Dutch in the late 1700s. By the 1870s the cake was well known and was mainly baked to use up the leftover egg whites from other baking projects.

- If your angel food cake shrinks or falls, the egg whites were beaten too long.
- Angel food and sponge cakes need to be cooled upside down to release the steam.
- Angel food cake can also be placed upside down on an ice cube tray to cool it.
- If angel food cake is tough you over-mixed the batter.
- These types of cakes are also called foam cakes.
- Angel food cake needs to be baked on the bottom shelf at 325°F to retain its moisture.

To improve the flavor of angel food cake, just add 1 teaspoon of almond extract to the batter.

- If the angel food cake is frozen and is frosted or filled, unwrap it and allow it to thaw in the refrigerator.
- Frozen angel food cake that is wrapped in aluminum can be thawed at 300°F for 15-20 minutes.
- If your angel or sponge food cake has poor volume, you may not have beaten the egg whites long enough. Only beat until the peaks stand straight up.
- Be careful not to over mix the batter on angel or sponge food cakes when you add the flour. The batter should just be smooth.

Cutting a Tiered Cake

- The top should be removed if it is a wedding cake and wrapped well and frozen for the first anniversary party.
- The cutting should begin with the 2nd layer, then the 3rd, and the 4th.

Chiffon Cake

- The original name for chiffon cake was "chiffon pumpkin pie" and was first mentioned in 1929 and served at the Beverly Hills Woman's Clubs "fashions for foods" event.
- The leavening of chiffon cakes is accomplished by using beaten eggs and a small amount of baking powder and using oil instead of shortening. Since they contain a large amount of beaten eggs folded into the batter they develop their "spongy" quality.
- If your chiffon cake has yellow streaks, you have added the yolks and the oil directly into the dry ingredients, instead of mixing it in a "well" in the center of the dry ingredients.
- Chiffon pies should be thawed in the refrigerator.

If your chiffon cake has a layer, you have either over-beaten or under-beaten the egg whites. Only beat the whites until they are stiff and look moist and glossy.

- Citrus fruit can be blended with custard, then set in gelatin and lightened with beaten egg whites.
- A crunchy nut crust is excellent on a chiffon pie.

Fat-type Cakes

These include sheet, layer, cupcakes, and pound cake. The formula for a fat-type cake must be precise to obtain the best results. The oven temperature is an important factor and should be checked for accuracy. The common problem of shrinkage with the cake pulling away from the sides of the pan is usually due to using too much liquid, shortening, or too hot an oven. Cakes must cling to the sides of the pan for support as they bake. The best cake pans for fat-type cakes are made of iron with a dull (not shiny) finish. Dull finishes tend to transmit heat more efficiently and faster.

- Always use cake flour for cake, not all-purpose flour. Cake flour consists of all soft flour and makes a lighter, more moist cake. All-purpose flour is a blend of hard and soft flours.

Never substitute a granulated sugar for a powdered sugar.

- Preheat the oven for about 10 minutes before placing a cake in.
- Baking powder is only fresh for about 6 months.
- There should always be more sugar than flour in the recipe.
- Whatever liquid is being used plus the eggs should more than equal the sugar.
- The volume of the eggs should always be more than the total shortening.
- If your recipe calls for 1 cup of shortening you can replace it with 1 cup of applesauce to lower the fat.

Never use oil in a cake recipe, it does not distribute evenly and causes baked goods to become grainy.

- If your layer cake has a coarse texture or is heavy and solid, you probably did not beat the sugar and shortening long enough.
- Butter cannot be substituted easily for other fats since it contains 16% water. If you do want to substitute it you have to multiply by 1.25 to make up for the water.
- You can make your cake even lighter and more moist by mixing 2 tablespoons of cornstarch in 1 cup of cake flour. Use this mixture in place of all cake flour.
- Over-beating the egg whites will sometimes cause a dry layer cake.
- Over-beating in general will cause excessive gluten to develop resulting in a poor textured cake.

- Never use baking powder in a chocolate cake. Chocolate has a high acid content and baking soda is recommended.

Recipes usually call for baking soda when they contain acidic ingredients. Baking soda will neutralize the acid. Some ingredients that call for baking soda to be added are buttermilk, molasses, sour milk, sour cream, yogurt, etc.

- If you have air bubbles in your batter, hold the pan about 5 inches off the floor and drop it. It may take 2-3 times to get out all the bubbles.
- The reason flour must be sifted is that flour tends to compact during storage or it is somewhat lumpy. Also it is best to aerate the flour to produce a lighter textured product.
- When butter or shortening is mixed with sugar it needs to be beaten for the complete time the recipe calls for or you will end up with a heavy, coarse-textured cake.
- If you don't care about cholesterol, a richer cake can be made by substituting 2 egg yolks for 1 whole egg.
- Never fill the baking pan more than $^3/_4$ full to leave room for expansion.
- When butter is called for in the recipe, do not melt the butter; just allow it to soften at room temperature. Never place it in the microwave or you will lose 40% of the flavor.
- Vanilla extract can be used to replace sugar. Five drops will replace $^1/_4$ cup of granulated sugar.
- If you are adding dried fruit to the cake, be sure and coat the fruit with the same flour that you are using in the cake and the fruit will remain in suspension and not fall to the bottom.
- Never use low fat margarine or whipped butter for baking.
- Bake all cakes on the center rack in the oven for the best results.
- Never open the oven during the first 15-20 minutes of baking time or the cake may collapse.
- If you use a glass baking dish lower the temperature in the oven 25°F.
- Cakes should be baked on the center shelf to allow for even distribution of heat.
- A dry layer cake usually indicates overcooking.
- If you notice a long hole or two in your layer cake it usually means that the batter was mixed too much. Batter should only be mixed enough to blend the ingredients.
- Allow a cake to remain in the pan for a few minutes before removing it and allow the steam to escape or it will turn to water.

Dome-top cakes are the result of adding too much flour to your batter. The batter around the edges tends to set before the batter in the center. This will also occur if there is too little baking powder or if it is not fresh.

- When placing a fresh-baked cake on a platter or plate, be sure and sprinkle a thin layer of sugar on the plate first so that the cake does not stick.

- If you use parchment paper on the bottom of your cake and find it hard to remove, just brush the paper with a small amount of warm water and peel it off.
- When you cut a round cake, always start at the center and go toward the edge.

Cut a whole round cake in half then cut your slices and move the two halves back together.

- Never wrap frosted cakes in aluminum foil, always use plastic wrap.

Pound Cakes

- These are mixed first by creaming the butter and sugar together, then adding the eggs and the dry ingredients last.
- Usually not a very sweet cake.
- Should be baked on the center rack for the best results.
- Always slice when they are cold.

Sponge Cake

Grandma's sponge cake contained no fat and tended to dry out very fast. Today's sponge cake does contain some fat, which gives it a longer shelf life. The fat comes from the addition of whole eggs. By adding the fat it also makes the sponge cake more palatable.

- Sponge cake requires timing, light-handedness, and correct temperature.
- Sponge cakes should be allowed to remain in their pan for about 3-4 minutes. This will allow time for it to contract and to firm up somewhat, making it easier to remove from the pan.

If you want the finest texture, use superfine sugar. Superfine sugar can be made by processing granulated sugar into a powder.

- It is best to use cake flour and no leavening.
- Make sure that the bowl and beaters you use to beat egg whites are 100% free of any hint of grease or the slightest spec of egg yolk.
- Don't worry about over-beating, the egg mixture needs to be very stiff.
- Once the eggs are beaten you will not have very much time. Fold the flour into the batter and bake immediately after mixing.
- Using the correct size pan is very important.
- Never grease a pan when making sponge cake.

Shortcake

- When mixing shortcake you can use a wire whisk since the dough is very light.

- Use a rubber or plastic spatula when folding the ingredients into the egg mixture.

SOLVING CAKE PROBLEMS

The Cake Fell in the Oven
- Usually this is caused by not baking the cake long enough
- Used too much baking powder
- Used too much baking soda
- The egg white were beaten to a foam

The Center of the Cake Erupted
- The oven temperature was too high
- The cake pan was too small for the amount of batter
- The ingredients were not in the proper proportion

There Were Holes Inside the Cake
- The oven temperature was too high
- There was too high a level of gluten, possibly from over-mixing

The Cake Was Too Chewy
- Too much gluten developed
- The flour used had too high a protein content
- There was too little sugar used
- There was too little fat used
- Once the flour and liquids were added, the batter was over-mixed

The Cake Was Too Crumbly
- The gluten level was too low
- Used too much sugar
- Used too much fat
- The cake was not mixed enough to blend the ingredients adequately

The Cake Was Very Grainy
- The oven temperature was not high enough
- Ingredients were not mixed properly

The Cake Was Too Heavy

- The oven temperature was too high
- Ingredients were not mixed adequately
- Too much sugar was used
- Too much fat was used

The Fruit/Nuts Sank to the Bottom

- The batter was not thick enough
- The fruit or nuts were not floured before adding them

CAKE FROSTINGS (ICINGS)

Buttercream

- Prepared by creaming the sugar and fat, which may be either butter or shortening, and eggs. The eggs will provide the consistency. The lightness will depend on the level of mixing and creaming.

Make sure you sift confectioner's sugar before adding to buttercream icing or it will not be smooth.

- Frostings made with butter can be placed on warm cakes.

Fondant Icing

- Composed of corn syrup and water, which is cooked to 240°F, then cooled off to 110°F, and must be worked immediately into creamy, white, very smooth icing.

Flat Icing

- Prepared with water, icing sugar, corn syrup, and a flavoring. When applying the flat icing to Danish or other pastry, be sure that it is at 100°F for the best results.

Cooking Secrets

General Icing Information

- Boiled icing is made by boiling syrup of sugar, water, and corn syrup, and adding a beaten egg while the mixture is still hot. This icing will hold peaks well when used on cakes.
- An iced cake will stay fresh longer.
- Icing has an important function, that of placing a protective coating on the cake, keeping the moisture in.
- Confectioner's sugar should be sifted before using to prevent lumps from forming.
- If you are going to add a liquid to confectioner's sugar that has not been sifted, warm the liquid first to avoid lumps forming.
- If you add 1-2 tablespoons of soft unsalted butter into confectioner's sugar icing, it will keep the surface of the cake more moist.
- The butter can be replaced in confectioner's sugar icing by using $1/4$ teaspoon of baking powder. The icing will remain creamy and moist.
- Icing won't get crumbly if you add a pinch of baking soda to the powdered sugar.
- To keep boiled icing from hardening, just add a small amount of white vinegar to the water while it is cooking.
- When cooked icing becomes granular, just add $1/4$ teaspoon of lemon juice and mix well.
- If you stir boiled icing prepared with sugar and water it will turn grainy.
- If you sprinkle a small amount of cornstarch on top of the cake the icing won't run down the sides.
- A light-bristled brush should be used on any areas that will be iced to remove any crumbs.
- All cooked frostings cannot be placed on a cake until the cake cools.

Never ice a cake until it cools down.

- Cut layers to give you more layers that can be iced.
- Food colorings can be used to change the colors of each layer of icing.

If you are worried about the cake falling apart when you frost it, just place it in the freezer for a few minutes until it becomes more solid.

- When icing the middle layer, ice the layer and allow it to dry for a few minutes before placing the top layer on.

Royal Icing

- Prepared by mixing together icing sugar, egg whites, and an acid agent, until a smooth consistency is developed. Used mostly in bakeries for display cakes since it hardens up well.

CASSEROLES

Casseroles became popular in the 1950s when certain dishes were manufactured that were easy to use for one-dish meals. Glass became the most popular material for casseroles, and tuna casseroles were the most popular. Women's magazines popularized the dish so much that it became a national phenomenon.

- If you prefer a crisp topping on your casserole, don't cover it while it is baking.
- Place cheese on top of a casserole during the last 10 minutes of baking if you want a cheesy topping.

CHEESECAKE

The first mention in print of cheesecake was in 1440. There are two main varieties, the Jewish cheese-cake invented by Jewish immigrants from Eastern Europe (New York cheesecake), which is prepared with a smooth cream cheese filling, and the Italian cheesecake, which is prepared with a ricotta cheese filling. The most famous cheesecake is prepared by Lindy's Restaurant in New York City.

- Never substitute a different size pan for the exact size recommended.
- Make sure that you blend the ingredients in the order given in the recipe for the best results.
- If you are preparing an unbaked cheesecake, be sure and mix all the ingredients until they are very smooth before gently folding in whipped cream.
- When you are mixing the ingredients, beat at medium speed only, and just until the batter is smooth.
- Over-mixing at high speeds can cause cracks to form as the cheesecake bakes.
- The cheese must be at room temperature when starting.
- It is best to use a 9 inch spring-form pan and butter the sides.
- The oven should never be opened for the first 25-30 minutes or it may develop cracks or partially collapse.
- Bake for 10 minutes at 550°F then reduce the heat to 200°F and bake for about 1 hour.
- When the edges are light brown and the center is almost completely set, turn off the oven, open the door ajar and allow the center to set for about 20-30 minutes. This is another method of reducing the incidence of cracks.

To avoid cracking, just place a pan of hot water on the bottom shelf before you preheat the oven.

- Always bake cheesecake on the center rack in the oven.
- Slow-baked cheesecake will not shrink as much when cooled.
- Egg-based cheesecakes should always be baked on low heat for the best results.

- If you get too much shrinkage, then the cheesecake was baked on too high a heat setting.
- Cheesecake usually takes $1^{1}/_{4}$ hours to bake.
- Cracks can be repaired with softened cream cheese or sour cream.
- The center of a cheesecake will firm up as it is cooling.
- Cheesecake should be served cool. Refrigerate overnight for the best flavor and texture.
- Always cut cheesecake with dental floss that is not waxed.
- To remove cheesecake from the pan, first make sure that it is cool, then invert it on a lightly sugared plate, then transfer it to your serving plate.
- Remember never to jar a cheesecake when it is baking or cooling.

COOKIES

Originally cookies were just small biscuits until the Dutch named them "koekie" or small cake. The name "cookie" was first used in America, while in England "cookies" are still called biscuits.

- Cookies are made from dough that is high in sugars and fats and lower in water content than other dough.
- Use only sugar cane or beet sugar for making cookies. Blended sugars have a tendency to cause cookies to spread too much.
- Flour does not have to be sifted when making cookie batter.
- Never use a thin cookie pan. If you don't have a thick one place one on top of another.
- Cookies with fats and a high water content will be soft.
- Be careful about using too much egg white in a cookie since that may dry the cookie out too much.
- Unbaked cookie dough may be frozen for 10 months if wrapped airtight.
- To keep soft cookies soft, just place $^{1}/_{2}$ apple or a slice of fresh bread in the cookie jar.
- Butter is the best shortening for making cookies.
- Using butter as the fat will cause the cookies to spread.
- A combination of shortening and butter will reduce the spread.
- The protein content will determine the color of the cookies in most instances. The more protein, the darker the color.
- Flour with a lower protein content will produce more tender cookies.
- Flour with a high protein content will produce chewy cookies.
- Sugar helps make the cookies tender, crispy, and crisp.
- Corn syrup will brown at a lower temperature than standard granulated sugar. It will also make the surface of the cookie crispier.
- When brown sugar is used the cookie may absorb moisture and become softer even when allowed to stand after being baked.

- If you want consistency in the quality of your cookies then you need to use the same brand and type of flour every time you bake them.

When using a cookie cutter, rock the cutter back and forth to release the dough if it won't release easily. This will eliminate any air holes that may appear.

- Too much shortening will make a cookie crumble too easily.
- Never use margarine, whipped butter, or any spread in a cookie recipe.
- If you over-stir cookie batter the cookies will be tough.
- When making oatmeal cookies, lightly toast the oatmeal on a cookie sheet at 185°F for about 10 minutes before adding it to the batter to give the cookies a nice brown color.
- Sugar cookies will remain soft if you roll them out in granulated sugar instead of flour.
- If you want crunchy cookies use 100% whole-wheat flour and use butter instead of shortening. Never use oil or the cookies will be soft.

Keep cookies soft and moist by adding 1 teaspoon of jelly to the batter (not preserves).

- The oven should be preheated for 30 minutes before placing cookies in.
- To make sharp edges on your cookies, dip the cutter in warm oil occasionally.
- Cold cookie dough will not stick to the rolling pin. Place the dough in the refrigerator for 20 minutes before you start.
- When working with cookie dough always keep the dough that you are not working with covered with plastic wrap to keep it moist until you are ready for it.
- If you add a small amount of additional baking soda to your recipe to reduce acidity, add about $1/4$ teaspoon per cup of flour. The cookies will get darker faster and will not puff up as much.
- Using high protein flour instead of all-purpose will cause the cookies to brown more. You can also substitute milk for part of the liquid.

If your cookies are too crumbly, just sprinkle a small amount of water on the flour before you mix in the other ingredients.

- To make a cookie with the texture of a cake, mix the shortening, eggs, sugar, and liquid together, then gently fold in the flour and leavening agent. If you want a more dense cookie, just mix the ingredients slowly.
- Check cookies when they are baking at least 3-4 minutes before the recipe says that they should be done.
- Burned bottoms on cookies are very common. To eliminate this problem, just rinse the bottom of

the pan under cold water after each batch or wipe the bottom with a wet towel to cool it off.

- If your cookies are not browning well, then place them on a higher shelf.
- Cookies will continue to cook if left on the pan so it is best to remove them from the oven just before they are finished cooking.
- Cookies should be cooled on an open rack not left in the pan.
- Make sure that your cookie jar has a loose fitting cover if you want the cookies to remain crisp. The air needs to be able to circulate.

Chocolate Chip Cookies

Chocolate chip cookies were invented by Ruth Wakefield in 1927 in Whitman, Massachusetts. Ruth was the manager of an inn near a popular tollgate and loved to prepare cookies. One day she added chocolate bits to her butter cookies and called them Toll House Inn cookies. Nestle offered Ruth a lifetime supply of cookies of they could publish her recipe on the back of their larger chocolate bars. Nestle started selling chocolate chip morsels in 1939 so that people would not have to chop up the chocolate bars.

- Never use margarine to make chocolate chip cookies; always use unsalted butter that has been softened at room temperature then melted in a double boiler.
- If you use cake flour it will create steam and puff up the cookie, but the cookie will not brown as much.
- If you use shortening instead of butter you will have less spread due to the high melting point of the shortening.
- Make sure that you use 3 times the amount of pure vanilla called for in the recipe. Do not use imitation or vanillin.

Use only superfine granulated sugar. Granulated sugar will not give the cookies as good a texture.

- If you use brown sugar, the cookie will be more moist and soft.

- If you use egg the cookie will have more moisture for puffing.

- Add 2 tablespoons of milk to the batter and the cookies will not be as stiff and hard.

- When using milk in the recipe, be sure that batter is cold before placing the dough on the cookie sheet.

- If you don't want to use milk, a teaspoon of sour cream will make the cookies softer.

- The best chocolate chips are semisweet Nestle Morsels. Other chips do not melt as well in cookies.

- The cookie sheet should be at room temperature when placing the cold dough on it.

- Real maple syrup can replace brown sugar if you wish, but be sure it is the "real" syrup, not an imitation.

TYPES OF COOKIES

Bars and Squares

- Dough is prepared into one pound pieces and then rolled out to the length of the cookie sheet. Place three strips on the sheet leaving some space between them.

- Flatten the strips with your fingers and shape them into equal 1 inch strips then egg wash them and bake.

- Slice when finished baking. It is important when making bar cookies to have the right size pan. If the pan is too small, the cookies will be too cake-like and when the pan is too big, the cookies tend to be too dry.

Drop Cookies

- The cookie dough is dropped onto the cookie pan by hand or with a spoon, then flattened out with a cookie die.

- If the dough is rich enough it will spread out by itself and does not have to be pressed.

Refrigerator Cookies

- Prepare the dough in $1\frac{1}{2}$ pound pieces, place on waxed paper and roll into bars that are 18 inches long.

- Refrigerate the dough for 8-10 hours then cut into $\frac{1}{2}$ inch strips and bake.

Rolled Cookies

- Chill a flour bag and roll the dough out on the bag in $\frac{1}{8}$ inch thick pieces. Cut into shapes and sizes that you desire with a cookie cutter and place on cookie sheet to bake.

- Make sure you dip the cookie cutter in water to stop the dough from sticking to it.

Sheet Cookies
- The cookie dough is spread out on cookie sheets, then sprinkled with raisins or nuts and baked.
- Once it is cool it can be cut into squares or any shape you desire.

SOLVING COOKIE PROBLEMS

The Cookie Spread Too Much
- Decrease, the amount of butter used and increase shortening
- Substitute egg for liquid
- Use cake flour
- Reduce sugar by just a few tablespoons
- Make sure that the dough has been adequately chilled

The Cookie Didn't Spread Enough
- Increase the butter or use all butter
- Add a small amount of additional liquid
- Add 1-2 tablespoons of granulated sugar

The Cookie Was Not Tender Enough
- Use low-protein cake flour
- Add 1-2 tablespoons of granulated sugar
- Add additional fat

The Cookie Was Too Soft
- Use higher protein flour or unbleached flour
- Reduce sugar by 1-2 tablespoons
- Reduce fat by 1-2 tablespoons
- Add a small amount of water to the flour before combining with other ingredients

The Color is Too Light
- Substitute corn syrup for the sugar
- Substitute egg for the liquid
- Use bread flour

The Color Is Too Dark
- Use water for the liquid
- Use cake flour or bleached all-purpose flour

Cooking Secrets

CUPCAKE

- Twenty cupcakes can be made with $2^{1}/_{4}$ cup of flour.
- Make sure that you only fill the cupcake holders about $^{2}/_{3}$ full, at the most, to leave room for expansion.
- Allow the cupcakes to cool for about 5 minutes before attempting to remove them.
- Cupcakes should be completely cool before you ice them.
- A butter cake recipe will make great cupcakes.

CREPE

Crepe is the French word for pancake and the most famous crepe is the "crepe suzette," which was named after Mme. Suzette, the star of a French comedy show presented at the Comedie Française theater in Paris.

- The batter is prepared from well-beaten eggs, all-purpose flour, soft butter, a pinch of salt, and milk.
- Serve with a sugary sauce prepared from orange juice and Grand Marnier (orange liqueur).

CROISSANTS

In 17th century Hungary, local bakers were baking at a very early hour of the morning and detected a surprise attack by Turks. They warned the officials who were able to fight off the attackers. The bakers, as a reward, were given the right to prepare a unique crescent-shaped pastry. The "croissants," shaped to represent the crescent of the Turkish flag, were first prepared in Budapest, Hungary in 1686.

- Chill the dough for 20-30 minutes (no more) before starting to turn the croissants.
- The butter should be evenly dispersed as the turns are made.
- Make sure that you brush off all flour when you are rolling the dough.
- All unused dough must be kept covered to avoid drying out.
- If you are working in an air-conditioned room that is under 68°F, allow the dough to acclimate to the temperature for 15-20 minutes before you start shaping it.
- Try not to roll the croissant too tightly.

DOUGHNUTS

In the early 1800s in England a woman made what she called "fry cakes" with dough that had been leftover from other bake products. The "fry cakes" were very tasty with the exception of the soggy centers. In 1847 a young man named Hanson Gregory accidentally poked his finger through the soggy center of the fry cake and everyone liked the taste, thus the first doughnut was born. Another story is that Hanson Gregory was a sea captain and placed the fry cakes on the spokes of the ship's wheel, making the holes.

- Doughnut dough should be allowed to rest for 20 minutes before frying to allow the air in the dough to escape giving the doughnut a better texture.
- By resting the dough the doughnut will also absorb less fat.
- If you place a doughnut into boiling water for 3-5 seconds as soon as it leaves the frying vat it will be lower in fat.
- Fry doughnuts at 365°F for 50 seconds on each side and only turn once.
- Never crowd doughnuts in the fryer.
- To stop doughnuts from becoming soggy and absorbing too much oil, add 1 teaspoon of white vinegar to the frying oil.
- The more egg yolk you use in a doughnut recipe the less oil will be absorbed.
- Doughnuts may be leavened with yeast if you are making raised doughnuts or baking powder if you are making cake doughnuts.

Glazed doughnuts will lose their glaze when frozen and thawed. Raised doughnuts will freeze better than raised doughnuts.

- Doughnuts are about 27% fat.

DUMPLINGS

- To avoid soggy bottoms on your dumplings, just wait until the dish is bubbling hot before you place them on top. They will also be lighter and absorb less moisture.
- Try using biscuit dough to make dumplings.
- When making potato dumplings, make sure that when you place them into the boiling water to cook that they immediately rise to the top and do not stick to the bottom. They should only simmer for 10 minutes.

Dumpling dough should not be mixed too much, just enough to combine all the ingredients.

- If possible place the dumplings on top of the vegetables or meat.
- Dumplings need to be simmered for about 10 minutes uncovered, then 8-10 minutes covered. Be sure that the cover has a dome so that the steam won't make them soggy. A top with a steam-release opening is best.

HUSH PUPPY

The name "hush puppy" was probably derived from the period just after the civil war in the late 1860s. Food was scarce and to feed their dogs people used to throw scraps of corn batter to them when they barked, saying "hush puppy." The hush puppy is basically a fried dumpling made from cornmeal.

- The basic recipe for cornmeal hush puppies is $1\frac{1}{2}$ cups of cornmeal mixed with $\frac{1}{2}$ cup of all-purpose flour. Then add 2 teaspoons of baking powder and $\frac{1}{2}$ teaspoon of salt.
- Add 1 well-beaten large egg that has been mixed with $\frac{3}{4}$ cup of milk and add 1 finely grated onion.
- The shape of the hush puppy is usually cylindrical and fat.

FRENCH TOAST

French toast was created to utilize French bread, which is prepared with no fat and therefore goes stale very quickly. Because of the short life span of the bread, the French used stale French bread to prepare a dish they called "pain perdu," which means "lost bread." The bread was soaked in a mixture of bread and milk then fried.

- The batter consists of 2 large eggs and $\frac{1}{2}$ cup of whole or nonfat milk. Whole milk makes a creamier product.
- Sourdough bread is usually preferred, but almost any bread can be used.
- The bread should be at least 2 days old. Fresh bread does not work as well.
- The bread must be allowed to absorb the mixture before placing it on the skillet.
- Unsalted butter is recommended.
- Sprinkle a small amount of powdered sugar on top before serving.
- Only turn the bread once as soon as the egg sets up.

FRUITCAKE

- The color of your fruitcake may be determined by the spices and fruits used.
- If you omit nutmeg and cinnamon and use only light-colored fruits such as golden raisins and

pineapple, the fruitcake will be lighter.

- Fruitcake will be fully cooked when you can insert a skewer and it comes out clean.
- Fruitcake batter will rise over the edges of a pan if the pan is filled more than $^2/_3$.
- To keep the outer edges from burning, bake a fruitcake slowly and place the pan into a larger pan filled halfway with hot tap water.
- Wait until the fruitcake cools before slicing it and use a serrated blade knife.

MERINGUE

- If the weather is rainy or even damp outside, the meringue peaks will not remain upright. High humidity will kill peaks.

Meringue recipes will work better if the eggs are 4-5 days old.

- All utensils must be very dry; egg whites do not like moisture.
- Adding 4-5 drops of lemon juice for every cup of cream also helps.
- Overcooking may cause beads to form on meringue.

Stronger peaks can be made if you add $^1/_4$ teaspoon of white vinegar for every 3 egg whites while beating.

- Egg whites must be at room temperature.
- When making meringue, be sure that there is no egg yolk left with the white or it will affect the result. Remove the slightest trace with a piece of paper towel.
- Add a small amount of baking powder as you are beating the whites.
- Add 2-3 teaspoons of sugar for each egg used.
- Beat with a hand mixer and only until they stand up.
- Another method to reduce weeping is mix 1 teaspoon of cornstarch with any sugar used in the recipe before you mix it in with the egg whites.

The sugar should be added gradually while beating the whole time. Only add a few spoonfuls at a time.

- To make a crispy crust on your meringue, just sprinkle the top with a finely sifter confectioner's sugar before you place it in the oven.
- It is easier to separate eggs when they are cold.
- When you have to store a meringue pie, be sure to rub butter or spray vegetable oil on the plastic wrap before placing it on the meringue to avoid the plastic sticking to the meringue.

- When cutting meringue, use a knife dipped in cold water.
- If you sprinkle very fine cake crumbs on top of a hot filling before placing meringue on, it will stop any leakage from ruining the pie.
- To eliminate meringue tears (weeping) caused by condensation, just allow the meringue to cool in the oven and turn the oven off just before the pie is done. Overcooking will also cause the problem.

MUFFINS

- Substitute buttermilk for milk in a muffin recipe for the lightest muffins.
- The secret to the greatest muffins is how well you combine the ingredients.
- The oven should be preheated for 10-15 minutes before baking the muffins.
- Separating the eggs will make muffins lighter. Mix the yolks with other moist ingredients then beat the egg whites until they are stiff before blending them into the rest of the ingredients.
- Muffin batter should be stirred gently or it will produce tough muffins.
- Muffin batter needs to be poured into the pan immediately when you stop stirring it.
- The muffin batter should be somewhat lumpy and not smooth.

Frozen muffins should be thawed at room temperature for 1 hour or heated, unthawed, at 300°F for 20 minutes.

- If you want a high-dome muffin, just grease the bottom of the tin and $\frac{1}{2}$ inch up the sides.
- If you add $\frac{1}{2}$ cup of raisins or nuts you need to increase the batter by adding 2-3 tablespoons of milk and $\frac{1}{4}$ teaspoon of baking powder.
- Muffins are easy to freeze and defrost well.
- To check whether the muffins are done, just insert a skewer into the muffin and if it comes out clean, the muffins are done.
- If you have a problem removing the muffins from the tin, just place them on a wet towel for 1-2 minutes or until they release easily.

English Muffin

The English muffin that is sold today was originally made by Samuel Bath Thomas who began making the muffins in 1880. Mr. Thomas used his mother's recipe that he brought with him from England to start a thriving business with a single product. The S.B. Thomas Company of New York makes the majority of the supermarket English muffins sold today.

- Use muffin rings or very clean (dishwasher clean) tuna cans.
- Only fill a muffin tin $\frac{1}{2}$ full and only turn once if using a grill.

- One of the best recipes to follow will be found in The Joy of Cooking cookbook.
- Make sure that the butter has been allowed to soften at room temperature and that it is unsalted.

PANCAKES

- Club soda should be used to replace milk or water in the recipe for the lightest pancakes. Make sure that the club soda is at room temperature.
- Mix the batter gently and never over mix.
- Adding a small amount of sugar will produce a nice brown pancake.
- Placing the batter in the refrigerator and keeping it cool until it is needed will slow the development of the gluten.
- The butter or oil can be left out of the batter, providing you grease the griddle well.
- If you add one teaspoons of white wine to waffle batter it won't stick to the waffle iron. The alcohol will evaporate during cooking.
- One tablespoon of "real" maple syrup added to pancake batter really improves the flavor.
- Different fruit juice can also be used in place of milk or water.
- When adding acidic fruit to pancakes, be sure and adjust for the acid by reducing the baking powder by $1/2$ teaspoon and adding $1/2$ teaspoon of baking soda.
- Only mix pancake batter until the ingredients are moist. The batter may still be somewhat lumpy, which is fine.
- If any lumps of flour are left, crush them. Don't keep trying to mix them in.
- Pancakes should be turned as soon as air pockets appear.
- The batter should always be mixed between batches to keep it aerated.
- Pancakes need to be cooked on a griddle with the temperature of 325°F for the best results. If a drop of water bounces on the griddle it is ready. If the griddle is too hot the water will jump off the griddle.
- The griddle should be wiped off with coarse salt wrapped in cheesecloth after each batch to stop any sticking.

Never use a spatula to press pancakes down. This tends to make them heavier.

- To keep the pancakes warm, place them on a cookie sheet with foil between the batches in a preheated 200°F oven.

Cornstarch Pancake Recipe

1 cup granulated sugar

2 tablespoons cornstarch

2 tablespoons unsalted butter

2 teaspoons of pure vanilla

2 cups boiling water

1/8 teaspoon nutmeg

Whisk the sugar and cornstarch, then add the boiling water a little at a time, while stirring constantly. Cook the mixture for about 9 minutes then add the butter, vanilla and nutmeg. Whisk and serve.

PASTRY/DANISH

- One of the best flours for making pastry dough is King Arthur's.
- Danish pastry is 23% fat.
- If you are using your own blend of pastry flour and the pastry is coming out too tender, reduce the amount of cake flour you are using.
- Ingredients for pasty making should be chilled or cold when starting.
- Puff pastry is basically very thin strands of gluten mixed with egg and kept separated by the fat. It is actually leavened by steam created by the hot air.
- The fat in puff pastry boils and bubbles then forms air pockets.
- Never put too much pressure on the rolling pin.

Pastry should be glazed as soon as it is taken from the oven to seal the surface.

Custard Cream Fillings for Pastry

- Never use copper bowls to store custard.
- Never place your hands in the filling since that is an easy way to contaminate it.
- Leftover custard should be discarded and never stored.
- Add any flavoring to the custard while the custard is still warm for the best results.

Dust should never come in contact with custard.

- Cool as fast as possible to avoid contamination.
- Never place custard in day old baked goods.
- Éclair paste dough should be made with bread flour so that when it bakes it will stretch and not tear apart.

- After adding egg yolks, bring the custard back to almost a full boil. This will inactivate the enzymes in the egg yolk. These enzymes are responsible for breaking down the starch and will ultimately cause the custard to become too thin.
- After filling keep under refrigeration.
- Custards are easily contaminated by bacteria.
- The cream can be brought to a boil if desired since it contains starch.

Pastry Dough

- Puff pastry dough is prepared from soft wheat flour, butter, and water.
- Timing when you add the salt is critical since you do not want tough gluten.
- Never use cake flour to prepare pastry dough because there is insufficient gluten development and the dough will not stay together adequately when it is being rolled out.
- Wondra flour can be substituted for pastry flour. However, the protein per gram is a little lower and the crust will not be as tender.
- Special margarine can be purchased from a bakery supply house to prepare pastry with. A combination of butter and special margarine may be used for flavor if so desired.
- Some bakers like to add salt to the flour instead of into the dough to distribute it more evenly, while other bakers like to add it to the liquid instead.

It is best to roll your pastry out on a sheet of waxed paper that has been lightly floured. When finished, invert the dough over your pan, or filling, and peel the waxed paper off.

- Place a small amount of butter between the layers of dough before it is folded several times. The butter or fat should be placed in pats or small globs. The more you fold, the more air pockets will form and the lighter the pastry.
- To stop pastry crust from becoming soggy, brush the surface with well-beaten egg white.
- Place the dough in the refrigerator for about 15-20 minutes before baking. If you leave it in too long, the fat will harden.
- When cutting the dough be sure and use a very sharp knife and cut straight down. Never pull the knife through the dough or cut the dough at an angle.
- The dough should be allowed to rest for 10-15 minutes between rolling and folding or dough can become tough.
- If the dough is not cut straight down, the end will puff up unevenly as the pastry bakes.
- Pastry dough should look like coarse crumbs.
- When making Danish dough it must rest for 4-8 hours after it has been rolled and folded. It should be placed in a "retarder" at 35°-45°F so that it can be easily worked.

Cooking Secrets

SOLVING PASTRY PROBLEMS

The Pastry Crust is Not Flaky

- The fat was not cut into the flour properly
- The pieces of fat were too small
- The fat was not cool enough
- The type of fat used melted too fast

The Pastry Crust Was Too Soggy

- The crust was not baked long enough
- The crust was baked with a filling that was too moist
- The pastry was baked with a filling at too low a temperature
- The top was not properly glazed
- The bottom did not receive adequate heat

The Pastry Crust was Too Tough

- The gluten (protein) development was too high
- The flour used was too high-protein flour
- The fat was not worked into the flour properly
- Excess water was added
- The dough was overworked

The Pastry Crust Lost Its Shape

- The crust was not chilled enough before placing the pastry into the oven
- The oven temperature was not high enough

The Pastry Crust Had Burnt Spots

- There were thin spots in the dough from poor rolling

The Pastry Crust Was Too Brown

- There was too much sugar used
- There was too much protein in the dough
- The oven temperature was too high
- The pastry was bake for too long a period of time

The Pastry Crust Was Too Soft

- The fat was worked into the dough too much
- The fat was too warm and was not chilled enough

The Pastry Crust Shrank Away from the Edges

- The dough was stretched too much
- Too much water was added to the recipe
- Dough was overworked
- Protein content was too high

PHYLLO (FILLO) DOUGH

- Frozen phyllo dough should be thawed in the refrigerator for at least 12-15 hours.
- Never thaw phyllo dough in a microwave.
- Clarified butter produces a crispy product.
- Never allow the phyllo dough to set or it will dry out very quickly. Prepare all ingredients before you unwrap the dough.
- Phyllo dough should be covered with wax paper and then a very damp towel placed on top to assure that the dough will not dry out.
- Fresh phyllo dough is easiest to work with.
- One pound of frozen phyllo dough contains about 22 sheets. Fresh dough contains about 25 sheets and is a little thinner.
- Baker's recommend 1½ teaspoons of clarified butter for each sheet of phyllo dough.
- Use olive oil or peanut oil to lightly brush on the dough before you bake any savory pastries in phyllo dough.
- Egg whites can be brushed on the phyllo dough instead of the oil.

When brushing butter on phyllo dough, start with the edges and work in. The edges tend to dry out much faster.

- If phyllo dough splits or tears, just brush the area with butter and place a small piece to patch the area.
- When cutting phyllo dough, use a metal ruler and make sure that the knife is very sharp.
- Once you complete the assembly using phyllo dough, be sure and brush the exterior with butter to prevent drying.
- Phyllo should be baked at 375°F on one of the upper shelves until just golden and not brown.
- If you have to bake phyllo when it is frozen, do so without thawing for the best results and to prevent sogginess.

PIZZA

About 200 years ago in Italy, pizza dough was rolled in the shape of a leg of a man's trousers that were worn at that time and called "calzone," which means "trousers" in Italian. These were prepared either as small appetizers or large ones to feed a family and included a variety of meats and vegetables. The first pizza parlor in America was on Spring Street in Manhattan, New York and opened in May, 1905. Pizza became a favorite food when service men returned home after World War II from Italy. The men had tasted pizza in Naples and wanted more.

The stylized pizzas that we have in the United States, such as Tex-Mex, Chicago, etc. did not really start until the mid-1970s. The best New York pizza is prepared with a very thin crust and in a coal-fired oven that can reach 750°F giving the pizza "New York blisters." The first pizza in Chicago (deep dish) was introduced in 1943 at Pizzerio Uno

Making the Crust
- To prevent a soggy crust on a homemade pizza, place the cheese on before the tomato sauce.
- If you add a small amount of olive oil to the dough while you are working it, it will produce a crispy crust with a soft interior.

Brushing olive oil on top of the dough before adding toppings is another pizza parlor secret in order to stop the ingredients from making the dough soggy.

- When the pizza is done, try brushing a small amount of olive oil around the outer crust to keep the crust from getting too hard.
- Some of the best pizza chefs in the United States sprinkle some extra virgin olive oil on top of the pizza just before placing it into the oven to keep it from becoming too crispy.
- Another trick to preventing a soggy crust is to sauté vegetables that have a high water content, such as peppers, onions, and mushrooms, to decrease their water content before placing them on top of the pizza.
- Pizza crust is easily cut with large kitchen scissors.

Pizza crust is best made with Gold Medal high-gluten bread flour. The crust will

be more tender and crisp.

- Never use all-purpose flour for making pizza crust or the texture will not be the same as using the Gold Medal flour.
- Pizza dough should be allowed to rise for at least one hour to double in size.
- After pizza dough rises it should be "punched" down and divided into balls, then allowed to rest for 15 minutes before being used.
- If you add a small amount of whole-wheat flour the crust will have a nuttier taste.
- If you add semolina flour it will produce a very crispy crust.
- If you use a food processor to mix the dough, the dough will be thoroughly kneaded when it forms one or two balls on the top of the blade.

Shaping Pizza Dough
- Dough should be lightly floured after it has rested for 15 minutes. The surface you are working on should be dusted with flour.
- When working the dough, use your fingertips and heel of your hand and work in a circular motion, continually flattening the dough. Flip it and continue to stretch it out until it is the size you want.
- If the dough is relaxed it will be easier to work.
- The pan that you place the dough on should be lightly dusted with cornmeal.

Freezing Pizza Dough
- Allow the batch to rise only once then punch it down and separate it into separate balls enough for one crust.
- Flatten the balls into discs and then wrap them separately with plastic freezer wrap or freezer bags that have had oil sprayed on the inside first. This will allow you to remove the dough without it sticking to the bag.
- Frozen pizza discs will stay fresh for 3-4 months.
- Thawing is best done by placing the disc in the refrigerator overnight.
- Frozen pizza dough should not be shaped until it is at room temperature.

Cheese for Pizza
- Mozzarella is the cheese of choice for pizza since it melts easily and does not become tough.
- Mozzarella originated in Italy and was made with the milk from water buffalo, which is where the term "buffalo mozzarella" originated.
- The best pizzas use the "real" Parmesan cheese, which is called Parmigiano-Reggiano. It is sold on the rind and is grated fresh.

Cooking Secrets

- Romano cheese is also used with excellent results.
- Imported provolone will add a somewhat sharper flavor.
- New England style pizza uses white cheddar as the cheese of choice.

Tomato Sauce

- It takes $1\frac{1}{2}$ cups of tomato sauce for a 12 inch pizza.
- The basic pizza parlor recipe for tomato sauce is one can of Italian style tomato puree, one large crushed garlic clove, one teaspoon of dried oregano, four fresh basil leaves, salt, and fresh pepper to taste. This is the basic recipe but not recommended if you want the best tasting pizza.

If you want the best tasting pizza never add the spices to the tomato sauce, only salt and pepper as desired. Spices should be added last on top of the ingredients after the pizza is complete. The acid in tomato sauce tends to reduce the potency of many spices, especially as the tomato sauce heats up.

Toppings

- If you use meats they are best if precooked, such as salami, pepperoni, sausage, ham, or hamburger.
- Tuna is an excellent topping, but should be a good quality and placed on in chunks.
- Because of their high fat content, meats such as sausage need precooking.
- Vegetables other than tomatoes should also be precooked since they may not cook through if they are thick, or their water content is too high.
- Grilling vegetables is recommended, however, they can also be sautéed or blanched.
- Sautéing vegetables allows you to add additional flavors, which enhance the taste of the pizza.

Baking the Pizza

- The oven should be at the highest temperature possible.
- The pizza should be placed directly on a special pizza screen, which looks similar to the screen

on your door, so that the heat can easily get to the bottom of the crust.

- If you have ordered a delivered pizza and the crust is soggy, just make sure that your oven has been preheated to 400°F before it arrives, then place it in for 5 minutes.
- Pizza will always taste better when prepared in a coal-fired or wood-burning brick oven or cooked directly on the heat source, which must be at least 550°F. Home ovens usually will not go over 500°F.
- Unglazed quarry tiles can be placed on the bottom of the oven, which does help. They must be at least ½ inch thick or they will crack from the intense heat.
- If you are going to use the tiles, be sure that the dough is at room temperature for the best results.

The finest all-natural, handmade pizza in the United States can be found in Las Vegas, Nevada at Fasolini's Pizza Cafe. Jim and Josie Fasolini are recognized as one of the finest pizza and Italian food chefs in the world.

POPOVER

- Popovers are easily leavened using only eggs and steam.
- Make sure that you have the eggs and milk at room temperature before you start mixing a popover batter.
- Eggs will create more volume at room temperature.
- If you follow the recipe to the letter, the popovers will come out great. If you try and alter the recipe you won't like the results.
- If you prepare the batter ahead of time and refrigerate it, be sure and allow the batter to return to room temperature for 45 minutes before using it.
- Popovers should only be made in an iron popover pan for the best results. The pan should never be filled more than half full to avoid spillovers.

Most bakers recommend that if you do not have an iron popover pan you do not even attempt making them.

- Always bake popovers on the center rack of the oven and at 425°F. If glass cups are used reduce the heat by 25°.
- Popovers may collapse if the oven door is opened during the first 20 minutes of cooking time.
- Popovers will collapse when they are removed from the oven if you undercook them.
- They should have a nice brown color when baked.

After the popovers have finished baking, puncture each one in several places with a skewer to release the steam and the insides will not be soggy.

- If you would like the insides to be somewhat crispy and very dry, just return the popovers to the oven for 8 minutes after you have punctured them but keep a close eye on them so that they do not burn.
- Popover batter should be mixed just enough to blend the ingredients. Even if it ends up thin it will be okay.

PRETZEL

The first pretzel was made in 605 AD in a monastery in southern France by a Franciscan monk. The pretzel was made during Lent when fat, eggs, and milk were forbidden. The monk decided to prepare dough of just flour, salt, and water, then twisted the dough into the shape of two arms crossed as in a "prayer." He called it a "pretiola," which is Latin for "little gift." The first pretzel was then given to children as a reward for saying their prayers. The first pretzel in the United States was introduced by Jochem Wessel in 1652 who made a pretzel and sold it to the Indians. This made settlers mad because he used "good flour" and they had to eat bran flour.

- The ingredients are 2 teaspoons of brown sugar, 1 teaspoon of fresh, dry yeast, warm water (105°-110°F), $3\frac{1}{2}$ cups plus 3 tablespoons of flour, $\frac{1}{4}$ teaspoons of salt, and 2 tablespoons of baking soda.
- Mix the brown sugar with $\frac{1}{4}$ cup of warm water until all the sugar is dissolved, then sprinkle yeast on top to moisten, then set it aside to rest for 10 minutes.
- Sift $3\frac{1}{2}$ cups of flour and the salt into a separate bowl, then stir in the yeast mixture and add $\frac{3}{4}$ cup of warm water and mix into dough.

Problems occasionally occur if you are using chlorinated water, which will reduce the effectiveness of the yeast.

- Add more warm water 1 tablespoon at a time if needed. The dough should be solid, but not sticky.
- Next you need to lightly flour your work surface with the remaining 2 tablespoons of flour, then turn the dough out and knead for 4-5 minutes.

- Form the dough into a ball, then coat the inside of a medium-sized bowl with cooking spray, and place the dough in the bowl, covering it with a clean towel.
- Allow the dough to rest for 30 minutes, then divide it into 8 equal pieces, flatten and cut the dough into rectangles about 2 inches by 3, making 16 pieces.
- Next roll out each piece to form a rope about 9 inches long and shape each rope into a pretzel bow or knot. Try and keep them the same size.

If salt comes into direct contact with the yeast, it can kill the yeast.

- Next add the baking soda to 2 cups of water and bring to a boil in a large saucepan.
- Drop the pretzels into the boiling water, only two at a time for 15 seconds, turning them once. Remove the pretzels with a slotted spoon and allow them to drain.
- Preheat the oven to 350°F and sprinkle pretzels with a small amount of salt or sesame seeds, then bake for 15 minutes or until brown.

QUICHE

- The biggest problem with quiche is a soggy crust. To make a crisp crust, just partially bake the pastry shell at 425°F for 15 minutes, remove it (remove lining if one was used) and brush it with egg yolk (or egg white) and return it to the oven to dry for only 2 minutes.
- Never pour the filling into the pastry shell until just before baking. This helps to prevent a soggy crust as well.

If you bake the quiche in a Pyrex dish, reduce the heat by 25°F.

- When you think that the quiche is done, just shake the pan lightly to see if is set. The quiche should be just barely firm.
- To be sure, just insert a skewer into the center. If the skewer comes out clean, the quiche is done.
- Quiche will continue to cook for a short time after it is removed from the oven and should be removed just before it has completed cooking.
- Quiche will curdle if overcooked and become very watery.

Quiche Lorraine
- Best to use a prebaked pie crust, since an unbaked one will probably be raw in the middle.
- Keep the filling $^1/_8$th from the top of the crust.
- Curdling will not occur if you only bake the quiche until you can insert a skewer into the middle and it comes out clean.

SUGARS USED IN BAKING

Granulated

Ultrafine
> Best for cakes and dry mixes and is usually used to coat confectionery pans.

Very Fine
> Excellent for dry mixing when producing cake mixes, puddings, and gelatin desserts.

Fine or Extrafine
> Standard granulated sugar we use as an all-purpose sugar in recipes and in our sugar bowls.

Medium Coarse
> Used to produce crystalline syrups in candies and other sweets. This sugar does not change very much when heated to high temperatures.

Coarse
> Used much like medium coarse sugar. It tends not to caramelize easily.

Powdered Sugars

Confectioner's (10X)
> Very fine granules, which makes a smooth textured icing.

Confectioner's (6X)
> Best for cream fillings, especially in biscuits, and as a topping for pies and pastries. Tends to mix well with melted fats.

Confectioner's (4X)
> Normally used in the production of chewing gums and as packing for marshmallows.

Medium Coarse
> Used for dusting mixtures that do not require the fine sugars. Usually used on doughnuts and related baked goods.

INVERT SUGAR

Produced from equal parts of two simple sugars, dextrose and levulose, and is sweeter than cane sugar. Found naturally in honey and molasses.

- Has the ability to retain moisture when used in cakes, which slows down the staling of cakes.
- Will enhance smoothness in icings.
- Helps a baked product obtain a rich looking brown crust through caramelizing.

TARTS

- The crust for a custard or fruit tart should be partially baked before the filling is added or the crust will not remain a separate layer. This is called "blind baking."
- Weights may be needed to hold the crust down when blind baking. Wrapping coins in a piece of aluminum will do.
- After shaping tart dough it is best to refrigerate it for 30 minutes to reduce the risk of shrinkage.
- In Europe bakers use wide rubber bands on either end of the rolling pin when rolling out tart dough to tell the correct height of the dough so that it is not too thick or thin.
- Unfilled shells need to be baked on the center shelf.
- After you shape the dough into a ball, place it in the refrigerator for 30 minutes to allow the dough to relax and distribute the moisture.
- Use a pastry cloth when you roll out the dough.
- Rolling the dough between two sheets of wax paper is ideal. The wax paper should still be floured.

Shells with fillings need to be baked on the bottom shelf.

- If you are making a glaze for a pear tart, the reduced pear syrup has to cool completely before any thickener is added or it will get lumpy.

- Be sure that any honey you use in a tart tastes good. Some honey does not have a good flavor.

- The shell will not become soggy if you quick-temper chocolate and brush it on the top of the bottom crust before adding the filling.

Orange Tart
- The best orange for tarts is the Valencia orange.

- Place the orange in the microwave for a few seconds to release more juice when squeezed.

- Canned mandarin oranges make an excellent substitute and work well. Make sure they are uniform in size for the best results.

For a real surprise, try using a new rasp from your local hardware store as a zester. The shards of zest look lacy and great.

- The whipped cream should be folded into the orange curd as soon as it is ready so that the gelatin will be incorporating as the cold orange curd cream begins to set up.

- Never use Seville orange zest, it is too bitter and will ruin the tart.

WAFFLES

Thomas Jefferson brought the first waffle iron to the United States from France. It was 100 years later when the waffle gained popularity and was sold by street-food venders in Philadelphia and New York. Belgian waffles were first introduced at the New York World's Fair in 1964.

- If you would like crispy waffles, just add $1\frac{1}{2}$ tablespoons of additional oil to the batter.

- Never open a waffle iron to check the waffle until it has cooked for 1 minute.

- When waffles are cooked, the lid will rise from the expanding dough.

- Frozen waffles should be heated without thawing.

- Waffle batter will keep for several days in the refrigerator, but be sure and place the batter in a larger container since it will expand.

- Using baking soda and eggs in the batter produce a very light waffle.

- If you want a crisper, brown surface, add 2 tablespoons of corn syrup to your recipe.

43

Pie Baking
SECRETS

PIES

- The bottom of the pan can be floured if you wish. Do not leave any globs of excess flour; shake out the pan well.
- The bottom of the pan can also be sprayed with vegetable oil if you prefer not to flour it.
- You will need to protect the edges of a single crust pie after it has baked for 15 minutes.
- Double crust pies need the edges of the crust protected after 30 minutes of baking. Aluminum foil can be used.
- Pies should be removed from their cooking pan and placed on a plate for easy serving and slicing.

Slicing pies in a metal pie pan dulls the knife and makes it more difficult to serve.

- If the pan is prepared properly, the pie should easily slip out of the pan.
- If there is enough fat in the dough, it will not be necessary to grease the pan to make the pie slip out easily.

Apple Pies

- Different varieties of apples can be used to provide different flavors and textures.
- Slice the apples thin so that they will be able to lie close together. Thick slices create too much air space.
- Thick apple slices usually drop to the bottom creating a space between the apples and the top crust.

The best apples for pies are Granny Smith, Pippin, Cortland, Jonathan, and Stayman-Winesap.

- Granny Smith apples are the most popular when preparing apple pie in the winter months.
- If you spray the exposed surfaces with a solution of powdered vitamin C and water it will keep the surfaces from browning too soon.
- For a milder cinnamon flavor reduce your recipe to $\frac{1}{2}$ to 1 teaspoon.

Cherry Pies

- If you are going to use sour cherries, use them as soon as you purchase them or freeze them. Sour cherries tend to deteriorate very quickly.
- If you don't have a cherry pitter, use an old style hairpin (if you can find one).
- The maximum amount of sugar should never exceed 1 cup.
- Butter does not go well in cherry filling. However, it is okay to use a crust made with butter.
- If you want to keep a nice cherry color, don't cook the cherry filling before you bake the pie.
- A small amount of almond extract is a great addition to cherries.

Chiffon Pie

- For chiffon pies, meringue is folded into the filling just before placing the cold mixture into the piecrust.
- If you place the chiffon filling into a crust that was not baked, the egg whites would get overcooked and ruin the consistency of the dish.
- The filling must be heated to a temperature of 160°-170°F to be sure that the enzyme that breaks down starch in the yolk is destroyed.

If the chiffon pie is to be eaten the next day, it is best to reduce the gelatin by $\frac{1}{4}$ of the amount recommended.

PIES

- If the custard is chilled in the refrigerator it should be stirred frequently during the first minute and then every few minutes until it starts to set up.

- If the custard becomes too stiff it will make it difficult to fold in the whipped cream.

- To remove a chiffon pie from the pie plate, just use a hot, damp dishtowel and run it around the bottom and sides.

Chocolate Cream Pie

- Always use a heavy well-insulated pan to keep the pie filling from burning.

- Remember never beat the filling too much after it has cooled or you will cause it to breakdown.

- If you want to eliminate the possibility of lumps, use a 10 loop piano wire whisk to prevent them.

- It is best to place the whipped cream on just before serving.

Cream/Custard Pies (General Information)

- When using a cream filling, coat the crust with granulated sugar before adding the cream to eliminate a soggy crust.

- Separate whites from the yolk when the eggs are cold, it will be easier. However, allow the whites to come to room temperature before using them.

- When cutting pies with loose fillings; spray your knife with oil before cutting and the filling won't stick to the knife.

- Cream pie fillings are always added to a prebaked piecrust.

- Toppings are added after the pie has cooled.

The preferred thickener for cream pies is "regular" cornstarch not "waxy maize" cornstarch.

- Custard pies should not be frozen, with the exception of pumpkin pies.

- The reason a custard pie shrinks away from the crust is that you have cooked it too long in an oven that was too hot.

- Custard pies are usually baked in the shell for 10 minutes at 450°F, then temperature is reduced to 300°F for 40-50 minutes.

- Cream and custard pies should be stored in the refrigerator.

Four step method

1. cald the milk and only some of the sugar in a round-bottomed pan.

2. In a separate bowl, mix the egg yolks, the rest of the sugar, thickener, and any flavoring.

3. Stir in the mixture in the bowl as soon as the milk and sugar has scalded but just before they boil. Mix until it boils and remove from the heat.

4. Flavorings can be added after removal from the heat.

Crumb Pie Crust/Topping

- Graham crackers can be used providing you add a small amount of sugar.
- If you are going to add nuts to the crust, additional sugar will be needed.
- Always add a pinch of salt and a small amount of vanilla to your recipe.
- The pie pan should not be greased or the crust may slip down. The rim, however, should be greased.
- For a crumb topping for an apple pie, combine $\frac{1}{2}$ cup of flour, $\frac{1}{2}$ cup of brown sugar, $\frac{1}{2}$ teaspoon of cinnamon, and 4 tablespoons of unsalted butter. Just barely blend the ingredients and crumble over the top of the pie.

Currant Pies

- If you use frozen currants, be sure they are defrosted before using them or they will not dissolve the thickener and the sugar.
- Make sure that the currants you use have no more than 4 seeds per currant.

Frozen Pies

- The oven should be preheated to 425°F. Bake the pie for 10 minutes before lowering the temperature to 400°F. Finish baking for about 40 minutes more.

Fruit Pies (General Information)

- When making a lemon pie, bakers rub a few sugar cubes over the top of a lemon then include these as part of the total sugar.
- Never substitute a granulated sugar for a powdered sugar if you run out.

Never place hot filling into a piecrust; always wait until it cools.

- Drain juices from fruit well and use with the thickener.

Always use glass baking pans when making fruit pies or the acid will discolor the filling and the pie tin.

- If frozen, bake without thawing at 450°F for 15-20 minutes, then reduce the heat to 375°F for 20-30 minutes or until the top has browned.
- Fruit pies do not hold up well and are best eaten on the day they are prepared.
- If you are making an apple pie with eating apples instead of baking apples, be sure and add 1 tablespoon of lemon juice to the filling.
- Fruit pies should be served just slightly warm. If served too hot, the filling will be too watery.
- When using fruit for pies make sure that the fruit is sweet enough otherwise more sugar needs to be added.
- Add 1 tablespoon of tapioca to the pie filling and it won't bubble over.

Another method of stopping bubble overs is to place a large tube of pasta in the center of the pie as a chimney to allow air to escape.

- Never use a microwave to bake a pie. The insides will cook long before the crust is done.
- Fruit pies can be stored at room temperature.
- Pies that are only made with berries tend to get bitter fast.
- The filling must be bubbling rapidly to be sure that the cornstarch will absorb enough liquid and thicken the fruit filling.

Fruit Pie Dough
- A method of keeping the bottom of the dough dry is to spread a thin layer of butter on the pie pan before placing the bottom crust in.
- Dough should be made the day before and allowed to rest in the refrigerator for 1 hour after it is rolled and shaped. This will prevent distortion and help the dough maintain its shape.
- It is best to decrease the amount of cornstarch used by 1 teaspoon if you are planning to eat the pie the next day. The pie will lose moisture overnight.

FRUIT PIE INGREDIENTS

FRUIT	QUANTITY	SUGAR	CORNSTARCH
Apple	8 cups	½ cup	4 tsp.
Apricot	4 cups	6½ Tbsp	2 Tbsp
Cherries	15 Tbsp	14½ Tbsp	2½ Tbsp
Current	3½ cups	1⅓ cups	3 Tbsp
Gooseberry	4 cups	1 cup	2¼ Tbsp
Peach	6 cups	½ cup	4 tsp.
Plum	4 cups	½ cup	2 Tbsp.
Rhubarb	4 cups	⅔ cup	4 tsp or 2 eggs

Ice Cream Pie

- The pie shell is fully baked first, then a soft ice cream is placed in and the pie frozen.
- Toppings can be placed on at the same time that the ice cream is placed in the crust.
- Whipped cream cannot be placed on top of the ice cream until just before serving.

Key Lime Pie

Originally a special lime was used to prepare key lime pie. These limes were brought to this country from the West Indies where they had been grown since the early 1500s and were probably brought there by Columbus. The lime trees were brought to the Florida Keys in 1839 and thrived there until a hurricane destroyed almost all the orchards in 1926. The key limes were replaced with a Tahitian variety, which we still use today and still call the pie a Key Lime pie.

- You can use either a pastry crust or a graham cracker crust.
- Be sure that the lime juice is squeezed fresh for the best results.

Lemon Pie

- The best lemons to use for lemon pie are the Meyer lemons from California. They have the mildest lemon flavor.

Nectarine Pie

- Make sure the nectarines are ripe and sweet but not mushy.
- Spray the nectarines occasionally with a spray of powdered vitamin C and water to prevent browning.
- Never add a hot liquid to the nectarines or it will cause the cornstarch to get lumpy.

Pecan Pie

- To brown the top better, use low-protein flour (cake flour) and eliminate the sugar, then add 1 teaspoon of lemon juice to the recipe.
- Refiner's sugar and unrefined brown sugar are the best for pecan pies. It will probably be necessary to obtain these in a baker's supply shop.
- The filling dries out easily and you need to check this pie regularly.

Pumpkin Pie

- Place a layer of mini-marshmallows on top of the bottom crust before pouring the filling in. As the pie bakes the air will expand inside the marshmallows and they will rise to the top providing a beautiful layer of browned marshmallows.
- Frozen pumpkin pies should be baked without thawing at 400°F for just under 2 hours, then

reduce the heat to 325°F until done.

- To be sure the pie is baked, insert a skewer into the center and if it comes out clean the pie is done.

- The cracking in the pie custard is caused by over baking.

Rhubarb Pie

- Never use rhubarb leaves, they contain a poison.

- If you don't like the tartness of rhubarb, strawberry can be added.

The combination of cherries and rhubarb makes one of the greatest pies ever baked.

- Two eggs can be added in place of the cornstarch to thicken the filling and provides custard that is excellent. The mild custard will not affect the tart flavor, which rhubarb lovers prefer.

Shoofly Pie

- Make sure that you use unsulfured molasses; the sulfured variety has a bitter taste.

Soft Pies

- Pecan, sweet potato, and pumpkin pies should be made in a very deep glass pie dish with a fluted rim.
- Prepared with an unbaked crust.
- The filling normally sets during the baking process. Most filling will contain eggs, which assist in the filling setting-up properly.
- A frozen pumpkin pie will take about 15 minutes longer than a fruit pie to bake. This gives the pie longer to dry out, reducing the excess moisture, which allows the filling to set better.

Thickeners

- Thickeners are not needed for apple pies.
- All other fruit pies should be thickened with a mixture of 2 tablespoons of cornstarch and 2 tablespoons of tapioca.
- Cornstarch has twice the thickening power of flour. For fruit pies NEVER use regular cornstarch, the gel obtained becomes too solid. The recommended cornstarch is "waxy maize."
- Acidic fruit pies may interfere with the thickening power of the starch used. Always add the pie filling after the thickener has set and never cook it with the acidic filling.
- The juice that was drained from the fruit should be brought to a boil and the thickener added. You can also use both the juice and the fruit together if you wish.
- After thickening with cornstarch bring the mixture back to a boil, which will clarify the mixture and set the thickener.
- Add any sugar, salt, butter, or other ingredients after the thickener has set and stir in until fully dissolved.
- Juices from pies will not run if you blend 1 egg white, beaten until stiff, with 2 tablespoons of sugar and add it to the filling before baking.

Pie Washes

To make the pie crust more appealing, many bakers use eggs, water, milk, melted butter, or sweet cream brushed on depending on the appearance desired.

CREAM WASH- Just brush the crust with cream before baking the pie to give the pie a glossy top.

EGG WHITE WASH- Use 1 egg white mixed with 2 teaspoons of water to provide a transparent golden brown color to the pie.

EGG YOLK WASH- Use 1 egg yolk and 2 tablespoons of water to make a golden crust.

BUTTER WASH- Provides a soft, rich-flavored crust.

MILK WASH- Makes the crust softer and not as shiny.

WATER WASH- Spray a mist water on top of the loaf to make a crunchier crust.

WHOLE EGG WASH- Makes loaves fancy by giving the surface a shiny bronzed surface. Use a whole egg beaten with 1 tablespoon of water gently brushed over the surface.

The Perfect Pie Crust
- Leaf lard is the best fat for preparing the flakiest piecrust. It has the largest fat crystals of any fat, which makes a flakier, lighter piecrust. Lard and shortening are 100% fat compared to butter at 80-90%. Shortening is the best choice after lard.

Never use bread flour when making piecrust dough. The protein content is too high and to compensate you would have to add more shortening to tenderize the gluten strands.

- Shortening should always be at room temperature or too much gluten will develop and the crust will be tough.
- A small amount of butter added will provide a nice flavor to the crust.

- Adding a teaspoon of white vinegar to the pie dough will produce a flakier piecrust.
- The shortening in a crust will usually provide 25-40% fat.
- If you freeze pie dough it must be thawed in the refrigerator, not at room temperature.
- Pie dough that is uncooked and unrolled can be stored in the refrigerator for 3-4 days and frozen for 2-3 months.
- If you don't want to add vinegar, substitute sour cream or whipped cream for any water.
- The perfect surface for rolling out pie dough is a piece of marble with a pastry-cloth on top.
- Mealy piecrust is made by rubbing the flour and the shortening until there is a very fine distribution of the flour in the shortening.
- The coolness of a marble surface helps to keep the fat firm, preventing the fat from being absorbed into the flour, which can cause a loss of flakiness.
- When rolling dough, if cracks develop, just remove a small piece from the edge, lightly dust it with flour, place a piece of plastic wrap over it, and roll it into the dough.

All ingredients and utensils should be very cold when preparing piecrust dough. Even the flour should be placed in the freezer for a few minutes before adding it in to the recipe.

- Sea salt is recommended by bakers in place of table salt since it tends to have a slightly sweet flavor.
- Sugar can damage gluten formation, making it excellent for piecrust dough.
- When you add baking powder to your recipe try using half the salt called for.
- A small amount of vinegar added to the ingredients when you add the liquid (if the liquid has no acidity of its own) will improve the dough, provide better elasticity, and reduces the risk of shrinkage.
- If you want a buttery, great tasting crust, try using all unsalted butter to replace the shortening. The crust will not be as flaky, but the flavor will make up for it.
- Try adding the butter in large ice-cold pieces so that when the water is added it will be completely absorbed by the flour. This will develop the maximum amount of gluten.
- Cutting the butter in may not allow for enough gluten formation.

It is always best to chill the shaped crust in the pie pan/plate, before baking, to relax the gluten and reduce shrinking. The entire filled pie can be chilled for 15 minutes if you prefer and the crust will not pull away when it is baking.

- Pastry flour (low-protein flour) is best for piecrust. Soft wheat flour will produce a sturdy crust. However, more shortening will probably be needed. Very little gluten is needed for the perfect piecrust.
- Try using half all-purpose flour and half cake flour and you will obtain a good blend of flakiness and a tender crust.
- If you add water to pie dough it must be ice water or at least be very cold. The water should be added to the dough until it just holds the dough together. Too much water will make the crust tough.
- Water has an important function in that it slows the gluten from developing, which allows the water to evenly distribute. This keeps the dough tender. Once you add the water, try and mix as little as possible.

When using ice water the shortening will remain solid and reduce the development of gluten.

- Use a pizza cutter to cut strips for a lattice top.
- To stop fruit juices from making the bottom of the piecrust soggy, just brush the bottom crust with lightly beaten egg white to seal it. Then refrigerate the crust for 10-15 minutes before using it.
- Never stretch the dough when placing it in the pan or it will shrink.
- To make thinner dough for pie shells, just coat your rolling surface with olive oil.

Blending shortening into the flour causes it to break into many pieces, coating all pieces with flour during the process. If you incorporate half of the shortening at a time, you will create dough with many pockets of shortening. As you roll the dough you tend to flatten out those pieces of shortening, which gives you flakes or the "flaky crust" you desire.

- Make sure a ready-made piecrust is fully thawed before using it.
- To make a different top on the pie, just cut out shapes from the piecrust dough with cookie cutters and place the shapes on top instead of a full crust.
- Pie ingredients should be cold when preparing a pie.
- If you are using a single piecrust, you will need to fold the edges under and flute the edges with your fingers. Fluting is just making and indentation in the crust so that it remains in place.

Phyllo dough can be used for piecrust and will make a fat-free crust. Use two leaves for a 9-10 inch pie, sprayed with vegetable cooking spray. Centered in the pan, then lay two more layers at right angles to first, then two more on the bias to fill any gap to be sure that the pan is full lined. Use a piece of damp paper towel to press the phyllo into the pan. Be careful not to tear the phyllo.

- If your crust is too crisp and you want it to be soft, increase the shortening you are using or add milk instead of water.
- For a double-crust pie, place the pie crust on the bottom, place the filling in, then place the second crust on top of the filling and press the two crusts together by fluting them against each other.
- Never make a pie in a warm or hot kitchen. It will affect the results.
- When mixing the dough, if you use your hands the crust will be flakier. Look at the dough while you are working with it. If you see can see small flakes of butter, the crust will be flaky; if it seems to stretch easily, it will be elastic enough so that it will not shrink.

If your dough has been refrigerated for more than 1 hour, allow it to remain at room temperature for 15 minutes before you work it.

- If the dough appears to be very fragile and breaks easily, fold it and refrigerate it for 25 minutes before working it again. The fat did not allow enough moisture into the dough.
- After the dough is mixed, roll it into a rough ball, wrap it and then refrigerate it for 45 minutes before rolling it out.
- Ceramic or Pyrex pie plates will give you the crispiest piecrust.
- Place a few slices of fresh white bread on top of your pie while it is baking and it will eliminate blistering. Remove the bread about 5 minutes before the pie has finished cooking to allow the crust to brown.
- When baking a crust for a cream pie or ice cream pie, always bake it in a preheated oven and on the bottom shelf. The crust should be pricked with a toothpick every 3-4 inches to allow steam to escape. Bake the crust uncovered at 450°F for about 14 minutes or until the crust has barely browned.
- To avoid a blistering piecrust, place a second pie pan on top of the crust as its bakes. This is called "double-panning."
- Glazing the top crust usually results in a tougher crust.
- Sprinkling sugar on the top crust will provide a bit of crunchiness and will not make the crust tough. It also helps to brown the crust.
- If you want a real crisp bottom on your pie, bake it on the floor of the oven for the first 25 minutes.
- If you have a problem removing pies from pans that have a graham cracker crust, just place the

pan in warm water for 10-15 seconds and it will come right out.

- If your piecrust sticks to the pan, it may be due to inadequate shortening, or the dough separating and the filling burning on the pan. This is another good reason not to stretch the dough to fit the pan.

The Right Size Crust for the Job

- For a fluted pastry tart pan - Cut the dough circle 1 inch larger than the pan.
- For a single piecrust - Cut the dough circle 3 inches larger than the pan/plate.
- For a double-crust pie - Cut both circles 2 inches larger than the pan/plate.

Special Piecrusts Secrets for Lengthy Cooking Times

- These pies are made with a filling that requires a longer baking time, which could damage the normal crust.
- If the recipe calls for a dairy product, substitute water.
- A small amount of apple cider vinegar (acid) should be added to retard browning.
- Use 50% cake flour and 50% of your regular flour.
- Leave any sugar out of the recipe.
- Reduce the amount of shortening.
- Make sure that you refrigerate the dough since the cold will cause the moisture to distribute more evenly.

- Placing the crust in the freezer to chill it is even better than the refrigerator and will help to retain the shape of the crust.

SOLVING PIE CRUST PROBLEMS

The Crust Didn't Brown Enough
- Make sure you used a heatproof clear glass dish or dark metal pie pan
- Add additional sugar or syrup

The Crust Browned Too Much
- The filling will need to be precooked or at least heated before placing it in the crust
- Use a light-colored pie pan
- The edges need to be protected with aluminum foil

Preparing
SOUPS & STEWS

SOUPS/STEWS

Croutons

- The best croutons are made from small cubes of bread that have been sautéed in butter or extra virgin olive oil with pepper flakes.
- Dust croutons with freshly grated Parmesan cheese before serving.
- Croutons should be served on the side not on the salad.

Soups

Removing fat from soup and stews can be accomplished in a number of ways:

1. Place the soup or stew in the refrigerator and allow the fat to rise, then remove it.
2. Use a separator cup for clear soups.
3. Place 3-4 ice cubes in a piece of cheesecloth and swirl around, allowing the fat to attach to the cheesecloth.
4. Swirl a piece of iceberg lettuce around in the soup or stew and the fat will adhere to it.

- Depending on the density of the vegetable they should be added at different times. If you wish to add them at the same time then you may want to steam some to soften them before adding them.
- Vegetables should be sautéed before adding them to soup to retain their individual flavors and keep them firm.
- A small amount of wine will intensify the flavor of soup. Recommended is a not too dry sherry, which should be added during the last 10-15 minutes of cooking time.
- Eggshells will clarify soups. Just add 3-4 eggshells and simmer for 10-12 minutes before straining out the eggshells for clear soup.

If the soup boils while you are trying to clarify it, it will not clarify.

- Cream of wheat is used by some chefs to thicken soup.
- Pasta should be precooked and added to soup a few minutes before serving.
- Flavors will blend better if soup is cooked in a lidded pot.
- Soup will have better flavor if allowed to rest in the refrigerator for 1-2 days.
- Always save leftover meat and chicken bones to provide additional flavor for soups and stews.
- If you are going to puree soup, allow the soup to cool first.
- Popcorn on top of soup is a great treat for kids.
- Salt should never be added to soup that has dairy products until just before serving to prevent curdling.
- If you have lumps in your soup use a wire whisk.
- Warm bowls should be used to serve soups in.
- If soup develops lumps, just place it in the blender.

Soups and Stews

- For the best tasting soups and stews, always refrigerate the dish for 8-10 hours to allow the seasonings a chance to produce a more desirable flavor.
- Try and remove as much fat as possible before thickening soup or stew for the best results.
- If you use flour to thicken the soup or stew and then add a dairy product such as milk it won't separate as easily.

When you use cornstarch or flour to thicken soup or stew, always add any acidic ingredient after you have completed the thickening for the best results.

- Acidic vegetables and fruits need to be added to a milk-based soup. Never add a dairy product to the acid.
- Most herbs lose potency very quickly, especially when added to a hot or boiling liquid. Best to add the herbs toward the last 20 minutes of cooking time.
- Parsley placed in a piece of cheesecloth and swirled around in soup or stew for 5-8 minutes will reduce a garlicky flavor.
- If you have over-salted the soup or stew, just place two pieces of raw potato in and stir for a few minutes while simmering, and then discard the potato.
- Too much salt can be overcome by adding 1 teaspoon of white vinegar and 1 teaspoon of brown sugar.
- If you want a rich brown color to the soup or stew, just caramelize 3-4 teaspoons of sugar and add that to the pot.
- Pureed okra makes an excellent thickener for soups and stews.
- For a great low fat soup or stew thickener, try using dehydrated potato flakes.
- Both salt and pepper tend to intensify the flavor of soups and stews and therefore should only be added just before serving.
- To keep the flavors in soups and stews never boil them, only allow them to simmer.

There are a number of rules to remember when reheating soups, sauces and stews:

- Foods that contain fats tend to oxidize more readily and this may impart a less than desirable flavor.
- When reheating, never place the food in an aluminum or iron pot, and never add salt until the food is almost completely warmed back up.
- Soups and gravies should only be simmered for about 2 minutes.
- Creamed soups should only be reheated at a slow simmer for about 2 minutes after they have reached a slow boil.

BISQUES

- Bisques are heavy cream soups that usually contain shellfish.
- They are usually made with a white base with fish puree and vegetables.
- The French sometimes thicken bisques with rice.

Shrimp Bisque

- Adding some shrimp shells to the soup will provide excellent flavor. Make sure you strain them out before serving.
- Cook the rice in the stock from the soup to pick up additional flavor.
- To add additional flavor try adding onions or jalapenos.
- Adding pureed rice and shrimp will add body and great flavor.
- Dry sherry adds flavor and has the ability to enhance the flavors of other ingredients.

CHICKEN SOUP

- Noodles should never be added in the beginning, only toward the end of the cooking, or they will get mushy.

To prepare the best chicken soup like your grandmother made the butcher will have to provide you with a "soup hen" not a young chicken.

- Noodles should be cooked before adding them to the soup if you want the soup to remain clear.
- Always remove as much of the fat as possible.
- Kosher salt should be used since it will not cloud the soup.
- Choose a heavy pot with a spigot on the bottom, which will allow you to drain off just the clear soup.
- Surface fat can be eliminated using a piece of paper towel or a piece of white bread as a sponge. Discard the bread before it breaks down.
- White pepper may be used if so desired.
- The chicken should be diced and precooked, then added about 10 minutes before the soup is finished cooking, allowing enough time for it to heat.
- Diced carrots and celery are frequently added toward then end of the cooking time.

When carrots are added to chicken soup and heated they release carotene and provide the color that old-fashioned chicken soups had.

CHOWDER

New Englanders were so upset by New Yorkers putting tomatoes in clam chowder and calling it clam chowder that they actually passed a bill in 1939 outlawing tomatoes in New England clam chowder.

- Always add clams or oysters near the end of the cooking cycle or they will become tough.
- To keep cream-based soup warm, use a double boiler or it may get scorched.
- All chowders contain milk and potatoes.
- Prepared as thick soup, never watery. If it becomes watery, use potato flakes to thicken.
- New England chowder contains cream, potatoes, onions, clams, clam juices, salt, and pepper.
- Manhattan chowder contains clams, tomatoes, and an assortment of vegetables.

COLD SOUPS

- Cold soups need additional flavor since the cold tends to reduce the intensity of the flavors.

Cold soups will not be as thick as they were when they were hot and may need additional thickening if that is the way you like them.

- The most popular cold soup is vichyssoise, which is prepared from potatoes and chives.
- Cold soups should be made the day before and refrigerated to allow the flavors to mingle.
- Be sure and chill the bowls or cups before serving cold soup.

Gazpacho
- Gazpacho is cold tomato and vegetable soup.
- The major vegetables are usually tomatoes, sweet red pepper, and scallions.
- The seasonings seem to vary depending on the recipe used.
- $^1/_4$ cup of olive oil and 3 tablespoons of fresh lime juice are always added.
- Traditionally it is served with white onions and bread cubes on the side.

Vichyssoise
- Normally prepared from leeks, onion, potatoes, and unsalted butter.
- The soup should be boiled for 40 minutes, strained through a sieve, and allowed to cool in the refrigerator before serving.
- Before serving most chefs add 1 cup of heavy cream to the soup as well as a sprinkling of fresh chopped chives.

CONSOMMÉ

- Clear, concentrated soup that has excellent flavor and can be used as a soup or stock base.
- Using ground beef and leeks help to improve the flavor.
- The main ingredients are usually meat and egg white
- It is best to start with a quality strong stock or broth. Weak stocks need to be reduced more so that the flavors will be stronger.

For serious consommé makers, you will need a pot with a spigot on the bottom to drain off the finished consommé without bothering the "raft" on top. After you remove the consommé from the spigot it should be strained through a sieve or china cap.

- When adding the proteins, be sure that the stock is cold so that the proteins will not cook as soon as they hit the liquid.
- Using egg whites help trap small particles and help to improve the flavor.
- Always allow the consommé to come to a simmer very slowly, don't try and rush it.
- The raft that comes to the surface is composed of proteins, usually albumin.
- Be very careful not to allow the consommé to boil or it may break up the raft and infiltrate the consommé, adding a lot more work to clarify the soup.
- Consommé should simmer for about $1\frac{1}{2}$ hours without disturbing the raft.
- Be sure and remove all fat from the surface.

CREAM SOUPS

- When making cream soups, try adding a small amount of flour to the milk to make it smoother.
- Simmer the soup until there is no starchy taste.
- Always thicken the soup before adding milk.
- When adding wine to cream soups it should be added just before serving or you risk curdling the soup.
- Never add cold milk or cream to simmering soup; always warm the milk or cream first.
- It is best to temper the milk or cream on low heat with some of the soup while you are warming it.
- The best wines for cream soup are sherry or dry white wine.
- When making tomato soup always puree the tomatoes separately from the milk or cream. Then add the puree very slowly to the milk or cream.

If you do add a dairy product to hot soup, do not allow it to boil or the dairy products will curdle.

- If curdling does happen, just strain the soup and place it in a blender on low for a few seconds then increase to high. Only fill the blender $\frac{1}{2}$ full.
- Curdling can be reduced, or even eliminated, by just preparing a thin paste solution of flour and water and mixing it into the milk or dairy product before adding it to the acid. The most common problem occurs when making tomato soup with milk.
- Never boil soup after you add milk or cream.

TOMATO SOUP

- A small amount of sugar should be added to tomato juice or tomato paste to bring out the flavor.
- A small amount of lemon juice added to the soup just before serving will bring out the flavor.
- If you are going to thicken the soup, never use flour, always use cornstarch.

Old Fashioned Cream of Tomato Soup

14 ounce can of whole tomatoes and the liquid

1 cup plain tomato juice

3/4 cup nonfat milk

1/2 pound red potatoes, peeled and diced

1 cup finely chopped red onions

1 1/4 cup red or yellow bell pepper, diced

3 tbsp. coriander, chopped

2 cloves of garlic, peeled and crushed

1/4 teaspoon fresh ground black pepper

1 slice of whole-wheat bread

1/4 teaspoon salt

Using a medium saucepan, combine the whole tomatoes, their liquid, the tomato juice, bell peppers, onions, 2 tablespoons of coriander, garlic, black pepper, salt, and the potatoes. Bring the mixture to a slow boil over medium heat; then cover the pan. Reduce the heat and allow the soup to simmer for 15 minutes. Remove the pan from the heat and allow it to cool for 6 minutes. Then place the mixture in a food processor and puree for about 1 minute or until it is smooth. Allow the machine to run and add the milk very slowly. Return the pureed mixture to the pan and cook only until it is hot (do not boil) then serve.

VEGETABLE SOUPS (GENERAL)

- For a richer flavor, mix 1 tablespoon of butter into the soup just before serving.
- When preparing vegetable soup, only pour enough water into the pot to cover the vegetables by two inches.
- Using too much water in vegetable soup tends to make the soup watery.
- Carrots will give vegetable soup a sweet flavor.
- When adding mushrooms to vegetable soup, always sauté the mushrooms separately, and then add them to the soup just before serving for the best flavor.
- Always begin with a clear tasty stock or broth. Make sure that the stock or broth is not cloudy.
- Make sure that the vegetables selected go well with each other. The average is 5-6 different vegetables.
- Be sure and slice all vegetables uniformly.
- Always cook all vegetables separately in clarified butter.
- Cook all pasta separately from all other ingredients before adding to the soup.

- Never add tomatoes to the soup until after you have removed it from the heat.
- Overcooking vegetables is a common problem with vegetable soup. Vegetables should have the same consistency as they would have when served as a side dish.

STEWS

- Stews are basically prepared from almost any combination of meats, vegetables, and seasonings you enjoy. Stew should always be relatively thick and not watery.

If you have a problem with tough stew meat, you may have added hot water when water was needed instead of cold water. Studies have shown that hot water added to boiling or simmering stew may cause the meat to become tough. Cold water does not have the same effect.

- To really thicken your stew sauce, just mix 2 tablespoons of potato starch in 3 tablespoons of water and add the mixture slowly while stirring it into the stew. If you do this for every cup of liquid in the stew it will really make it thick and good.

Mulligan's Irish Stew Recipe

2 pounds of potatoes, sliced to about 1/2 inch thick

3 pounds of shoulder lamb, cut into 1 inch cubes

3 stalks of celery, chopped

2 medium carrots, chopped

4 large red onions, sliced into small chunks

1/4 teaspoon thyme

2 cloves garlic

1 teaspoon freshly ground black pepper

1 teaspoons salt

6 cups of pure cold water

Irish stew is normally prepared in layers. Using a large stew pot (or preferably a large, covered casserole that can be placed directly from the oven to the table), place a layer of potatoes on the bottom of the pot, then add a layer of onions, and then the lamb (or other meat). Sprinkle on the seasonings and add the garlic cloves. Place any remaining onions on top of the lamb, then the rest of the potatoes on top of the onions. Add just enough cold water (about 4-5 cups) to cover the last layer of potatoes. Slowly bring the stew to a boil, cover the pot and reduce the heat and barely simmer for 1-2 hours. Stop the cooking as soon as the meat and vegetables are just tender and not overcooked and mushy.

If the water is evaporating, add a small amount at a time as it is being lost. Preheat the oven to 350° F. (176.7° C.) Place the stew into the oven and check regularly to be sure that it is not boiling, only simmering.

- To tenderize the meat in stew, just add ½ cup of strong tea. The tannic acid will tenderize beef and not add flavor to the stew.
- A small amount of quick-cooking oats added to stew will thicken it.
- If you have over-salted the stew, just add a can of peeled tomatoes or a small amount of brown sugar.

If you place 3-4 wine corks in your stew it will tenderize the meat. Cork contains a chemical that has the ability to tenderize meats. The chemical is activated and released when placed in hot liquid. Remove the corks before serving.

- When thickening stews, if you are using flour, be sure and sprinkle the flour over the meat and do not stir for about 3 minutes. This will eliminate the floury flavor and help brown the meat.
- Never allow stews to boil, you will lose flavor.

GELATIN

- If powdered gelatin is wrapped and stored properly in a cool, dry location it will last forever.
- A 11/4 ounce envelope of powdered gelatin is capable of gelling 2 cups of liquid.
- Gelatin must be soaked in a cold liquid for about 3-5 minutes before dissolving it. This will soften and activate the granules allowing them to dissolve efficiently when heated.

Gelatin will not set up if it is allowed to boil.

- Gelatin will not set up if you add certain foods, which contain enzymes that break gelatin down such as kiwi, papaya, pineapple, figs, guava, and ginger root.
- If any of the harmful enzyme-containing foods are cooked or canned, the enzyme will be destroyed and the foods can be used.
- If you are going to make different layers of colored gelatin, be sure and wait until the first layer is good and sticky before placing the next layer on.
- Make sure that you rinse molds that will be used for gelatins with very cold water or spray the insides with vegetable oil before adding the gelatin. This will make it easier to remove the mixture.

Too much, gelatin produces a rubbery textured mixture.

- To speed the setting up, just place the bowl containing the gelatin mixture in a larger bowl filled with ice cubes and cold water. Stir until the desired consistency is obtained.
- The freezer will usually set it up in about 20 minutes, but don't forget about it.
- If the gelatin sets too fast, just place the mold in a larger bowl filled with WARM water, then mix until the desired consistency is obtained.

STOCKS

Stocks are the basis of many soups and sauces. There are four basic stocks: brown, white, poultry, and seafood. Stocks are prepared from a liquid that fish, meats, or poultry are cooked in. The liquid is then seasoned and usually cooked for 8-10 hours to assure that the flavors are adequately incorporated into the stock. The liquid is then removed leaving the flavored residue or stock. Stocks may be frozen and used as needed.

- Kosher salt is the preferred salt that most chefs use when preparing a stock.
- Kosher salt contains no additives, which may cause the stock to become cloudy.
- Salt is important to stock but should be added after it has cooked for 10 minutes. Salt has the tendency to concentrate and ruin the stock when added too early, especially as the liquid reduces.
- Salt will help draw the albumin (a protein) from the bones to keep the stock clear.

The bones and meat from older cows will have more flavor for stock and their bones will have 8 times more gelatin than their meat. The bones are more important to making stock than the meat.

- If you prefer to purchase stock in the supermarket, it may be sold under a number of different names. These include bouillon, broth, or consommé.
- An excellent poultry stock can be made using the turkey carcass from thanksgiving dinner. If you don't have the time right away, just freeze the carcass, well wrapped in freezer paper. Try to use it within 2 months for the best results.

Preparing stock in aluminum pots should be avoided. The aluminum tends to impart a bitter taste to stocks and will stain the pot if the stock is stored in it.

- Chefs always prefer veal bones when preparing stocks since they tend to provide a more delicate flavor than beef bones. Veal bones contain more collagen and therefore have a better thickening ability.
- Stocks are usually prepared from the liquid that fish, chicken, or meats are cooked in.
- There are two types of canned broth to choose from: ready-to-serve, which has liquid added, and condensed, which requires that you add more liquid.
- Stock should be kept frozen until needed, especially if it contains an animal product.
- Next time you prepare soup or stock, try placing a pasta strainer-basket into the pot, or just use a large pasta pot. The basket can be removed and will contain many of the ingredients you may wish to dispose of or keep.
- Always use cold water, which is usually purer than hot water. Hot water tends to leach more impurities from water pipes and may give the stock an off-flavor.
- Make sure that all fat has been trimmed away before adding meats to the stockpot.
- Hot water added to gelatin should never be over 180° F. (82.2° C.) for the best results. If your recipe calls for an equal amount of sugar to gelatin, the cold water step is not required since the sugar will stop the clumping. However, you still never pour hot water into gelatin. Always place the gelatin into the water.

Always simmer stock with the pot uncovered. Condensation may affect the final result. Stock should never be boiled or it may become cloudy.

- When you simmer bones to extract the flavor, foam may be created the surface, which is composed of a protein (albumin) and a number of impurities (mineral residues) that are released from the bone. This foam is usually bitter and needs to be completely removed. Even leaving a hint of the foam may alter the desired taste.

- If you are really in a hurry and need a stock that can easily be prepared in about 30 minutes, the following should solve your problem:

Recipe for Speedy Stock

2 cans of a low-salt broth   1 large stalk of celery, chopped

1 teaspoon of beef stock   1/2 large onion, sliced

1 1/2 cans of pure water   1/8 teaspoon thyme

1 medium carrot, chopped small   1/8 teaspoon celery powder

Place all the ingredients in a large saucepan and bring to a slow boil, then reduce the heat and simmer uncovered for about 20-30 minutes. Strain the stock through a fine sieve.

- Salt should not be added to stock during the first 10 minutes of cooking time.
- Salt helps draw the albumen (protein) from the bones, which will keep the stock clear.
- Always simmer stock with the pot uncovered. Condensation may affect the final product.
- Never boil stock or it may become cloudy.
- Make sure that you do not stir stock more than 3 times during the first hour or it may become cloudy.
- The bones provide gelatin for the stock, which is important.
- Never cover stock since this may cause an increase in bacteria around the lid.
- Gelatin from the bones is important, since the stock should become completely gelled when cooled down. The stock can be spooned as needed.
- Stocks should be kept frozen until needed, especially if they contain an animal product.
- If refrigerated for storage, stock can be kept for about 6 days. After more than 6 days in the refrigerator the stock should be boiled for 8-10 minutes before using.

When dissolving dry gelatin, never pour hot water directly on the gelatin. This causes clumping and reduces the ability of the gelatin to dissolve properly. Try using a small amount of cold water until it is dissolved, then add the additional hot water.

- When the stock is finished, you should strain it only once through a fine mesh strainer before refrigerating for 2-3 hours.
- Remove the stock and skim off the fat that has risen to the top, producing an almost fat-free broth with the flavor intact.
- Canned broth should be placed into the refrigerator overnight to allow the fat to rise. Remove

the fat before using for a low fat broth.

- If your gelatin develops a thick rubbery skin it is probably because it sat out in the air too long without being covered. The only other reason is that it has aged too long before being used.

- The stock is the very flavorful residue leftover after the liquid has been removed.

Brown Stock

- Brown stock is usually prepared from beef or veal bones, which are grilled producing a rich, brown color and are included in the initial stages of preparation whenever possible.

- Veal bones are preferred for brown stock since they have better flavor.

- Brown stock can be reduced until it is syrupy or even very dark, if desired. Brown stock is usually very concentrated and very little is needed to flavor sauce. It is easy to overpower with a brown sauce and detract from the flavor of the dish. Any stock can be more concentrated by boiling it down more.

- Use a tall pot to reduce evaporation.

Brown Stock Recipe

3 1/2 beef shank	8 fresh peppercorns
(butcher will easily supply)	4 quarts pure water
3 tablespoons of vegetable oil	2 bay leaves
3 red onions, sliced	1 3/4 teaspoons of sea salt
4 fresh celery stalks, diced	(iodized salt is okay)
3 medium carrots, sliced	1/2 teaspoon ground black pepper
4 sprigs of parsley, whole	1/2 teaspoon dried thyme

Step One:

- Using a large pan with 1 1/2 to 2 inch sides, add the vegetable, oil, and the beef bones that have been broken into chunks, and bake in a 450° F. (232.2° C.) oven until they are brown, turning occasionally.
- This should take about 10 minutes.
- When the bones are brown add the onions, carrots, and celery to the mixture and bake until the vegetables start to brown. Remove from the oven.

Step Two:

- Place the mixture into a large pot. Add one cup of boiling water to the baking pan and scrape all the residues into the water. Add this to the large pot; then add the thyme, bay leaves, peppercorns, parsley and 4 quarts of cold water.
- Bring the stock to a slow boil over medium heat, then reduce the heat and allow

---

the stock to simmer for 5 hours.
- Remove any fat that rises to the top for the first hour using a piece of white bread as a sponge or a thin wooden spoon. Remove from the heat and strain the mixture.
- Allow the stock to cool to room temperature. Stock will freeze for 6-8 months but will only last for a few days in the refrigerator. If any more fat rises to the top, allow it to remain until you are ready to use the stock, then remove it. The fat will protect the stock from outside contamination.

Chicken Stock

- Chicken stock is a clear liquid prepared from chicken parts and simmered with vegetables, herbs, and spices.
- Always use a tall pot to reduce evaporation.
- The cooking should be started in cold water, which will improve the extraction of flavors.
- Use overripe vegetables to add flavor and utilize the soluble pectin they have developed.

Fish Stock

- Fish stock is prepared from fish bones and poached fish or shellfish.
- If you sauté the bones and vegetables first it will improve the flavor that will be released.
- The intensity of the flavor of fish stock is totally dependent on the quality of the fish, not the cooking time. However, if you cook the stock for more than 20 minutes it will usually become bitter. If you want to cook it longer start with a larger amount.
- Ripe or even overripe vegetables provide more flavor to fish stock.

Steps to Clarify Stock

1. Stock needs to be strained through a piece of cheesecloth or a very fine sieve.
2. For each quart of stock add 1 beaten egg and a crumpled-up eggshell. Stir the egg and eggshell into the stock and bring to a slow simmer (do not stir). Foam will form on the surface as the heat rises.
3. Allow the stock to simmer for 15 minutes, remove from the heat, and allow the stock to rest for 30 minutes.
4. Gently move the crusty foam aside and spoon the stock into a sieve lined with 3 layers of lightly moistened cheesecloth.

Cooking Secrets

Vegetable Stock

- Vegetable stock is prepared from onions, carrots, and celery, then flavored with garlic and other herbs. The formula is usually 60% onions, 20% celery and 20% carrots.

   Strong-flavored vegetables are usually not used to prepare stock.

- Dark-colored bones are too deteriorated to be used in stock.

White or Veal Stock

- Originally prepared with only veal bones, providing a clear stock that contains very little flavor of its own. The stock, however, is now made with veal, beef, or poultry bones, or a combination.

White Stock Recipe

4 pounds of bones, broken into small chunks (meaty if possible)
1 cup red onions, chopped
2 large carrots, chopped
5 celery stalks, chopped
3 cloves of fresh crushed garlic
2 bay leaves
1/2 teaspoon thyme
3 cloves
1 teaspoon black peppercorns
Small bunch of parsley
Add salt to taste

Place the bones in a large stockpot and cover the bones with water by about 4 inches. Cover the pot and bring to a boil, then pour off the water with foam and residues. Cover with water again to the same level and simmer for 7 hours, adding cold water as the water evaporates. Continually skim the surface to remove the foam and debris. Only stir the pot 2-3 times to make sure that the bones do not stick to the bottom of the pot.

Add the vegetables about 2 hours before the cooking time is completed then add all the seasonings 30 minutes before the end. Cover a large bowl with three layers of cheesecloth and strain the stock. Discard all the bones and vegetables. Cool the stock as rapidly as possible. The stock will keep for about 2-3 days in the refrigerator and may be frozen for 4-6 months.

NOTE:

Most quality stock bases are not sold in markets. A 1 pound jar of base is capable of making 5 gallons of stock. However, the better brands of bases are almost all sold directly to restaurants and chefs. One of the best stock bases is produced by the L. J. Minor Corporation of Cleveland, Ohio.

Blanching Bones for Stocks

- The bones first need to be rinsed in cold water. All blood and residue need to be removed.
- Do not use fresh bones.
- The bones should be placed in a stockpot and covered with cold water.
- Don't start the bones in hot water; it slows down the extraction.
- Bring the water to a boil and allow any impurities to rise to the surface as foam.
- Skim the surface frequently to remove the foam.
- The bones should be drained and rinsed well before being placed in the stockpot.

SOLVING STOCK PROBLEMS

The Stock Is Losing Too Much Water, Too Fast

- Use a tall, narrow pot to reduce evaporation

The Stock Does Not Have Enough Flavor
- Starting with cold water will increase the level of flavor extraction
- Ripe or overripe vegetables will add additional flavor
- Pectin adds flavor, is more available, and is easier to extract from older vegetables

The Stock Is Too Greasy and Cloudy
- The stock was probably allowed to boil and the fat emulsified
- The foam was not removed at regular intervals
- The stock was stirred too much causing the fat to emulsify

GLAZES

- Glazes are actually just a stock that has been reduced to a point that it will coat the back of a spoon. They are used as flavorings in many sauces. They should be used in moderation since they are a concentrated source of flavoring. Glazes are the original bases and are still thought of as a base.

- Even though the glaze has been reduced from a stock, it will not taste like the stock. The types of glazes are basically the same as the stocks they were prepared from such as chicken, meat, or fish.

Guidelines for preparing a glaze
- The stock should be reduced over medium heat.
- The surface should be skimmed frequently to remove any debris or skin.
- When reducing by at least $1/2$ a small saucepan should be used.
- Continue reducing over low heat until the glaze is syrupy and coats the back of a spoon.
- Glazes will store well in the refrigerator for at least 3-4 weeks if not contaminated and sealed well. Glazes may also be frozen for 2-3 months.

Cooking Secrets

Desserts & Candy
MAKING TIPS

DESSERTS, CANDY, AND CHOCOLATE

CANDY

- One of the most important factors in cooking candies is to follow directions to the letter.
- Always use a heavy pan that conducts heat well. A poor pan will easily scorch and burn candy.
- Never use fructose in hard candy, it has the tendency to retain moisture.
- When making candy, chefs always use a pan larger than they need to avoid sugary syrups boiling over.
- The temperature recommended is very important and a higher temperature to speed up a procedure will not produce good results.

- Temperature must be controlled when cooking syrup since the lower the temperature the softer the candy. The higher the temperature the harder the candy.
- Candy recipes are very precise and they cannot be doubled to make a larger batch to save time.

When boiling syrup the sugar may tend to crystallize. To resolve this problem, just put a pinch of baking soda in the syrup while it is cooking to reduce the acidity.

- When adding water to a candy recipe, always add very hot water for the best results and a clearer candy.
- Cane sugar is best for candies; blended sugars will cause candies to become sticky.
- Most candies do not freeze well and never taste the same if they have been frozen. Hard candy may crumble when thawed and jellies become granular.
- Candy will store well in as airtight a container as possible for about 3 weeks.
- Different candies should be stored separately.
- If you have a problem with candy boil-over, just place a wooden spoon across the top of the pot. A better method, however, to reduce the risk of catching the spoon on fire is to just rub a thin layer of oil about 1-2 inches down the inside of the pot from the top.

Remember to always wash off any spoon you use to stir syrup with before using it again. Crystals tend to cling and crystallize on the spoon and can damage the syrup.

- It is better not to make candy if the weather is rainy or if the humidity is over 50%. If you must cook under these conditions the temperature should be increased by about two degrees above recommended.
- The best temperature to make chocolates, divinity, fudge, and hard candy is between 62°-68°F with low humidity.

- Marshmallows are made from corn syrup, albumen, granulated sugar, and gelatin beaten into a soft spongy consistency.
- Marshmallows are best stored in the freezer. Dip in hot water for a few seconds to thaw and separate.
- If you are going to make taffy, try not to use molasses or it may boil over easily. If you do use molasses, use a large pot.
- Make sure that when you are melting sugar you do so over low heat and be sure that ALL the sugar crystals have melted. If any crystals have clung to the sides of the pot and did not melt this will cause a problem.

If you have a problem with sugar melting, cover the pot and allow the steam to melt the rest of the crystals.

- When using sugar to prepare syrups, remember that sugar has the tendency to attract moisture from the air and thus keeps foods moist.
- Cakes are lighter because the sugar slows the gluten from becoming stiff.
- Sugar has the tendency to lower the freezing point of most liquids, which keeps ice cream in a state of a semisolid.
- When using sugar on meats it will help retain the natural moisture.

EASY TO PREPARE SUGAR SYRUPS

THIN SUGAR SYRUP- One cup of granulated sugar added to two cups of water.

MEDIUM SUGAR SYRUP- One cup of granulated sugar added to one cup of water.

HEAVY SUGAR SYRUP- One cup of granulated sugar added to $^3/_4$ cup of water.

THICK SUGAR SYRUP- One cup of granulated sugar added to $^1/_2$ cup of water.

In a small saucepan, add the sugar to the water and stir gently over low heat. Do not allow the mixture to boil until the sugar is completely dissolved. When boiling begins, stop stirring and continue to boil (uncovered) for about 1 minute. Flavorings can be added either before or after cooking. If you overcook the syrup, just add $^1/_4$ cup of boiling water and cook again.

THREAD STAGES OF SUGAR SYRUP

The thread stage is used to determine the actual temperature of the sugary syrup. In order for the candy to set up it must crystallize into sugary syrup. Cook the syrup in a small saucepan over medium heat until it reaches the desired temperature. If you do not have a thermometer, the following will be useful:

Thread Stage
> 230° F. to 234° F. (110° C. to 112.2° C.):
> Syrup will form a soft light thread.

Soft Ball
> 234° F. to 240° F. (112.2° C. to 115.6° C.):
> Syrup will form a small ball that will flatten out by itself when removed.

Firm Ball
> 244° F. to 248° F. (117.8° C. to 120° C.):
> Syrup will form a firm ball that tends to flatten out when pressed
> between your fingers.

Hard Ball
> 250° F. to 265° F. (121.1° C. to 129.4° C.):
> Syrup will form a hard ball that has just a little give to it when squeezed.

Soft Crack
> 270° F. to 290° F. (132.2° C. to 143.3° C.):
> Syrup tends to separate into hard threads that are bendable.

Hard Crack
> 300° F. to 310° F. (148.9° C. to 154.4° C.):
> Syrup will separate into threads, which are hard and very brittle.

Caramelized Sugar
> 310° F. to 338° F. (154.4° C. to 170° C.):
> Syrup will become a golden color.

- When sugar is cooked above 350° F. (176.7° C.) it will turn black and burn.
- When making sugar syrup, always watch the bubbles since they tend to become smaller as the syrup thickens. If the bubbles get too small before it thickens, better start over.

Caramel
- Caramel sauce is prepared from sugar and water. The mixture is cooked until it is a dark brown color.
- Caramel candy is prepared from sugar, milk or cream, honey or corn syrup, and butter.

CHOCOLATE

Chocolate is made from the cacao bean. The majority of the world's cacao beans come from West Africa. The largest producers are Ghana, the Ivory Coast, and Nigeria. The earliest known chocolate plantations were started by the Mayans in 600 AD in the Yucatan Peninsula. The word "chocolate" is derived from the Mayan "xocolatl."

CHOCOLATE SAUCE/SYRUP

- When preparing chocolate sauces there are a number of tips that you should be aware of. The following will help you obtain the perfect sauce:
- If a liquid is used in the recipe, always melt the chocolate in the liquid, not separately, for the best results. Use low heat and stir continuously.
- The microwave is excellent for melting chocolate. Just place the chocolate in a large measuring glass and cook until melted while keeping an eye on it to be sure it doesn't cook too much.
- Most chefs melt chocolate in a double boiler over simmering (not boiling) water.
- Always use the type of chocolate called for in a particular recipe and always use the highest quality chocolate you can find.
- Ganache is one of the finest blends of chocolate sauce you will ever taste when made properly. It consists of melted semi-sweet chocolate, heavy cream, and unsalted butter. It is definitely not a healthy food since it is high in fat, cholesterol, and calories.

Ganache Recipe

In a small saucepan heat 1 cup of heavy cream and 2 tablespoons of butter to boiling. Place a 12 ounce bag of chocolate semi-sweet morsels into a medium bowl and pour the hot butter-cream mixture over the chocolate and stir until smooth. When it is cool, it will remain somewhat soft and should not harden.

Grandma's Hot Fudge Heaven Sauce Recipe

> 4 ounces of bittersweet chocolate (4 squares)
>
> 12 ounce can of quality evaporated milk
>
> 3 tablespoons of salted butter
>
> 2 1/2 cups confectioner's sugar
>
> 2 teaspoons of pure vanilla extract

Combine the chocolate, sugar, and evaporated milk on the top of a double boiler with simmering water in the bottom. Stir occasionally until the chocolate has melted completely. Remove from the heat and whisk in the pure vanilla and butter until the mixture is smooth. Enjoy!

Chocolate Cherry Delight Sauce Recipe

> 1/4 cup quality unsweetened cocoa powder
>
> 1/2 sweet cream
>
> 1/3 cup Karo(r) syrup
>
> 1/2 cup granulated sugar
>
> 2 teaspoons real vanilla extract
>
> 1/4 pound of salted butter
>
> 2 ounces of bittersweet chocolate (2 squares)
>
> 1 tablespoon of a quality cherry brandy (optional) or use
> maraschino cherry juice

Using a small saucepan, whisk the cocoa and sugar together on medium heat. Slowly, add the cream (or half-and-half), the Karo(r) syrup (or any corn syrup), butter, and chocolate. Stir continuously until the mixture comes to a boil and is smooth. Remove the sauce and immediately add the cherry brandy or cherry juice and the vanilla. Best to serve the sauce hot or at least warm.

Chocolate Peppermint Cream Sauce Recipe

4 ounces of bittersweet chocolate (4 squares)
1/2 cup granulated sugar
1/4 pound of unsalted butter
1 cup of heavy cream
1 teaspoon of a good quality peppermint extract

The chocolate can be melted in a double boiler over simmering water (not boiling). As soon as the chocolate is melted, add the sugar and butter. After you have stirred them in add the cream and allow the mixture to remain on low heat over direct heat for 3-5 minutes and just simmer. Remove the sauce from the hot burner and add in the peppermint extract slowly, while continually stirring.

- Tempering chocolate is the process of melting it, cooling it, and then melting it again. This process produces a more lustrous, glossy, and stable mixture and is called for in many chocolate recipes. There is an exact science to obtain the right consistency and it takes some practice.
- However, there is a "quick-tempering" method that utilizes a small amount of oil that will speed the process up considerably. The end product will be a little thinner, but will not make a difference in most recipes and decorative uses.

The quick-tempering method:

Use 1 tablespoon of vegetable oil (preferable a neutral oil such as canola or safflower), or clarified butter, or even a solid shortening. Stir 1 tablespoon of the oil into every 3 ounces of melted chocolate you use, over low heat. Quick-tempered chocolate will only hold up for 2-3 days, but the candy is usually long gone before that.

Chocolate Sauce

- If too much heat is applied to chocolate sauce it will burn or clump up.
- Chocolate is best melted in a double boiler with the water simmering, not boiling.
- Only use the type of chocolate called for in the recipe; do not substitute.
- Buy the best quality chocolate; there is a difference.
- When making chocolate sauce you need to use a heavy saucepan to control the heat more easily.

Chocolate-Covered Fruit

- Use the best brand of bittersweet chocolate and melt it to dip fruit into for a great dessert.
- Place a toothpick into each piece of fruit, dip it, and then place it on a cookie sheet in the refrigerator to harden.

Coating Chocolate

- Normally used in candy making.
- Has a high percentage of cocoa butter, giving candy a hard, shiny finish.
- This is a special chocolate that is hard to use unless you are experienced.

Cocoa Powder

- Dried and powdered chocolate liquor with at least half of the cocoa butter removed.

  The "Dutched" variety has alkali added to make it darker and less acidic.

- Some of the cocoa powders that are used for cooking have sugar added.
- The best quality will be the unsweetened variety.

Confectioner's Chocolate

- Not really chocolate. Made from vegetable oil instead of cocoa butter.

Couverture (covering)

- This special kind of chocolate contains more cocoa butter than standard chocolate.
- The cocoa butter content is usually between 33%-38%.
- Used for coating truffles and similar confectionery products.
- Commonly used in "enrobing" or "hand-dipping."

Chocolate Fondue

- Chocolate fondue makes a great dessert treat, just mix 8 ounces of chocolate chips with $1/2$ cup of whipping cream. Melt in a double boiler and stir until it is smooth. Remove from the heat and mix in $1^1/4$ teaspoons of pure vanilla extract. Dip grapes or strawberries in the fondue.

Chocolate Mousse

- For a different treat, try pouring $1/4$ cup of Grand Marnier into the egg yolk and chocolate mixture just before it begins to thicken.

Chocolate Pudding

- When making pudding from scratch mix together the water and cornstarch very thoroughly and set it aside.
- Mix the other ingredients in a large saucepan. Mix the sugar, cocoa, and salt stirring well with a wooden spoon, then mix in the warm milk and make a smooth paste.
- Place the saucepan over medium heat and bring to a boil while stirring continually for 2-3

minutes before adding the chopped chocolate. Stir until all has melted and is smooth.

- Gradually add the heavy cream and the cornstarch mixture (be sure it is well mixed) and stir for about 5-6 minutes or until it thickens and boils.
- As it cooks, make sure that you stir around the bottom of the pot with a wooden spoon to avoid lumps.
- After you pour the pudding into the individual cups, place a piece of plastic wrap directly on top of the pudding to prevent skin from forming.

If you would like coffee-flavored pudding, substitute 1 tablespoon of coffee liqueur or Kahlua for the vanilla extract.

- Toasted nuts can be added to provide a different taste treat.

Melting Chocolate
- When you are melting chocolate, water droplets, excess condensation, and high temperatures may cause the chocolate to stiffen prematurely. To alleviate this problem, just add 1 teaspoon of corn oil to the pan and stir. More oil can be added if needed to assure the proper consistency.
- When melting chocolate, spray the inside of the pot with an oil spray to make it easier to remove all the chocolate.
- If you need to grate chocolate, make sure you allow it to warm to room temperature first to make the job easier.

Make sure that no water gets into chocolate when it is melting or it may cause the chocolate to harden and clump up.

- If chocolate does get hard and clumps up, just add 1 tablespoon of corn oil for every 6 ounces of chocolate and reheat while stirring until it becomes smooth again.

- If you scorch chocolate even the slightest bit discard the batch.
- Chocolate squares that are wrapped in paper can be melted in the paper.
- If a white coating appears on chocolate it is because the chocolate has been around moisture and the moisture has drawn the sugar to the surface and crystallized it.
- If you are preparing a recipe that calls for melted chocolate, remember to always melt the chocolate in the liquid for the best results. Use low heat and stir continuously.
- The microwave does a good job of melting chocolate.
- Chocolate is best melted in a double boiler over simmering water not boiling water.
- Chocolate should be cooled to room temperature before you add it to cookie dough or any cake batter.

Help! My chocolate had a seizure

If your chocolate turns from a shiny, smooth liquid to a dull, very thick paste it has what is called a "chocolate seizure." Seizing happens when you do not follow instructions to the letter.

The following are the most common problems that cause seizure:

- The temperature got too hot and it was not stirred continually.
- Milk and white chocolate are more susceptible to seizing.

Moisture got into the pot. Even a small amount of moisture from a metal spoon can cause a seizure. Use a wooden spoon.

- Fondue chocolate can change if too much moisture gets into the fondue pot from the fruit that is being dipped in.
- Never add cold cream or milk; be sure it is the same temperature as the chocolate.
- Even large amounts of liquid can be added to chocolate as long as the liquid is the same temperature or has at least been warmed.

Milk Chocolate
- Contains chocolate liquor and cocoa butter, sugar, milk solids, and vanilla.
- Best for eating and not for baking.

Semisweet or Bittersweet Chocolate
- Chocolate liquor that has sugar, cocoa butter, and vanilla added.
- Bittersweet chocolate has a little less sugar than semisweet chocolate.
- Semisweet chocolate morsels can be substituted for semisweet chocolate in all recipes.
- To make bittersweet chocolate, use 1 ounce of unsweetened chocolate and mix it with 4 ounces of semisweet chocolate.

Unsweetened Chocolate
- Contains about 50% cocoa butter in the chocolate liquor.
- Does not contain sugar or any other added ingredients.
- This is not to be confused with bittersweet chocolate.

Unsweetened Baking Chocolate (Premelted)
- Liquid blend of cocoa and vegetable oil. Best to use the standard unsweetened chocolate.

White Chocolate
- Contains no chocolate liquor and is not really chocolate.
- This is made from cocoa butter, sugar, milk solids, and flavorings.
- Quality white chocolate is at least 100% cocoa butter.

HOT CHOCOLATE (COCOA)

- The basic formula for great cocoa is to place $2\frac{1}{2}$ teaspoons of unsweetened cocoa, $2\frac{1}{2}$ tablespoons of granulated sugar, and a pinch of salt in a saucepan, then add $\frac{1}{2}$ cup of cool tap water and place over medium heat. Cook until thick, then slowly add $1\frac{3}{4}$ cup of milk while stirring continuously. Do not allow the cocoa to boil.
- If you would like foamy cocoa, just beat it slightly with an electric beater.
- To spice it up a little, just add $\frac{1}{2}$ teaspoon of peppermint schnapps.
- Cocoa does not mix well with water and tends to remain in suspension for only a short period of time. The heat from the water will cause the particles to remain in suspension only as long as the drink is hot. As the drink cools, a percentage of the particles will fall to the bottom of the cup.
- When mixed with hot milk, however, the fat in the milk tends to hold the chocolate better in suspension.
- A great drink in the summer is to take a cup of ice, a cup of whole milk, and 3 tablespoons of a quality cocoa and place it into a blender until the ice cubes are gone. Makes a great chocolate chiller. Ice water can be added in place of the milk if you prefer.

Recipe for homemade hot chocolate

1 pint heavy cream   6 ounces semi-sweet chocolate bits (finely grated)
1/4 cup whole milk   1 tsp. vanilla (not imitation)

Using a double boiler, melt the chocolate; then slowly stir in the cream, vanilla, and milk. Continue to heat the mixture to a point just below boiling, stirring constantly. Serve topped with whipped cream.

- Mixes should only be used to prepare hot chocolate drinks. They contain milk, or cream powder, and sugar, or a substitute.

- Only pure cocoa or "real" chocolate should be used when recipes call for cocoa powder or chocolate.

- There are new chemicals being added to some cocoas used for hot drinks. These new ingredients are called texturing agents and are tapioca-based products that will help keep the cocoa powder in suspension better, providing a smoother, more enjoyable drink. The new product is called Textra™ and is manufactured by National Starch Company. It actually gives the product a mouth-feel similar to that of fat, without the fat calories.

- Hot chocolate does have caffeine; however, it only has about 1/10th the amount found in a cup of regular coffee.

- The better grades of hot chocolate powders are sweetened with sugar; however, there is a sugar-free hot chocolate available that uses Nutrasweet™. The amount of sugar is low in hot chocolate and the real sugar is preferable to an artificial sweetener.

- Most European cocoas are less sweet than the American varieties. Europeans prefer a cocoa that does not have the sweet taste so that they can enjoy the flavor of the chocolate more.

- White hot chocolate is hot chocolate without the "chocolate liquor," which make real chocolate "real." It does have a smooth, creamy flavor and is a favorite of many hot chocolate connoisseurs.

- If you purchase one of the better brands of cocoa powder, such as Mont Blanc, it should stay fresh for at least a year.

- A new item from the Sunbeam Company is now being sold called the "Cocomotion." The Cocomotion is a European-designed machine that is capable of heating, aerating, and blending 4 cups worth of hot chocolate in 10 minutes. The machine has a clear plastic chamber that shows the mixture being prepared. The unit is priced at $49.95, which includes a recipe book.

- If you want to eliminate the skin that forms on top of hot chocolate, just beat the drink for a few seconds until it gets frothy.

- Try mixing a teaspoon of cornstarch and a pinch of salt in a small amount of water and adding it to the pot of hot chocolate to improve the taste and texture.

FUDGE

The word "fudge" was originally used to denote a negative act or to cheat. The term was picked up, however, by college women in the early part of the 20th century to pertain to the fact that they were going to "fudge" and eat candy to help them gain the 15 pounds that was expected of a freshman to gain during their freshman year. The term relating to the 15 pounds was first used at Wellesley and Vassar colleges and the candy was called "Wellesley fudge" and "Vassar fudge."

- Plastic or rubber spatulas may melt if the fudge gets too hot and should not be used.
- Raw sugar is not the best sugar for fudge.
- The best chocolate is Hershey's for fudge.

Fudge is made from three ingredients; sugar, liquid (usually milk), and chocolate. A forth ingredient such as extra flavoring may be added to the fudge.

- Corn syrup and honey do not produce good results.
- If you use any other nut except walnuts, only use $^3/_4$ cup instead of 1 cup.
- It is okay to make fudge when it is snowing since the humidity is usually low. If it is a wet, heavy snow the humidity will be too high.
- Powdered sugar should not be used in fudge.
- Brown sugar can be used to replace white sugar but only up to $^1/_2$ of the total sugar used in the recipe.
- If you want to use milk chocolate only use half milk chocolate and half semi-sweet chocolate.
- When making fudge you need to continue with all procedures until completely done.
- A variety of extracts can be added to fudge to produce great flavors. Some of the favorites include mint, lemon, vanilla, orange, and maple. However, only add $^1/_4$ teaspoon of an extract to fudge
- Always use a wooden spoon to mix fudge and mix until it starts to become firm before adding any raisins or nuts. Metal spoons get too hot.

The Basics of Fudge Making
- The mixture of milk, sugar, and butter are brought to a boil.
- The boil must be held for 5-10 minutes to reduce the amount of water and supersaturate the sugary slurry.

If you live at sea level, you will have less trouble with your fudge setting up than people who live at high altitudes or in humid climates.

- If you use semi-sweet chocolate bits, the milk will make the taste similar to milk chocolate.
- If you use milk chocolate as your base the fudge may be too milk chocolate unless it is to your liking.
- Using milk chocolate will make very sweet fudge, which many people do not like.
- Nuts, cherries, or raisins can be added after the fudge is finished cooking and is ready to be cooled.
- If you do not add any nuts or raisins a 9 by 9 inch pan will do.
- Insulated pots may cause the fudge to cool too slowly.
- If fudge is wrapped as airtight as possible it can be frozen for about 12 months.
- Fudge can be poured into a lightly buttered glass dish or a tin-foil lined pan that has been lightly buttered.
- The texture of fudge will become creamier if allowed to remain at room temperature for the first 18 hours after it is poured into the pan.

Fudge won't set up?

- If you have a problem with fudge setting up, just add 1 teaspoon of cornstarch when you start mixing in the ingredients.
- Divinity fudge tends to attract moisture and cannot be made on humid days.
- Placing the fudge in the refrigerator may harden it temporarily, but when it gets back to room temperature it will start to soften again.

Too much butter is a common problem.

- If the water content is too high it won't set properly.
- Poor grades of margarine that have been substituted for quality butter will also cause this problem.

Paulette's Fudge Recipe

5 ounces of quality unsalted butter (stick)

2 3/4 cups of granulated sugar

2/3 cups of evaporated milk (not condensed milk)

12 ounces of semi-sweet chocolate chips or bits

7 ounces of quality marshmallow crème

3/4 cup of fresh walnuts (chopped)

1/4-1/2 cup of raisins (good quality)

1 teaspoon of pure vanilla extract (best quality)

Use a 13 by 9 inch pan or equivalent and grease it lightly with the butter wrapper.

Mix the sugar and milk in a 3 quart saucepan, stir continually, and bring to a boil. The butter should be added after you mix the sugar into the milk and after it starts to boil.

Boil gradually and start with a medium heat and then go to high.

Do not allow crystallization around the inside top of the pot. Wipe it clean.

Boil for about 7-8 minutes on medium-high heat. It should be a rolling boil.

Use a candy thermometer and boil until the temperature reaches 235°F.

Remove from the heat and stir in the butter.

Chocolate chips, marshmallow, and vanilla should be in a separate heat-safe bowl.

Carefully pour the hot butter, sugar, and milk mixture over the chocolate chip mixture and stir until combined.

Add any remaining ingredients or raisins and mix well, then pour into the prepared pan.

The fudge should be cooled at room temperature and should set up perfectly.

Slice as soon as it sets up but is not completely solid.

DESSERTS

Baked Alaska

Baked Alaska was invented by Benjamin Thompson around 1800 in Massachusetts. He studied the resistance of egg whites to heat and was able to place a crust on top of ice cream. The dish was originally known as "omelette surprise" and then "Alaska-Florida Cake." The dessert was originally prepared and served at Delmonico's Restaurant in New York City by Chef Charles Ranhofer in 1867.

- The sponge cake used must be trimmed to 1 inch in thickness.
- The cake cannot be covered with more than 3 inches of ice cream.
- Freeze the cake and ice cream until solid.

- The egg whites must be beaten until stiff before adding 1 teaspoon of pure vanilla, $^1/_2$ teaspoon of cream of tartar, and $^2/_3$ cup of granulated sugar.
- The frozen ice cream/cake is removed from the freezer and the egg whites are spread in swirls around the ice cream and shaped into a dome.
- Bake in a preheated oven at 500°F just until the top of the dome is golden brown, which should only take about 3 minutes.
- The dessert must be served immediately.

Frozen Desserts
- To remove a frozen dessert from a mold, just place a very hot towel around the mold for a few seconds.

Tiramisu

Originated in the Italian province of Tuscany and was originally prepared for the Grand Duke Cosimo de Medici III and called "duke's soup." The dish did not gain popularity in the United States until the 1980s. The original tiramisu that is still served along the banks of the canals in Venice is composed of ladyfingers, lightly moistened with marsala and espresso, then layered with sweetened egg yolks and enriched mascapone cheese. It is sold chilled with a light dusting of cocoa powder.

- Make sure that the egg yolks and confectioner's sugar are mixed together until they are just pale and thick.
- Then beat in 1 tablespoon of the liqueur and sweet marsala, add the mascarpone cheese, and only beat until smooth and somewhat thick.
- In another bowl combine the coffee or espresso and 1 tablespoon of the liqueur. Place 3 ladyfingers into the bottom of the glasses you are using, then slowly drizzle the coffee mixture over them.

Ladyfingers are sold in different sizes. Usually, two 6 ounce packages will be enough for two layers.

- Spoon in half of the mascarpone mixture and sprinkle with grated milk chocolate.
- Repeat the layers of ladyfingers, coffee, mascarpone mixture, and chocolate and refrigerate for about 2 hours before serving.

Kids
CAN COOK TOO

COOKING WITH KIDS

The following recipes and cooking secrets can all be done by kids. However, adult supervision is always recommended to be on the safe side.

Marshmallow PB Squares

1 cup chocolate chips

1/2 cup margarine

2 cups Rice Krispies™

Colored sprinkles for garnish

3/4 cup butterscotch chips

1 cup smooth peanut butter

2 cups colored mini-marshmallows

Melt the chips, margarine, and peanut butter on low heat until all melted and smooth. Add the Rice Krispies™ and mini-marshmallows. Combine everything in a large bowl. Place the mixture on an 8 by 8 square pan and garnish with the colored sprinkles. Refrigerate until it is firm then slice into squares.

Chefs Secrets

Don't wait until it is hard or it will be too difficult to cut into squares.

Peanut Butter Brittle

1 cup sugar

1 1/4 cup roasted peanuts

1 teaspoon "real" vanilla extract

1/2 cup corn syrup (white)

1 teaspoon unsalted butter

1 teaspoon baking soda

- Mix the sugar and corn syrup and place in a 1 1/2 quart casserole dish.
- Place the casserole dish in the microwave and microwave on high for 3-4 minutes.
- Add the peanuts, stir, and microwave for another 4 minutes or until just golden brown.
- Add the butter and vanilla to the mixture; stir well, and microwave on high for 2 min.
- Remove from the microwave.
- Add the baking soda and stir until it gets foamy then quickly pour the mixture into a lightly greased cookie sheet.
- Allow it to cool for about 30-50 minutes.

Chefs Secrets

Do not refrigerate while it is cooling or it may get sugary. When you remove the bowl from the microwave it will be too hot to handle so use an insulated glove.

Peanut Fruit Loops

20 ounces of almond bark

2 cups Rice Krispies™

8 cups Fruit Loops™

2 cups colored mini-marshmallows

2 cups salted peanut pieces

· Melt the almond bark in the microwave in a safe dish.

· Remove from the microwave.

· Mix in the remaining ingredients.

· Drop a spoonful at a time on a lightly greased cookie sheet.

· Chill in the refrigerator and enjoy!

Bisquick Pizza

8 tubes of buttermilk Bisquick™ biscuit mix

8 cups pizza sauce

8 cups mozzarella cheese

· Cut each biscuit into 2-4 pieces depending on the size desired.

· Place the pizza sauce and any favorite topping on top.

· Bake 20 minutes at 325°F.

· Remove from oven. Place the cheese on top, then return to oven just until the cheese starts to melt.

· Remove and enjoy!

Pig Cookies

1 cup soft butter

2 large eggs

1 teaspoon "real" vanilla extract

1 teaspoon baking powder

1 1/2 cups sugar

1 cup sour cream

3 cups all-purpose flour

1/2 teaspoon salt

Frosting

1/2 cup butter

2 teaspoons "real" vanilla extract

4 drops of food coloring

36 Large marshmallow halves

4 cups confectioner's sugar

6 tablespoons whole milk

pink sugar waffle cookies

Reese candy bar sprinkles

Cookies
- Cream the butter and sugar.
- Add the eggs, sour cream, and vanilla and mix well.
- In a separate bowl combine the dry ingredients. Then add the mixture to the creamed mixture and blend well.
- Drop by tablespoon onto a lightly grease baking sheet.
- Preheat oven to 375°F.
- Bake for 10-12 minutes or until the edges are just brown.
- Cool on a wire rack.

Frosting
- In a medium saucepan, melt the butter, then add the sugar, vanilla, milk, and food coloring.
- Mix until smooth.

Frost the cookies.
- Cut the sugar wafer in triangles and place two on each cookie for ears.
- Using a toothpick, poke two holes in each marshmallow half for the nostrils then press brown candy bar sprinkles into holes.
- Place noses on cookies then add dark brown candy bar sprinkles for eyes.

Worm Hunt

2 small packages of instant pudding	3 1/2 cups whole milk
1 tub frozen whipped topping	1/2 cup margarine
8 ounces cream cheese	1 cup confectioner's sugar
1 small bag Oreo™ cookies (crushed)	12 gummy worms

- Mix the pudding and whole milk together in a medium bowl.
- Add the whipped topping and set aside.
- In another bowl cream the cream cheese, sugar, and margarine until smooth, then add to the pudding mix.
- Beat on medium speed until all is well-blended.
- Use a clean flowerpot and alternately place in the pudding mix, cookie crumbs, and worms, ending up with the cookie crumbs on top so that it looks like dirt.

- Place in refrigerator for 2 hours.
- Insert some artificial flowers so that it looks like the flowers are growing out of the pot.
- Serve each kid an individual small flowerpot or have the kids look for the worms in their dessert if you scoop out and serve from a larger pot.

Orange Sunrise

3 cups orange juice

2 medium bananas (sliced)

cranberry juice cocktail

1/4 cup honey

ice cubes

- Place the orange juice, bananas, and honey in a blender.
- Add the ice cubes until you have 6 cups of the mixture.
- Cover and blend on low speed for 30 seconds or until smooth.
- Divide the mixture into 8 glasses and pour the cranberry juice on top.
- The cranberry juice will sink to the bottom making an orange sunrise.

Steamy Chocolate Pudding

Ingredients:

1/2 cup all-purpose flour

1/4 cup whole milk

2 tablespoons sugar

1 large egg

1 teaspoon baking powder

2 teaspoons cocoa

2 teaspoons strawberry jam

1 ounce butter

- Sift all the dry ingredients into a large bowl.
- In another bowl, cream the butter and sugar.
- Add the egg to the creamed mixture and mix well with a wooden spoon.
- Make a "well" in the dry ingredients and pour in the creamed mixture.
- Mix well until all ingredients are blended.
- Spray cups with a vegetable spray and place 1 teaspoon of strawberry jam into each cup.
- Place half of the pudding mixture in each cup then loosely cover with glad wrap.
- Cook on high for 2 minutes for 2 pudding cups.

Veronica's Pizza Sticks

Ingredients:

8 ounces pepperoni

1 tablespoon Parmesan cheese

8 ounces pizza sauce

11 ounce package of refrigerated bread sticks

8 ounces mozzarella cheese (shredded)

1 tablespoon garlic powder

- Place the rolled out bread sticks on an ungreased cookie sheet, then place 2 pepperoni slices on the end and sprinkle with the mozzarella cheese.
- Fold the bread stick over and twist it up.

Cooking Secrets

- Mix the Parmesan cheese and the garlic powder and sprinkle over the bread sticks.
- Place in preheated 350°F oven for 6-8 minutes until a nice light brown color.
- Heat the pizza sauce in a pan on stove.
- Dip the pizza sticks in pizza sauce and eat.

Sandy's Speedy Quesadillas

4 large tortillas
8 slices American cheese   sour cream
4 pieces of paper towel   salsa (mild)

- Tear the cheese slices in strips.
- Place one tortilla on one piece of paper towel on a plate and add the cheese strips from 2 pieces of cheese spaced evenly.
- Roll the tortilla up as tight as you can, then move the tortilla to the edge of the paper towel nearest you.
- Roll the tortilla up in the paper towel and place on the plate and place the plate in the microwave for about 15-20 seconds depending on the power.
- Add salsa and sour cream if desired.

Sheryl's Marshmallow Teeth

8 medium red apples   bag of mini-marshmallows
smooth peanut butter

- Cut the apples into wedges.
- Spread the peanut butter onto one side of each apple wedge.
- Place the wide side of two wedges on a piece of paper towel and insert the teeth into the peanut butter. The peanut butter will hold the marshmallow teeth and it will look like a set of false teeth.

Deborah's Popsicle Marshmallows

2 cups of chocolate chips   waxed paper
1 cup of smooth peanut butter   lollypop sticks
bag of colored mini-marshmallows or large white marshmallows
chocolate or multi-colored sprinkles

- If you are using the large marshmallows, the lollypop sticks work better.

- Rounded toothpicks work best with the mini-marshmallows.
- Place the stick into the marshmallow so that it looks like a lollypop.
- Next dip the top of the marshmallow into the peanut butter and place them on a piece of waxed paper.
- Place the chocolate chips in a microwave-safe dish and melt them.
- Watch them closely so that they just melt and do not burn.
- Dip the peanut butter end of the marshmallow into the melted chocolate chips and then dip into the sprinkles
- Allow them to cool on waxed paper.

Robin's Putt'in on the Ritz

8 oz box Ritz™ Crackers
8 oz jar pasta or pizza sauce with mushrooms
20 slices of thin pepperoni
8 ounces of shredded mozzarella cheese

- Place Ritz crackers on a large dinner plate, salt-side down.
- Spoon pasta or pizza sauce on top of the crackers, then place the pepperoni slices on top of the sauce and top with the shredded cheese.
- Place the plate in the microwave for 1-2 minutes depending on the power or until the cheese melts.

Dana's Chocoana Banana

4 popsicle sticks   1/2 pound of chocolate squares
4 ripe bananas

- Peel the four bananas and place them on a plate.
- Melt the 1/2 pound of chocolate squares in the top of a double boiler.
- Place the Popsicle sticks or lollypop sticks in the bananas.
- Place the melted chocolate in a location where the children can easily reach in the pot and assist them in dipping the bananas into the melted chocolate and placing them on a plate.
- Place the plate into the freezer for at least 1 hour.

Little Paulette's Orange Fizzy

6 ounces of canned frozen orange juice   1/4 cup granulated sugar
1 cup whole milk   1 teaspoon "real" vanilla
1 cup cold tap water   10 ice cubes

- Measure out and place all ingredients into a blender.
- Place top on blender and fizz away.

Ashleigh's Mini, Mini Pizza

8 English Muffin halves   8 cup mozzarella cheese (grated)

1 can or jar of pizza sauce (8-10oz)   pizza toppings that you like

- Lightly toast the English muffin. If this step is left out the pizza will be soggy.
- Spread a thin layer of pizza sauce on top of each muffin then sprinkle the top with the cheese and your toppings.
- Place the pizza muffin in a 425°F oven until the cheese melts and just barely starts to bubble. This takes about 5 minutes.
- Allow the pizza muffin to cool for a minute or so and enjoy.

Kaylena's Caramel-Fudge Apples

8 medium Rome or Delicious apples   8 ounces of caramels

8 wooden skewers   8 ounces of fudge drops or chocolate squares

2 tbsp room-temperature butter   1 cup chopped peanuts or walnuts

3 tbsp cool tap water   (optional)

Colored or chocolate sprinkles may be used instead of the fudge

- Wash the apples in cool tap water and remove the stems.
- Insert the wooden skewers into apples.
- Heat the butter and water in the top of a double boiler.
- Melt the caramels and fudge.
- With adult supervision dip the apples into the caramel mixture and twirl them to be sure they are well coated.
- Roll the apples in the nuts and sprinkles if desired and place them on a piece of waxed paper to cool and dry.

Cooking
FOR CATS AND DOGS

SPECIAL TREATS FOR YOUR CAT

It's Tuna Time

3/4 small can of tuna   1/2 cup whole-wheat flour

1/2 cup nonfat powdered milk   1 large egg (beaten)

1 tablespoon corn oil   1/4 cup of water

- Place the tuna in a large bowl and mash well.
- Add the flour and milk and mix together.
- Slowly stir in the water, egg, and oil and mix well.
- Shape into 1/2 to 3/4 inch balls and place on greased baking pan.
- Press the balls gently to flatten.
- Bake the tuna treats at 350°F (175°C) for 10 minutes, then remove from oven.
- Allow the treats to stand for 5 minutes before tuning the treats over and baking for another 10 minutes.
- Place the treats on a wire rack to cool.
- Store in a well-sealed plastic container in the refrigerator.

Super-Vita Meal for Cats

5 chicken livers (cooked in water & chopped)

2/3 cup small curd cottage cheese

1/4 up biscuit mix

2 tablespoons corn or safflower oil

Pinch of salt

Mix all the ingredients together in a medium bowl and store in refrigerator. Best to use an airtight plastic container.

Fussy Cats Special Food

1 cup of canned or cooked chicken

2 ounces of chicken broth

1/2 cup cooked white rice (or brown)

1/2 cup broccoli (chopped and cooked)

1/2 cup carrots (chopped and cooked)

Place all the ingredients into a food processor and blend well. Then store in the refrigerator in a well-sealed plastic container.

Fishy Treats

1/2 cup canned salmon

1 tablespoon of corn oil

1 medium egg (beaten)

1 cup of breadcrumbs (whole wheat preferred)

1/4 teaspoon of Brewer's yeast

Crush the salmon in a medium bowl into very small pieces. Add the rest of the ingredients and mix well. Place 1/4 teaspoons full on a greased cookie pan and bake for 7-8 minutes at 350°F (175°C). Cool and store in the refrigerator in a well-sealed plastic container.

The Cat's Meow

2 chicken livers (cooked, chopped)   2 cans of sardines in oil

1/2 cup parsley (chopped)   2/3 cup cooked rice

Place all the ingredients into a food processor and mix well. Store in a well-sealed plastic container in the refrigerator.

The Cat's Fillet

1/2 pound of fillet of sole   1 1/2 tablespoons of freshly chopped chicken liver

1 tablespoon of soft margarine   1/4 cup cheddar cheese (shredded)

1 tablespoon of all-purpose flour   2/3 cup cooked rice

1/2 cup of low-fat milk   2 tablespoons parsley (chopped well)

1/2 teaspoon of saltv   Water

- Place the fillet of sole on a greased baking dish and sprinkle with the parsley.
- Add just enough water to cover the bottom of the dish.
- Melt the margarine in a saucepan and add the flour then heat until it just starts to boil.
- Slowly add the milk to the margarine mixture and stir well until the mixture gets thick.
- Remove the margarine mixture from the heat and add the cheese, chicken liver, and salt while stirring until all the cheese has melted.
- While you are making the cheese sauce place the sole in a preheated 450°F (230°C) oven for 10 minutes, cool and flake with a fork.
- Place the flaked fish and the rice into the cheese sauce and mix well. Cool and refrigerate in a well-sealed plastic container.

SPECIAL TREATS FOR YOUR DOG

Barker's Delight

3 jars of any meat baby food

1 jar mixed vegetable baby food

1 1/2 cup of wheat germ

Mix the wheat germ and baby food into dough then roll into 1 inch balls. Place the balls on a cookie sheet and press each one down flat. Bake at 350°F (175°C) for 30 minutes before cooling on a wire rack and refrigerating in a well-sealed plastic container.

Treats to Bark For

1 large egg

1/2 cup nonfat dry milk powder

2 cups of whole-wheat flour

1/2 cup chicken broth

1 tablespoon brown sugar

2 chicken livers (cooked)

1/2 cup corn oil

Place all the ingredients into a large bowl and mix well. Roll the dough out on a well-floured work surface and cut into small pieces in any shape you desire. Place the pieces on a greased baking sheet and bake at 300°F (150°C) for about 25-30 minutes then cool on a wire rack before storing in the refrigerator in a well-sealed plastic container.

They Do Back Flips for This One

4 pounds of ground chuck
(cooked and drained well)

8 egg yolks

4 cups of oats

4 cups of wheat germ

1/2 cup corn oil

1/2 cup honey

8 envelopes of unflavored gelatin

Place all the ingredients into a large bowl and mix well. Form into small balls and store in the freezer. Thaw only the amount desired for 2-3 days. These are used for a treat and can also be used for weight gain.

Special Treat

1 cup dry dog food (ground fine)

1 pound of ground chuck
(cooked and drained well)

1/4 cup molasses

1/4 cup corn oil

1 cup hot tap water

1 cup wheat germ

1 egg yolk

Mix all ingredients in a large bowl and roll into small meaty balls. Store in freezer and only thaw enough for 2-3 days at a time.

Doggie Treats

1 cup of chicken

1 cup of whole-wheat flour

2 cups of standard oats

2 large eggs

1 1/4 tablespoon of garlic powder

1 tablespoon of parsley

2 tablespoons of soy sauce

1/4 cup of powdered whole milk

Place the chicken in a medium saucepan and cook in chicken fat for 15 minutes, then simmer for 35 minutes adding a small amount of water. Remove from the heat and allow the chicken to cool for about 20-30 minutes. Slice into small pieces and place all ingredients into a food processor and blend, but do not liquefy.

Place tablespoon-size or larger globs on a cookie sheet and bake at 250°F. for 40-50 minutes, then allow to set-up in the sun (out of the dog's reach) to fully dehydrate for a few hours. Allow the biscuits to cool for another 12 hours before allowing your pet to devour them.

Making Doggie Biscuits

3/4 cup of rye flour

1 3/4 cup of whole-wheat flour

3/4 cup of bulgur

1/2 cup of cornmeal

1/2 cup of Brewer's yeast

1 teaspoon of dry yeast

1/2 cup of reduced fat dry milk

1/4 cup of warm tap water

1 cup of defatted chicken or turkey broth

1/4 cup of dried parsley

1 large egg (beat with 1 tablespoon of whole milk)

- Place the warm water and dry yeast in a bowl and stir until all the yeast is dissolved, then add the broth.
- Place the flours, Brewer's yeast, bulgur, dry milk, cornmeal, and parsley in another bowl and mix well.
- Stir the liquid mixture into the dry mixture and mix well, forming a stiff dough.
- If the dough is too difficult to work, add a small amount of warm water to loosen it up.
- Roll the dough out on a floured surface to about 1/4 to 1/2 inch thickness, then cut with a cookie cutter into biscuits.
- Place the biscuits on a cookie sheet and lightly glaze with a beaten egg and bake at 300°F. for 40 minutes.
- Allow the biscuits to remain in the oven overnight to thoroughly dry out.

Sweet Treat

1 pound of chicken livers

2 tablespoons of molasses

2 large eggs

1/2 teaspoon of garlic powder

do not use the salt)

1 1/2 cups of cornmeal

Place the chicken livers, eggs, and molasses in a food processor and puree. Add the rest of the ingredients and mix well. Pour out the mixture into a greased baking pan (9 by 9) and bake at 400°F (205°C) for 30 minutes or until a knife comes out clean. After you cool, cut the treats into bite sized pieces and refrigerate in a well-sealed plastic container.

Doggie's Having a Ball

2 cups of dry dog food (ground fine)

1 pound of ground chuck (cooked and drained)

1/4 cup molasses

1/4 cup wheat germ oil

Place all the ingredients into a large bowl and mix well. Form into small balls. Store them all in the freezer until ready to use. Only thaw enough for 2-3 days at a time.

Doggie Bagels

2 cups of whole-wheat flour

2/3 cup of beef broth

1 large egg

1 teaspoon of garlic powder

3 1/2 tablespoons of quick oats

- Blend the broth and egg together in a large bowl.
- Add the blend to the flour.
- Blend in the oats and garlic powder.
- Form the dough into a ball.
- Using a floured work surface roll the dough into about 1/2 inch thick pieces.
- Shape into bagels making the hole with your thumb. Arrange on a shallow baking pan, allowing space between each bagel.
- Microwave the bagels on high setting for about 10 minutes then allow them to cool on a wire rack before refrigerating.

Sweet Treats

1/2 cup honey

3 cups whole-wheat flour

4 1/2 ounces of wheat germ

1/4 cup soft margarine

1/4 cup almonds (finely chopped)

1 large egg (beaten)

Pinch of salt

- Mix together flour, wheat germ, almonds, and salt.
- Cut in margarine with your hands until the mixture is crumbly.
- Add the egg and honey. Then form the dough into small balls.
- A small amount of water may be added if needed to make the mixture easier to work.
- Using a floured surface, roll out the dough to about 1/2 inch thickness. Then cut into any shape you wish.
- Place the pieces on a greased baking pan.
- Bake at 375°F (190°C) for 20-25 minutes or until golden brown. Cool on wire racks and refrigerate.

Drying
FOODS

THE PROCESS OF DEHYDRATION

Drying foods is an excellent method of preserving space. It allows you to store more items in a smaller space. Dried foods do not have the nutritive value of canned or frozen foods, nor do they taste the same, nor do they have as good an appearance. However, they do provide more variety and a certain level of nutritive value.

TEMPERATURE

The initial part of the drying process utilizes the highest temperatures and the lowest humidity, which results in the fastest drying out of the food. This temperature is usually between 150°-160°F (65°-70°C) to allow the moisture to evaporate quickly from the food. Food tends to lose heat during rapid evaporation and the air temperature can be high without the temperature of the food increasing.

However, as soon as the surface moisture is lost and the rate of evaporation slows down, the food will warm up. The air temperature must then be reduced to 1400F (600C). As the food reaches the end of the drying process, the food can scorch easily and must be watched closely.

Every fruit and vegetable has a critical temperature above which an off taste will develop due to scorching. You don't want the temperature to cook the food, just dehydrate it.

HUMIDITY

The higher the temperature and the lower the humidity, the more rapid will be the rate of dehydration. Humid air tends to slow down dehydration. Do not try and dry foods on a humid day or "case hardening" will occur. The cells on the outside of the food give up their moisture faster than the cells on the inside. When this occurs the surface becomes hard and will prevent the escape of moisture from the inside cells.

The moisture in the foods escapes into the air through evaporation. The trapped air will take on as much moisture as it can hold and then no further drying can take place. Therefore, the ventilation around the oven or drying unit must be adequate.

DRYING UNIFORMLY

Try to stir the pieces of food frequently and shift the racks if using an oven or moving the food around even in a dryer. Heat in a dryer varies in different locations. It is best to just spread thin layers of uniform-sized pieces of food on each drying rack.

DIFFERENT TYPES OF FOODS

If you have never tried drying foods it would be best to try and dry a few foods in the oven. You may want to see what dried foods really taste like before trying to dry a large batch. It will also help you to familiarize yourself with the drying process.

You will find that fruits are easier to dry than vegetables since the moisture in them tends to evaporate faster. The best fruits to dry are apples, cherries, peaches, apricots, and pears. The easiest vegetables to dry are corn, peppers, onions, green beans, and peas.

Don't bother to dry vegetables if they have been stored for a long period of time. The best vegetables for drying are fresh from the farm. Supermarket vegetables are usually not as good to dry as fresh. Herbs of all types are easy to dry, especially the leaves, seeds, and blossoms.

Beef, lamb, and venison can easily be dried to make "jerky." Fish tends to dry well and retains most nutrients. Foods with high moisture content such as iceberg lettuce, melons, and cucumbers do not dry well.

TIPS TO BE AWARE OF

- Cleanliness and sanitation are a must.
- Expect the flavor to be somewhat different than you are used to.
- The texture will change.
- It takes time and patience to dry food.

EQUIPMENT

- Kitchen oven
- Drying racks
- Storage containers
- Food scale
- Electric fan to circulate the air
- Thermometer to check oven temperature
- Blancher for vegetables
- A sulfur box for fruits

Wooden slats or a stainless steel mesh screens are the best to use for racks. Never use a solid metal tray or baking sheet since the air cannot circulate around the food. However, pieces of meat for jerky can be placed on the metal oven racks as long as they are big enough not to fall through the spaces. Also, never use racks made from galvanized screening, aluminum, copper, fiberglass, or any types of vinyl. These metals will cause an acid reaction and will darken the foods as well as cause harmful compounds to be formed.

DIFFERENT METHODS

Commercial Food Dryer

This method uses less electricity than an electric oven and will provide automatically controlled heat. Drying will take a little longer since the average temperature runs about 1200F (500C).

- Preheat the dryer to 125ºF (52ºC).
- Gradually increase the temperature to 140ºF (60ºC).
- It will take you about 5-10 hours on the average to dry fruits or vegetables.

Oven Drying

This is probably the simplest method of drying since you do not have to buy any special equipment. It is faster then trying to dry in the sun or even using a food dryer. However, the big drawback is that you are only able to dry a limited amount of food. An average oven can only hold about 5 pounds of food at a time.

- Set the oven on the lowest possible setting and preheat to 140ºF (60ºC).
- Never use the broiler of an electric oven or the food on the top tray will dry too fast.
- Ovens with pilot lights may dry the food without any other heat source.
- The oven temperature must be kept between 140º-160ºF (60º-70ºC).
- Place an oven thermometer on the top tray halfway back where it can easily be seen.
- Check the thermometer every 30 minutes.
- Arrange about 1-2 pounds of prepared food in a single layer on each tray and place one tray on each oven rack.
- Be sure and allow at least 1$\frac{1}{2}$ inches between the sides, back, and front of the trays for air circulation.
- If you have the room in the oven you can use small blocks of wood (at least 1 inch high) to place additional trays in the oven.
- Never dry more than 4 trays of food at a time. The lighter the load, the faster the food will dry.
- Keep the door to the oven ajar. The moist air needs to escape. For electric ovens keep the door opened about 5 inches, and 2 inches for a gas oven.
- Change the location of the trays. Rotate them from top to bottom about every $\frac{1}{2}$ hour.
- Stir fruits and vegetables every $\frac{1}{2}$ hour so that they will dry evenly. Turn jerky regularly or it will stick to the rack.

Sun Drying

This was the only method of drying food in the old days. It utilizes the sun's heat and natural air movement. The temperature, however, must be around 100°F with low humidity.

- Make a natural draft dryer, which traps the heat from the sun and protects the food from insects and birds.
- When food is placed on the drying racks they need to be covered with cheesecloth or netting to keep the dust off.
- The dryer must be placed in direct sunlight.
- Keep dryer away from animals and small children.
- Bring the dryer indoors at night if the temperature drops more than 20°F from the daytime high.
- If you get dew at night it will place the moisture back into the food.
- Fruits and vegetables take 3-7 days to dry in the sun.

HOW TO DRY FRUITS

Selecting and Cleaning

Be sure and start with high quality fruits that are fully ripe and not damaged or bruised. Sanitation during all phases of the drying process is very important.

Pretreatment

All fruits need some type of special treatment before you can dry them. They may need to be cored, pits removed, washed, skinned, or sliced. It's best to slice them in uniform pieces for the even results. Fruits like cherries need their skins cracked before you can dry them since the skins are waxy and tough.

Cracking the Skins

There are a number of fruits that cannot be dried unless their skins are cracked. These include cherries, grapes, plums, and even blueberries. Their waxy coating has to be removed or the moisture will not release easily. To crack the skin you must do the following:

- Place the fruit in boiling water for 30-60 seconds, then dip them into very cold water.
- Boiling water works better than a lye bath since lye can be dangerous.
- Be sure and drain them well on paper towel before drying.

Light-Colored Fruits Vs Oxidation

There are numerous light-colored fruits that will easily turn brown when exposed to the air, allowing oxidation to take place. Oxidation will ruin the flavor, texture, aroma, and appearance of fruits. The following will assist you in reducing or eliminating this problem:

- For apples use 2 teaspoons of ascorbic acid (vitamin C) to 1 teaspoon of water and brush on all exposed surfaces.
- For all other light-colored fruits use 1 teaspoon of ascorbic acid to 1 cup of water.
- The solution can be either sprinkled on or brushed on with a very soft bristle brush.
- The above amounts should be enough for about 5 quarts of fruit.
- Commercial products are available but the cost is much higher and they do not do a better job.
- Never soak the fruits in vinegar or salt before drying.
- The more you soak a fruit the more water-soluble vitamins will be lost, especially vitamin C.

Using Sulfur

Sulfuring stops the oxidation of fruits and protects them from drying out and browning. It also will reduce the loss of vitamin A and C as well as having anti-microbial properties. There are two common methods of sulfuring foods:

1. Using sulfur fumes, a method which takes too much time and equipment.
2. Soaking the fruit in a sulfite solution.

To prepare a sulfite solution you add 1-2 tablespoons of sodium bisulfite to 1 gallon of water and mix well. After preparing the fruit soak it for only 5-10 minutes. Use a plate to hold the fruit under water and soak the light-colored fruits a little longer then the darker fruits. You can get sodium bisulfite in most drugstores or health food stores. Never use garden-grade sodium bisulfite.

BE SURE AND ONLY USE FOOD-GRADE SODIUM BISULFITE

Steam Blanching

As an alternative to sulfuring, try steam blanching your fruits. This method is not as effective and more vitamins are destroyed in the process. The drying time will also be longer and this is not a preferred method.

Starting the Drying Process

- Pretreated fruits should be arranged in a single layer on drying trays.
- Place the trays into the drying oven.
- Be sure they are $1\frac{1}{2}$ inches apart.
- Juicy fruits such as apricots need to be halved and the pits removed.
- Pieces should be set on the tray cut-side up for the best results.
- The drying time will depend on the size of the pieces and their uniformity.
- When the drying process is completed the pieces should be leathery.
- Cut into a piece of fruit to be sure that it is still not moist.

Making Fruit Leather

To prepare fruit leather, just puree any kind of fruit then spread the fruit on a baking sheet to dry. Cover the baking sheet with plastic wrap before pouring the pureed fruit out. Try and form a layer about $\frac{1}{4}$ inch thick. If you wish you can sweeten the pieces with honey or other sweetener as well as adding nuts, coconut, or even spices on top. Remember the drying process will cause the flavors to concentrate, so a little goes a long way.

Using Dried Fruits

If you are going to use dried fruits in a dish it is best to rehydrate them first by soaking them in cold water for about 2 hours or until they are somewhat plump. Another method is to pour boiling water over the fruit, just enough to cover and simmer for about 15 minutes. However, if you overcook them the fruit will become mushy and not be very good to use.

DRYING VEGETABLES

There are many vegetables that can easily be dried. You must, however, start with fresh vegetables that are mature and only purchase the amount you can dry efficiently at one time. Never dry more than 5 pounds if you are going to use an oven. Be sure and clean them thoroughly and remove any bad spots or bruises. The pieces should be uniform for the best results.

Blanching Is a Must

Almost every vegetable should be blanched in boiling water before being prepared for drying. The boiling water kills the enzymes, which will cause the vegetables to lose their color and flavor during the drying process. Only a few vegetables do not need to be blanched. These include mushrooms, onions, and okra. Vegetables can also be steam blanched, which will reduce the amount of water-soluble vitamins that are lost. After blanching be sure and place the vegetables in cold water and dry thoroughly.

Drying

The same rules for drying fruits will apply for drying vegetables. The only difference is that when vegetables are dry they will shatter when hit with a hammer instead of being pliable.

Handling Different Vegetables

- Some beans, such as any mature bean, soybeans, and peas can be partially or completely dried right on the vine.
- Carrots, parsnips, potatoes, and turnips are best stored fresh and not dried. They will last for months in a cool, dry location.
- Broccoli and asparagus will be better if frozen and not dried since drying will affect their flavor.
- Remember you can dry different vegetables at the same time as long as they are uniform in size.
- The exception to this is vegetables that are going to be used in soups. They should be dried separately from all other vegetables.

Using Dried Vegetables

Soaking is usually not required when using dried vegetables. However, presoaking them will shorten their cooking time. To reconstitute vegetables, just soak 1 cup of dried vegetables in 2 cups of water for 2 hours. Most vegetables will return to their normal size and shape. Don't throw the water that you use to reconstitute them away since the water contains some nutrients and can be added to soups and sauces.

DRYING HERBS

Preparation

- The stalks should be cut when the leaves are mature and the plants have just started to bloom.
- Only use the tender, leafy tops and flower clusters. Discard all leaves below 6 inches from the top of the stalk.
- These will not be as pungent as the top leaves.
- Be sure and remove any dead or discolored leaves.
- Rinse the herbs with cold water and wash off any dust and dirt.
- Remove the excess moisture by blotting with paper towel.
- If you plan on drying dill, harvest the plant as soon as you see that the seeds are ripe.

Air Drying

To air dry herbs just tie 6-8 stems together in a small bunch. Then you need to tie a large brown paper bag around the bunch to protect the herbs from too much light. Make sure that the leaves do not touch the sides of the bag or they may stick to the bag, which will affect the way they dry. You will need to make a few holes in the bag for ventilation and then hang the bag in a warm, dry location with good air circulation. It should take about 2 weeks to dry herbs.

HERBS SHOULD NEVER BE SUN-DRIED. THE LIGHT WILL DESTROY THE NATURAL AROMA

Oven Drying
To oven dry herbs, just place the fresh leaves on racks in a single layer allowing about 1 inch around the racks as well as between them so air can circulate freely. The oven should be set on the lowest temperature setting so that the herbs will dry slowly. Be sure and keep the oven door propped open slightly for ventilation. It will take about 2-4 hours to dry the herbs.

Microwave Drying
You can dry herbs in a microwave. However, the herbs need to be placed between paper towels and placed on a rack. Use the medium setting and it should only take 2-3 minutes before the herbs are dry. The leaves should be crumbly and brittle. If they are not, continue drying them for another 30 seconds.

Storing Herbs
- Shake the leaves from the stems as soon as the leaves are dry and throw away the stems.
- The leaves can be crushed and stored, however, the whole leaf will retain its flavor longer.
- Be sure and store herbs in an airtight container.
- They can be placed into a plastic bag. Blow into the bag and seal it up fast. The carbon dioxide from your breath will preserve the herbs.
- Store in a cool, dry location for longer life.
- To check to see if the herb is still potent, rub the herb in your hands and breath in the aroma. If no aroma, the herbs are bad.

Using the Herbs
The herbs should be cut up, chopped, or ground up into very fine bits before adding them to a food. Grinding with a mortar and pestle is an excellent method of powdering herbs. Herbs should be added to the liquid in a recipe for the best results. The amount of the herbs used depends on your taste preferences.

Remember if a recipe calls for fresh herbs, you can substitute dry herbs, but only use a fourth of the recommended amount. $1/4$ teaspoon of dried herbs equals 1 teaspoon of fresh.

Herb Use Rules to Follow

- When using herbs in soups or stews add the herbs during the last $\frac{1}{2}$ hour of cooking.

- When adding to uncooked foods you should add the herbs 3-4 hours before serving. You can also add the herbs and allow the dish to remain overnight to release the flavor.

- If you want to release the flavor faster for cooked dishes, just place the herbs in a small amount of liquid such as lemon juice, vegetable oil, or other liquid that is being used in the recipe for 8-10 minutes before adding them to the dish.

DRYING MEATS

Preserving meats has been done for thousands of years, using salting, smoking, and drying methods. Making jerky from beef was the only way that the early settlers had to incorporate meat into their diets safely. Jerky was sun-dried back then. Now, however, it is made in the oven with controlled temperatures. Making your own jerky is still somewhat popular these days, although it is easier to just buy it at your local supermarket.

Jerky

The word "jerky" was derived from the Arawak Indian word "charqui." It refers to meat that has been dried and cured. The best jerky is made with wood smoke and sunlight.

- Jerky can be made in a smoker for the best flavor.
- The best cut of meat is a sirloin tip roast, which is very lean and has very little fat.
- The roast should be sliced across the grain and into $^1/_4$ inch strips.
- Jerky is best prepared at a low temperature using very little smoke. The temperature should be under 150°F for the best results.
- Electric smokers work very well when preparing jerky.

Preparing the Meat for Drying

- Only dry lean meats. Fat will get rancid too easily.
- The best meats are beef and venison.
- Partially freeze the meat before slicing to make it easier to slice.
- Only slice with the grain into long, thin, even strips.
- Be sure that the strips are $^1/_8$ to $^1/_4$ inch thick, about $1^1/_2$ inches wide and about 5-10 inches long.
- Thin slices will dry faster.
- If you are going to use any wild game, be sure and freeze the meat for at least 30 days at 0°F to reduce the risk of any parasite larvae.
- You can season the meat according to your taste. However, too much seasoning will overpower the flavor of the meat.
- The oven temperature must be maintained above 140°F or spoilage may occur.
- The meat can be marinated overnight in a crockery, glass, or stainless steel bowl. The temperature should be 40°F and 12 hours is the minimum time in the marinade.
- Be sure that the marinade does not contain any oil or you may have a problem with rancidity.

Standard Jerky Marinade Recipe

5 pounds of lean meat

2 tablespoons Worcestershire Sauce

1/2 teaspoon garlic powder

2 teaspoons hickory smoke-flavored salt

1/2 cup soy sauce

1/2 teaspoon pepper

1/2 teaspoon ground ginger

- Combine all the ingredients in a large bowl and mix well.
- Add the strips of beef or venison and mix to coat all surfaces well.
- Cover and refrigerate for 8-10 hours.
- Remove strips and remove excess moisture with paper towels.
- The soy sauce can be replaced with other sauces, such as teriyaki, sweet and sour, or hot sauce.

Drying Methods for Beef

The oven is probably the easiest way to dry meats and make jerky. Use the oven racks and be sure that the meat strips do not touch each other and that there is enough space between the strips for air circulation. Turn them at regular intervals or they will stick to the rack. Maintain 140°-150°F (60°-65°C) and use an oven thermometer to be sure of the temperature. The oven door needs to be slightly ajar and you can even place a small fan near the door to keep the air circulating properly.

Testing for Dryness

The jerky must be dry enough or it will spoil fast. However, you don't want it too hard or it will be difficult to eat. The final product should be dark brown, almost black, and be hard and dry. When you bend it, it should snap like a green twig, not a dry stick. The jerky must be cool before you test it. The final product will be pliable and about a fourth of its original weight.

Storing Jerky

- As soon as the meat has dried in the oven, remove the racks.
- Pat off any fat beads that may have formed.
- Allow the jerky to cool. Remove it from the racks. Store in a clean, airtight container in a cool, dry location.

Section 4

Grandmother's
HOME REMEDIES

INTRODUCTION

GRANDMOTHER'S HOME REMEDIES

We've all heard the expression: "Grandmother knew best."

My grandmother was the kind of woman who always had a pot of coffee on the stove, something wonderful-smelling in the oven, and the answer for any question I could dream up. Nothing threw Grandma. "I've lived through some tough times," she used to say to me. "It'll take more than a cough or two to keep me down." Whenever I got sick, Grandma had just the thing to make me feel better. Like her mother and grandmother before her, my grandmother had a host of home remedies that could cure whatever ailed you. Unfortunately, these invaluable pieces of homespun advice were rarely written down.

This book is about grandmothers' home remedies. Not just the ones my grandmother used, but those handed down from generation to generation in families everywhere. Many of the remedies described in this book originated in Native American culture. Many may remind you of your own grandmother. Others will be new to you, but may soon become part of the legacy you pass on to your family.

My grandmother and women like her relied on common items they grew in their herb gardens, kept in their cupboards, or bought at the general store. The nearest doctors were often miles away-a distance that seemed farther before the invention of the automobile. When Grandma was a girl, people turned to home remedies the way we turn to our neighborhood pharmacy. In this book, you'll find tried and true natural treatments to alleviate many common illnesses. The remedies use everyday items-herbs and foods that are easy to obtain.

It's important to note that the remedies do not take the place of our physicians or prescribed medication. They are provided as another source of information about how a number of illnesses were treated before modern medicine came of age. Many of the remedies have been very successful. All are without side effects when used as recommended.

As you leaf through this book, I hope some of Grandma's spirit comes through. I also hope you will be reminded of your own grandmother and great-grandmother, who have passed on a precious oral tradition that must be cherished. My goal is that this book will help you perpetuate their legacy.

49

Touchy
SUBJECTS

Consisting of three layers, the skin is the body's largest organ. It acts as a shield between the body and the thousands of foreign substances that can damage it. Our environment contains pollutants that could harm and even kill us if allowed to gain entry. The skin reacts to these harmful elements by breaking out, flaking, scaling, and itching. It may redden, change color, crack, and become dry.

Clear Up Your Complexion:
ACNE

This common skin condition occurs when the sebaceous glands become clogged or are not regenerated in sufficient quantity to handle the load. These glands, which lie just beneath the skin, produce natural oils that keep it lubricated. Whiteheads, blackheads, or pimples form when these clogged pores release bacteria.

For serious blemishes, try washing with Fels-Naptha soap. It's strong stuff for oily skin. If your skin is normal or dry, you'll need something gentler for your face.

Clearing Up The Outside From The Inside

Grandma, like mothers everywhere, swore that all the high-fat food we love so much does a number on our complexions. Scientists may not be quite as convinced. To be on the safe side: Avoid chocolate, chips, and fried foods.

Eating more brown rice is good for improving overall health. It is also good for your complexion. To ward off pimples and other facial blemishes, make brown rice a regular part of your diet.

Keep the skin and body hydrated by drinking at least eight glasses of water daily. This is an effective method of keeping the skin clear and clearing wastes from the body.

Studies show that zinc deficiency may contribute to acne. Be sure to check with your doctor before taking a supplement: Too much zinc can have harmful side effects.

Spread It On Thick

To help fight pimples, use a paste of onion and honey. Cook one sliced onion in one-half cup of honey until it is tender. Mash the onion with a fork to form a paste and allow the mixture to cool. Apply the paste to the problem area and leave it on your skin for an hour before rinsing with warm water. Use this treatment every night before going to bed until your complexion is clear.

An application of egg whites helps distribute the skin's natural oils more evenly. This eliminates dry and oily patches. Swab the egg whites onto your face with a cotton ball. After five minutes, rinse your face. Studies have shown that certain amino acids in the protein of egg whites may have anti-inflammatory properties. Most small blemishes and pimples shrink or disappear in a matter of days.

Oatmeal has long been used to control the spread of acne and speed healing. Prepare the oatmeal as directed (without the milk, brown sugar, and raisins, of course!) and apply it to the face. Let it stand for ten to fifteen minutes before washing it off. The abrasive action of the oats cleanses deeply and increases circulation in the affected area. This speeds healing.

Acne and eczema, as well as psoriasis, have responded well to a paste made from the grain amaranth and placed on the affected area. Amaranth may also be taken as a tea. Cover two teaspoons of the fresh seeds with boiling water. Simmer the brew on low heat for five to six minutes. Remove the tea from the heat, add two to three amaranth leaves, and allow the brew to steep for thirty to forty minutes. Two cups a day should alleviate a number of skin problems.

Urine For A Surprise
Some folk remedies are a little strange. Others are downright unappealing. I've heard that this particular cure is quite effective. So if you are really desperate about your acne, you might consider trying it: Capture your first urine of the day. Apply it with a washcloth to blemished skin. A baby's urine, which is purer than an adult's, works even better.

Super Strawberry Facial
If you have a chronic skin problem, try Grandma's Super Strawberry Facial. It takes a little while to prepare, so you have to plan ahead. About four hours before you'll want to go to bed, combine a cup of mashed strawberries in two cups of white cider vinegar. By the time you're ready for bed, your facial should be ready. Make sure you strain out all the solids and keep the liquid. Apply it liberally to your face. Don't worry: It dries quickly. In the morning, rinse your face with warm water. This is as good an astringent as anything you can buy. Your face will feel clean and tight. It shouldn't be long before you can kiss those pimples goodbye.

Make An Astringent At Home
Blackheads respond well to lemon juice, a substance with wonderful astringent properties. Rub lemon juice over the blemished skin before going to bed. In the morning, rinse with cool water. After a couple of days, you should see results.

Vinegar is a mild acid that cleans the affected area and reduces bacteria levels. Apply apple cider vinegar to the skin with a cotton swab. Allow it to stand for ten minutes before removing it with a mild soap.

You'll find cucumber toners in most expensive lines of skin care products. Cucumber extract soothes skin and helps dry acne. Squeeze a cucumber and apply the juice to your blemishes with a cotton ball. After fifteen minutes, rinse your face.

ERASING THE PAST

If you had a serious acne problem in the past, you probably still have scars. To fade them, apply a paste consisting of one teaspoon of honey mixed with a teaspoon of nutmeg. Rinse it off after twenty minutes, using cool water. Repeat this procedure twice a week. You should notice a difference within a couple of months.

Out, Out Damned Spots

In our teen years, we discovered that our grandmother had a real pet peeve about pillowcases. She blamed many common skin irritations and blemishes on dirty pillowcases and insisted we change ours every week. When you spend six to eight hours rubbing your face on a piece of cloth, she reasoned, you are bound to slough off dead skin and other residue that may contain bacteria. This idea also reinforced one of Grandma's favorite expressions: "Cleanliness is next to Godliness."

Buttermilk Facial Balm

Cousin Ruth had a terrible problem with acne as a teenager. She was very self-conscious about it. Grandma hated how unhappy it made her. "But you're such a pretty girl, Ruthie," she would say. She started asking her friends and neighbors for a sure-fire cure. It was Miss Betsy, the lady next door, who came up with just the thing. Here's the recipe she shared with Grandma: Bring one-third of a cup of buttermilk to a boil. Take it off the stove and immediately start adding honey. Add enough honey to make a paste thick enough to stay where you put it. Once the paste has cooled, dab it on the problem areas with your fingers. Wait fifteen minutes before rinsing it off. Cousin Ruth used it. And before we knew it, her pimples and blackheads were gone.

Stop Hiding Those Hands:
AGE SPOTS

Age spots are areas of increased pigmentation. Caused either by aging or by excessive exposure to sunlight, these skin spots are generally harmless. However, if they change color or cause discomfort, consult a physician immediately. As Grandma used to say: "An ounce of prevention is worth a pound of cure." Take care of your skin by using a sunscreen with an SPF factor of at least fifteen whenever you're going outside. Aloe vera preparations can postpone the appearance of these spots as you age.

Taking a zinc supplement may help fade age spots. But consult your physician before trying this remedy: High doses of zinc can have harmful side effects.

Rub It In To Rub Them Out

Mix onion juice with twice as much vinegar and rub the liquid into the age spots twice a day. The brown patches should disappear before your very eyes.

Vitamin E oil is highly beneficial to the skin. It can promote healing of cuts, prevent or fade scars, and relieve dry skin. It also appears to help fade age spots. Before you go to bed, rub some vitamin E oil into the brown patches. Let it work overnight. You should notice a difference in a few weeks.

Lemon juice can bleach out age spots for a time. Dab a small amount on the spots and allow it to dry. For the best results, do this at least two or three times each day. It may be two to three months before you see results.

Give It Some Time

Apply buttermilk compresses to the area for twenty minutes twice a day. The mild lactic acid found in milk products appears to be the active ingredient. Everyone's skin is different, so treatment time may vary.

Gota kola has, for hundreds of years, been used to alleviate memory problems. This herb also works on age spots. Mix a solution of one-quarter teaspoon of powdered gota kola, one-half cup of very hot water, and one-eighth teaspoon of Korean ginseng. Make a poultice and place it on the spots. Let it stand for ten minutes. Do this twice a day. You should see results in about one month. Gota kola is an effective bleaching agent but may work more slowly than some of the other treatments.

Fountain Of Youth Food

Chickpeas are a veritable fountain of youth. Low in fat and high in fiber and nutrients, they will keep you feeling youthful and energetic. You can also use them to fade age spots. You can buy chickpeas dried or canned. If dried, prepare them according to the directions on the package. Mash a small bowlful and add enough water to make a paste. Rub the chickpeas over the brown spots. After the paste dries, wash your hands. If you do this every day, your hands will begin to look years younger.

Leave It In The Locker Room:
ATHLETE'S FOOT

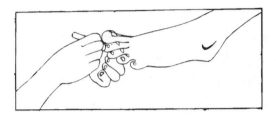

Athlete's foot thrives in dark, warm locations. To avoid this very contagious fungal infection, don't walk barefoot in a gym or locker room.

When Grandma could get to the store, she stocked up on over-the-counter antifungal remedies to have on hand for whoever needed them. Try Desenex or Tinactin. Some people like the dryness of powder. Others enjoy a cream's moisturizing effect.

Rubbing your feet to remove dead skin cells may help relieve the problem and prevent the fungus from spreading.

Grandma's Secret Foot Soak
Here's one of Grandma's favorite recipes for athlete's foot: Mix one-half cup of chlorine bleach, one-quarter cup of apple cider vinegar, and two tablespoons of salt in one gallon of warm water. Soak your feet for twenty minutes twice a day until the problem goes away.

Smelly Solutions
Garlic can destroy foot fungus. Dust your feet with garlic powder-not garlic salt-before putting on your socks.

Another effective way to kill the fungus is to soak your feet in a vinegar bath. Mix one-half cup of apple cider vinegar in one gallon of warm, filtered water. Soak your feet for at least ten to fifteen minutes twice a day. Then let them air-dry.

Gooey But Good for You
Other effective natural treatments include applying tea tree oil directly to the site and diluting fifteen drops of eucalyptus oil in one tablespoon of olive oil. Apply either solution twice a day.

Soak some cloth with honey and tape it to the bottom of your feet. You'll want to wear socks to keep the mess from seeping all over. Wear this honey poultice to bed. Take it off in the morning and wash your feet. Dry them thoroughly and apply powder or cornstarch to keep them dry. Your athlete's foot should clear up quickly.

Home Remedies

Break off a piece of your aloe vera plant to cure athlete's foot. Rub the gel into your feet in the morning and in the evening. If you don't have a green thumb, you can buy aloe vera gel or juice at the local health food store. Even stubborn athlete's foot has been known to respond to this treatment.

Beachy Keen

Everything is better at the beach-including your athlete's foot. Salt seems to kill the fungus that causes the itching. If you can't take frequent strolls at the seaside, dissolve two teaspoons of salt in a pint of warm water and soak your feet for five to ten minutes a day. Do this until the problem clears up.

The Dry Idea

Keeping your feet dry helps keep athlete's foot at bay. After you bathe or shower, pay careful to the areas between your toes. If toweling doesn't seem to dry your feet thoroughly enough, take aim with your blow dryer. Cornstarch or baking soda can help keep feet dry.

My grandmother was a practical woman. It made sense to her that an antiperspirant that could keep your underarms dry could do the same for your feet. Try a roll-on or spray to combat athlete's foot.

Some people didn't take Grandma seriously when she told them to wear white socks to get rid of athlete's foot. But Grandma wasn't kidding! White socks are free of dyes that may aggravate skin problems. To prevent foot fungus, choose socks made from absorbent, natural fibers.

Aloha To Foot Fungus

You'll think you're in the islands when you use Grandma's Pineapple Footbath to rid your feet of fungus. You'll need to plan for this remedy, since you have to soak your feet in pineapple juice for an hour. When the calypso music ends and the hour is up, dry your feet and sprinkle them with baking soda. If you repeat this every day, your athlete's foot should clear up quickly.

Keep Your Socks On

A foot soak is very relaxing. But adding astringent ingredients-such as Epsom salt, lemon juice, vinegar, black tea, chlorine beach, or borax-will help kill bacteria, reduce sweating, and eliminate foot odor. Mix one-quarter cup of white vinegar and two to three tablespoon of Epsom salt in a half gallon of water for an effective, germ-fighting foot soak.

Once again, baking soda comes to the rescue! Sprinkle it on your feet to absorb odor. Place a small amount in your shoes or socks.

Take The Pressure Off:

BEDSORES

These ulcers form when too much pressure on a bony area restricts circulation. This causes the death of cells and tissue. Most bedsores form at the base of the spine and result from lying in bed for prolonged periods. Massage the area to improve circulation. Change positions regularly to prevent bedsores.

Eat one cup of spinach each day for a week. Garlic also helps speed healing.

Sore Spots:

BOILS

Boils are also called furuncles. These round, pus-filled red bumps are usually due to infection, poor hygiene, food allergy, or stress.

Kitchen Cures

Apply honey directly to the boil. Or use very warm clay packs four or five times a day if you can. You can also use an onion poultice. Put the onion between two pieces of cloth. Do not put the onion directly on the boil.

You can use pumpkin, lemon, and figs to bring a boil to a head. Apply slices of fresh pumpkin to the boil, replacing them until the boil is better. Warm a lemon in the oven, cut it in half, and tape it to the boil. Leave the lemon on the boil for an hour The Biblical prophet Isaiah suggested using figs to cure a boil. Roast a fresh fig, cut it in half, and place the flesh on the boil. Hold the fig in place with a bandage or cloth and don't take it off for a couple of hours. Warm the pulp from the other half of the fig and refresh the treatment. It won't be long before the boil is gone.

Home Remedies

Grandma knew as much about baking as she did about home remedies. When somebody got a boil, she drew on both these skills to make a poultice of bread and milk. You don't have to use homemade bread, but my grandmother recommended it.

Try a warm oatmeal poultice on a boil. Hold it in place with a bandage. Leave it on overnight.

Slices of raw potato or cooked onion may also help bring a boil to a head.

Grandmother's Egg-cellent Boil Cure

Grandmother had a very unusual method of eliminating painful boils. She would boil an egg and remove the thin membrane that lies just under the shell. She'd place the membrane on the boil and cover it with a bandage. This method will bring most boils to a head by morning. Important note: To prevent salmonella poisoning, boil the egg for at least fifteen minutes before removing the membrane. Eggs, even if unbroken when purchased, may be contaminated with bacteria. Placing any part of a raw egg near an open wound may be cause for concern.

Boil Brews

A milk-based poultice will help bring a boil to a head. Gently heat one cup of milk, gradually adding three teaspoons of salt as the milk nears the boiling point. Remove the milk from the stove and add flour until the mixture forms a paste. Apply the paste to the affected area, making sure that it is not hot enough to burn the skin. In a few days, the boil will break. Pus will drain and the pain will disappear.

If you have a boil, brew yourself a cup of tea. After you enjoy the beverage, put the still-warm tea bag on the boil. The warmth helps draw out the toxins, and acids in the tea may kill bacteria.

Fill a small bottle with warm water and carefully place it on top of the boil. The suction will draw out pus.

Fat Will Do The Trick

Beef fat is bad for your arteries but good for a boil. Melt some fat and add it to a small amount of pine sap. Apply it to the boil.

Bacon fat can also help rupture a boil. Place it on the affected area and secure it with a gauze dressing or bandage. Keep the bacon fat fresh until the boil is better.

Another of Grandma's favorite remedies was to place a small amount of coal tar under a bandage and leave it in place overnight. Coal tar has an excellent drawing effect but is a bit messy. Bandage the boil carefully: Coal tar will contaminate an open wound.

A "Fishy" Boil Cure

When you're a kid, you don't care if something is good for you. If it tastes bad, you want to stay as far from it as possible. Grandma used cod liver oil to treat a number of ailments, and I tried to avoid each and every one those remedies. At least with a boil, the cod liver oil went on the outside, not down the throat. To make your own "fishy" boil cure, combine a tablespoon of cod liver oil with a tablespoon of honey. Put a handful of the mixture on the boil and bandage it. Make sure you change the bandage at least every eight hours.

The Black-And-Blue Blues:

BRUISES

Bruising occurs when the skin is not broken but underlying tissues are injured. Small blood vessels rupture. This causes localized pain, swelling, and discoloration.

Tea And C

Drink twelve ounces of orange juice a day. Vitamin C strengthens blood vessel walls. Taking a Vitamin C supplement of 500 to1,000 milligrams a day will also work wonders for repeated bruising.

Severe bruises involving broken blood vessels and skin discoloration respond well to ledum. Take this herb as a tea or apply it to the affected area.

Fade Away

To reduce swelling and fade black-and-blue marks more quickly, apply an ice pack to a bruise or immerse the affected area in cold water. Do not place ice directly on skin or use water cold enough to cause discomfort. This remedy works by constricting blood vessels and reducing bleeding beneath the skin.

Gently apply witch hazel to the bruised area to speed healing and fade discoloration. Like cold water, witch hazel constricts blood vessels to lessen bleeding. Natural witch hazel may be more effective than commercial preparations. Boil one teaspoon of powdered leaves or twigs in a cup of water. Strain and cool the ointment. Apply it to the bruised area.

Don't Knock It 'Til You Try It

Apply a poultice of grated turnip to a bruise to promote healing. Leave it in place for up to half an hour.

Boil a small amount of comfrey leaves for ten minutes. Let the liquid cool. Soak the bruised area in the mixture or apply it as a poultice.

Carefully apply a salve of parsley and a teaspoon of butter to a bruise. It should soothe the sore area and help fade the black-and-blue mark.

Keep It From Coloring

To prevent a bruised area from discoloring, try any of these three remedies. Right after you bump into the end table or against the car door, head for your kitchen and break out the sugar. With moistened fingers, gently rub sugar across the injured area. The next day, you should wake up without any trace of black or blue.

You can also prevent a bruise by applying a paste made from a couple of tablespoons of arrowroot and a little water. The paste will dry and flake, leaving behind unblemished skin.

When you get a bruise, eat a banana and rub the skin with the inside of the peel. To completely ward off a bruise, tape the peel to the injured area and leave it there overnight. By morning, there should be no bruise to speak of.

Don't-Drink-Me Tea

Try this Italian cure to relieve the pain and swelling of a nasty bruise. Brew a tea from one large tablespoon of oregano and a cup of boiling water. Let it set for ten minutes, then strain it. Wrap the wet oregano in a piece of cloth and apply it to the bruise. Save the liquid to refresh the oregano leaves.

How To Sweeten Up A Bruise

Grandma kept a huge jar of blackstrap molasses in her kitchen, but not with her baking supplies. She kept the molasses in the cupboard with the other ingredients for her home remedies. Whenever I came home black and blue from horsing around at school, she'd dip a piece of brown paper in the molasses. She'd secure it to the bruise with a bandage. When she took the paper off several hours later, the bruise would be almost gone.

Too Close To The Flame:

BURNS

There are three different degrees of burns. First-degree burns, the least serious, only redden. Second-degree burns also blister. Third-degree burns, which are the most serious, destroy skin and underlying muscle. Third-degree burns require immediate medical attention. They can result in serious infection.

When Grandma could get to the store, she'd buy some over-the-counter remedies that helped relieve the pain of burns. Many of these commercial preparations contain active ingredients to deaden pain as well as ingredients to fight infection. Many also contain aloe vera, which is soothing to burned skin.

Sweet Relief

My grandmother sometimes burned herself taking a pie out of the oven. Whenever that happened, she'd put a small piece of thin-rolled pie crust dough on the burn. By the time the dough dried up and fell off, the pain from the burn would be gone.

For a sweet burn cure, apply honey to the affected area to ease pain. Bacteria will not grow on honey, so this treatment promotes healing and prevents infection. Some people feel the honey is more effective if combined with sauerkraut or comfrey root.

Layers of apple butter can help heal a burn. Spread apple butter over the affected area and apply more as each coat dries. Keep this up for a day or two. By then, the burn should be well on its way to healing.

Swell Advice

Place a cold compress on the affected area to reduce swelling and pain. Elevate the burned area to reduce swelling.

Quick Relief

Apply aloe vera to first-degree burns right away. Apply it to second- and third-degree burns after healing begins.

If you're outside and need an immediate treatment for a burn, apply mud to the area to cool the skin.

A burned tongue can really hurt. For a severe problem, wash your mouth with cool water until it starts to feel better. You may also want to try a few drops of vanilla extract to ease the pain.

Hot wax, tar, or melted plastic can cause burns. Use ice water to harden the material before trying to remove it.

Don't Eat Your Vegetables

Apply layers of sliced raw potatoes to the burn. Refresh them every few minutes. The starch in the potatoes will form a protective coating to soothe the skin. You can also use a piece of fresh pumpkin or onion.

Mushrooms and radishes straight from the refrigerator can soothe a burn. Slice a mushroom and put the pieces on your burned skin to promote healing. Puree radishes to make a poultice. Apply it to the burn.

The Carrot Juice Cure

Grandma had an unusual treatment for a burn or a scald. She would immediately soak the affected area in ice water, then bandage it with a dressing dipped in pure carrot juice. She repeated this three or four times a day for about three days.

Grandma's Open-Cupboard Cures

Try the Vinegar and Brown Paper Bag cure for a burn. Soak a piece of a brown bag in white cider vinegar. Placing the paper on the affected area should have a cooling effect and relieve the pain.

Apply baking soda mixed with extra virgin olive oil to a burn. It will promote healing and reduce scarring of first- and second-degree burns.

Vitamin E oil helps skin heal more quickly and prevents scarring and blistering. Apply it liberally several times a day, then bandage the area with sterile gauze. This vitamin's antioxidant properties may help reduce inflammation.

Vanilla extract relieves the pain of a grease burn.

Place a piece of charcoal on a burn and leave it there for at least an hour. The pain will quickly subside. When you remove the charcoal, much of the redness should have disappeared.

Comfort From Within

Once a burn has started to heal, make a strong tea from blackberry leaves. Apply it as a compress two or three times a day to speed healing.

To relieve the discomfort of second- and third-degree burns, increase the low-fat protein in your diet to at least 3,000 to 4,000 calories a day. Drink at least eight to ten glasses of water a day.

Smoothing The Rough Spots:

CORNS AND CALLUSES

Calluses form when the body builds up layers of dead skin to protect tissues that are repeatedly rubbed the wrong way. Corns are the painful result of pressure that forces the body to build up layers of skin.

You're Soaking In It

Give your feet a soothing bath in oatmeal water. Add a little less than two cups of oats to five quarts of boiling water. Boil the liquid down to four quarts, remove it from the heat, and strain it. Save the liquid. Soak your feet for twenty minutes or more.

A good warm soak, in plain water or in water enhanced by a variety of ingredients, will soothe tired feet and reduce the discomfort of corns and calluses. Try adding a little vinegar, iodine, Epsom salt, or baking soda to the water for added effectiveness.

Stop It Before It Starts

Grandma preferred to prevent a problem whenever she could. She didn't have much patience with fancy shoes that didn't fit right and caused foot problems. Comfort, comfort, comfort was her motto. She particularly recommended avoiding high heels and shoes with pointy toes.

Callus And Corn Coverage

Dissolve six crushed aspirin tablets in one tablespoon of water. Apply the powder to the corn or callous. Don't use this remedy if you are allergic to aspirin.

Soak one crumbled piece of bread in one-quarter cup of vinegar. Let it stand for thirty minutes. Apply the

bread to the corn as a poultice and tape it in place. Leave the poultice on overnight. By morning, the corn should come off easily. Repeat the remedy until it does.

Tape a piece of pineapple peel to your corn, with the flesh of the fruit against your skin. Replace the pineapple every day until the corn is gone.

There is nothing nicer than a hot cup of tea. And you can recycle the used tea bag as a remedy for your corns. After your morning tea, secure the tea bag to your corn. Leave it in place for half an hour. Do this every day. The corn will disappear in a week or two.

Getting Ready For Bed
Before going to bed at night, rub some vitamin E oil into a corn or callus. Massage the area for a couple of minutes. Let your feet air-dry for a few minutes before putting on socks and turning in. After a couple of treatments, a corn should fall off and a callus should soften.

Secure a small piece of lemon to the corn, pulling on socks to keep it in place overnight. Keep doing this until the corn is gone.

Soak an onion in some white vinegar. Before going to bed, tape a piece of the onion onto the corn. By morning, you should be able to remove the corn. If it proves to be stubborn, repeat the process.
If a corn or callus is really bothering you, apply lemon juice or vinegar as a poultice and leave it on overnight. It will help soften the spot so you can remove the dead skin.

Grandpa's Pampered Feet
Hardworking folks like my grandmother know the importance of taking care of their feet. When Grandpa

came home complaining about his "aching dogs," Grandma would just shake her head and reach for the basin. Before Grandpa could change out of his work clothes, Grandma would have his feet soaking in castor oil. Then she would use an emery board or pumice stone to remove the dead skin. Although he complained and moaned the whole time, we knew Grandpa loved all the pampering.

Farewell To Flakes:

DANDRUFF

Dandruff is due to malfunctioning scalp glands that cause drying and scaling of the skin. Itching and burning may occur in serious cases, and a physician should be consulted before any treatment at home.

In some cases, exposure to sunlight will help. Also try eating one serving of yogurt a day for a week.

Nothing Flaky About This Cure

Grandmother's favorite method of getting rid of dandruff was her Special Scalp Massage. Mix one cup of apple cider vinegar in one cup of water. Add ten mint leaves. Boil this mixture for five minutes, then allow it to stand at room temperature for twelve hours. Strain the liquid and massage it into the scalp twice each day for seven days. There is no need to rinse: The mixture will evaporate and will not leave an odor.

Wash Those Flakes Right Out Of Your Hair

A shampoo of the herb bay laurel eliminates dandruff. Prepare the solution with one quart of boiling water and three to four teaspoons of crushed bay laurel leaves. Allow it to steep for thirty minutes, strain, and let it stand in the refrigerator for one hour. After you wash your hair with your normal shampoo, massage some of the tea into your scalp. Repeat the treatment a second time. This time, let the tea stay on your scalp for one hour before rinsing. For best results, this herbal shampoo must be used regularly.

A traditional Arab remedy for dandruff recommends washing the hair with a mixture of one cup of beet juice, two cups of water, and one teaspoon of salt. If you've ever dripped beet juice on your clothes, you

Home Remedies

know that it acts as a dye. So if you have light-colored hair, don't use this remedy. Unless you fancy something in a light pink.

Try a lemon rinse to banish dandruff. Apply the juice of half a large lemon to your hair, wash your hair with your regular shampoo, and rinse. Mix the other half of the juice with two cups of water. Apply it to your hair and rinse again. Use this lemony rinse every other day until you are without flakes.

Shampoo your hair as you normally would and rinse with chive tea. To make the brew, steep a tablespoon of chives in a cup of boiling water for twenty minutes. Used once a week, this treatment should solve your dandruff problem.

Thyme For A Cure

Grandma would brew a batch of thyme rinse to treat dandruff. Using two cups of water, boil four tablespoons of dried thyme for ten minutes. Strain and cool the liquid. Use half of the mixture to rinse damp hair, making sure it gets to the scalp. Keep the other half for another time.

A derivative of thyme oil is an active ingredient in Listerine. If you'd rather go to the drug store than the health food store, massage Listerine into your wet scalp with a cotton ball. Wait an hour or so before washing your hair. Repeating this several times a week for a couple of weeks should clear up the dandruff.

A Flowery Solution

Grandma recommended washing your hair with a mixture of ginger and chamomile flowers- an ounce of each-to cure dandruff. She'd tie the herbs up in a handkerchief and boil it for ten minutes in a gallon of water. She'd let it cool and store it in a tightly sealed bottle. Grandpa had problems with dandruff from time to time. So she'd have him wash his hair and rinse with a handful of her Ginger-Chamomile Brew. She'd tell him not to rinse it out. Before long, the flakes would be gone.

If Grandma didn't have time to whip up her ginger brew, she'd snip a leaf off her trusty aloe vera plant for a quick scalp soother. She'd squeeze out the gel and rub it into Grandpa's hair and scalp. Then she'd wrap his head in a towel. The next morning, Grandpa would wash his hair without shampoo, letting the aloe vera go to work. Grandpa's dandruff would soon be history.

Here's The Rub

Grandma always recommended that we massage the scalp to keep the skin healthy. She often turned to the items on her kitchen shelf to prepare home remedies. For dandruff: Wash your hair, massage in a little warm olive oil, wrap your head with a towel, and leave it on overnight. In the morning, brush your hair to loosen dandruff flakes. Rinse out the oil. One of the causes of dandruff is a dry scalp, and an occasional warm oil treatment will remedy that in a jiffy. You don't want to overdo it, though: Too much oil can make the problem worse.

One way to relieve your dry scalp without making your hair oily is to use this massage and soak method. Warm enough peanut oil to massage into your entire scalp. After applying the oil, rinse with lemon juice. Let both ingredients work for fifteen minutes before shampooing with baby shampoo. You can use corn oil in much the same way.

Flaky, Scaly, Itchy: Dermatitis

Dermatitis is an allergic reaction that causes flaking, scaling, and itchy skin. Metals are frequently the cause, but creams, ointments, and certain plants can also be responsible. Dermatitis tends to spread and can become a serious problem.

Combine the herb goldenseal and vitamin E with a small amount of honey to add consistency. Leave the mixture on the affected area for twenty to thirty minutes. Use it at least three times a day.

How To Be A Smoothie: Dry Skin
NATURE'S HEALING HAND

A traditional Hawaiian remedy for dry skin is kukui nut oil. The pleasant-smelling oil is great for both face and body. It's quickly absorbed and doesn't leave a heavy, greasy feeling.

For dry skin care, try cleaning your face with whole milk. Add one teaspoon of castor oil to three tablespoons of warm milk. Shake well to mix and apply it to your face with a cotton ball. This milk-and-oil mixture is terrific for removing makeup and dirt.

A chamomile-and-lavender preparation can alleviate dry skin.

Over-The-Counter Curatives

For chronic dry skin, try Eucerin. This over-the-counter product contains mineral oil and lanolin, ingredients that help your skin retain moisture.

The farm hands at Grandma's stumbled onto a great treatment for dry skin: Bag Balm, a product that helps soothe a mother cow who is nursing. Bag Balm is especially good for stubborn, dry skin on the bottom of the feet. Apply it thoroughly before bedtime and put on socks to keep it from staining the sheets. You can also use Vaseline on the tough skin of elbows, knees, and feet. Take a bath or shower before bed, then apply the jelly.

Petroleum jelly is also an effective facial moisturizer. Glob some onto your fingertips and rub it on your face and neck. Keep adding water to thin the layer of jelly on your face until it no longer feels greasy.

Nutrition Solution
Sulfur tends to keep the skin smooth and youthful in appearance. Sulfur is found in onions, garlic, asparagus, and eggs.

Another Reason To Quit
Smoking dries skin and causes premature wrinkling around the mouth and eyes.

Pamper Your Face Fresh:
FACIAL MASKS

Facials are a wonderful way to keep skin healthy and beautiful. It's best to apply facials in the evening, when your skin will be free of makeup for several hours. Facial masks are most effective after a shower or bath, when your face has been gently steamed and the pores are open. Always start with a clean face and neck and apply the mixtures with an upward, circular motion.

The Banana Mask
This is an excellent mask for dry skin. It's also recommended to reduce or prevent fine lines and wrinkles. Mash a ripe banana and add a drop or two of peanut oil. Spread it on your face and neck and leave it on for about half an hour. Then rinse your skin with lukewarm water. You may apply this mask every day or every other day to promote softer skin.

The Cocoa Powder Mask
Cocoa powder is a popular baking ingredient. It also makes one of the best masks for dry skin. Mix two cups of cocoa powder, two tablespoons of dairy cream, and one to two tablespoons of extra virgin olive oil. You may have to experiment with the consistency and the proportions of the ingredients until you have a thick paste that won't drip once applied. The olive oil will prevent the mixture from drying out prematurely. The mixture is approximately twenty-five to thirty percent linoleic acid. This is the ingredient that will do the job. This inexpensive preparation was the reason Grandma's never had the money to purchase all those fancy skin preparations, but her skin always looked great.

The Eggplant Yogurt Mask
This is a fine mask for oily skin. Combine one quarter of a small eggplant (with its skin intact) and one cup of plain yogurt in a blender. Spread the mixture over your face, being careful to avoid the delicate skin around your eyes. Leave the mask on for twenty minutes, then rinse with lukewarm water. You might

want to follow this treatment with an astringent or toner. Keep chamomile tea in a spray bottle in your refrigerator and spritz the tea on your face after you rinse off the mask. Or use it any time as a quick skin refresher.

The Egg White Wrinkle Mask

This mask is said to smooth wrinkles associated with age. You can apply it three or four times a week. Mix the white of an egg with some sweet cream. Lightly spread the mask around your eye area and let it set for half an hour to an hour. Rinse with lukewarm water.

The Honey Mask

Apply unheated honey to your face with your fingertips. Spread the honey with an upward, circular motion. After twenty minutes, rinse with lukewarm water. This sticky mask should help rid your complexion of blackheads and blemishes. You'll feel refreshed.

The Honey-And-Cream Mask

This is another mask with a good reputation for smoothing wrinkles. Thoroughly mix one teaspoon of honey with two tablespoons of heavy whipping cream. With your fingertips, gently massage the mixture into the fine lines and wrinkles on your face. Leave the mask on for at least half an hour. You'll feel a gentle tightening. When you've had enough, rinse your face with lukewarm water. I've heard that some people have made this a part of their evening ritual. Many swear by the results. You be the judge.

The Oatmeal Cleansing Mask

In a blender, reduce one cup of uncooked oatmeal to a powder. Mix the powder with the white of one egg, one-half cup of skim milk, and three drops of almond oil. Spread the mask on your face and neck-avoiding the tender area around your eyes. Leave it on for half an hour before rinsing with lukewarm water.

The Oily Oatmeal Mask

Add vegetable oil to make cooked oatmeal easy to spread. Massage the mixture into your face and neck. After half an hour, wash it off with lukewarm water. If used daily, this mask may reduce wrinkles.

The Papaya Mask

You'll need a blender for this one. Peel and puree a ripe papaya. Spread the pureed fruit on your face. After twenty minutes, rinse with lukewarm water. This refreshing mask will remove dead skin cells.

The Too-Much-Sun Mask

This mask is not for sunburns. It's for skin that has endured years of sun abuse-the kind often called leathery. Mix two tablespoons of flour into two tablespoons of raw honey. Add enough milk to make the mixture the consistency of toothpaste. Smooth the paste onto your face and neck with your fingertips, avoiding the delicate area around your eyes. After twenty minutes, rinse your skin with lukewarm water. Pat your skin dry. Follow with a toner and moisturizer.

Soothing Relief:

ITCHING

Rashes, skin irritations, and allergic reactions can cause chronic itching.

A Dab Will Do You

A salve made from chickweed can control itching. Add one and one-half cups of diced chickweed to two cups of extra virgin olive oil heated with five tablespoons of beeswax. Heat the combined ingredients in a 200° oven for two hours. Strain the mixture before the wax solidifies. Pour it, while warm, into a clean jar that can be tightly sealed.

Rubbing freshly sliced carrots on an itchy spot can give you relief. Slices of raw onion will also do the trick.

One way to prevent itchy, dry skin is to moisturize regularly. Especially in the winter months. For best absorption, apply moisturizer after a bath or shower, while your skin is damp.

Taking The "Bite" Out

If you suffer from mosquito bites, you may get welcome relief from witch hazel. Just dab it on the bite and your urge to itch will go away. Witch hazel may also help reduce swelling.

In the summertime, Grandma used to give us ice to rub on our mosquito bites. It always stopped the itching for a while. The swelling went down, too. Taking a cool shower is another way to temporarily relieve itchy skin.

Immerse Yourself In Relief

Among its many uses, baking soda helps relieve the itching associated with chicken pox, insect bites, and other afflictions. Make a paste with baking soda and water and dab it on the bite or itchy spot. You'll find it will soothe the itch and keep you from scratching-an important factor in aiding healing. You may even try pouring baking soda in your bath. If you prefer showers, pour some baking soda into your hands and apply it to your wet skin. Leave it on for a few minutes before rinsing. Don't make the bath or shower water too hot: The hot water will make you feel even itchier.

Salt water will not only help stop itching, it can dry blisters and kill some kinds of fungus. Landlubbers can make a soak by adding two tablespoons of salt (Table salt will do.) to a pint of lukewarm water. Soak for five to ten minutes and repeat as needed.

An oatmeal bath can soothe such skin ailments as allergic reactions, eczema, poison ivy, and chicken pox. Pour some oatmeal into netting fine enough to keep the oats inside. Even a sock or old pantyhose will do. Place it in the bathtub (like a tea bag) while the water is running. Enjoy a good long soak. Make sure the bath water is warm, not hot. One bath might do the trick, but repeat the process for a few days if necessary. You may also try a finely ground oat product called colloidal oatmeal. You can find one or more varieties at your local pharmacy. Take colloidal oatmeal baths once or twice a day.

Snacking Solutions

Here's a snack that can help to relieve itching: Mix a few teaspoons of ground flaxseed with dried fruit and nuts. Ground flaxseed or flaxseed oil can relieve the itch of psoriasis. If you are taking anticlotting agents or aspirin, check with your doctor before consuming flaxseed or flaxseed oil.

Changing your diet may alleviate itching. Make sure to eat plenty of leafy green vegetables, fish, dried fruit, and other foods rich in iron. Taking iron supplements can be beneficial, too. Ask your doctor about the recommended dosage.

In Need Of A Manicure:
NAIL PROBLEMS

Nails can become fragile, dry, ridged, or brittle. They can develop white bands.

An Ounce Of Prevention

My grandmother wore rubber gloves when she did the dishes, but this practice seems to have gone out of fashion. You can still buy these gloves, and they're terrific for protecting your hands and nails from harsh detergents and bleach. If you find you are sensitive to rubber gloves, don't throw them out. Simply wear vinyl gloves under the rubber ones, and you should be fine.

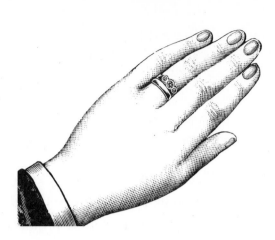

Nail Nutrients

Approximately one cup of carrot juice a day should relieve dryness and brittleness. Increase your intake of whole grains to strengthen nails and eliminate ridges. Hangnails and white bands are usually signs of a low-protein diet.

If you have a problem with splitting fingernails, eat six raw almonds a day. The almonds are a good source of protein, vitamins, nutrients, and linoleic acid, which helps keep nails healthy. You'll have to keep this up for a while before you see results.

Smoothing The Rough Edges

While you're making your hands look lovely with moisturizers, don't neglect your nails. Hand creams often improve hard, brittle nails. Massaging in a little petroleum jelly can strengthen nails that break easily. But be careful: Too much moisturizing cream will make soft nails too soft.

If you browse the shampoo aisle of your local store, you may notice a few brands that claim to have been developed by horse trainers. Well, horse trainers have also developed a product that's terrific for hands and nails. Hoof Saver is a cream vets and animal trainers use on horses. Great for maintaining strong, hard nails, it's inexpensive and contains many of the ingredients found in the hand creams people use. Look for Hoof Saver in feed stores.

You're Soaking In It

Here's a remedy the character Madge would love (If you remember Madge, you're dating yourself). Steep one tablespoon of horsetail in a cup of boiling water. Once the horsetail cools a bit, strain it. Then soak your fingers in it. If you do this every day, you'll see improvement in about a month.

Dulling The Shine:

OILY SKIN

Squeaky Clean

A liquid made from lemon grass and licorice root can benefit oily skin.

Here's a good cleanser for oily skin you can mix up at home. Mix one tablespoon of powdered milk in water until the water takes on a milky consistency. Apply the mixture with a cotton ball, gently rubbing it into your face and neck. While your skin is still moist, wipe off the makeup and dirt with a tissue. Pat dry.

Toning Up

If you don't mind smelling like a pickle, this toner is terrific for restoring the pH balance of your skin. Mix one tablespoon of boiled water with one tablespoon of apple cider vinegar. As soon as the liquid cools to a comfortable temperature, dip a cotton ball in it and apply it to your face. Your skin will feel smooth and tight. But the fumes from the vinegar may make your eyes a little teary.

Cucumbers have long been used as a beauty aid. Here's a cucumber toner you can make yourself: Squeeze two cucumbers in a juice extractor and bring the liquid to a boil. Skim off any froth. Place the liquid in a bottle or jar and keep it in the refrigerator. You can use this toner twice a day, after you've washed your face. Mix one teaspoon of the cucumber juice with two teaspoons of water. Gently apply it to your face and neck. Let your skin dry before using a moisturizer.

From The Inside Out

If you have oily skin, try drinking yarrow tea each day. Yarrow is a natural astringent that can reduce the oils in your skin. Use one tablespoon of dried yarrow to one cup of boiling water. Let it steep for about ten minutes. Strain the tea before drinking.

The Nasty Side Of Nature:

POISON IVY AND POISON OAK

When bare skin of susceptible individuals comes into contact with the sap of poison ivy or poison oak, it reddens, blisters, swells, and develops a rash. Scratching makes the problem worse and may spread it to other parts of the body. Animals that come into contact with the plants can spread the sap to humans.

Cleaning Up

To relieve the rash, wash the affected area with alcohol immediately after contact. Combine the juice of two limes with one quart of water mixed with equal parts of white oak bark tea. This solution should be applied with a wet cloth or bandage that is changed when it dries. This treatment should reduce the severity of the attack and hasten healing.

Soap is a wonderful remedy for taking care of poison ivy or poison oak-before the rash appears. After contact with the plants, be sure to scrub the exposed area with soap to wash off the resin. Getting the resin off your skin will keep you from breaking out in a rash. Thoroughly washing the area within one to two hours of exposure should prevent a problem. Any kind of soap should work fine, but some people swear by Fels-Naptha. I recommend scrubbing with this soap before going into an area where the plants are known to be, then scrubbing again after you leave the area.

Some people find that household bleach helps remove the resin of poison ivy or poison oak. Wash the area well with a soap like Fels-Naptha. Then soak a cotton ball in a half-water, half-bleach mixture and dab it on the area. If you do this three times the day you first notice blisters, you should see a definite improvement. Bleach can irritate skin, so test a small area before you proceed.

Herb Help

The herb goldenseal has been reported to relieve symptoms in just a few hours and even cure the rash in a day. Make a paste or purchase the liquid form for fastest results.

Here's a hot idea that must be used cold: In summertime, when poison ivy poses the biggest problem, make a batch of mugwort tea. Keep it in a jar or bottle in the refrigerator until needed. As soon as you realize you've come into contact with poison ivy, wash your skin with the refrigerated tea. If applied soon enough after the contact, mugwort tea can rid your skin of the rash-causing oil. But only if the tea is cold. Hot tea will open your pores and make the rash worse.

Friendly Foods

If poison ivy or poison oak is driving you bananas, this is the perfect cure for you. Peel a banana and set the fruit aside. You'll need only the peel for this remedy. Rub the inside of the peel on your rash every hour for one whole day. Use a new banana peel each time. If you're lucky, someone you know will have a banana bread recipe as good as Grandma's.

Placing tofu directly on a poison ivy rash can stop the itching and cool and soothe the skin. Hold the tofu in place with gauze pads.

Oatmeal is a great remedy for all kinds of itchy skin ailments. It's especially good on poison ivy and poison oak. Fill some fine netting (or a sock or old pantyhose) with oatmeal and put it in a bathtub that's filling with warm water. Hot water will make the rash worse. Have a good long soak. For even more itch control, leave the oatmeal residue on for a little while before rinsing. To calm patches of poison ivy or poison oak, make a paste out of oatmeal and tepid water. Leave it on the rash until the itching subsides.

Getting Muddy

If you're camping or away from home, try putting fresh mud on the poison ivy or poison oak. The mud will help draw out the infection.

Fire With Fire

When I was young, it seemed I was always getting into trouble-and I always paid for it. I used to love to play in the woods with my friends. More often than not, though, we'd run into some poison ivy or poison oak and one of us would soon be covered with an itchy red rash. Grandma had shown me what the offending plants looked like, but defensive botany didn't seem important to a kid who just wanted to have fun.

Grandmother's remedy for the rash these harmful plants cause was jewelweed. Also known as impatiens or touch-me-nots, this plant often grows near poison ivy and poison oak. Grandma would boil a few of the plants in a gallon of water and strain the plant matter out. She always kept a jar of it handy in the summer. And she always made enough for me and my friends.

Getting Past The Rough Patches: Psoriasis

This skin disorder is characterized by patches of silvery scales or reddish areas on knees, elbows, or at the waist. It may be triggered by stressful events or extreme nervousness. It may be hereditary.

Taking cod liver oil in capsule form one or two times a day has had excellent effects on alleviating psoriasis and relieving its symptoms. Giving up caffeine also has a positive effect.

From The Herb Garden

Birch bark has been used on eczema, psoriasis, and numerous other skin problems throughout the years. Make a tea by boiling about three tablespoons of the powdered bark in one quart of water. Simmer it for ten minutes and let if stand for one hour. Strain the mixture well and pour it on a cloth. Leave the cloth on the affected area for at least one to two hours.

Apply a poultice of yellow dock, chaparral, and goldenseal to soothe the affected area and improve healing time.

Turning Red:
RASH

Baby's Delicate Skin

Babies get rashes all the time. Curing them is child's play. Since diaper rash is caused by too much wetness, a common-sense solution is letting the baby's skin air-dry before diapering. Both fresh air and sunlight are good for skin. A little airing can help heal or prevent diaper rash.

If you don't have time for a good air-drying, use your blow dryer. Make sure you keep the heat low and don't get the dryer too close to your child. A baby's skin is sensitive, and you don't want to replace a rash with a burn.

A good diaper can help prevent diaper rash. If you use disposables, use the super-absorbent varieties that keep moisture away from the skin. If you prefer cloth diapers, try double-diapering and eliminating the rubber pants.

Healing The Hurt

One of Grandma's sure-fire remedies for baby rash was to place a thin coating of egg whites on the affected area. The egg whites coat and protect the area and promote healing.

Grandma kept cornstarch in her kitchen cupboard. She would rub a little on a baby's bottom to dry skin and help soothe diaper rash. You can always use baby powder, but never use talcum.

A variety of over-the-counter ointments can help protect your child's delicate skin. Many people swear by Desitin Ointment. Others prefer petroleum jelly or A and D Ointment. Yeast can infect a diaper rash. If this is the case with your child, try an over-the-counter antifungal treatment such as Gyne-Lotrimin, which is normally used for vaginal infections. Please contact your pediatrician before using any over the counter products.

Don't Do Anything Rash

For a sweet remedy, try gently rubbing honey on the rash. Honey has a smooth, creamy texture and its antibacterial properties are well known.

Although this remedy won't cure the problem, an application of apple cider may be very soothing. It can also alleviate the sting of sunburn.

Try putting cornstarch on your rash. It will keep the rash free of moisture and can alleviate itching. One warning: You should not use cornstarch if you are prone to yeast infections.

Ease prickly heat and other such rashes by rubbing the sensitive area with the inside of a watermelon rind.

Soaking It In

Oatmeal is a terrific remedy for skin rashes. Put oats in a fine netting (Try a sock or an old pair of pantyhose.) and place it in a warm bath. Soak in the tub for at least half an hour. Make sure the water is not hot: Hot water can make rashes feel worse. An alternative to oatmeal is finely ground oats called colloidal oatmeal. You can find different brands of colloidal oatmeal at your pharmacy or in the bath section of your sundry store. Sprinkle the colloidal oatmeal in a tub filling with warm water. Soak for at least twenty minutes, then carefully pat your skin dry. A colloidal oatmeal bath twice a day should relieve the discomfort of many common skin rashes.

Another bath additive you can try is dry mustard. Put a few tablespoons in a warm bath to soothe itching and promote healing. My grandmother used to suggest this remedy to our neighbor, whose husband got prickly heat. Like the oatmeal bath, this bath will soothe itching and keep you from scratching. That's an important part of the healing process.

Don't Overreact

If you are prone to rashes on your hands, be wary of harsh detergents and dishwashing liquids that can cause allergic reactions. Try switching to a non-allergenic brand for a few weeks. If your rash goes away, your old detergent was probably the culprit. To make sure, try the old detergent again. If the rash comes back, you have definitely found the cause of your discomfort. Some people with especially sensitive skin also get rashes from rubber gloves. If you suspect this is the case, protect your hands by wearing vinyl gloves under your rubber gloves.

Ring Around The Rosy:
RINGWORM

Ringworm responds to raw garlic placed over the rash and secured with a bandage.

Overexposed:
SKIN CANCER

Skin cancers have been treated with tea prepared from chaparral. Place the tea in a poultice and apply it for thirty minutes three times a day.

Too Much Of A Good Thing:
SUNBURN

Excessive, prolonged exposure to ultraviolet light can burn bare skin.

Taking The Sting Out
Take the heat out of sunburn by applying apple cider vinegar. Dilute the vinegar in water (Try one part vinegar to two or three parts cool water.) and apply it to the areas that are burned. That hot feeling you get from too much sun should disappear and the stinging sensation will subside. You may even find that applying the vinegar solution will prevent peeling.

Cold clay poultices are very effective. Placed on the affected area with a washcloth, cooled green tea will also have a soothing effect. The poultice should be left on for about thirty minutes every few hours.

Another soothing sunburn remedy is a cold milk compress. Put equal parts of milk and ice in a quart container and add about two tablespoons of salt. Soak a washcloth in the milky mixture and place it on the raw area. Leave the washcloth on for up to fifteen minutes. Repeat this three or four times during the day.
Try spreading yogurt or sour cream on a sunburned face. Leave the mask on for twenty minutes and let it take the heat out of your burn. Rinse your face with lukewarm water.

Buttering Us Up
When one of us kids came home glowing like a firefly from a nasty sunburn, Grandma would grab one of her handy kitchen helpers: butter. She used the freshly churned variety. You may find that a can of evaporated milk will also do the trick. Milk has been known to ease sunburn, but be sure to use whole milk. It's the fat content in the liquid that soothes raw skin.

Don't Forget To Moisturize

Aloe vera gel does wonders for relieving the pain of sunburn and helps moisturize the skin. Many of today's commercial brands of skin care products include aloe vera. If you have an aloe vera plant at home, cut off a leaf, break it open, and spread the gel right on your burn. It's soothing and lubricating and promotes healing. So you'll feel better in no time. If you don't have a plant handy, you can purchase aloe vera gel at your local health food store.

Another soothing solution for sunburns is vitamin E. Cut the capsule open and spread the oil on the tender area. It will ease sunburn pain and lubricate your skin to guard against peeling and blistering.

Grandma's Secret Anti-Wrinkle Lotion

My grandmother's skin always looked great. She had few wrinkles, despite her advanced years. Whenever anyone asked about her complexion, she would say, "Clean living is my secret." One day I saw her preparing a lotion from avocados, and she swore me to secrecy. The oil that was Grandma's secret makes one of the best suntan lotions. Avocado oil will also keep the skin in excellent condition and slow the effects of aging on your complexion.

Rub-A-Dub-Dub

Try taking a baking soda bath to relieve sunburn pain. Sprinkle about a cup of baking soda into lukewarm water and soak for fifteen to twenty minutes. You might want to follow this with one of the topical remedies.

Another bath additive good for sunburn pain is colloidal oatmeal. Look for colloidal oatmeal at you pharmacy or sundry store.

How about a milk bath to take the heat and sting away? Empty a package of powdered non-fat dry milk or a quart of low-fat milk into a tub of warm water. A half-hour soak should soothe sunburn pain.

THE EYES HAVE IT

The delicate skin around the eyes is very susceptible to sunburn. Tea bags are a good remedy for sunburned eyelids. Cool, wet tea bags placed on the eyelids will feel great and promote healing. Tea is also soothing for other sunburned skin. Try brewing a pot of strong tea, letting it cool, and applying it to sunburned legs, arms, backs, etc.

Here's another eye-easing remedy: Prepare a poultice made from grated apples and place it on your eyelids. Then lie back and relax-it helps if you can leave the poultice in place for about an hour.

Another good poultice for sunburned eyelids is made by lightly beating the white of one egg. Place the poultice over your closed eyes and get a good night's sleep. Remove the poultice when you wake up. You should notice improvement.

Frog Prints:
WARTS

These contagious clusters of cauliflower-like growths can appear anywhere on the body. They are usually caused by a virus. To prevent the spread of warts, bandage them and don't pick at them.

Simple Medicine
Take two aspirin. . . Another remedy for warts is aspirin. But you don't swallow it. Instead, dip your hand in warm water and place a damp aspirin tablet on the wart. Bandage the wart or cover it with a gauze pad and tape it in place. Put the aspirin on the wart before going to bed. That one application should do the trick. Your wart should be history in just a few days. This remedy is not recommended for those who are allergic to aspirin.

Applying iodine several times a day can help dissolve a wart. This remedy may take a while. The wart should fall off within a few weeks.

Here is a cure for plantar warts-the warts that appear on the soles of the feet. These warts can spread, so don't pick at them. Rub castor oil on a plantar wart each night before you go to bed. Keep this up until the wart's gone.

Salt is also used as a cure for warts. Moisten some table salt and place it on the wart, then cover it with a bandage. Keep this treatment up until the wart disappears.

Kitchen Cures
One of Grandma's remedies for warts was to strap on some blackstrap molasses. Apply a poultice of the

Home Remedies

molasses to the wart and keep it on as long as you can. She also fed us a tablespoon of blackstrap molasses each day. After about two weeks of the molasses treatment, the wart should drop right off.

Go figure-placing a fresh, crushed fig on the wart for half an hour each day will make the wart disappear. Be sure the fig is very mushy.

Try putting a used tea bag on the wart for fifteen minutes every day. Your wart should be toast in a week and a half.

Here's an egg cure-sort of. Soak your hand in water in which eggs have been hard-boiled. Do this for ten minutes a day until the wart disappears. For some reason, this remedy works specifically for warts that appear on the hands.

Place fresh, crushed garlic directly on the wart. Cover it with a dressing for twenty-four hours. The wart should develop a blister and, eventually, drop off. Castor oil has also been used with varying success.

Meadow-cine

Picking dandelions can have positive healing effects on warts. When you break the dandelion off at the stem, a white, milky substance will appear. Put this on the wart several times a day until the wart goes away. Be careful, though. Dandelions may cause a rash for people with sensitive skin.

Turn Back The Clock:
WRINKLES

The herb cleavers has been used as a facial cleanser and astringent with excellent results. It far outshines most expensive over-the-counter preparations. To prepare a mixture, bring one quart of pure, filtered water to a boil. After removing the water from the heat, add three to four tablespoons of cleavers. Then cover the mixture and allow it to steep for forty-five minutes. Apply the mixture by lightly saturating a small towel and placing it over your face for ten minutes. Do this three or four times a day for four days. The effects will become evident in about two weeks and will remain for three to four weeks.

50

Bed-Ridden
BLUES

Stuck With The Sniffles:
COLDS

Colds are caused by a virus, and their symptoms include various kinds of upper respiratory discomfort. Mucous should be allowed to flow freely, since this is how the body rids itself of infection. The many forms of the cold virus make this infection difficult to fight.

A Few Tips On Prevention
"An ounce of prevention is worth a pound of cure." That was my grandmother's sage advice. Grandma recommended eating certain foods to help ward off colds and flu, and modern science has confirmed the benefits of eating more broccoli, parsley, and apples. The old adage that an apple a day keeps the doctor away may well be true! Grandma also recommended drinking raw sauerkraut juice every day to keep cold germs away. This has the added benefit of keeping you regular.

If someone at work has been coughing on you or one of your children has come down with a cold or the flu, take a cinnamon oil preventative immediately. Add five drops of cinnamon oil to a tablespoon of water. Drink it down and repeat three times a day.

The shiitake mushroom has an important place in traditional Asian medicine. If you feel a cold coming on, add these tasty mushrooms to your favorite dish. Take shiitake mushroom capsules if you prefer.

Tea And Sympathy

Grandma always said that when you've got the sniffles, something warm to drink and few warm words went a long way toward helping the patient recover. Here are a few soothing suggestions:

Several herbal teas have a significant effect on cold symptoms. Goldenseal tea stands out as one of the best. It is known to contain antibiotic properties.

Make a tea with cayenne pepper, which can help prevent a cold or speed relief. Use just a pinch if you're not used to hot food. The capsaicin in the pepper helps loosen mucous.

Try this congestion-curing tea: Steep two teaspoons of dried mullein leaves in one cup of boiling water for ten minutes. You can find this herb in health food stores. It helps soothe sore throats. It also breaks up mucous, easing congestion.

A tea made with slices of fresh ginger root or powdered ginger will help break up mucous and reduce fever. It may also boost the immune system.

Try this very citrus cure that allows you to use your favorite liquor: In a saucepan, combine the juice of one orange, one lemon, and one grapefruit with a tablespoon of honey. Be sure to stir the mixture as you bring it to a boil. Add an ounce or so of brandy or whatever you have on hand. Enjoy!

Don't Knock Chicken Soup

Chicken soup works wonders. Heating the soup releases a chemical that promotes nasal drainage and relieves other symptoms. Other foods that may help are garlic, onions, and hot peppers.

Drink a broth made from potato peels one or two times a day. The peels should be approximately one-half inch thick and should include the skin. Clean the skin thoroughly with a good organic cleanser and a vegetable brush. Boil the peels for twenty to thirty minutes with two stalks of celery. Drink the broth after it cools.

Don't Forget To Flush

Drinking a lot of water can help flush toxins and germs out of the body. You can also re-hydrate with unsweetened fruit juices and various kinds of herbal teas, including the ones mentioned here.

Rub It In And Breathe Deeply

Rub oil of eucalyptus into your chest two or three times a day. Inhaling this oil clears up congestion and opens airways. You can also place seven or eight drops of eucalyptus oil in hot bath water or six or seven drops in a cup of boiling water. Place a towel over your head and inhale the vapors.

If you have a chest cold, try rubbing your chest with a salve made from the white of one raw egg and four teaspoons of mustard. Place a hot compress on top of the mixture and reapply four or five times as the compresses get cold. After the last compress cools, wash off the salve and turn in for the night. Make sure you don't sleep in a draft. You should sleep more soundly that night and feel a lot less congested in the morning.

To clear chest congestion, heat a cup of white wine and inhale the vapors.

Grandma's Cold Concoctions

Place one tablespoon of the powder of slippery elm bark in one-half cup of boiling water. Add one-quarter cup of pure honey and the juice of half a lemon. Pour the mixture into a jar and shake. Swallow one to two teaspoons every three hours.

My grandmother used the sunflower seeds she harvested from her garden to make a great cure for our family's colds. Follow her recipe by boiling one-half cup of sunflower seeds in five quarts of water, reducing the liquid by a little more than half. Add one-quarter cup of honey and three-quarters of a cup of gin. My grandmother instructed the cold-sufferer to take two teaspoons of the mixture at each meal. Honey acts as an expectorant, and this remedy works especially well on a cold accompanied by a cough and chest congestion.

Grandma's Hot Dog Helper

Grandma used to say a good old-fashioned mustard plaster was the best way to lick a cold. She claimed mustard plasters could relieve almost any cold symptom. They are still used in many rural areas of the United States and Canada. To make a plaster, mash the leaves and stems of a fresh mustard plant into a thick pulp. Cover the chest with a thin layer of Vaseline. Then apply the plaster. Cover it with a cloth or towel, taping it down. It is essential to use Vaseline to protect the skin against blisters and any other adverse effects of the mustard. For the best results, the plaster should be left on overnight. Whenever Grandma used a mustard plaster, she made sure to tuck us in real tight. By placing pillows on either side of us, she made sure we didn't move around too much during the night. We stayed snug as bugs in a rug.

Smelly Solutions

Garlic appears to contain a substance that fights infections of all kinds: bacteria, viruses, and fungus. Garlic can also help ward off or cure a cold. Fresh garlic is most effective, but you can also take dried garlic in capsules or tablets.

Onions, like garlic, have traditionally been used to fight colds. If you're not an onion fan, look for onion preparations at your health food store.

Keep On Moving

When you come down with a cold, you feel sluggish. Your natural inclination is to rest. Grandma couldn't have disagreed more. She recommended getting out for a short walk- nothing too strenuous, just enough to get the blood going-bundling up if it was cold outside. In fact, it appears that exercise may stimulate the body's natural infection-fighting abilities.

A "Hard" Cure for Your Cold

Grandpa kept a flask of whiskey in the pie safe in the hallway. "Just for medicinal purposes," he always assured us. In fact, several traditional remedies for the common cold involve alcohol. Brew a mug of very strong black tea. Add one tablespoon of honey, one tablespoon of cognac, one-quarter teaspoon of cinnamon, and one teaspoon of butter. The tea should be as hot as you can stand. You should wake up the next morning with soggy sheets, having sweat out the cold during the night.

If you prefer rum to cognac, try this remedy that combines the juice of one lemon and three teaspoons of honey with four teaspoons of rum. Before you go to bed, add the mixture to a glass of hot water and drink it down. You should feel much better in the morning.

Hot And Cold Cures

Just before turning in for the night, soak in a hot tub with ginger powder added to the water. Stay in the bath for about fifteen minutes to get the full benefit. To keep from getting chilled, dry off well afterward and dress warmly for bed. The ginger should help you sweat and rid your system of toxins. If the ginger does its job, you may have to change into fresh, dry pajamas during the night. By morning, you should feel noticeably better.

In traditional Chinese medicine, acupressure points are stimulated to relieve cold symptoms and cure the infection. Put a cube of ice on the bottom of each big toe. Leave the cubes in place until they melt. Do this three times a day until the cold clears up.

Soothing The Tickle:
COUGHS

Soothing Solutions

Grandma's remedy for the cough associated with the common cold was hot tea with lemon and honey. The honey coats the throat and relieves the cough for a few hours. Another of Grandma's remedies was elderberry juice. It can calm the cough reflex for a long period of time. Fresh elderberries should be placed in a juicer with a slice of fresh lemon. Every three hours, drink four to six ounces of the juice sweetened with one-half teaspoon of honey or blackstrap molasses.

Something Everyone Can Inhale

Put eucalyptus oil in a vaporizer and inhale the fumes.

Add ginger to very warm bath water. After your bath, wrap yourself in a terrycloth towel. The ginger will make you sweat and loosen the mucous.

Peppermint, in its many forms, can be great for coughs. Put a drop of peppermint oil on your tongue to calm a coughing fit. Add a few drops of the oil to a cup of boiling water and inhale the vapors to relieve congestion. Make a tea of fresh peppermint leaves and drink it with a little honey. You might even try a piece of peppermint candy. Grandma always had some in her purse, just in case.

If your congestion and cough keep you awake at night, take a warm bath before retiring. Add a couple of drops of pine oil to the water. The relaxing vapors should open your bronchial passages and help you breathe more easily while you sleep.

Break It Up

Some hot, spicy foods seem to help reduce a cough's severity and break up the mucous and congestion usually associated with it. Try cayenne capsules, hot Chinese mustard, and red horseradish. Apply hot onion packs to the chest and back at least three times a day. The onions should be sliced, steamed, and placed between soft cloths. Place a heating pad over the onion pack.

Control The Urge

Herbal cough drops help control the cough reflex. There are a number of effective herbs, such as eucalyptus and horehound.

For fast cough relief, make a tea of slippery elm. Your health food store sells lozenges whose active ingredient is slippery elm.

Throaty Solutions

A bay leaf poultice works wonders to relieve chest congestion and coughing. Add twenty bay leaves to a cup of boiling water. Cover it and let it stand for fifteen minutes. Wrap the warm, moist leaves in a cloth. Place the cloth on your chest and cover it with a towel to retain heat. Save the liquid to refresh the bay leaves. After an hour, reheat the liquid before soaking the leaves in it.

Gargle with a mixture of warm water and three tablespoons of dark corn syrup. This will relieve a hacking cough.

Breakfast Breakthroughs

The fat in dairy products can coat the throat and soothe a dry cough. Warm a cup of milk (not skim) and add two teaspoons of sweet butter. Drink two to three cups of this a day until the cough is gone. Milk contributes to mucous production, so you shouldn't try this remedy if you're coughing up phlegm or feel congested.

Certain ingredients in oatmeal can ease coughing. Make thick oatmeal by following the package directions but reducing the water by one-quarter cup. Flavor with honey to taste. Don't add milk, for the reasons already noted. Eat one cup of warm oatmeal four times a day or whenever the cough flares up.

A Honey Of A Cough Remedy

Grandma had a few "sweet" cures for a cough. All of them involved honey. In the first, she combined six medium-sized onions, coarsely chopped, with one-half cup of honey in the top of a double boiler. She simmered the mixture for two hours, then stored it in a tightly sealed jar. She'd warm it up and give the cough-sufferer a teaspoon every two to three hours. She made her other "sweet" cough cure from one teaspoon of horseradish and two teaspoons of honey. She used the same dosage as her other honey remedy-one teaspoon every few hours.

Here's a tasty cough remedy you'll enjoy even when you're well. Combine the juice of a large lemon, two tablespoons of honey, three cloves, half a cinnamon stick, and enough hot water to top off a mug. The steam will ease your congestion, and the lemony warmth will soothe your throat. Drink a mug every three hours to relieve an irritating cough.

Use root vegetables and something sweet to quiet a persistent cough. Cut the middle out of a rutabaga or yellow onion and fill the cavity with brown sugar or honey. Let it stand overnight and drink the juice in the morning. You can also cut a hole in a beet, add brown sugar or honey, and bake the vegetable until it's soft. It's a tasty way to knock out a cough. A turnip will work, too.

Barley Makes It Better

Sometimes I dream about my grandmother's beef barley soup. That's how good it was. Although I have the recipe, it never tastes quite the same when I make it. Grandma was simply magic in the kitchen. When someone in the family had been hacking for a few days, she'd make a big pot of her soup and whip up a cough remedy while she was at it. She'd add the juice of one lemon to a cup of cooked barley and liquefy it. She'd give the cougher a cup of her barley brew to drink slowly, every four hours.

Liquor Is Quicker

Mulled wine was the beverage of choice in merry old England, especially around the holidays. Add a cinnamon stick, three cloves, a tablespoon of honey, and a few pieces of lemon peel to three cups of dry red wine. Make sure you stir while heating it and try not to splash onto countertops: Red wine can stain. Enjoy up to three cups a day. It should help relieve your coughing. But even if it doesn't, you'll feel much happier.

Just one sip of whiskey should relax the cough reflex. Many commercial cough syrups contain alcohol.

Homemade Cough Syrups

Try these folksy recipes for cough syrup: Combine the juice of one lemon, one-half cup of olive oil, and one cup of honey. Heat the mixture for five minutes. Remove it from the heat and stir for several minutes. Take one teaspoon every two hours. Or mix one-half cup of water with one-half cup of apple cider vinegar. Add one teaspoon of cayenne pepper and enough honey to sweeten to your individual taste. Take a tablespoon at bedtime and any time you have a severe coughing fit.

For a dry cough, boil three unpeeled potatoes. Retain the warm water and sweeten it with honey. Take a tablespoon of it whenever you feel a coughing fit coming on.

Cut off a small piece of fresh ginger root. Wash and chew it, swallowing the juice. This should soothe your throat and ease your cough. Ginger root is a little pungent for some people's taste. If it's too strong for you, try one of the other remedies.

Boiled Bean Cough Cure

It doesn't seem that eating mashed kidney beans should help relieve a cough. But Grandma relied on her

Boiled Bean Cure for the worst of the worst-those deep, persistent coughs that nothing seems to help. Soak the kidney beans overnight to soften. In the morning, drain off the water and tie the beans in plastic wrap or a tea towel. Beat the beans with a saucepan, bowl, or whatever is handy. Boil the bruised beans in two cups of water with three cloves of minced garlic for about two hours, until they are soft. Watch the level of liquid and add more water if the beans get too dry. Whenever you have a coughing fit, eat a tablespoon of the beans.

Cure By The Cupful

A speedy cure for a bad cough is a warm cup of dill tea. Make the brew from one teaspoon of dill and a cup of boiled water. Let it stand for seven minutes before straining it. If you don't like the taste, sweeten it with a teaspoon or two of honey. Drink three cups throughout the day. If the cough isn't gone, repeat the treatment the next day. But you probably won't have to.

If you've had a cough so long it feels like you were born with it and you think you may have pulled a muscle in your back from the endless hacking, it's time for fenugreek. On the first day, drink a cup of tea made from this powerful herb every hour or so. The next day, reduce the dosage to four cups spaced evenly throughout the day. You should be able to feel the chest congestion breaking up, and the cough should soon fade away. Since fenugreek is such strong medicine, turn to this remedy only when the others have failed and your cough is very persistent.

Licorice root has long been a staple in traditional healing. It is especially effective in treating upper respiratory ailments, including sore throats, colds, and coughs. Brew a tea from licorice root or look for tea bags at your local health food store.

Grandma's Sunflower Cough Syrup

My grandmother often turned to her garden for her home remedies. Every year, she planted a row of beautiful sunflowers at one end of the garden, next to the peas. At the end of the season, she harvested the seeds and kept them on hand for snacks and cures. To treat a cough, she would whip up her Sunflower Cough Syrup. She'd cook one-half cup of the seeds in five cups of water, boiling it down to about two cups of liquid. She'd strain out the seeds and add about one-half cup of honey. From the pie safe in the hall, she would take the bottle of whiskey or whatever Grandpa had on hand "for medicinal purposes" and add about three-quarters of a cup to her cough syrup. She stirred it up and sealed it tightly in a bottle. She would give the cougher a teaspoon or two four times a day. When you make this at home, you can use any hard liquor you happen to have on hand.

It's Hotter Than Heck In Here:

FEVER

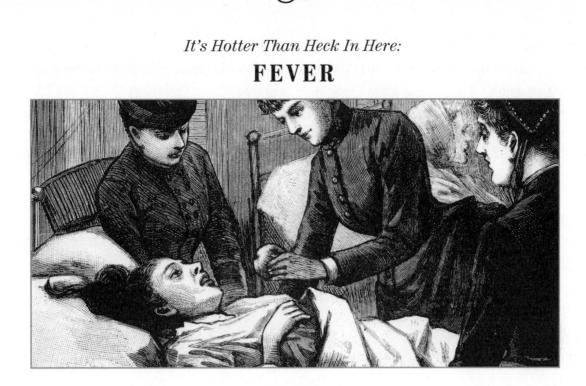

Normal body temperature ranges between 98 and 99° Fahrenheit. If your fever is higher than 102° degrees Fahrenheit, you should consult a physician.

Fevers affect zinc absorption, so avoid supplements containing this mineral. Lobelia extract reduces fevers. Take one-half teaspoon every three to four hours. If stomach discomfort occurs, reduce the dose to one-quarter teaspoon.

Cool It

Fevers respond well to rubbing alcohol dabbed on the feet, palms, and wrists. This increases heat evaporation through the skin and cools the entire body.

Evaporation helps cool the blood. If you're running a fever, try taking a cool bath or shower, splashing your face with cool water, or applying a cold compress to your forehead or wrists.

Out Of The Frying Pan

Heat can also reduce a fever by inducing a therapeutic sweat. Take a hot bath or lie in bed under lots of warm quilts. Once you start perspiring, come out from under the blankets and let your sweat evaporate. This will help cool the blood. Don't work out to cause sweating. And be sure to drink plenty of liquids.

Teas, in many varieties, have long been used to reduce fevers. The warmth will help induce a sweat. Brew a cup of black tea and add some sugar or honey. Let the tea cool for a minute, and slip in an ice cube. Sip it slowly while resting in bed. Take a second cup if needed.

Grape Idea

Try eating grapes throughout the day to relieve a fever. You can also drink pure, unsweetened grape juice. It's best when diluted and should always be at room temperature.

Put It On

For a homespun fever remedy, soak a folded piece of brown paper bag in white vinegar. Place it on the forehead.

Fry some onions and put them in a bag or pillowcase. Place it on the chest, layered between towels. Cover the top towel with a heating pad. This should cause sweating, which will help break the fever. If you put onion slices in your socks before bedtime, the fever should be gone in the morning.

Drink It Up

Lemon balm has proven an effective fever remedy for Grandma and many other home healers. Steep leaves in boiling water to make a tea, and add lemon and honey. Two or three cups should break a fever.

Grandma's "Fishy" Fever-Beater

Grandma swore by cod liver oil. The rest of us swore that it tasted really awful, so she tried to mix it with other things to help it go down more easily. Mix up a batch of Grandma's Fever Beater by combining two to three tablespoons of lemon juice, one-half teaspoon of cod liver oil, and honey to taste. Remember: Cod liver oil is strong-tasting stuff. So go easy on it.

Down For The Count: Flu

This highly contagious viral infection usually affects the respiratory tract. It spreads through the air and tends to mutate. This makes it difficult to cure.

TEA FOR FLU

Yarrow tea has positive effects in reducing the severity of symptoms. Catnip tea enemas reduce fevers.

Try a tea made from echinacea or ginger. Sip it slowly every three to four hours.

A Spoonful Of Relief

The fruit of the gooseberry plant is called alma or amalaki. One alma contains more vitamin C than seven oranges. Take one to two teaspoons of alma a day if you think you have the flu. It should lessen the symptoms and boost the body's immune response.

Take one tablespoon of blue or black elderberries in syrup form three times a day. This syrup is available in most health food stores. In recent years, studies have been conducted in Israel on this remedy.

In One Nostril And Out The Other

In our family, the flu spread like wildfire. Grandma made us use a nasal wash to keep our sinuses free of the virus. To make the wash: Add one-half teaspoon of fennel seed to one cup of water and allow it to simmer for ten minutes. Add one-eighth teaspoon of sea salt and cool the mixture to room temperature. Drain out all the fennel seeds and place the mixture in a neti pot. Lean over the sink and tilt your head to one side. Pour half of the mixture into one nostril: It will drain from the other side. Then pour the balance of the wash into the other nostril.

When It Hurts To Swallow:
SORE THROAT

This ailment is a severe irritation of the mucous membrane at the back of the throat. It may be caused by an environmental irritant or infection.

Here's a note about prevention: During the cold and flu season, it's important to be aware that germs can spread. Make sure to wipe telephones, door handles, and other shared surfaces-even the television remote-with a disinfectant spray. You can also use Lysol Disinfectant Spray on pillowcases and bed linens to keep sick family members from re-infecting themselves.

Grandma's Works-Every-Time Tea

Grandma had a great remedy for sore throats. This tea made from fresh hyssop works wonders. To prepare the tea, place two to three teaspoons of the dried herb in a cup of boiling water. Allow it to steep for ten to twelve minutes. Two to three cups a day should help relieve the problem.

Grandma's Gargles

Whenever I had a sore throat, my grandmother had me gargle with salt water. She would stir about a teaspoon or two of salt water into a glass of lukewarm water. The amounts are not exact. That's because when it came to measurements for cooking and baking, my grandmother's technique relied on sight, not science. She would make me drink a glass of the salty water several times during the day and night until I started feeling better.

Try gargling every hour with a solution of one-half teaspoon of sea salt with a small amount of chlorophyll added. For that annoying sensation of postnasal drip, Grandma would use a vinegar-and-water gargle. She claimed that it reduced the excess mucous in the back of the throat. Add about a tablespoon of apple cider vinegar to a glass of lukewarm distilled water and gargle. Sometimes the vinegar stung my throat. Then Grandma would use the honey-and-lemon remedy instead.

Another good gargle for a sore throat is hydrogen peroxide. Gargling with this solution three times a day should bring relief. I recommend mixing water with a three percent hydrogen peroxide solution.

One way to get rid of laryngitis is an apple cider vinegar one-two punch. Mix two teaspoons of apple cider vinegar in one glass of lukewarm water. Gargle the first mouthful and spit it out, then swallow the next. Repeat this pattern until you've finished the glass. You can repeat this every hour. Many people have found their voices can be heard again after about seven doses. This remedy can also be good for sore throats. You will probably need to repeat this vinegar-gargle swallow for two or three hours before you notice a difference.

Nothing To Sneeze At
This remedy that may sound strange, but give it a try. Add some cayenne pepper to ginger ale. This won't get high marks for flavor, but both the cayenne and the ginger will lubricate and heal the throat.

Sweet And Sour Solutions
Another of Grandmother's sore throat remedies was honey and lemon. Squeeze some lemon juice or reconstituted lemon juice on a tablespoon of honey. Then lean back and let it trickle down the back of your throat. I don't think this went a long way toward healing the sore throat, but it got rid of the persistent scratchy feeling long enough for me to fall asleep. And as far as remedies go, honey and lemon is very easy to take-especially for children.

A tea made from raw honey and lemon juice will soothe the affected area. Honey is the only food that will not grow bacteria. Coating the throat with honey will reduce the level of bacteria growth and speed healing.

Grandma's Garden-Variety Cure
Among the plants in Grandmother's herb garden was one she relied on for the cough and sore throat season: hyssop. She told us how her grandmother had brewed her the soothing tea when she was a little girl. Hyssop makes an excellent tea for quieting the coughing that can irritate a sore throat. Two teaspoons of the dried herb should do the trick. Steep it in boiling water for several minutes. If you have fresh hyssop on hand, steep the herb longer but use the tea more sparingly. Tea, in general, is good for the throat: The heat is soothing, and drinking a lot of liquids is always recommended as a way to keep the throat lubricated. Hot liquids can also help unstuff your nose.

Cures For Suckers
One way to numb a sore throat is to suck on a clove. It will be hot, but hold it in your mouth and let it warm your throat. It will also lubricate your throat and ease dryness. Try doing this before bedtime to ease discomfort and help you fall asleep. Be careful not to swallow the clove: It can upset your stomach.

If sucking on a clove doesn't appeal to you, try zinc lozenges. Many people claim that zinc lozenges will get rid of your cold as well as your sore throat. Try this remedy and decide for yourself. You'll find zinc lozenges in your local health food store.

Tea You Don't Swallow

When you have a sore throat, it is important to get lots of rest and drink lots of non-dairy liquids. And while drinking herbal tea can make you feel much better, here's another way chamomile tea can give you relief: Brew some chamomile tea and let it cool just enough so you can handle the heat. Soak a white towel in the tea, wring it out, and place it on your throat. Once the towel loses its heat, dip it in the tea again. Wring it out and reapply.

Here's a tea you gargle with, but don't swallow: Steep three non-herbal tea bags in a cup of boiling water until the tea is very, very dark. Let the liquid cool slightly and gargle. Remember: Don't swallow. Repeat this every hour until you begin to feel better.

Put The Hoarse Out To Pasture

Try this remedy for hoarseness. Boil one-half cup of anise seed in one cup of water for fifty minutes. Strain the anise seed. While the liquid is still hot, add one-quarter cup of raw honey and one tablespoon of cognac. Take one tablespoon every half hour.

Grandma's Vampire Vapors

Here's a remedy that is wonderful for the throat but not so appealing to the nose: garlic. Grandma knew that garlic had a lot of wonderful properties. So whenever she felt a tickle on the creep, she would reach for the garlic. She said it cleared her sinuses and soothed her throat. Grandma would either put a garlic clove in her mouth or rub garlic oil on her neck. Neither of these remedies is recommended if you're expecting company, but Grandma swore her smelly solution did the trick.

See No Evil,
HEAR NO EVIL, SMELL NO EVIL

Clear The Canal:
EAR INFECTION

Ear infections increase pressure in the outer or middle ear. The canal becomes inflamed and swelling occurs. This may cause a temporary loss of hearing in the affected ear. These infections are very painful for both adults and children. A physician should be consulted.

Earache "Don'ts"

"Don't go out of this house without a hat!" Grandma would say to us in the winter. It was good advice. The ears can be extremely sensitive to cold. Sometimes only a little chill or a strong wind can make them ache. Take care of your ears by wearing a hat, scarf, or earmuffs.

If you have an earache, blow your nose gently. Forcefully blowing your nose can push mucous deeper into the sinuses and into the passage between the throat and ears.

Home Remedies

Sit Up Straight

Just sitting up can help reduce the pain and congestion of an earache. Elevating the head helps clear the passages that run between the throat and middle ear. This equalizes pressure.

Warming Trends

Heat is one of the best remedies for earache pain. Put a washcloth in a bowl of water and microwave it for forty-five seconds. Hold the washcloth against your sore ear. Then direct the airflow from your blow dryer into your sore ear, keeping if far enough away so your skin and hair don't get burned.

Fill a handkerchief or clean sock with one-quarter cup of table salt. Wrap a rubber band around the sock to make a ball and warm it in the oven on low heat. Lie down with the sock against your ear. The heat should relieve your pain. Some people claim this remedy works better if you add one-quarter cup of raw bran to the salt.

If your child has an earache, try the hug remedy. Put one hand over one ear and press the child's other into your chest. Your body's warmth will ease the ache.

Splish, Splash, Don't Do Anything Rash

Getting water in your ear while swimming or showering can be very annoying. If you have a problem with swimmer's ear, put a few drops of jojoba or mineral oil in your ears before diving in.

Stick It In Your Ear

A number of substances can be placed in the ear to relieve pain. Buy garlic oil capsules at your local health store. Poke a hole in one of the capsules and let the oil drip into your ear. Seal the ear with a cotton ball. The pain should begin to diminish within half an hour. You can also try mixing four drops of onion juice and one teaspoon of warm olive oil. Place this in the ears the same way, making sure to plug the ears with cotton. Apply three drops to each ear in the morning and evening.

Alleviate pain by placing a few drops of warm olive oil in the ear along with a drop of tincture of lobelia. Children who live around smokers tend to have more ear infections than other children. Do not use this method before seeing a physician: It will cause problems if the eardrum has been perforated.

If the idea of putting something into your ear canal makes you uncomfortable, try this remedy instead. Put some castor oil on a cotton ball and add a little black pepper. Place it on the outside of the ear to relieve pain.

Grandma's Russian Remedy

My grandmother called this cure for an earache her Russian Remedy. That's because it contains vodka, something she allowed in the house only for medicinal purposes. I had a terrible time with earaches when I was little, as many children do. Grandma'd get out her medicine dropper and the vodka and gently put no more than four drops into my ear. I don't think it was ever more than five minutes before my ear felt much better.

Silence Is Golden:
RINGING EARS

Ringing may affect one or both ears and can be caused by poor carbohydrate metabolization. Fluid retention in the semicircular canals, or wax buildup, may also cause ringing in the ears.

Quit It

If you have a terrible headache, you may take more than the recommended dose of aspirin or other analgesics. These over-the-counter drugs contain substances that can make your ears ring. Stop taking the drug. The ringing should stop when the medication wears off.

For persistent ringing in the ears not caused by medication, take fenugreek tea. Drink it in the morning, in the afternoon, and before going to bed. To make the tea, add one teaspoon of fenugreek seeds to a cup of boiling water. Steep it for twenty minutes. It will take a couple of weeks to take effect.

Get Rid Of Waxy Buildup

Ear wax is often the culprit when you have ringing in the ears. To get rid of the buildup, put a teaspoon of warm (not hot!) sesame oil into each ear. Seal the ears with cotton balls. Let the oil work for a couple of minutes to loosen the wax, then remove the cotton and wash out your ears. An easy way to wash out the ears is to take a shower and let the water stream into the ears. Both the oil and wax will flow out. Hopefully, the ringing will be a thing of the past. You can use castor oil in much the same way to cure chronic ringing in the ears.

To remove ear wax, place a few drops of warm olive oil in the ear. Seal the ear with a piece of cotton while keeping your head tilted to the side. Remove the cotton and add a few drops of hydrogen peroxide. The oil will soften the wax. The bubbling action of the hydrogen peroxide will loosen the wax and carry it out of the ear canal.

To eliminate ear wax that can contribute to ringing ears, fill a syringe with warm water. Gently squirt the water into the ear. The wax will wash out in a few minutes. Of course, you should always be careful when dealing with the ears.

Dip a cotton ball in warm oil that has been sprinkled with black pepper. Place it carefully in the ear and leave it there for five minutes. This will reduce ear wax.

Hot Blooded

Problems with blood supply and circulation can contribute to ringing in the ears. To redistribute blood flow and get rid of the ringing, put a heating pad on your hands and feet.

Stick It In Your Ear

My grandmother believed in onion juice as the cure for ringing ears. Place two drops in your ears three times a week.

EYE PROBLEMS

Smoking, high sugar intake, and drinking too much coffee can blur vision or make eyes burn or become bloodshot, irritated, or sensitive to light.

The herb eyebright has, for centuries, been used to alleviate many eye problems with great success. It may be taken as a tea or in capsule form. If eyebright is not available, goldenseal may be substituted.

Seeing Red:
BLOODSHOT EYES

The best way to treat any ailment is to get to the root of the problem. Bloodshot eyes can be caused by lack of sleep or too much hard drinking. If you have this problem and neither of these causes fits the bill, you may have a vitamin deficiency. Try taking a supplement of B2 according to your doctor's instructions. Or take brewer's yeast, which is an excellent source of B vitamins.

A Spicy Solution

Grandma recommended this old country cure of using ginger to treat bloodshot eyes. She'd make a wet paste from two tablespoons of ginger and a little water. We'd put the paste on the soles of our feet, pull on thick socks to save the sheets, and go to bed. When we woke up in the morning, Grandma could see the whites of our eyes.

How Many Fingers?:
BLURRED VISION

If you have a problem with blurred vision, treat it with alfalfa. Look for alfalfa tablets at your local health food store. Thoroughly dissolve one tablet in a cup of boiling water. Cool and strain the mixture and store it in a tightly sealed bottle. Put one drop in each eye daily, preferably in the morning. It should help clear up your eyesight.

In The Pink:

CONJUNCTIVITIS

To treat conjunctivitis, or pink eye, grate an apple or raw red potato and make a poultice. Close your eyes and apply the poultice for at least thirty minutes. The pink eye should clear up within two or three days.

Chamomile tea makes a fine eyewash to treat conjunctivitis. Bathe your eyes twice a day until the condition heals. You can also use fennel tea to wash your eyes. Steep a teaspoon of fennel seeds in one cup of boiling water for five minutes. Strain out the seeds and let the tea cool before using it. If your eyes are irritated, put a couple of drops of milk or castor oil into each eye.

I Can See Clearly Now:

EYESIGHT

It sounds like a cliche, but drinking carrot juice can help improve your eyesight. Drink a small glass twice a day. You'll soon be seeing better than ever.

Chew On This

My grandmother's favorite snack was fresh sunflower seeds harvested from her garden. She had remarkable eyesight for a woman her age. As it happens, sunflower seeds contain many nutrients that are good for the eyes. Make them a staple of your diet, eating one-half cup every day.

Traditional Asian healers recommend ginger to strengthen eyesight. Chew a piece after every meal.

Get Some Shuteye:

EYESTRAIN

If you spend a lot of your day reading or staring at a computer screen, you probably suffer from eyestrain. Traditional Chinese medicine prescribes acupressure to relieve tired eyes. Pinch the center of your index and middle fingers, thirty seconds on each finger. Your eyes should feel refreshed in a matter of minutes. If they don't, repeat the procedure.

Rest For The Weary:

IRRITATED AND TIRED EYES

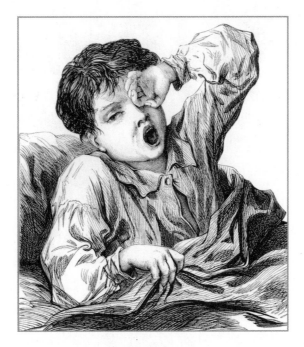

Keep Them Covered

To beat eye irritation, peel an over-ripe apple and place the flesh on your closed eyes. Use gauze or cloth to keep the apple in place and leave it on for thirty minutes.

There are several poultices that can be applied to the eyes to reduce irritation and inflammation. Try grated Irish potato, papaya pulp, or cooked mashed beets. Apply the poultice twice a day and leave it on for at least fifteen minutes.

Several herbs can be used in compresses to soothe tired and irritated eyes. Make fennel tea by steeping a tablespoon of fennel seeds in two cups of boiling water. Allow it to steep for fifteen minutes, then apply it to the eyelids with cotton or cloth. You can also use horsetail. Measure a teaspoon of this herb and steep it in boiling water for ten minutes. Leave the warm compress on your eyelids for ten minutes at a time. Keep wetting the cotton until your eyes are soothed.

Close your weary eyes and apply a warm compress of rosemary tea to soothe and refresh them. You can use fresh rosemary, the dried herb, or tea bags. Let the tea steep for ten minutes in boiling water. Soak some cotton or a cloth in the tea, put it on your eyelids, and relax for ten minutes or more.

European Eye-Cup Cure

Chervil has been used in Europe to relieve severe eye inflammation. Prepare the herb by placing one-quarter cup of diced leaves in one cup of boiling water. Boil it for five minutes, then remove it from the heat. Allow the tea to cool to body temperature and apply the mixture with an eye cup.

Just Resting My Eyes

Sometimes Grandma's common sense pointed out things that should be obvious but manage to elude us anyway. Grandma always said that if we were tired, we should rest. She believed the same thing was true if our eyes were tired. When I'd spent too much time going over homework and my eyes were bothering me, she'd send me into the front room to lie down, rest, or nap for twenty minutes or so. I'd get up feeling fresh, ready to wrestle with long division once more.

Don't Flip Your Lid:
STYES

Tea Treatments

To cure a stye, brew a handful of parsley leaves in a cup of boiling water. Allow it to steep for ten minutes. Soak a washcloth in the tea, lie down, and place it over your closed eyes for fifteen minutes. Also try this remedy on puffy eyes.

If you have a stye, save the tea bag from your afternoon cup of tea. Apply it to your closed eye with gauze or cloth before going to bed. Leave it on overnight. The stye should be gone in the morning. You need to use black tea- not herbal-to get the right active ingredients.

Swab It Away

Simply swabbing with a little castor oil on a piece of cotton can help clear up a stye in a matter of days.

Fools Gold?

One of the most popular folk remedies for a stye is to rub it with a gold wedding ring. This may fall more into the category of superstition than science. But what could it hurt to give it a try?

Lose The Luggage:

UNDER-EYE PUFFINESS

If you tend to wake up with under-eye puffiness, brew yourself a cup of black tea. After you enjoy the beverage, apply the cooled tea bag to your closed eye. Pretty soon, your eyes should look much less puffy. The gentle acid in the tea causes the tissues to contract.

In old movies, you'll sometimes see a starlet relaxing with cool slices of cucumber on her closed eyelids. It's a great way to refresh tired eyes and can also help reduce under-eye puffiness.

NOSEBLEEDS

Nosebleeds may be caused by injury or excessive dryness that makes the delicate nasal blood vessels rupture. Sudden changes in atmospheric pressure will also cause these small vessels to break.

Giving It Lip Service

Putting a wad of paper, cotton, or gauze inside your mouth-between your top lip and gum-may help slow and, eventually, stop the bleeding.

You may also try putting pressure on the outside of your upper lip. Place a strip of cardboard or paper between your upper lip and nose. Press firmly, squeezing for about a minute or so. Your nosebleed should stop. This effective remedy works with known acupressure points.

In A Pinch

Pinch the center of your nose (just below the bony part) with your thumb and forefinger. Keep pinching for several minutes. Your nosebleed should stop.

Hot And Sour Stoppers

Here's a hot tip: Drink a glass of warm water with one-eighth teaspoon of cayenne pepper added. It should stop the bleeding.

Vinegar can help control a nosebleed. Wash the temples, nose, and neck with a cloth that's been soaking in vinegar. In addition, drink one-half glass of water with two teaspoons of vinegar.

Grandma's Silver Dollar Nosebleed Stopper

Grandma used a special treatment when one of us kids got a nosebleed. To stop the bleeding, she'd reach for the magic silver dollar she kept in the freezer for such occasions. She'd press the coin to the back of our necks. And just like magic, the bleeding would stop. Grandma's other chilly solution for nosebleeds was reserved for the adults-but both worked equally well. First she made the adult sit up with the head tilted down. (You can tilt your head back if you like, but the blood will run down your throat and may cause a stomachache. Just make sure your head is above your heart.) Then she wrapped ice in a dishtowel and placed it on the back of the neck. It always seemed to help. Ice packs work well, too.

Things That
GO BUMP

The Buzz Factor:
BEE STINGS

In the United States, most problem bee stings are due to honeybees and yellow jackets. If you are allergic and get stung, seek medical care immediately. The stinger should be carefully removed with tweezers as soon as possible.

It can be tricky to remove a stinger without releasing the poison into the body. Grandma was the expert bee-stinger remover around her house. She would pass a wet bar of soap over the area, and the stinger seemed to come right out.

Take The Sting Out Of The Sting

For quick relief, apply ammonia on a cotton ball to a bee sting.

Since ancient times, mud or clay packs have been used to alleviate the discomfort of stings of all kinds. The cooling sensation and the mild drawing action help relieve the pain.

Ice packs or a few ice cubes placed in a piece of cheesecloth will dull the pain of a sting.

Tears And Celery

More than once when I was young, I ran into an angry hornet. If you've ever met a hornet, you know that their stings tend to cause more pain and discomfort than any other type of insect sting. Grandma would dry my tears, then have me chew a small piece of celery stalk. She'd place the pasty mixture of saliva and celery on the site of the sting. Try this in an emergency. You will be pleasantly surprised that the throbbing and pain will subside in a short time. Two or three applications will probably be needed to bring the sting under control.

Swell Ideas For Reducing Swelling

To reduce pain and swelling, crush a charcoal tablet and place the powder on a cotton ball. Attach it to the sting with a bandage.

A slice of cold onion placed on a bee sting or insect bite will stop pain and swelling.

Grandpa always had a chaw of tobacco with him, even though he tried to hide it from Grandma. It proved handy when any of us kids was stung by a bee. Moistened tobacco applied to a bee sting can help reduce pain and swelling.

Aspirin is one of the most common home remedies for a variety of complaints, even bee stings. Make it into a paste with water and apply it to the sting to reduce pain and swelling. Don't try this remedy if you're allergic to aspirin.

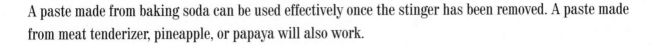

A paste made from baking soda can be used effectively once the stinger has been removed. A paste made from meat tenderizer, pineapple, or papaya will also work.

Putting The Pressure On:
BLEEDING

For a serious cut or gash, try placing powdered cayenne pepper or powdered kelp on the injury to stop the bleeding. Native Americans have used this treatment for hundreds of years. Apply the cayenne (also called capsaicin) to the wound and place a dressing over it. Within a few minutes, the bleeding should have stopped. The cayenne increases peripheral circulation, bringing additional blood-clotting agents to the area.

You Should See The Other Guy: Cuts And Scrapes
CLEANED AND DRESSED

One of the best treatments to promote rapid blood coagulation is an herbal bandage that uses yarrow. Both the leaves and the flower tips can be pressed into the wound before it is washed and bandaged.

Whenever you need to stop the bleeding from a small cut, rinse the area thoroughly and dress the wound with papaya pulp, cayenne pepper, a moist tea bag, goldenseal powder, or aloe vera gel.

An Oily Solution To Scarring
Applying vitamin E oil will help a cut heal more quickly and prevent scarring. Applying the membrane from inside an eggshell will also keep a scar from forming.

Sweet Ways To Guard Against Infection
One of the best natural ways to prevent infection of a cut or serious bruise is to use juniper berries. Crush fresh berries to make a paste, apply it to the wound in a poultice, and keep the poultice in place for three to four hours.

Home Remedies

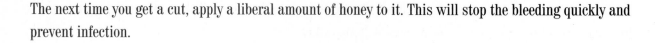

The next time you get a cut, apply a liberal amount of honey to it. This will stop the bleeding quickly and prevent infection.

When It's Muggy And Buggy:
OTHER INSECT BITES

Most insect bites are harmless. But some cause some discomfort and may require professional medical attention. Examples are tick bites that can transmit Lyme disease or Rocky Mountain spotted fever and mosquitoes that may carry malaria.

Just Say No
Avoid alcoholic beverages if you will be in an area with mosquitoes. Alcohol causes the blood to come closer to the surface, making you a tempting target.

Say Ahhh
Rub brewer's yeast and garlic into the affected area to help relieve discomfort. A slice of raw potato may also help.

Meat tenderizer can relieve pain and itching. Dissolve one-quarter to one-half teaspoon in a small amount of warm water. Apply it to the bite.

Be Quick With A Tick
Ticks should be removed from the skin as soon as possible. Use a lighted match and tweezers. Hold the flame near the tick until it withdraws, then use the tweezers to remove it.

Creepy Crawlers Beware:
PESTICIDE

Finely ground black pepper will rid your home of silverfish, ants, roaches, spiders, and most other crawling insects. Grandma used to sprinkle a small amount inside the cabinets in every corner and especially under the sink. We never saw a bug.

Rattle Battle:

SNAKEBITE

Symptoms may vary, depending on the toxin released. So it is always best to see a physician.

Symptoms may be alleviated by using a poultice of white oak bark and comfrey. Comfrey salve is also very effective on the affected area. Drink echinacea tea three or four times a day for at least three or four days.

Time For The Tweezers:

SPLINTERS

Place an ice cube on the splinter for a few seconds before trying to remove it. This will numb the area.

A Lousy Way To Lose Weight:

TAPEWORM

Pomegranate seeds have been used to chase tapeworms for hundreds and hundreds of years. Just dry the seeds of nine pomegranates in direct sunlight or in a low-temperature oven overnight. Crush the dried seeds into a powder with a mortar and pestle or hammer. Add one tablespoon of the powder to a six-ounce glass of unsweetened pineapple juice. Drink this three times a day, preferably on an empty stomach.

Watch Them Wiggle:
WORMS

Many varieties of worms can infest the human body. They may cause loss of appetite, diarrhea, nausea, anemia, colon disorders, and rectal itching. Worms are more common in children because of their poor bathroom habits.

What's In A Name?
The herb wormwood is recommended in capsule form. Black walnut extract is also excellent. Chaparral tea, taken three times a day on an empty stomach, will also have excellent results.

53

Quit Your
BELLYACHING!

Letting The Air Out:
COLIC

Colic is probably caused by intestinal gas. Symptoms include crying, clenched fists, bulging abdominal area, and whining.

There are many benefits to breast feeding your baby. Breast milk contains the nutrients a baby needs, boosts the child's immunity, and lets you snuggle and bond with your baby. However, if you eat dairy products, your breast milk may cause colic in your child. Experiment with your diet. Eliminate dairy and get the calcium you need from such sources as whole grains and leafy green vegetables. This remedy works in about half of all cases of colic.

Home Remedies

Grandma's Rock-A-Bye Baby Method

When babysitting for colicky infants, Grandma used to place one to two ounces of ginger ale into their bottles. She said this would almost always soothe the discomfort. The soda's carbonation helps release gas. Getting the baby to burp on your shoulder will also solve the problem. Grandma's favorite remedy: Rock the baby in a rocking chair.

Baby's Belly Brews

Brew a tea of one teaspoon of fennel seed and one-quarter teaspoon of sugar. Cool and strain the tea and pour it into your child's bottle. It will calm the baby and help get rid of gas.

Add one ounce of fresh peppermint leaves to a pint of boiling water. Steep the brew. The peppermint tea should be lukewarm when given to the child. One-quarter cup will usually ease the symptoms and help the child sleep. You can also try letting your child suck on a peppermint stick. Not all children can tolerate peppermint's pungent taste. If your baby has trouble with it, try another remedy.

Make a tea from caraway seeds to soothe a colicky baby. Steep a tablespoon of caraway seeds in a cup of boiling water for ten minutes. Cool the tea and strain out the seeds. A couple of teaspoons should be enough to ease gas pains and soothe the infant. You can give the tea to the baby in a bottle.

The Tried And True

Put corn syrup on your child's pacifier to help ease colic, or add one-quarter teaspoon of brown sugar to an eight-ounce bottle of milk. This should help the baby expel gas. Of course, you don't want to overdo the sugar. That wouldn't be good for the baby's teeth.

My grandmother found that simple cures were often quite effective. Warmth will help soothe a colicky baby. Try filling a hot water bottle with warm water and place it on the child's stomach. Or just hold your baby close and soothe the child with the warmth of your body and your loving touch.

White Noise Works

Grandma had a way with children. Neighbors often brought colicky babies to the house to ask for her help. She would tell them to take the baby for a long buggy ride. That would do the trick every time: The child would stop crying and, usually, fall asleep. The repetitive motion and steady noise-not the horse-were the important elements. Try wrapping your baby in a blanket and putting the child in a laundry basket. Place the basket next to your clothes dryer and turn the dryer on for twenty minutes. The sound of vacuuming may also help your baby relax. The vibration can help the baby's intestine do its work, relieve gas, and ease the colic.

Fridge Fright:
FOOD POISONING

Here's an antidote for food poisoning caused by bad shellfish: Bring two pints of water to a rapid boil, add two teaspoons of cherry bark, one tablespoon of fresh grated ginger root, and one finely diced onion. Allow the mixture to simmer for ten minutes. Then remove it from the heat and allow it to steep for thirty minutes. Drink two cups while the brew is still warm.

A Raging Inferno:
HEARTBURN

This burning sensation in the abdomen is related to the release of excess hydrochloric acid, which irritates the stomach lining and the esophagus. Alcohol, carbonated beverages, citrus fruits, tomato products, certain spices, and other foods can cause this reaction. So can more than two cups of coffee a day.

Tranquil Tummy Teas
A tea made from ginger soothes the stomach and controls the release of excess acid.

Slippery elm bark has, for many years, been used to ease an acid stomach and relieve heartburn discomfort. Look for this herb at your local health food store. Add one teaspoon of the bark itself or of a powder made from it to a cup of boiling water. Sip the tea, and you should feel better shortly.

Undoing A Sugar Overdose
You know how kids are. They love sweet stuff, and sometimes they don't know when to quit. That's exactly the way I was as a child. Especially at Grandma's house, where so many delicious treats awaited me in her kitchen. Whenever I ate too many of her goodies, Grandma would shake her head and say, "Poor thing. You've got a sore tummy, haven't you?" Then she'd whip up her favorite remedy to settle a stomach sickened by eating too many sweets. She'd mix a cup of warm water, the juice of half a lemon, and a teaspoon of salt. She'd put her arm around me and tell me to drink it down slowly. Before very long, I was feeling much better and looking for my next cookie.

Chew On This

Sometimes you can chew your way to heartburn relief. Chew a mouthful of dry oats until they're soft enough to swallow. Your favorite chewing gum can also reduce stomach acid and prevent heartburn.

Eat six unblanched almonds. Chewing them very slowly and thoroughly can help reduce stomach acid and soothe the discomfort.

You can also eat raw, peeled carrots to counteract heartburn. Chew each bite slowly and thoroughly.

Make-It-Better Beverages

Place one thoroughly washed, unpeeled raw potato in a juicer. Add an equal amount of water and drink the juice three times a day. Make fresh potato juice every time.

Grandma preferred leaf lettuce, but she always grew some iceberg lettuce to use in her heartburn remedy. Puree a few lettuce leaves and three-quarters of a cup of cold water in your blender. Sip the green liquid and prepare for relief.

One tablespoon of raw apple cider vinegar, mixed with cold water and sipped slowly during a meal, is an effective treatment. Do not consume any other liquid with your meal.

This remedy sounds like it would do more to upset your stomach than settle it. But many people swear by it. Combine an egg white with two tablespoons of olive oil and drink it.

Simple But Effective

Activated charcoal is highly absorbent. Take a capsule of it to absorb the excess stomach acid that causes heartburn.

Dissolve one teaspoon of baking soda in a glass of water and drink it. This remedy will help neutralize stomach acid. Don't use too much baking soda. Don't use this remedy after an especially large meal. It's full of salt and can create too much pressure on a full stomach.

Feel The Burn? Reach For Peppermint!

Grandpa loved to eat, and Grandma was a wonderful cook. Unfortunately, Grandpa sometimes overdid it at the dinner table and ended up with heartburn. While Grandpa walk ed around the house to keep the blood moving so he could digest all that food, Grandma made him a nice, warm cup of tea from peppermint leaves grown in her garden. The peppermint soothed Grandpa's stomach, and pretty soon, he'd be ready for dessert.

Spelling Relief:

INDIGESTION

This condition is usually a stomach disorder, but it may also relate to the small or large intestine. Symptoms include bloating, flatulence, abdominal pain, belching, a burning sensation, or nausea. The problem may result from consuming liquids with meals. Doing so neutralizes enzymes needed to break down foods.

Mint, papaya, peppermint, chamomile, and fennel are useful in alleviating symptoms. For inflammation of the colon, a slippery elm enema should provide fast relief.

Before The Burn

You may know that certain foods always seem to irritate your stomach. Foods that are hard to digest or that produce gas often cause stomach problems or aggravate existing conditions. If you just can't resist foods that don't agree with you, try taking a capsule of activated charcoal with the food. Or take one tablespoonful of olive oil before you eat. You may find that you can then enjoy foods you hadn't been able to tolerate.

If you like vegetables but they don't like you, there's no need to despair. Just sprinkle fresh lemon juice on vegetables more than three hours before you plan to eat them. This marinade makes the veggies easier to digest. It also adds a nice flavor.

If you're going to serve a hard-to-digest meal, this side dish does double duty. Sprinkle some steamed zucchini with raw, grated almonds. It's tasty and will aid digestion.

Daikon, a Japanese radish, is a wonderful digestive aid. It's crisp, refreshing and very effective, especially when eating oily or fried foods. Add one or two tablespoons of raw, grated daikon to salads. Or eat a few slices with your meal.

Here's a hot tip for indigestion sufferers: cayenne pepper. Sprinkled on all kinds of food, it will aid digestion. Be careful not to use too much: A little cayenne pepper goes a long way.

Grandma's Brown Rice And Fresh Barley Belly Soup

A soup made from brown rice and fresh barley should help alleviate bloating and flatulence. Boil five parts of water to one part of the grain mixture for ten to twelve minutes. Then allow it to simmer for forty-five minutes before straining. Allow the soup to cool before you eat it.

Home Remedies

Natural Acid Neutralizers

Papaya is another natural cure for stomach pain. This tropical fruit has long been recognized as a digestive aid. After a meal, drink papaya juice, eat the fresh fruit, or take papaya pills. Most health food stores carry a number of brands of papaya products. Check them out and see which works best for you.

For acid ingestion, you may find kelp tablets to be a welcome relief. This form of seaweed forms a gel that soothes upset stomachs by binding up stomach acid. A caution to those who must watch their salt intake: This is not the cure for you. Kelp (and other seaweed) is very high in sodium.

How about a spicy solution to your stomachache? Try chewing cardamom seeds. This fragrant spice has long been recognized as a digestive aid. Chewing cardamom seeds can relieve nausea and discomfort and help relieve gas buildup. The seeds have a pleasant flavor, too. Other fragrant spices can also be helpful. Try anise seeds and caraway seeds. They'll soothe your stomach and, like the cardamom seeds, they can sweeten your breath.

If you suffer from acid indigestion, try chewing a teaspoon of dry rolled oats. Make sure you chew the oats thoroughly before you swallow. They will soothe you and help neutralize the acid in your stomach.

Grandma's Grapefruit Granules

Grandma's herb garden and her abundance of home remedies gained her some notoriety with her friends and neighbors. This is one that a lot of her friends adopted as their own. I'm sure an awful lot of medicine cabinets around the country contain a jar of Grandma's Grapefruit Granule. You can prepare this remedy well in advance so you'll have it on hand when an upset stomach strikes. Grate a grapefruit peel and let the shavings dry on a paper towel. Once the shavings are completely dry, place them in a jar. Close the jar tightly and store it in your medicine cabinet. The dried peel keeps very well. The next time your stomach is upset, reach for the jar and chew a teaspoon of the peel. Make sure you chew it thoroughly, so that the granules are saturated with saliva. You'll thank Grandma, just like her friends and neighbors did.

Tea-rrific Tummy Ache Tamers

To settle your stomach, boil one teaspoon of alfalfa seeds in one cup of water. Let the seeds steep for approximately five minutes. Strain the tea and drink it half an hour after your meal.

If you have stomach discomfort from overeating, drinking fenugreek tea can make you feel better in no time. Crush one teaspoon of the seeds in a cup of boiling water. Steep it for approximately five minutes. Strain the crushed fenugreek seeds and sip the tea.

Sipping a cup of sage tea can help banish the bad breath and the white coating on the tongue that can accompany an upset stomach.

If you suffer from a nervous stomach, try this soothing tea. Steep one-half teaspoon of dried marjoram and one-quarter teaspoon of dried oregano for ten minutes in a cup of hot water. Strain the herbs and sip the tea. Drink another cup in two hours if the first cup doesn't do the trick.

Other teas that will soothe your upset stomach are chamomile and peppermint. Drink a cup at the first sign of discomfort. Sip more as needed.

Cookin' Up A Cure

This home remedy may be a little hard to take, but it really seems to work. At the first sign of stomach discomfort, boil one sliced onion in one cup of milk. Drink the mixture while it's still warm. It's difficult to swallow, but it's better than the stomach pain.

Another way to neutralize acid is to drink raw potato juice. To make the juice, grate and squeeze a potato (through cheesecloth, if you have it). One tablespoon diluted in one-half cup of warm water should make you feel better. Be sure to drink it slowly.

Sometimes overeating brings on a sensation known as a sour stomach. Or you may feel that something you've eaten doesn't agree with you. Here's a quick remedy that many people find helpful for settling their stomach: Add one teaspoon of apple cider vinegar to a glass of water. If the sour taste is too much for you, you may want to add some honey.

Speaking of honey, this natural nectar has been found to bring sweet relief for some stomach pain. A tablespoon or two of honey can do wonders to relieve stomach cramps. This is no new-fangled remedy: The appreciation of honey's curative qualities dates to ancient Egypt.

Tartar For The Tummy

When I was a child, Grandma gave me cream of tartar in water whenever I had a stomachache. She always had it on hand for baking and it always made me feel better (after a good belch or two).

Arrowroot is terrific for settling the stomach. Grandma made arrowroot paste by combining one tablespoon of arrowroot with enough water to get the right consistency. She mixed it until it was smooth. Then she boiled and cooled the paste and added one tablespoon of fresh lime juice.

Without Sugar Or Spice

For stomach ailments, many doctors recommend the BRAT diet. This bland diet works particularly well if you have the stomach flu. It consists of foods that are easy to take on an upset stomach: bananas, rice, applesauce, and toast. Easy to remember, easy to digest.

Shower Yourself With Relief

Sometimes a hot shower is all you need to feel better. Let the hot shower water run on your stomach. You should feel better-and more relaxed-within ten to fifteen minutes.

When The Room Is Spinning:
MOTION SICKNESS

This disorder occurs when the brain receives conflicting signals through the vestibule apparatus in the ear and sensory nerves.

Take four to five charcoal tablets approximately one hour before a trip. Ginger capsules are just as good, but you need to take two to three of them one hour before the trip and every three hours after that.

On The Road

Whatever mode of transportation you use, sit near a window and look out. Focus on faraway objects. If that doesn't work, try sucking on a lemon.

Some people believe that the delicate skin on your inner wrist can signal your brain to let up on the motion sickness. Pinch the skin on your inner wrist just an inch below your palm. Keep it up, alternating wrists, until you feel better.

When you start feeling queasy, it's important to get fresh air. If you're traveling by car, train, or bus, open a window and breath deeply. If you're on a boat, stay on deck. Open the overhead fan on a plane.

Motion Potions

If you get seasick, try taking marjoram tea. Drink a cup of tea before boarding a ship.

You can also try peppermint or chamomile tea. Both are excellent for soothing the stomach and relieving nausea.

Not quite so soothing a thought is this peppery drink. In a cup of warm water, mix one-eighth teaspoon of cayenne pepper. Drink it all. You can hold your nose if you like.

Belly Flops:
NAUSEA

If you're finding it difficult to keep your food down, try peeling and eating half a cucumber. It will feel very soothing and refreshing. It won't irritate your system.

Tummy Tonics

Fresh ginger or ginger capsules seem to reduce nausea and even eliminate it in many cases. In some countries, ginger powder is prescribed after surgery to alleviate the nausea induced by anesthesia.

Try placing a few drops of peppermint tincture under your tongue. The queasy feeling should pass in a few minutes. You can find a large variety of herbal tinctures at health food stores.

Peppermint tea is another herbal alternative to ease stomach discomfort. If you don't have the tea handy, try peppermint candy.

Chamomile tea is a popular remedy for an upset stomach. You can find many brands of chamomile tea in any grocery or health food store. Chamomile tea is also very soothing and can help when you feel stress. It's great before bedtime, too. Note: If you are sensitive to ragweed, chrysanthemums, or asters, you should avoid chamomile.

Yarrow tea can provide quick relief from nausea. Drink one cup when you start to get that queasy feeling. Cloves, cinnamon stick, and ginger are all good for relieving nausea. Steep a couple of cloves in boiling water for five minutes. Or try cinnamon stick or one teaspoon of powdered ginger. Any of these teas will help relieve your nausea.

From The Soda Fountain

Believe it or not, soda can help relieve nausea. Sipping ginger ale is a good preventive measure for nausea. You might also try Coca-Cola for an upset stomach. Cola syrup is also terrific for nausea. You can find this over-the-counter-item at your pharmacy. One teaspoon of this sweet syrup works very well.

Chewing on ice chips can also curb nausea.

Bumpy Ride Candy

Whenever we traveled long distances, Grandma kept candies in her purse. Her favorite was barley sugar, and she always had a supply handy for long, bumpy rides. Any hard candy is a good deterrent for carsickness, but barley sugar always reminds me of Grandma. The best thing about this remedy is that if your kids get carsick, you won't have to coax them to take their medicine!

MANAGING MORNING SICKNESS

Two or three capsules of powdered ginger root each morning can help prevent morning sickness.

Another morning sickness remedy is vitamin B6. It is most effective for women who have severe morning sickness and who vomit several times a day. Check with your doctor before you start taking the vitamins. Like many vitamins, too much B6 can be harmful.

Eating crackers can often allay nausea due to morning sickness. Many women swear by soda crackers. Keep a box in the car and keep some in your purse. When that feeling comes over you, you'll be glad you have them handy.

If you suffer from morning sickness, you may get some relief from drinking one teaspoon of bicarbonate of soda in half a glass of water. Or try drinking carbonated mineral water.

A Sore Spot:

ULCERS

Ulcers may occur anywhere along the gastrointestinal tract. But they most often develop when the stomach is unable to secrete enough mucous to protect its delicate lining from hydrochloric acid it secretes.

When it comes to ulcers, prevention is the key. If you suffer from ulcer pain, avoiding milk and foods that are fried, spicy, acidic, or fatty could keep your suffering at bay. While these foods don't cause ulcers, avoiding them may keep you from getting a flare-up.

Although you should avoid spicy foods, cayenne pepper is a very helpful spice to use in ulcer healing. Drink one-eighth teaspoon of cayenne pepper in a glass of water twice daily. If you can stand the taste, work your way up to one-quarter teaspoon of the pepper.

A Dairy Don't

Never drink milk to soothe the stomach. The calcium in milk tends to stimulate acid production. The only milk that may be helpful is almond milk.

Soothing Stomach Savers

Ulcers respond well to a tea made from chamomile or bayberry. Cayenne capsules also tend to promote healing by increasing circulation.

Some people find that ginger root can calm an ulcer flare-up. Licorice has been known to have the same effect. Deglycyrrhizinated licorice, known as DGL, can help protect the stomach's lining. DGL is available in health food stores.

Drinking catnip tea before each meal can make a noticeable difference in the pain of many stomach ulcers. Steep a tea bag or one teaspoon of catnip in a cup of boiling water. After five minutes, strain the tea and drink it.

Rejuvenate With Juice

Fresh cabbage juice will ease the problem but must be consumed as soon as prepared. Exposure to air can reduce the juice's potency.

One tablespoon of aloe vera juice after each meal is an extremely effective remedy.

Whole-Grain Goodness

You might want to check with your doctor before you try this barley water remedy. To six cups of water, add two ounces of pearled barley. Boil the mixture down until only about half of the liquid remains in the pot. Strain the barley, which can be used for cooking, and drink the tea. You may add honey and lemon to taste.

54

The Party's
OVER

One More Round:
ALCOHOL DEPENDENCY

A healthy, nourished body is the foundation of all wellness. Beating alcoholism requires a change in lifestyle. It may be easier if you eat more healthily, getting most of your calories from whole grains, vegetables, and fruits. Try to cut out all high-fat, sugary, and processed foods that may contribute to your alcohol cravings.

Herbal Easers

Easing alcohol cravings facilitates the process of eliminating alcohol dependency. The roots and leaves of the herb angelica have properties that seem to lessen the desire for alcohol. A person who is trying to quit drinking should drink three cups of angelica tea every day. To brew the tea, use one teaspoon of angelica and a cup of boiling water. Steep it for ten minutes, then strain. If you like honey and lemon, add them to taste.

Native Americans used chaparral to heal many ailments. This herb helps purify the system, rid the liver of toxins, and lessen the urge to drink. Look for chaparral capsules at your local health food store. Take one each day to combat alcohol dependency.

Cut Out The Cravings

Sucking on-but not swallowing-a clove is one of the best ways to curb the appetite for alcohol. Cloves are thought to contain a substance similar to Antabuse, a drug that short circuits the biochemical pathways that let the body break down alcohol efficiently. Ingesting alcohol causes discomfort.

To reduce alcohol dependence, try leaving the liquor out of your next Bloody Mary. Mix glass of tomato juice mixed with the juice of a lemon. Sip it slowly. Tart beverages seem to ease alcohol cravings.

Next-Day Nasties:
HANGOVER

Prevent The Unpleasantness

Before you go to your next party, try eating six raw almonds to prevent drunkenness. A peanut butter sandwich can have the same effect.

Alcohol, which acts as a diuretic, depletes fluids the body needs. It would be wise to drink at least eight ounces of water for every beer and twelve ounces of water for any other alcoholic beverage consumed. Snacking on raw vegetables and whole-grain foods while drinking will usually eliminate a hangover. The liver needs a number of B vitamins and minerals in order to metabolize alcohol. When you consume a lot of alcohol, the liver becomes overworked and unable to locate the required nutrients. This is one cause of a hangover.

Before you go to bed, take two aspirin with plenty of water. This should prevent a hangover. Taking aspirin before or while drinking may cause you to get more drunk in less time.

Sober As A Judge

In addition to drinking plenty of water to fight off a hangover, you might want to orange juice or some other fruit juice. The natural sugar helps your body fight off the effects of the alcohol. The vitamin C and potassium also help.

Like fruit juice, honey is high in fructose. This natural sugar can improve the body's ability to burn off alcohol. If you need to sober up in a hurry, take two teaspoons of honey every few minutes. You may take up to two pounds of honey, depending on the amount of alcohol you've ingested.

To cure a hangover, take two tablespoons of honey every minute for five minutes. Repeat the process thirty minutes later.

When you've had too much to drink, eat as many cucumber slices as you can. The enzymes in the cucumber will reduce the effects of the alcohol.

Eating certain foods after a night of partying really does seem to help cure a hangover. Eat a grapefruit, chewing slowly, to dispel hangover symptoms. Liquefy some fresh radishes in your juicer and drink a small glass of the juice. You should sober up quickly.

When You're Feelin' Poorly

"Go sleep it off!" That's common sense and very good advice when you've had too much to drink. Unfortunately, it may be difficult to follow. That's because alcohol interferes with your body's natural sleep rhythms. If you wake up with a hangover, try to nap throughout the day to relieve the symptoms.

The next time you wake up with a nasty headache, sick stomach, and lots of regret, drink a glass of water with one-eighth teaspoon of cayenne pepper. It will provide a quick pick-me-up.

One of the most unpleasant aspects of a hangover is the perception that the room is spinning. It makes you feel more nauseated and can make it difficult for you to fall asleep. Lie down on your bed and keep one foot on the floor to stop the sensation.

Traditional Chinese medicine prescribes ginger tea for nausea due to a hangover. You can also stimulate acupressure points to get rid of the other symptoms. To relieve the overall feeling, massage the flesh between your thumb and forefinger. Rub each thumb below the knuckle to relieve your pounding headache.

It may sound a little funny, but rub one-quarter of a lemon on the skin under each arm after drinking too much. It will help you feel better.

It Gets In Your Eyes:

SMOKING

The Just Say No Remedy

Although smoking wasn't known to be harmful in Grandma's day, this remedy really worked for anyone who wanted to kick the habit. Place two tablespoons of powdered slippery elm bark in a small mixing bowl. Make a small indentation in the center and pour in a small amount of honey or blackstrap molasses into it. Stir the mixture with the back of a wooden spoon until it forms thick dough. Roll small pieces of the dough in a mixture of powdered slippery elm bark flavored with a dash of cinnamon. Suck on a piece of dough every time you crave a cigarette.

Breaking The Chain

Drinking marjoram tea won't exactly curb your desire to smoke. But it will act as a deterrent. (Or should I say irritant?) Marjoram tea dries the throat, so you won't enjoy those cigarettes quite as much as you have been. Marjoram is naturally sweet, so you won't need to add a sweetener. Drink half a cup of this tea in the morning, whenever you'd smoke your first cigarette, and every time you feel a strong urge to smoke.

This refreshing alternative can help you stop smoking. Whenever you feel an urge to smoke, break an orange into sections. Eat all the pulp after you've sucked out the juice.

Sucking on a clove can eliminate your cigarette craving.

Some people find that a few cups of tea made from slippery elm bark can curb their desire to smoke. You can buy this tea at most health food stores. Eating a handful of raw, unshelled sunflower seeds can take your mind off of smoking.

Extra

Grandmother's
FAVORITE TIPS

GRANDMOTHER'S FAVORITE FOOD TIPS:

- Always store eggs in a closed container or the original carton for longer life and to avoid the egg absorbing refrigerator odors.

- If you place an apple in a bag of potatoes, the potatoes will not sprout.

- A new plastic storage bag for fruits and vegetables is now on the market. The bag is tinted green to lessen the effects of light reducing the potency of the vitamins. Produce stored in these bags will last 10 times longer than standard plastic storage bags and in tests over a 12 day period 50% more of the vitamin C was retained.

- The best method of reducing or eliminating the browning of fruits can be achieved with the use of ascorbic acid or vitamin C. Pure ascorbic acid is available in most supermarkets or drug stores. While some people tend to use lemon juice, it is not as effective and may impart more of a lemon flavor, which may not be desirable for many foods.

- To avoid milk from curdling when it's being boiled, just add a pinch of baking soda to the milk.

- To remove an unbroken egg that has stuck to the carton just wet the carton. If the egg is broken throw it out.

- To desalt a ham, use ginger ale or low fat milk. To remove the rind, slice it lengthwise and cook that side down. For a caramelized top, just dust the ham with light brown sugar.

- To keep a roast moist, rub olive oil on the roast and put celery sticks on top.

- Cook shrimp in the shell whenever possible for better flavor and use 3 tablespoons of salt to 1 quart of water to cook. Allow the water to boil before you add the shrimp and always rinse immediately after cooking.

- For great fried chicken soak the meat in buttermilk first.

- Never salt a food before placing the food into a fryer. The salt tends to draw moisture out of the food and will cause splattering. The moisture will also cause the oil to decompose more readily.

- If you soak cabbage in ice water it will eliminate the odor. Add vinegar or lemon juice to retain the color of red cabbage.

- Always add warm milk to mashed potatoes and use Idaho potatoes for the lightest and Yukon Gold if you like them buttery.

- For moist and crispy chocolate chip cookies, add sour cream. Use only butter or shortening, never margarine or whipped butter.

- For the best results, use glass pie pans to bake fruit pies.

- For the very best meatloaf use ground round, soak your breadcrumbs in tomato juice and along with diced onion and celery, try adding grated cheese and red wine or dark beer. The flavor's great.

- To preserve the juices, never put salt or pepper on a steak until it's done.

- To cook pasta, start with cold water and bring it to a rolling boil. Be sure to use plenty of water to avoid mushy pasta.

- To stop freezer burn on ice cream place plastic wrap on the portion that is left over.

- If you like flavored coffee just grind up a little of your favorite spice along with the coffee beans.

- Apple sauce is a substitution - you can replace the fat with applesauce in many recipes.

- To keep herbs fresh, store them in plastic bags.

- If the grill gets too hot, place lettuce leaves on the coals to eliminate flare ups.

- To keep those cookies from burning in the oven, double up on the cooking pan.

- To keep ice cream cones from leaking, place tiny marshmallows at the bottom. It does the trick.

- When you're choosing marinade, buyer beware - some of them actually dry out meats.

- When you're buying steak remember that if the fat on the steak is white, the steak will be more tender than if the fat is yellow. Yellow indicates grass-fed, white indicates corn-fed.

- To avoid a sticky knife, spray the blade with vegetable oil before you cut the cake.

- If you wrap an onion in foil and add it to the BBQ coals, it will add a smoky onion flavor to the grilled food.

- Love French fries but hate the calories? Add a teaspoon of vinegar to the oil when frying to reduce oil absorption.

- To keep pickles fresh and crisp, add horseradish to the pickle jar.

- When ice cubes remain in the freezer tray or the icemaker for more than a few days, they may pick up refrigerator odors or contaminants from the air when the door is opened. It would be best to wash the ice cubes before using them for the best results.

- To keep celery fresh longer, wrap it in foil. It will last 2-3 weeks.

- A pinch of baking soda in milk will increase shelf life by 2-3 days.

- When you're making gravy, be sure not to add too much flour. If the gravy burns, add 1 tsp. peanut butter to take away that burnt flavor.

- When you're cooking BBQ, add the sauce 15 minutes before the food is done and you'll eliminate bitterness and burning.

- For fluffy pancakes substitute club soda for whatever liquid the recipe calls for.

- One easy method of reducing the salt level in sauces and soups is to dip a sugar cube into the dish and run it back and forth, covering the surface only once and before the cube melts. Salt is attracted to sugar and a percentage of the salt will adhere to the cube. Then discard the cube.

- Out of sugar? Drops of real vanilla can replace the sugar in many recipes.

- To reduce the odor when you're cooking broccoli, cauliflower or cabbage, damp a cloth with vinegar and place it on top of the pot.

- To speed up cooking time on a baked potato, insert a nail into the potato.

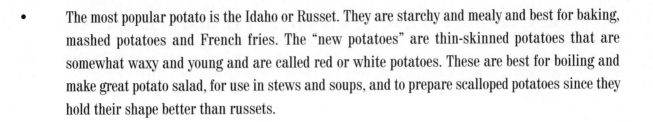

- The most popular potato is the Idaho or Russet. They are starchy and mealy and best for baking, mashed potatoes and French fries. The "new potatoes" are thin-skinned potatoes that are somewhat waxy and young and are called red or white potatoes. These are best for boiling and make great potato salad, for use in stews and soups, and to prepare scalloped potatoes since they hold their shape better than russets.

- You can increase the shelf life of cottage cheese if you turn the container upside down in the refrigerator.

- Salad won't be soggy if you place a saucer upside-down in the bottom of the salad bowl. The water goes down under the saucer and keeps the salad dry.

- To keep eggs fresh, rub vegetable oil on the shell - eggs have 300 pores.

- When cooking vegetables, add a small amount of milk or vinegar to the cooking water to retain the color of the vegetables.

- To naturally tenderize meat, use kiwi, papaya, tomato or fig juice as a marinade. For a tender beef stew, add a half a cup of tea to tenderize the beef with tannic acid.

- Light brakes down milk. Make sure to use a non-see through container and add a pinch of baking soda to retain freshness.

- Never re-use oil you've used for deep frying - it's can cause food poisoning.

- Use paper towels or wax paper in the microwave, never use plastic wrap.

GRANDMOTHER'S FAVORITE HOME TIPS:

- If you dust your light bulbs you will increase the available light by 50%. That includes the insides of lampshades.

- A scorch can be removed by rubbing a raw onion on the scorched area and allowing the onion juice to soak in thoroughly for at least 2-3 hours before washing.

- Lemon extract will remove black scuff marks from shoes and luggage.

- Stains from ballpoint pens can be removed with hairspray or milk.

- Mix equal parts of salt and white vinegar and scrub the cup to remove stains from tea and coffee.

- If you place a small piece of chalk in a silver chest it will absorb moisture and slow tarnishing. Calcium carbonate (chalk) absorbs moisture very slowly from the air. If you break the chalk up and expose the rough surface it will be more efficient.

- Almost any soft rubber ball including tennis balls can be brought back to life and the bounce returned by leaving the balls in an oven with only the pilot light overnight. This will cause expansion of the air inside the ball.

- One of the best methods of removing chewing gum from a child's hair is to use a small amount of non-chunky peanut butter (not the natural kind).

- If a child's shoelaces get raggedy on the tips, just dip the tips in glue and allow them to dry.

- To remove a broken light bulb, turn off the electricity, then try placing a $^1/_2$ a raw potato or $^1/_2$ a raw apple into the broken base and screwing it out.

- To remove grass stains, scrub the stain with toothpaste before washing.

- To clean stuffed animals that cannot be washed in the washer, just place them in a cloth bag and add baking soda, then shake.

- A pipe cleaner dipped in white vinegar can be used to clean the holes in an iron after it is completely cool. Make sure it's unplugged.

- To shine chrome fixtures, try rubbing them with newspaper while they are still damp. Baby oil and a soft cloth works well. Aluminum foil will also do the job.

- To keep plants moist while you're on vacation, place yarn in a glass of water and put the end in the plant. It's a long drink of water.

- To eliminate wrinkles in sheer curtains just add a packet of gelatin to the rinse cycle.

- To get rid of water stains make a mixture of vegetable oil and salt or use baking soda.

- For a brighter finish on your mirrors, wipe them down with rubbing alcohol.

- 2 antacid tablets in a toilet bowl will give the bowl a clean shine!

- If you want to make a bar of soup last longer, try unwrapping it before you use it and allow it to dry out.

- To ward off fleas from a pet's sleeping area, try sprinkling a few drops of lavender oil or Brewer's Yeast. Fleas hate oil of lavender, hopefully your animal won't.

- Flying insects will fly away if you keep basil plants around the house. And if you keep the plant well watered from the bottom it will give off additional aroma. Hanging small muslin bags with fresh dried basil will also repel anything with wings!

- All diamonds and gold jewelry can be cleaned using a 50/50 solution of vinegar and warm water. Dip a soft toothbrush into the solution and brush gently. (Opals, emeralds and pearls are too delicate for this type of treatment.)

- To stop dust from settling on artificial flowers, just lightly spray the flowers with hair spray.

- Dust on your electronics? Wipe your computer or TV screen with a dryer sheet to repel dust.

- To remove auto scratches, try rubbing a small amount of toothpaste on the surface. It will remove minor scrapes.

- Lipstick on the collar? Try removing it with Vaseline.

- To keep flowers fresh longer, add crushed egg shells to the bottom of your vase.

GRANDMOTHER'S TIPS FOR HEALTH & BEAUTY:

- To add shine to your hair and remove shampoo buildup, try adding 2 tablespoons of apple cider vinegar to the rinse water.

- According to Grandma, this face mask smoothes wrinkles associated with age: mix an egg white with some sweet cream, lightly spread it around your eye area and let it set for half an hour to an hour. Rinse with lukewarm water.

- Try the vinegar and brown paper bag cure for a burn. Soak a piece of brown bag in white cider vinegar. Place it on the affected area and it should have a cooling effect and relieve pain.

- Grandma's cabbage cure works for arthritis and is also helpful for back pain. Steam cabbage leaves for 10 minutes until slightly wilted. Wipe the sore area with olive oil and rub the cabbage leaves on top as soon as it is cool enough for you to stand. Be careful not to burn your skin. Place a towel over the area to retain the warmth. Leave it on for an hour and then repeat the whole process.

- Blackheads respond well to lemon juice which has wonderful astringent properties. Rub lemon juice over the blemished skin before going to bed and rinse with cool water in the morning. After a couple of days you should see definite results.

- To make an astringent that will soothe skin and help dry out acne, make your own cucumber toner. Juice a cucumber and apply the cucumber extract to your blemishes with a cotton ball. After fifteen minutes, rinse your face.

- Heartburn? Take a mouthful of dry oats and chew until soft enough to swallow. Your favorite chewing gum can also reduce stomach acid and prevent heartburn.

- For migraine headaches try inhaling strong Chinese mustard.

- Makeup melting? Spray mineral oil on your face and let it dry before you apply your make-up. It will last longer, especially in summertime.

OTHER HELPFUL TIPS FROM GRANDMA:

- Pour salt on a leech and it will shrivel up, fall off and die.

- Mind your P's & Q's is a beer fact: when you order beer or ale in an English pub it is ordering in P's (pints) or Q's (quarts). When a customer would get a bit unruly and had too much to drink, the bartender would tell them to "mind their P's & Q's."

- To remove auto scratches, try rubbing a small amount of toothpaste on the surface. It will remove minor scrapes.

- To keep flowers fresh longer, add crushed egg shells to the bottom of your vase.

Favorite Tips

Index

Grandmother's
10th ANNIVERSARY
EDITION

A

Abalone, 252–253
Air freshener. See Odor removal tips
Alfalfa juice, 75
Alligator, 204
Almond, oil, 145
Aluminum foil, 101, 108, 449
American diet (typical), 167
Anchovies, 265–266
    too salty (remedy), 607
Apples, 440–441
    applesauce, 66
        substitution for fat, 165
    juice, 65
    pies, 814
    poor flavor (remedy), 607
    and potato sprouting, 970
Apricot, juice, 66
Artichokes, 9–10
    tips, 608
Arugula, 3
Asparagus, 11–12
    juice, 75
    tips (remedies), 608
Auto scratch removal tip, 977
Avocado
    juice, 75–76
    oil, 145
    unripe, 608

B

Bacteria/molds/yeast in foods, 95, 102, 106, 445
    and cooking temperatures, 95, 186
    garlic stored in oil alert, 172
    and herbs, 113
    honey and Botulism, 290
    Listeria, 213–214
    and meat, 202, 210, 232, 233
    and poultry, 246, 247
    and poultry stuffing, 244
    vaccinations for chickens, 241
    and vinegar, 707
    See also Toxic food
Baked Alaska, 859–860
Baked goods. See Breads/baked products
Baking powder
    and chocolate cake, 783
    and flour ratio in bread, 771

Baking soda, 713–714
    and acids, 783
    tips, 714–716
Baking staples
    storage times, 449, 617
    See also Flour; Sugar
Banana, 66, 441
    Dana's Chocana Banana, 867
Barbequing, 719
    adding Smokey onion flavor (tip), 972
    sauce, 136, 720
        Grandma's, 137
Barley grass, juice, 76
Barracuda, 266
Basil, 197, 200
Bathroom cleaning
    Bathroom Fixture Cleaner, 487
    Ceramic Tile Cleaner, 486
    Cleanser for Shower Nozzle Residue, 487
    disinfectant formulas, 485–486
        Herbal Disinfectant, 487
    General Bathroom Cleaning, 487–488
    Porcelain Stain Remover, 488
    Removing Soap Residue from Washcloths
    formula, 485
    Super Tub and Tile Cleaner, 486
    Toilet Bowl Cleaner formulas, 483–484
    See also Mildew removal
Beans (dry), soaking tips, 430
Beans (edible pods), 13
    cooking tips, 13–15
    varieties, 15–16
Beans (shell varieties), 16
    cooking tips, 19
    pinto, 18, 430
    storing, 19
    See also Soy beans/products
Beauty products
    eye makeup
        Makeup Remedy for Black Eye, 555
        Making Eye Shadow, 554
        mascara formulas, 554
        remover formulas, 552–553
    glitter gels, Sparkler Gel, 586
    hand/face creams, 560
        formulas, 560–563
        Glycerin Hand Lotion, 584
        Soapless Hand Freshener, 587
    leg wax formula, 587
    lip gloss formulas, 585
    lip salves, 585
    lipstick, 584
        formulas, 586

problems/remedies, 609
storage tips, 430
Broiling, 721
broiler times, 721
meats, 394–395
Bromelain, 70, 442
Broth, 185, 195
frozen cubes, 241
Brownies, 780
Brussels sprouts, 23
juice, 76
Bubble and Squeak, 204
Buffalo, 210, 222–223
Buffalo fish, 272
Buffalo wings, 746
Buns, cinnamon, 780
Butter, 164, 174
black, 183
brown, 182
burned, 609
clarified, 181–182
compound, 182
dish, 180
ghee, 182
grades, 180
money-saving strategies, 424–4255
tips, 183
Buttons (tips for), 345–347

C

Cabbage, 23–25
cooking odor tip, 970
in home remedies, 976
juice, 76
problems/remedies, 609
storage tips, 430
varieties, 25–26
Cabinets, problems/solutions, 349–350
Caesar Salad, 4
Cakes, 780
Angel Food, 781
baking tips, 456
Chiffon, 781–782
cutting tips, 781
Fat-type cakes, 782–784
fruitcake, 796–797
problems/remedies, 609
problems/solutions
center erupted, 785
chewy, 785
crumbly, 785

fell in oven, 785
fruit/nuts sank, 786
grainy, 785
heavy, 786
holes, 785
Shortcake, 784–785
Sponge, 784
See also Cheesecake
Calcium sources, orange juice, 72
Can openers, 377
Candy/candy making, 299–300, 301
Baby Ruth, 306
caramel, 848
chewing gum, 307
sugarless, 309
defrosting, 302
jellybean, 307
lollypop, 305
M&Ms, 310
storage, 303
sugar syrups, 847
thread stages, 848
sugaring, 609
tips, 313, 845–847
Canned goods, shelf life, 618
Canning, soups, 187
Canola oil, 145–146, 156
Capon, 752
Caramel, 848
sauce, 848
Caramelization, 6
Carbohydrates, in fruits and vegetables, 64
Carob, 164, 309
Carp, 272, 276
Carpet cleaning/deodorizing, 506
formulas, 507
Carrots, 26–28
growing tips, 28
juice, 76
limp, 610
storing, 430, 431
Casseroles, 788
Catfish, 272, 417
The fisherman's formula for catfish fillets, 283
Cauliflower, 28–29
problems/remedies, 610
Caviar, 273–274
Celeriac, 31
Celery, 29–31, 431, 972
juice, 76–77
Celtuce, 31
Cheese
melting tips, 133

E

E. coli, 71, 186
    in beef, 202, 210
Easter egg dye, 669–670
Edible bugs, 203
Eel, 267
Egg whites, whipping secret, 711
Eggplant, 38–39
    problems/solutions, 611
Eggs
    baked, 760
    as binders, 178
    boiled, 426, 753–754
    deviled, 754
    eggnog, 755
    fried, 755–756
    grades, 426
    measurements, 425
    money-saving strategies, 425–428
    omelet, 756
    poached, 756–758
    quail, 757
    raw, 757–758
    scrambled, 758–759
    shirred, 760
    substitutes, 427–428, 755
    tempering, 129
    tips, 970, 973
    undercooked, 611
    yolks, 760
Emu, 209, 210
Emulsifying, 111
Endive, 3
    juice, 77
Exhaust hood, problems/solutions, 356–357
Extracts, vanilla, 140

F

Farina, 763
Fat, in non-vegetable proteins, 215
Fat drippings
    separation for gravy, 172–173
    tips to avoid smoking, 179
Fats, 141, 171
    in baking, 176
    categories, 141–142
    "caul fat," 183
    chemical composition, 142

cis-form fatty acids, 144
content in common foods, 169–170
and diabetes, 211
digestion of, 154
essential fatty acids (EFA), 143, 154–155
facts about, 163–167, 174–176
good/bad, 142, 158, 165
and gravy, 172–173
hydrogenation, 143–144
lard, 163, 175
measures, 184
medium chain triglycerides (MCT), 142–143
omega-3 fatty acids, 143, 155
replacements, 156
"schmaltz," 175
shelf life, 170
shortening, 170
trans-form fatty acids, 144, 156, 157–159
    avoiding (tips), 159
    health risks of, 158, 159
    and processed foods, 155
types
    monounsaturated (MUFA), 142
    polyunsaturated (PUFA), 142
    saturated (SFA), 142
See also Butter; Lower fat; Oils
Fennel, 39
    juice, 77
Ficin, 69
Filbert. See Hazelnut
Fillo (phyllo), 803
Fire extinguisher, salt, 712
Fish, 245, 409
    aquafarms, 276, 279
    cooking methods
        baking, 413
        broiling, 413–414
        frying, 414
        grilling, 414–415
        microwave cooking, 415
        poaching, 415
        sautéing, 415–416
    cooking tips, 275, 277, 278, 281, 282, 413
        frying secrets, 284
    forms of, 251, 411
    freezing, 102, 275
    freshwater, 272–273
    inspection, 251, 411
    money-saving strategies, 409–411
    new varieties, 276
    purchasing tips
        fresh fish, 250, 410
        frozen fish, 251, 410–411

I

Index

ground, 244
money-saving strategies, 403–404, 406–407
plucking, 245
shopping tips, 246
See also Capon; Chicken; Rock Cornish Game
Hens; Squab; Turkey
Powdered food, corn/soybean mix for famine relief, 5
Pregnancy
and fish consumption, 277
Grandma's Nipple Ointment, 701
information (free), 605–606
Itch-Reducing Balm for Pregnant Women, 560
morning sickness remedies, 694, 962–963
stretch marks, 563
formulas, 564
Reducing Pregnancy Stretch Marks, 556
Pressure cooking, 726
Pretzel, 808–809
Processed foods, and trans-fatty acids, 155
Prosciutto, 739
Prunes
hard (remedy), 614
juice, 75
Puddings
chocolate, 852–853
Steamy Chocolate Pudding, 865
problems/solutions, 615
Punch, bland, 614

Q

Quail, 248
eggs, 757
Quiche, 809
soggy crust, 615

R

Radishes, 55
Raisins, problems/solutions, 615
Range top, 373
tips, 374
unclogging burners, 715
Rattlesnake, 228
Refrigerator, 374
freezer efficiency, 98, 108
lined vegetable bins, 8, 430
problems/solutions, 374–375
Refrigerator Freshener product, 682
tips, 374–377, 519, 711
Rhubarb, 55

Rice
burned, 615
flour, 763
Roasting, 726–727
Roasting meats, 395–396
Rock Cornish Game Hens, 750
Romaine, 3
Rubber ball revitalization tip, 974

S

Sablefish, 268
Safflower oil, 148
Salad, 435
crispness, 973
dressing (shelf life), 618
Salami, 203–204
Salmon, 268–269
Salmonella
control device, 247
and pet treats, 206
Salsa, freezing, 102, 114
Salsify, 56
Salt
at river/beach, 712, 977
in bread making, 772
fire extinguisher, 712
and grooming products, 710
household cleaning tips, 711, 974
in meat cooking, 233–234
reducing in sauces and soups, 131, 972
and stock, 193
substitute, 113
unclogging drain, 709
vinegar and sugar to reduce, 707
windshield deicer, 712
Sardine, 269
Sauces
barbeque, 136–137, 972
egg-based, 130
with flour/lump elimination, 131, 197
higher-fat, 135
Hollandaise, 131, 132, 196
hot pepper, 114
lower-fat, 135
mole, 137
reheating rules, 829
salt reduction, 972
soy, 124–125
speedy, 134
steak, 124
sweet, 137–139

T

U

V

W

Y

Z

Index